DIEU ET MON DROIT

...th by the Grace of G...

...shall come *Greeting* Whereas *John Elliotson* Doctor of Physic *Sir Astley*...

...to us that a society was formed in the year One thousand eight hundred and five by a considerable number of...

...has published eighteen volumes of transactions which have had a very extensive circulation *And whereas*...

...Have of our especial grace certain knowledge and mere...

...that the said *John Elliotson Sir Astley Paston Cooper* and *John Yelloly* and such others of our loving subjects...

...*And We do*...

...*Provided*...

...*In witness*...

...wn Seal.

# The History of the Royal Society of Medicine

Dame Deirdre Hine, President of the Royal Society of Medicine 2000–02.
Portrait by Bob Tulloch (2001).

# The History of the Royal Society of Medicine

## Penelope Hunting

The ROYAL
SOCIETY of
MEDICINE
PRESS Limited

©2002 Royal Society of Medicine Press Ltd
1 Wimpole Street, London W1G 0AE, UK
207 E Westminster Road, Lake Forest, IL 60045, USA
http://www.roysocmed.ac.uk

British Library Cataloguing in Publication Data
A catalogue record for this book is available from the British Library
ISBN 1-85315-497-0

Phototypeset by Phoenix Photosetting, Chatham, Kent, UK
Printed in Great Britain by Ebenezer Baylis, The Trinity Press, Worcester

# Contents

Acknowledgements                                                                                    vii
Abbreviations                                                                                        ix
List of illustrations                                                                               xi
Preface                                                                                            xix

Introduction                                                                                         1
Chapter 1: The founding of the Medical and Chirurgical Society                                      5
Chapter 2: The Medical and Chirurgical Society                                                     23
Chapter 3: The Royal Medical and Chirurgical Society                                               67
Chapter 4: Advances in Medicine and Surgery                                                       127
Chapter 5: The Society at Hanover Square                                                           157
Chapter 6: The Royal Society of Medicine, 1 Wimpole Street                                        177
Chapter 7: The first Sections of the Society                                                      213
   Section of Medicine                                                             217
   Section of Surgery                                                              219
   Section of Pathology                                                            225
   Section of Epidemiology and Public Health, originally Epidemiology              230
   Section of Odontology                                                           238
   Section of Obstetrics and Gynaecology                                           244
   Clinical Section                                                                254
   Section of Dermatology                                                          258
   Section of Clinical Neurosciences, originally Neurology                         263
   Section of Laryngology and Rhinology, originally Laryngology                    269
   Section of Otology                                                              275
   Section of Radiology, originally Electro-therapeutics                           279
   Section of Experimental Medicine and Therapeutics, originally Therapeutics      289
     and Pharmacology
Chapter 8: From Anaesthetics to Proctology                                                        301
   Section of Anaesthesia, originally Anaesthetics                                 301
   Section of Paediatrics and Child Health, originally the Study of Disease in     309
     Children
   Section of Rheumatology and Rehabilitation, originally Balneology and           316
     Climatology
   Section of Psychiatry                                                           323
   Section of the History of Medicine                                              330
   Section of Ophthalmology                                                        333
   Section of Tropical Medicine and Parasitology, originally Tropical Diseases     342
     and Parasitology
   United Services Section, originally War                                          344
   Section of Urology                                                              349
   Section of Orthopaedics                                                         356

Section of Comparative Medicine 365
Section of Coloproctology, originally Proctology 369
**Chapter 9: From Endocrinology to Primary Health Care** 381
Section of Endocrinology 382
Section of General Practice 388
Section of Pharmaceutical Medicine and Research, originally Library 394
    (Scientific Research)
Section of Occupational Medicine 398
Section of Measurement in Medicine 403
Section of Clinical Immunology and Allergy 407
Section of Medical Education 409
Section of Plastic Surgery 411
Section of Oncology 414
Open Section 419
Section of Hypnosis and Psychosomatic Medicine, originally Medical and 422
    Dental Hypnosis
Section of Accident and Emergency Medicine 424
Section of Clinical Forensic and Legal Medicine, originally Clinical Forensic 427
    Medicine
Section of Geriatrics and Gerontology 430
Section of Respiratory Medicine 432
Cardiothoracic Section, originally Cardiothoracic Surgery 434
Section of Transplantation, originally Organ Transplantation 436
Section of Nephrology 436
Section of Sports Medicine 438
The Fora 439
**Chapter 10: The Society in the 20th century** 455

**General Bibliography** 479
**Appendix: Presidents of the Society 1805–2000** 481
**Index** 483

# Acknowledgements

First and foremost I thank Dr Anne Grocock, Sir Donald Harrison and Sir David Innes Williams for overseeing this project from conception to completion, and for their encouragement.

I have the highest regard for the staff of the RSM Library, all of whom were helpful and courteous throughout. I especially thank Margaret Hoyes who guided me round the catalogue, Sheron Burton who advised on copyright, Claire Jackson who introduced me to the archives, Mark Wilmshurst and Stephen Ford who know where to find obscure books and illustrations, and Ian Snowley who brought the information up to date. The Academic Department provided a regular supply of faxes and the Finance and Membership Departments came forth with documents and illustrations.

I am grateful to Professor Margaret Yelloly for corresponding about her ancestors and to the many Fellows of the Society who provided background information, books, papers and illustrations and made comments and improvements to the text. The advice of Dr Lawrence Razavi on a wide range of subjects was greatly appreciated.

The following made major contributions to the histories of the Sections:

Professor Charles Calnan and Dr Darrell Wilkinson wrote on the Section of Dermatology, Dr Anthony Cullen on the Section of Comparative Medicine, Dr Neville Davis on the Section of Clinical Forensic and Legal Medicine, Dr Campbell Mackenzie and Diana Berry on the United Services Section, Dr Anne Mathieson on the Section of Hypnosis and Psychosomatic Medicine, Mrs Veronica Rose on the Section of Pharmaceutical Medicine and Research. I thank them all for their time and effort.

Many Presidents of the Sections, longstanding members and those interested in the history kindly helped by giving interviews, corresponding, offering suggestions, correcting mistakes and adding to the typescript: Dr Julian Acland, Dr Aileen Adams, Dr John Ashley, Sir Roger Bannister, Dame Josephine Barnes, Dr Alexander Bearn, Mr Larry Benjamin, Professor Roger Berry, Professor John Blandy, Mr J Barton Booth, Professor George Browning, Mr Ian Burn, Mr Martin Conybeare, Dr Beryl Corner, Dr John Costelloe, Dr PDO Davies, Professor John Davis, Dr Neville Davis, Professor John Dormandy, Mr Bryce Douglas, Mr Leslie Dunn, Dr Anthony du Vivier, Professor David Easty, Professor Harold Ellis, Dr Carice Ellison, Professor John Emery, Sir Terence English, Dr John Ferguson, Baroness Ilora Finlay, Dr Cyril Fisher, Mr JA Fixsen, Professor Malcolm Forsythe, Dr John Fysh, Mrs Jean Gaffin, Dr NS Galbraith, Mr Anthony Golding, Dr Andrew Griffiths, Professor DI Haslock, Dr Deric Hawkins, Mr Basil Helal, Dr Rosalind Hinton, Dr Barry Hoffbrand, Dr James Hooper, Dr John Horder, Dr Douglas DC Howat, Mr Andrew Irvine, Mr John Kirkup, Mr RHS Lane, Miss AR Leon, Mr Michael Laurence, Dr Mary Lindsay, Dr John McMullan, Mr Andrew McIrvine, Dr Jean Macqueen, Mr Adrian Marston, Professor MD Mason, Professor RL Maynard, Dr David Melville, Professor Peter Millard, Dr Richard Moore, Professor John Moorhead, Dr Gerald Nash, Dr Katharine Orton, Dr Peter Orton, Professor Charles D Pusey, Mr Myrddin Rees, Mr Brian Reeves, Dr F Clifford Rose, Mr James Roxburgh, Mr Peter Saunders, Mr Adam Searle, Mr Barry Scheer, Mr Peter Schurr, Dr Anthony Batty Shaw,

Professor Thomas Stapleton, Dr Geoffrey Storey, Mr Brent Taylor, Dr Adrian Thomas, Dr John Thurston, Professor Anthea Tinker, Mr Graham Venn, Mr Richard Vercoe, Mr Denys Wainwright, Professor Michael Warren, Dr Diana Wetherill, Ms Katharine Whitehorn, Dr Robert Willcox, Mr Gordon Williams, Professor R Wootton and Dr Luke Zander.

# Abbreviations

BL: British Library
BMA: British Medical Association
BMJ: *British Medical Journal*
Bulletin: *Official Bulletin of the Royal Society of Medicine*
CM: Council Minutes of the Medical and Chirurgical Society, later the Royal Medical and Chirurgical Society and from 1907 the Royal Society of Medicine
  CM followed by Section name indicates Council Minutes of that Section
DNB: *Dictionary of national biography*
Duke: Duke University Medical Center, History of Medicine Collections, Durham, North Carolina, USA
GM: General Minutes, Medical and Chirurgical Society, later Royal Medical and Chirurgical Society and from 1907 the Royal Society of Medicine
  GM followed by Section name indicates General Minutes of that Section
GMC: General Medical Council
JMB: *Journal of Medical Biography*
JRSM: *Journal of the Royal Society of Medicine*
M & P: Moore, Norman, and Paget, Stephen, *The Royal Medical and Chirurgical Society of London. Centenary 1805–1905* (1905)
MCS: Medical and Chirurgical Society
MSL: Medical Society of London
Munk's Roll: Munk, W, *et al, Lives of the Fellows of the Royal College of Physicians of London* 9 vols (1878-1994)
Plarr's Lives: Power, Sir D'Arcy, *et al, Plarr's Lives of the Fellows of the Royal College of Surgeons of England* 7 vols (1930–95)
PRSM: *Proceedings of the Royal Society of Medicine*
RCP: Royal College of Physicians
RCS: Royal College of Surgeons of England
RMCS: Royal Medical and Chirurgical Society
RSM: Royal Society of Medicine
Transacs: *Medico-Chirurgical Transactions*
Wellcome: Wellcome Institute for the History of Medicine Library

Manuscript and documentary references in the Notes indicate material in the archives of the Royal Society of Medicine unless stated otherwise.

# List of illustrations

Royal Charter of Incorporation, 1834; endpapers

Frontispiece
Dame Deirdre Hine, President 2000–02

**Colour plates between pages 156 and 157**

Plate 1
Members of the Medical Society of London, 1800

Plate 2
The Crown and Anchor Tavern

Plate 3
Dr William Saunders

Plate 4
Dr John Yelloly

Plate 5
Dr Alexander Marcet

Plate 6
Dr Edward Jenner

Plate 7
1807 Vaccination scene

Plate 8
Sir Astley Cooper

Plate 9
Bright's disease

Plate 10
Henry Patten

Plate 11
Henry Patten's diseased liver

Plate 12
*Liber de homine*, 1474

Plate 13
57 Lincoln's Inn Fields

Plate 14
King William IV signs the Obligation Book, 1834

Plate 15
The Royal Charter, 1834

Plate 16
'The Flight of Aeneas' by Bacon, 1769

Plate 17
Chimneypiece attributed to Chambers

Plate 18
Library catalogue, 1879

Plate 19
Paper by Benjamin Travers, 1813

Plate 20
Dr T Bateman's *Cutaneous diseases*, 1817

Plate 21
International Medical Congress, 1881: Baroness Burdett-Coutts' garden party

Plate 22
President's badge, 1890

Plate 23
Key to 20 Hanover Square, 1890

Plate 24
Sir John MacAlister

Plate 25
Invitation to first House Dinner, 1892

Plate 26
The menu, 1892

Plate 27
20 Hanover Square, 2000

Plate 28
Centenary seal, 1905

Plate 29
Supplemental Charter, 1907

**Colour plates between pages 332 and 333**

Plate 30
Royal signatures in Obligation Book, 1912

Plate 31
Conversazione, 1912

Plate 32
President's badge and chain, 1927

Plate 33
Grant of arms, 1927

Plate 34
Coat of arms, 1927

Plate 35
Presidents' robes

Plate 36
Celsus' *De medicina,* 1478

Plate 37
Section of Surgery President's badge

Plate 38
Section of Pathology President's badge

Plate 39
Section of Odontology President's badge

Plate 40
Section of Neurology President's badge

Plate 41
Section of Obstetrics and Gynaecology
President's badge

Plate 42
Samuel Cartwright

Plate 43
Sir St Clair Thomson

Plate 44
Section of Laryngology and Rhinology
President's badge

Plate 45
Section of Otology President's badge

Plate 46
Section of Radiology President's badge

Plate 47
Dr W Withering, *Account of the foxglove,*
1785

Plate 48
Section of Anaesthesia President's badge

Plate 49
Section of Paediatrics and Child Health
President's badge

Plate 50
Section of Physical Medicine President's
badge

Plate 51
Section of Psychiatry President's badge

Plate 52
History of Medicine Section President's
badge

Plate 53
Sir William Osler

Plate 54
Section of Ophthalmology President's
badge

Plate 55
Paper by Dr Ida Mann, 1941

Plate 56
United Services Section President's badge

Plate 57
Section of Urology President's badge

Plate 58
Section of Orthopaedics President's badge

Plate 59
Section of Comparative Medicine
President's badge

Plate 60
Section of Coloproctology President's badge

Plate 61
Section of General Practice President's
badge

Plate 62
Section of Pharmaceutical Medicine and
Research President's badge

Plate 63
Section of Occupational Medicine
President's badge

Plate 64
Dr Edward Jenner's enquiry into cow pox,
1798

Plate 65
Dr John Elliotson

Plate 66
Section of Accident and Emergency
President's badge

Plate 67
Section of Clinical Forensic and Legal
Medicine President's badge

Plate 68
Section of Sports Medicine President's
badge

Plate 69
Bright's disease, 1827

Plate 70
Transplantation performed by Saints
Cosmas and Damian

Plate 71
Sir Richard Doll, 1999

Plate 72
Reopening of 1 Wimpole Street, 1986

Plate 73
1 Wimpole Street: the conservatory

Plate 74
1 Wimpole Street: the Library

Plate 75
1 Wimpole Street: the main reception area

Plate 76
Supplemental Charter, 1999

**Illustrations in the text**

**Chapter 1**
Dr George Birkbeck                                    7

The Freemasons' Tavern                           8

Letter from Sir Joseph Banks, 1805        10

Dr Matthew Baillie                                    11

Obligation Book, 1805                              13

Council Minutes, 1805                             13

Verulam Buildings, Gray's Inn               14

2 Verulam Buildings                                 15

First donations to the Library                  19

**Chapter 2**
Dr John Bostock                                        27

Dr Richard Bright                                      29

*Tractatus de corde*, 1669                          31

Dr James Blundell                                     32

Blundell's apparatus                                 33

Nerves of the face: Sir Charles Bell, 1830   35

Dr Peter Roget                                          38

*Medico-Chirurgical Transactions*, 1809   41

Drawings by W Clift, 1809                     46

'Dry gangrene', 1839                                47

Sir Benjamin Brodie                                 49

Sir Henry Halford                                     52

The Hippocratic oath                              54

First Library catalogue, 1816                  56

Professor Samuel Cooper                        57

Lincoln's Inn Fields                                  59

**Chapter 3**
The seal of the RMCS                             69

The Society's houses in the West End   72

53 Berners Street, interior                      73

Ground plan, 53 Berners Street, 1847   75

Dr Benjamin Babington                          79

Professor J Czermak                               80

Dr John Snow's proposal form, 1843    83

Paper by Robert Liston, 1836                 86

Guillemeau on eye disease, 1580s         88

Eustachi's *Tabulae anatomicae*, 1728     90

Joseph Toynbee                                        91

Dr Charles West                                       92

Dr Marshall Hall                                      93

Sir Richard Quain                                    95

Hodgson's disease, 1815                         98

Chamberlen obstetrical instruments   100

Pathological Society seal                        103

Epidemiological Society seal                 104

Obstetrical Society seal 105

Fellows of the Obstetrical Society, 105
c.1867

Odontological Society seal 106

Clinical Society seal 106

Honorary Fellows of RMCS, 1863 107

Marshall Hall method of resuscitation, 111
1856

Dr J Fothergill's description of diphtheria, 115
1748

Dr W Turner's book on baths, 1562 116

Marshall Hall bookplate 117

Charles Darwin, 1868 118

Sir Thomas Barlow, 1883 120

Chapter 4
Robert Liston, 1847 128

Dr J Snow's chloroform inhaler 129

FW Hewitt's 'gasometer', 1899 131

Sir Thomas Spencer Wells 132

Lord Lister 134

R Lawson Tait 136

Lister's carbolic spray in use 136

JW Hulke 137

Drawings by Sir Frederick Treves 139

Removal of a cerebral tumour, 1885 140

Sir Jonathan Hutchinson 141

Hutchinson's teeth, 1858 142

Sir Henry Thompson 143

Sir James Paget's proposal form, 1840 145

Paper by Sir Henry Morris, 1879 145

Paget's disease, 1876 146

Sir Felix Semon 147

Sir Morell Mackenzie 147

Myxoedema, 1877 148

Sir William Watson Cheyne 150

A poem about syphilis, 1530 152

Chapter 5
Hanover Square in the late 18th 159
century

Ground plan, 20 Hanover Square, 1877 159

Alterations to 20 Hanover Square, 160
1889–90

Timothy Holmes 161

Hanover Square, 1905, interior 162

MacAlister at Hanover Square 164

The MacAlisters' drawing-room 164

Charles Hewitt 165

20 Hanover Square, c.1907–10 166

Frontispiece to centenary volume, 166
1905

Sir Samuel Wilks' Diploma, 1905 168

Sir Richard Douglas Powell 169

Sir William Selby Church 170

Seal of the RSM 174

Chapter 6
2–5 Henrietta Street, Estate Plans, 178, 179
c.1797–9, 1807 and 1911

Architects' drawing, 1 Wimpole 183
Street, 1910

1 Wimpole Street, 1912 184–85

Dr William Harvey on the circulation 187
of the blood, 1628

Council Club dinner menu, 1913 192

Professor Marcus Beck 192

Invitation to Medical Officers, 194
1914–18

Emergency Surgical Aid Corps 195
dinner invitation, 1919

Sir Humphry Rolleston 199

The Gold Medal of the RSM 202

Viscount Dawson of Penn 204

Dr W Turner's Herbal, 1568 206

**Chapter 7**

Inaugural dinner of the RSM, 1907   215

Ketham, *Fasciculus medicinae*, 1513   220

Sir John Bland-Sutton   222

The Norman Tanner Medal   225

Sir Almroth Wright   226

Sir Alexander Fleming   228

The Jenner Medal   231

Sir Arthur Newsholme   232

The Hutchison Medal   237

The Odontological Society's Museum   239

Rösslin's birth figures, 1513   246

Dr Amand Routh   247

The Blair-Bell Medal   250

Paper to Clinical Section, 1908   255

Dr F Parkes Weber   256

Clinical Section dinner, 1934   257

Founders of the Section of Dermatology   259

JH Sequeira's case of 'kératodermie blennorrhagique', 1910   260

Dr GB Dowling   262

Dr Thomas Willis on the nervous system: illustration by Wren, 1664   263

The Hughlings Jackson Medal   264

Sir Terence Cawthorne   278

Röntgen and his apparatus   280

Radiation injury, 1908   283

Dr Russell Reynolds' apparatus, 1934   286

Section of Radiology dinner, 1937   287

Programme of meetings of Section of Therapeutics and Pharmacology, 1907–08   290

Professor WE Dixon   291

**Chapter 8**

Society of Anaesthetists conversazione invitation, 1897   302

Dr G Marshall's apparatus and Dr F Shipway's apparatus, 1919   303

RJ Minnitt's intermittent-flow machine, 1934   304

The Henry Hickman Medal   306

Phaer's *Boke of children*, 1546   309

Dr D Winnicott's squiggles, 1953   314

Balneological and Climatological Society, 1895   317

Bright's *Treatise of melancholy*, 1586   323

Card from Professor Freud, 1935   325

The Lang Medal, and William and Basil Lang   335

A myope class, 1913   336

Mayou's slit lamp, 1926   337

Sir Rickman Godlee   344

Sir James Watt   346

W Cheselden's operation for stone, 1723   350

E Hurry Fenwick   350

H Winsbury-White   355

Sir Thomas Fairbank   359

Study of Surgeon's Hands by Hepworth, 1947   362

GK McKee's paper on metal in bone surgery, 1957   363

Sir Frederick Hobday   366

Sir Thomas Clifford Allbutt   366

Proctologists' dinner menu, 1912   369

F Swinford Edwards   370

JP Lockhart-Mummery   370

The John of Arderne Medal   375

**Chapter 9**

Paper by Dr C. Hilton Fagge, 1871   383

Endocrinologists' dinner menu, 1946   384

Sir Walter Langdon-Brown   385

Boord's *Breviarie of health*, 1587 — 389

Lord Hunt and Dr George Abercrombie — 390

Plaque to Dr John Fry — 393

Ramazzini's *Diseases of workers*, 1716 — 398

Dr Percy Cliffe — 403

The Ellison–Cliffe Medal — 404

Equipment for measurement in medicine, 1975 — 404

de Ketham's woodcut of Petrus de Montagnana, 1513 — 410

The founders of British plastic surgery, c.1948 — 412

Tagliacozzi on plastic surgery, 1597 — 412

Carpue's restoration of the nose, 1816 — 413

Cancer of the stomach from Baillie's *Morbid anatomy*, 1812 — 415

Sir Ronald Raven — 417

Open Section meeting, 1991 — 421

Open Section's 25th anniversary, 1999 — 422

*A & E Letter*, 1988 — 426

Floyer's *Medicina gerocomica*, 1724 — 431

Dissertation on asthma, 1725 — 433

Ossification of the heart from Baillie's *Morbid anatomy*, 1812 — 434

Heald's *Injuries and sport*, 1931 — 438

Forum on Clinical Haemorheology, 1982 — 441

Venous Forum, 1983 — 442

The 'vein man', 1513 — 443

Forum on Angiology, 1987 — 446

Forum on Clinical Pharmacology and Therapeutics, 1988 — 446

Forum on Computers in Medicine, 1989 — 447

Forum on Quality in Health Care, 1992 — 447

Inauguration of Telemedicine Forum, 1997 — 448

Inauguration of Catastrophes and Conflicts Forum, 1999 — 449

**Chapter 10**

New fourth floor, 1 Wimpole Street, 1953 — 461

Chandos House, Queen Anne Street — 463

Ballroom, Chandos House — 464

Logo of RSM Foundation — 465

Western District Post Office, c.1915 — 470

Site of Western District Post Office — 471

Proposed lecture theatre, 1 Wimpole Street, 1979 — 471

Commemorative Medal — 476

The illustrations are from the collections of the Royal Society of Medicine with photography by Argentum, with the exception of the following who kindly gave permission for reproduction: page 59 Alan Godfrey Maps; pages 350 lower, 355 Professor John Blandy; pages 403, 404 lower Dr Carice Ellison; page 471 EPR Design Ltd; page 362 Fitzwilliam Museum (copyright Alan Bowness, Hepworth Estate); pages 256, 259, 262 Dr Andrew Griffiths; Plates 2, 13 and pages 8, 14, 159 top Guildhall Library, Corporation of London; pages 178, 179 Howard de Walden Estates Ltd; Plate 27 Knight Frank; page 72 London Topographical Society; Plate 1 Medical Society of London; page 438 from CB Heald's *Injuries and sport* (1931) by permission of Oxford University Press; page 470 Post Office Archives; page 390 Royal College of General Practitioners; page 56 Royal College of Physicians; pages 237, 250, 264, 375, 404 top The Royal Mint; page 366 left Archives and Historical Collection, The Royal Veterinary College; Plate 70 Society of Antiquaries of London; page 164 Mrs Jean Somervell; Plates 7, 21 and page 165 Wellcome Library, London.

The illustration on page 226 is from Sir Zachary Cope's biography of Almroth Wright (1966) which Cope (President of the Section of Surgery 1930–40 and the History of Medicine Section 1954–56) presented to the RSM Library. Page 228 is a portrait by Karsh from André Maurois' biography of Fleming (1959); page 80 is reprinted from a paper by FS Brodnitz 'One hundred years of laryngology' in *Transactions of the American Academy of Ophthalmology and Otolaryngology* vol 58 (1954) pp. 663–69 with permission of Elsevier Science.

# Preface

Although there are many valid reasons why an organization would wish to publish its history, perhaps the commonest is to commemorate a specific period of time or special occasion. In 1905 an account of the origins and development of the Royal Medical and Chirurgical Society of London was published to celebrate its centenary.

This was initiated at the request of the then President, Sir Richard Douglas Powell, and his Council and was edited by Norman Moore MD, Honorary Librarian, and Stephen Paget FRCS, an Honorary Secretary. It was a modest production, given free to each Fellow and compiled from the Minute Books, *Proceedings* and *Transactions* of the Society. The purpose was to give an outline of the Society's origins and also to commemorate 'the Founders and Benefactors', although considerable space was devoted to the Society's turbulent foundation by a group of physicians and surgeons who had seceded from the long-established Medical Society of London. The manner in which the founding purposes of 'a Society comprehending the several Branches of the medical profession be established in London for the purpose of conversation on professional subjects, for the reception of communications and for the formation of a library' had been pursued was described, as was an account of the first 50 Presidents.

In 1907 a momentous change transformed the Royal Medical and Chirurgical Society into the Royal Society of Medicine by the merger of 15 societies. Many of these were 'specialized' and the merger was a landmark in the gradual acceptance of specialization. Inevitably, the amalgamation resulted in dramatic growth in both the number of Fellows and the stature of the Society. It was therefore no surprise that once again at the request of the President and Council a second history covering the period from 1805 to 1955 should be written, this time by Maurice Davidson MD. This also included a review of the origins of the Medical and Chirurgical Society and utilized the facilities of the Society's Library and archives to add greater detail to the earlier publication. By this time the Society had moved from 20 Hanover Square to 1 Wimpole Street, and Davidson's account closed with brief biographies of the Presidents, finishing with Sir William Gilliatt (1954–56). Whereas the first volume had been published by the Aberdeen University Press, the second was published by the Royal Society of Medicine itself, and was not given free to the Fellows! The concluding paragraph expressed hope and belief in the future of the Society, which contained within its fold 'workers in many different branches of medicine, minds of different mould and calibre, fostering a judicious blend of Science and Art. This keeps the balance between crabbed age and impetuous youth'.

In 1996, conscious of the approaching bicentenary (for despite a change in name it was generally accepted that the Royal Society of Medicine could date its origins to 1805) thoughts turned towards celebrating this important milestone with a commemorative publication. The project had first been discussed during the presidency of Sir Gordon Robson (1986–88) but despite preliminary proposals it had not been pursued. Perhaps it was the planning of the Society's millennium celebrations that prompted an urgent reappraisal of the bicentenary book during the presidency of Sir Christopher Paine (1996–98). The project was then discussed in depth by the Honorary Officers with consideration being given to matters such as content and cost. The proposal that was submitted to Council for approval and support was that a bicentenary book should be published by RSM Press Ltd and be edited by RSM members, mainly from the Section of the History of Medicine, and professional historians. Sir David Innes Williams (President 1990–92) summarized the Honorary Officers' discussion document, emphasizing a general wish that the volume should avoid the dullness of a straight factual record of 200 years of events and personalities. Since it was hoped to publish several years before the bicentenary date of 2005 the contents should attempt to follow the spirit of a subtitle, *Valere Vita*: the Society and the Profession.

It was hoped that such a book would be of interest not only to RSM members but to all who were concerned with the social history of medicine. Sir David also emphasized the urgent need to record on tape the recollections of those who had been closely involved with the Society's affairs, while they were still available! Since it was expected that such a venture would take at least two years to complete a small subcommittee of past Presidents was set up, which while supporting Sir David's proposals agreed that advice from a professional historian was needed, and Professor Bynum of the Wellcome Institute for the History of Medicine was approached. He proved enthusiastic, agreeing to assist in our search for a professional author who could take on such a commission within the time scale envisaged.

Although 2005 as a publication date had some attraction since it met the chronological 200 years of gestation, the granting of the second Supplementary Charter, formally signed in Letters Patent of 10 February 1999, 165 years after King William IV had granted the original charter incorporating the Royal Medical and Chirurgical Society, appeared more appropriate. Search was therefore made for a historian who could complete a manuscript by the end of 2000 and fortunately Dr Penelope Hunting, who had recently written *A history of the Society of Apothecaries*, was willing to take on this commitment. A Memorandum of Agreement was signed in March 1998 and the final typescript was delivered as agreed in December 2000.

While the subcommittee had been disbanded, David Innes Williams and I maintained a 'watching brief' on the developing manuscript, with the primary aim of discussing the chapters and their contents as they emerged. To the credit of Dr Hunting any suggestions or observations that we made were received with both consideration and appreciation. Our liaison proved useful, for as her researches progressed many of the original concepts as to chapter contents and headings changed. Together we agreed a format, saving considerable time, and conversations with several senior Fellows of the Society who had important contributions to make regarding past events were recorded on tape. The recordings followed planned guidelines in order to ensure confidentiality and the results added valuable information to our archives.

While reading the final manuscript it became clear that we had been wise to choose the granting of the new Supplementary Charter of 1999 as our closing date. It followed dramatic changes in the Society's administration, a major revision of its by-laws and illustrated a period of vigorous development of its purpose as defined in the original charter of 1834.

This book traces the origins of the Society from its foundation in 1805 to its present site in Wimpole Street. Its compilation by a professional historian with experience of searching archives from a wide variety of sources has resulted in the most comprehensive account ever recorded of this Society. In every way this book has fulfilled our original concept of a social history describing the development of a Society that has evolved, and continues to evolve, within the context of the medical, dental and veterinary professions. In so doing the Society has responded to the pressures of scientific advances, public expectation and professional interaction without at any time attempting to exert a political influence. As such it has met all our expectations.

Sir Donald Harrison
President 1994–96

# Introduction

MEDICAL SOCIETIES FLOWERED in response to the Enlightenment, an intellectual movement that overthrew ancient conventions by the power of reason, scientific enquiry and belief in the ultimate progress of humanity. In England the publication of Dr William Harvey's revolutionary work on the circulation of the blood (1628) launched the medical Enlightenment and his experimental approach became the tool of scientific medicine. Fortified by the philosophy of Descartes, by the application of physics to medicine by Boerhaave and by experiments in chemistry in the laboratories of Oxford and London, medicine was given a scientific basis that inspired a spirit of discovery. This spirit was evident in the inventions of Dr Erasmus Darwin and in the teaching of the leaders of the Scottish Enlightenment; it was manifested in William Cheselden's *Anatomical atlas*, in the radical Dr Thomas Beddoes' experiments and Dr William Withering's manual on the value of digitalis in heart disease. With the work of William and John Hunter and Dr Edward Jenner's discovery of the smallpox vaccine these advances represented some of the enlightenments that impelled medicine and surgery forward in 18th-century Britain.

During the period of Enlightenment progressive intellectuals, authors, scientists, physicians and surgeons questioned and experimented; they founded clubs and societies to feed their desire for knowledge and conviviality. The medical establishment, however, was ill-equipped to face the challenges and discoveries of scientific medicine. Discounting the disreputable 'quacks' and charlatans, the medical profession was divided into three tiers with the Royal College of Physicians determined to maintain its status at the pinnacle of the hierarchy. The Royal College of Surgeons was not established until 1800 and its predecessor, the Surgeons' Company, wielded little power. At the base of the hierarchy apothecaries and surgeon-apothecaries struggled for recognition, obtaining legal sanction to practise medicine in 1704, but it was not until 1815 that the Society of Apothecaries gained a significant role.

In these restricting circumstances it was the Royal Society that took the lead in encouraging the exploration of medical science in this country. Granted a royal charter in 1662, with a high proportion of medical Fellows among its membership and under the influence of the physician Sir Hans Sloane, first as Secretary and later as its President for 13 years, the Royal Society fostered scientific investigation and experiment. Physicians, scientists, apothecaries, botanists, philosophers, mathematicians, astronomers and aristocrats became Fellows. They attended meetings, presented and witnessed experiments and discoveries and submitted papers to *Philosophical Transactions* – one-fifth of those published between 1665 and 1848 were on medicine, anatomy and physiology. It was this learned Society that was the prime example to the many medical societies founded in England during the late 18th and early 19th centuries for the dissemination and discussion of scientific medicine at meetings, through papers and publications and by the creation of medical libraries.

Another precedent, second only to the Royal Society, was the Medical Society of Edinburgh, founded in 1737 and incorporated by royal charter in 1778. It was formed by 10 students and their masters 'for the laudable purpose of promoting an Ardour for

Medical Enquiries' and it possessed a medical library and a Hall.[1] The supremacy of the medical faculty of Edinburgh University following its foundation in 1726 attracted the keenest students, who found that membership of the Society was essential to their success. Astley Cooper was an assiduous member; John Yelloly, William Saunders, George Birkbeck and his contemporaries John Bostock and Peter Roget belonged to the Royal Medical Society of Edinburgh in the last decades of the 18th century, and when they migrated to London to pursue their careers they sought, founded and joined similar societies. The founders of the Medical and Chirurgical Society of London, which developed into the Royal Society of Medicine, had all been prominent members of the Royal Medical Society of Edinburgh.

As scientific and artistic horizons widened during the Enlightenment, new societies were founded in London – the Society of Antiquaries in 1707, the Royal Society for the Encouragement of Arts, Manufactures and Commerce in 1754, the Linnean Society in 1788, the Royal Institution in 1799, followed by the Horticultural Society of London, the London Institution and the Geological Society in the first decade of the 19th century. Medical societies were part of this trend and were formed to cater for the interests of physicians, surgeons, apothecaries, medical students, teachers and practitioners, and they provided a platform for the most distinguished members of the medical profession. These societies were distinct from the medical licensing bodies and the medical dining clubs in that their *raison d'être* was to advance medical knowledge. They remedied, to some extent, the deficiencies of the system by bridging the divisions between physicians of the College, surgeons and apothecaries and they fulfilled an educational purpose at a time when medical education was haphazard.

The first medical school attached to a hospital opened in 1785 at the London Hospital, but the first hospital built specifically for teaching, Charing Cross, did not open until 1834. Generally, the education of medical students was informal and irregular: those aspiring to join the profession clustered around an eminent teacher such as John Hunter at his Great Windmill Street School and gleaned what practical experience they could by 'walking the wards' in attendance upon a leading physician or surgeon. With the founding of student medical societies in the 1770s a further, much-needed educational resource became available. The first and most famous was the Physical Society of Guy's Hospital, originating in 1770 when Dr William Saunders began to lecture there. Its meetings provided a forum for dissertations, the description of medical cases and discussion between students, staff and practitioners in the neighbourhood. Dr Saunders was its first President, supported by Astley Cooper, Dr Babington, Dr Haighton and Dr Curry, who were to be leading figures in the Medical and Chirurgical Society on its formation in 1805.

The Middlesex Hospital Medical Society was formed in 1774 for students, and its counterpart at St Bartholomew's Hospital originated in 1795 (it was renamed the Abernethian in 1832 in recognition of its founder, the surgeon John Abernethy).[2] The teachers, lecturers and leaders of the London medical milieu – Abernethy, Dr Fordyce, Dr Fothergill, Dr Sheldon, Dr Simmons, Dr Lettsom, William and John Hunter and Dr Saunders – personally inspired several medical societies, which might be attended by students, graduates, senior members of the profession or an intermingling thereof. The founders looked to the examples of the Royal Society of London and the Royal Medical Society of Edinburgh, and they sought to promote the education of the medical profession by sharing their skills, experience and most importantly their researches, experiments and discoveries in the exciting and apparently limitless new field of scientific medicine.

John Hunter was particularly active in the London medical societies by reason of his status as a teacher and anatomist. He revolutionized surgery and gave impetus to the study of morbid anatomy, inspiring his nephew Dr Matthew Baillie to write the first important book on the subject in English. Hunter's surgical methods, lectures and the personal influ-

16

ence he exerted moulded the next generation: he urged his pupils to enquire, to experiment, to try, and at another level he founded and promoted medical societies where cases and research could be presented and discussed. Hunter was the founder or co-founder of the Society for the Improvement of Medical and Chirurgical Knowledge in 1783, which met at Slaughter's Coffee-house, and of the Lyceum Medicum Londinense based at Hunter's lecture room from 1785; he was also an originator of the Pow-wow, a society for scientific medical conversation that held 'a delightful monthly meeting' at the Thatched House Tavern.[3] Hunter's medical societies were ridiculed by some: one pamphleteer derided them as medical tea-sipping societies,[4] yet there was no denying their popularity – as their proliferation and longevity was to prove. After John Hunter's death in 1793, his pupils sustained the societies he founded and formed new ones, including one which took his name, the Hunterian, founded in 1819 with Sir William Blizard as its first President.[5]

John Hunter and Dr John Lettsom enjoyed membership of another society called the Athletae, for the promotion of health by exercise. Its meetings often took place at Lettsom's villa in Camberwell, where dinner was followed by outdoor pursuits. Dr Lettsom, who personified the current ideal of progress and moral improvement, built up a large London practice and supported several philanthropic institutions and societies, notably the Medical Society of London, which he founded in 1773 for physicians, surgeons and apothecaries. This was the parent of the Medical and Chirurgical Society of London, formed in 1805, renamed the Royal Medical and Chirurgical Society in 1834 and from which the Royal Society of Medicine descended in 1907.

1 Gray, John , *History of the Royal Society of Medicine 1737–1937* (1952) p. 54.

2 JB Bailey, Librarian of the RMCS from 1884 to 1887 and afterwards to the Royal College of Surgeons, wrote a general account of the medical societies of London: Bailey, JB, 'The medical institutions of London' in BMJ 6, 13 July, 1895 pp. 24–26, 100–03. See also Dukes, Cuthbert E, 'London medical societies in the eighteenth century' in PRSM vol 53 (1960) pp. 699–706; Rolleston, Sir Humphry, 'Medical friendships, clubs and societies' in *Annals of Medical History* n.s. vol ii May 1930 no 3 pp. 249–66; Power, Sir D'Arcy, *British medical societies* (1939); Hale-White, Sir William, 'The Physical Society' in *Guy's Hospital Gazette* vol 33 (1919) pp. 379–84, 396–401; Pitt, G Newton , 'Reflections on John Hunter as a physician and on his relation to the medical societies of the last century' in the *Lancet* (i) pt 2, 9 May 1896 pp. 1270–74.

3 'Pow-wow was an outlandish word for conjurer, and hence the members were tickled at the idea, and this name, which was proposed by John Hunter, was chosen.' See Cooper, Bransby B, *The life of Sir Astley Cooper Bart* (1843) vol ii pp. 239–40.

4 *Reflections on a letter addressed to the Governors of St George's Hospital by John Hunter* (1793) p. 19.

5 It has been estimated that John Hunter influenced more or less directly some 500 students and practitioners, see Pitt, G Newton, *op cit*. Another authority estimated that his pupils probably numbered nearly 1,000, see Porritt, Sir Arthur, 'John Hunter: distant echoes' in *Annals of the Royal College of Surgeons of England* vol 41 (1967) pp. 1–24.

# Chapter 1

# The founding of the Medical and Chirurgical Society

THE FORMATION OF the Medical and Chirurgical Society was the direct result of discontent within the ranks of the Medical Society of London. The latter had been founded with the aim of uniting in one association physicians, surgeons and apothecaries, and it remains the oldest surviving medical society in London. Nevertheless its existence has been threatened several times, not least when many of its distinguished members abandoned it and established the Medical and Chirurgical Society in 1805.

## The Medical Society of London
The first meeting of 10 of Dr Lettsom's friends to inaugurate the Medical Society of London was held on 19 May 1773, when it was resolved to found a society that would secure and promote 'the collective experience of the three primary divisions of the profession'.[1] Among the 29 members joining the following July stood Dr James Sims, whose dominance as President for 22 years was to split the Society, and Dr William Blizard (later Sir William), the founder of the medical school at the London Hospital and an original member of the Medical and Chirurgical Society in 1805.

Possibly because Lettsom's attention was diverted towards the promotion of the Royal Humane Society and the Royal Sea Bathing Infirmary at Margate, the Medical Society of London soon lost momentum: fewer papers were submitted by members and the meetings were dominated by Dr Sims and his supporters. A dispute led to the expulsion of Dr Whitehead from the chair in 1784, damaging the Society's prestige and bringing the threat of dissolution, which was narrowly averted by Sims' election as President in 1786. Under his leadership the Society rallied, benefiting from Lettsom's gift of the freehold property at Bolt Court, Fleet Street (Plate 1), and there were even rumours of a royal charter.[2] In the opening years of the 19th century dissension surfaced again, this time over the conveyance of Dr Sims' library to the Society. This apparently generous act aroused suspicions of deceit when it was revealed that the library comprised 6,000 volumes and not the 8,000 that had been promised as the basis of an agreement that gave Sims an annuity. Sims managed to retrieve the situation and engineered his re-election as President, and his reign continued unchallenged until 1805.

## A split in the Medical Society
In the first years of the 19th century younger men came to the fore in the Medical Society, namely Dr John Yelloly (who chaired the Council meetings for the session of 1803–04), Dr George Pearson (he and Yelloly were on the Library committee), Dr Alexander Marcet, Mr Dimsdale (these two both sat on the Council) and the Registrar, CR Aikin. They were increasingly frustrated by the oligarchic presidency and with the retrogressive nature of the Society at a time when prospects of reform, scientific progress and advances in medicine and surgery were exciting the profession.

The desire for change became evident in October 1804, when proposals were made for new laws to put the Society on a more democratic basis, and for improvements to the accounting procedure and to the Library. There was no progress on any of these points and during the winter of 1804 the activities of the Society practically ceased: Council meetings were adjourned and cancelled and only two papers were submitted. In February 1805 reform was again mooted, this time at a Council meeting attended by Yelloly, Marcet, Aikin, the President Dr Sims and ten other Council members. These proposals were directed against Sims' long and obstructive tenure of office by a motion that no gentleman who had served as President in the preceding three years was eligible for re-election and that two Vice Presidents should be elected annually on the same conditions. The Society then divided into two parties – the supporters of Sims and the opposition – and in a series of confrontational Council meetings resolutions were passed, and then rescinded. Matters came to a head at a special general meeting on 29 April where, although the reformers were well represented, Sims won the day. With proposals for new laws blocked and while Sims continued as President there was no future for the reformers in the Medical Society. They therefore resigned and formed the Medical and Chirurgical Society, which was based on more liberal principles and given a democratic constitution. This left just a core of loyal supporters at the Medical Society: 'Doctors Lettsom, Clutterbuck, Hancock, Pinckard and a few others of eminence adhered to the old establishment and maintained its existence by their learning and experience', the Registrar Thomas Pettigrew recalled.[3]

An influential figure at Guy's Hospital, Dr William Saunders (Plate 3), had submitted his letter of resignation even before the stormy meeting of 29 April. He claimed that the Medical Society was divided and biased against some of its members: 'I have never attended the meetings of the Medical Society', he wrote, 'as I understand that a spirit of party has excluded from its Councils some of the most learned and intelligent of its members I beg to resign my seat as one of the Council'. Replying, the Registrar begged Saunders to reconsider his resignation, to no avail.[4] Others followed Saunders' lead: Mr Frederick Skey withdrew from his engagement with the Society in April and the following month Dr Yelloly resigned as a trustee. Even the Society's founder, Dr Lettsom, penned a letter of resignation in March 1806, intimating that an element within the Society had conspired in recent elections 'to unite in the expulsion of its most distinguished, and literary members, and in the introduction of their own partisans'. Lettsom was persuaded to withdraw his resignation and subsequently he put forward suggestions 'to heal the disunion and promote the harmony of the Society' by the annual election of the President by ballot.[5] By this time the energetic Dr Henry Clutterbuck was chairing Council meetings and with the support of Dr George Birkbeck he mounted the final campaign to remove the main cause of dissension, Dr Sims, from the presidential chair. Objections to his oligarchy were compounded by a scandal: £87 that should have been in the hands of the sub-Librarian could not be found. Lack of confidence in the management of the Society then verged on mutiny, and both Birkbeck and Dr Walker refused to accept the honour of Orator. The Council Minutes record 'no business' in March 1808, Clutterbuck's proposal for the use of sealed lists in the election of officers was defeated in September and once the revered Dr Lettsom indicated that he supported reform, change was imminent.[6]

Birkbeck later recounted how he and Clutterbuck 'stood before the Society as innovators on bad customs, having been the first to tear from the chair of the Society the nearly immovable Dr Sims, who lorded the members in high style, and stood (or rather sat) resolutely in the way of all improvement, and wholly impeded the progress of science in the institution. Great was the strength of Sims, but his tower fell beneath the assault of his assailants. So obstinately indeed, had he fixed himself in the seat, that but for the opposition then made, he would, had death spared him, doubtless at that very moment have been sitting in the chair, the leather of which was so thoroughly identified with the nether integuments of the Doctor, that they had almost become united by the process of vital adhesion. Most reluctantly was he dragged therefrom. Some such a task had he, Dr Birkbeck, and his respected colleague at the Aldersgate Street Dispensary' [Henry Clutterbuck].[7]

Dr George Birkbeck, founder of the London Mechanics' Institute and after whom Birkbeck College, London University, is named. He joined the Medical and Chirurgical Society in 1807 and was elected President in 1825.

Lettsom's desire to see the reform of the Society he had founded, combined with the aggressive tactics adopted by Clutterbuck and Birkbeck had the desired effect: Sims submitted his letter of resignation in November 1808. He claimed credit for the Society's recovery from the brink of dissolution in 1786 and alleged that it would have died without his leadership and benefactions. 'This I feel to be one of the most awful moments of my life', he concluded pitifully. He was compensated by the gift of a piece of plate, and a committee was appointed to alter the laws of the Society forthwith.[8]

## Seceders found the Medical and Chirurgical Society

Meanwhile, Yelloly, Marcet and Saunders, leading the seceders from the Medical Society of London (MSL), had founded its offspring, the Medical and Chirurgical Society of London (MCS). Sims' obstinacy, together with the vetoing of reforms and improvements while he was still in a position of power, 'was the immediate cause of the secession of a considerable number of the most able and influential members of the Society'.[9] Frustration with the management of the MSL kicked the MCS into life; there were, however, as Yelloly pointed out, other reasons for the foundation of the Medical and Chirurgical Society, in particular the deficiencies of the Royal College of Physicians. The College was a regulatory body for the examination and admission of physicians to the profession; it was concerned with corporate business and the administration of memorial lectures. Criticism centred on its exclusive, regressive nature: it did not encourage communications on medical topics, its publication had lapsed and its Library was accessible only to a few. *The picture of the present state of the College of Physicians* (1817) described the current state of affairs: 'So long as the present system continues, the College can never make a figure as a learned body. The Licentiates have no interest in adding to its reputation, and the Fellows are too few to give brilliance, deep science, and interest to its transactions, which present only here and there a rich but scattered ray. It was these illiberal restrictions that perhaps led to the institution of the Medical and Chirurgical Society, which presents an assemblage of talent in every department of medicine, and a considerable part of that drawn from the College to enrich another soil'.[10]

### The membership

On 22 May 1805 at a meeting of physicians and surgeons at the Freemasons' Tavern, Great Queen Street,[11] it was resolved unanimously 'that a Society comprehending the

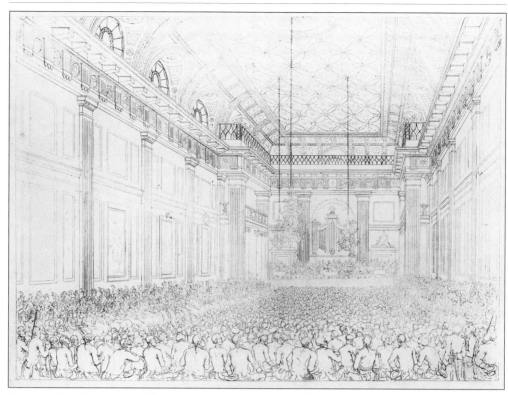

Interior of the Freemasons' Tavern, Great Queen Street, Holborn, where a group of physicians and surgeons met to found the Medical and Chirurgical Society of London on
22 May 1805.

several Branches of the medical profession be established in London, for the purpose of conversation on professional subjects, for the reception of communications, and for the formation of a library'.[12] The union of the various branches of the profession within the new Society was an essential principle. Yelloly wrote of 'the plan which has been pursued since the commencement of the Society of endeavouring to form an union of all descriptions of the profession. Fellows and Licentiates, Surgeons and Apothecaries are all necessary to form a Society of sufficient magnitude and respectability'.[13]

The new association was named the Medical and Chirurgical Society of London and its affairs were to be conducted by a President, four Vice Presidents, a Treasurer, three Secretaries (one being the Foreign Secretary) and a Council elected annually. The next clause, that no gentleman was eligible for the office of President for more than two years in succession, was a pointed reference to the difficulties experienced with the leadership of the MSL. Members – there were 26 founder-members present at this inaugural meeting – were to pay six guineas admission fee and an annual subscription of three guineas. In future, admissions were to be by personal nomination, followed by a ballot (three-quarters of the votes in favour were required for election), although to put the Society on its feet certain gentlemen were invited to become members without ballot. This gave the founders the opportunity to recruit James Parkinson (who first described Parkinson's disease in 1817), David Dundas (later Sir David, and serjeant-surgeon to George III), Dr John Haighton (one of the soundest obstetricians in London and a recipient of the Medical Society's silver medal) and Everard Home (John Hunter's pupil, brother-in-law, co-executor and the destroyer of his papers, later a baronet and President of the Royal College of Surgeons). Other important invitees were the royal apothecary Everard Brande and Dr Richard Croft, who attended Princess Charlotte in childbirth with fatal outcome (the combination of public criticism and personal remorse led to his suicide in 1818).

## Honorary members

Another category of Honorary members was created for 'gentlemen who have eminently distinguished themselves in sciences connected with medicine, but who are not of the medical profession'. Science was perceived as paving the way to progress and the leading scientists of the Royal Society and the Royal Institution were men of stature whom the MCS wished to cultivate. Accordingly invitations for Honorary membership were sent to Sir Joseph Banks, President of the Royal Society from 1778 to 1819, to Sir Charles Blagden, its Secretary from 1784 to 1797, to Dr John Aikin (editor of the *Monthly Magazine* from 1796 to 1806) and to Humphry Davy, Professor of Chemistry at the Royal Institution from 1802. Davy had recently flirted with a medical career, an idea he abandoned on being appointed director of the laboratory at the Royal Institution. Famous for his invention of the miner's safety lamp (first used in 1816), Davy received a baronetcy in 1818 and was elected President of the Royal Society in 1820.

Some of his peers were suspicious of Davy's methods, not least his experiments with 'laughing gas'. Dr John Bostock thought he came to hasty conclusions and that his lectures were merely 'to amuse the Lords and Ladies, who came in their carriages for their weekly Luncheon of philosophy'. Dr Wollaston, on the other hand, another early Honorary member of the MCS, was regarded as a serious chemist: 'the first chemical philosopher now alive in this country... the most acute man of the age on all philosophical subjects'.[14] The reserved, meticulous Wollaston had much in common with Dr Alexander Marcet (Plate 5), the Society's first Foreign Secretary, and he collaborated with Smithson Tennant in developing a method of producing malleable platinum.[15] Tennant was also one of the first Honorary members of the MCS; he is credited with the discovery of osmium and iridium and was Professor of Chemistry at Cambridge University from 1813. Wollaston, Secretary of the Royal Society from 1804 to 1816, Smithson Tennant and Marcet travelled to France together in 1814 to visit scientific friends; unfortunately Tennant died on the return journey and was buried at Boulogne.

The Honorary member Charles Hatchett was another of this group of Fellows of the Royal Society whose names feature large in the history of chemistry: Hatchett had discovered columbium (niobium) in 1801 and was well known as a mineral analyst and chemical manufacturer. Mr Edward Howard was also pleased to accept Honorary membership of the MCS; he was a brother of the Duke of Norfolk and the resourceful inventor of a new method of processing sugar, which made him a fortune. The patronage of Banks and Davy signified approval from the Royal Society and the Royal Institution respectively, and in 1806 Dr James Edward Smith, President of the Linnean Society, accepted Honorary membership, signalling approval from the country's second oldest scientific society.

Letters of acceptance addressed to Yelloly allude to the honour of being connected 'with a body so respectable as this new Society' (so wrote Sir Joseph Banks, who was usually wary of any new society that might detract from the stature of the Royal Society).[16] Wollaston saw the offer as the approbation 'of my endeavours to promote sciences connected with medicine'. Dr Haighton was concerned that the time of meetings should not interfere with his professional engagements and Dr William Heberden, physician to George III, was one of the few who declined to join because 'he should be very little able to attend' the meetings. Significantly, Sir Lucas Pepys, President of the Royal College of Physicians, and his successor, Sir Francis Milman, both refused Honorary memberships. Pepys' excuse that his 'public and private avocations are such as will prevent my accepting' might be interpreted as disapproval of the new Society by the College of Physicians, beleaguered as it was by demands for reform from associations that appeared to threaten its status.

Sir Joseph Banks, President of the Royal Society, was one of the first to accept Honorary membership of the Medical and Chirurgical Society. His letter of acceptance dated 10 July 1805 conveys his 'best thanks ... for the honor they have done me in choosing me an honorary member of their body'. He expressed 'infinite satisfaction' in being associated with 'a body so respectable as this new Society appears to be'.

## Distinguished physicians and surgeons

The founder-members of the Medical and Chirurgical Society were, as contemporary correspondents and reports emphasize, highly respectable, if not distinguished gentlemen. Mr A Cooper, the Society's first Treasurer, is better known as Sir Astley Cooper, twice President of the Royal College of Surgeons and surgeon to King George IV, whose innovative surgery was first described in the Society's *Transactions*. Dr William Saunders, the Chairman of the meeting of the nascent Society on 22 May 1805 and its first President, was physician to the royal family, a popular teacher at Guy's Hospital and the author of treatises on mineral waters, the use of mercury and diseases of the liver. He had been the first to resign from the Medical Society of London and as one of the senior physicians in London he added weight and dignity to the new Society. Yelloly remembered that he 'went with us heart and hand', as did Dr Matthew Baillie, Sir Walter Farquhar, Dr Pitcairn, Mr Cline and Mr Abernethy.[17] Baillie, author of *Morbid anatomy of some of the most important parts of the human body* in which he described emphysema and cirrhosis of the liver for the first time, counted George III, Lord Byron and the historian Edward Gibbon among his patients.[18] Baillie took an active part in the affairs of the Society from the beginning, becoming a Council member and later President (1808–10). The surgeon John Abernethy lectured at St Bartholomew's Hospital and was the founder of the medical school there. Another co-founder of the MCS was one of Abernethy's teachers, Sir William Blizard, twice President of the Royal College of Surgeons. His contemporary Dr Gilbert Blane, President of the MCS from 1813 to 1815, was known as 'Chilblaine' on account of his cold manner; he achieved fame through his introduction of citrus juice to the British navy. One of the Society's first Secretaries, Charles R Aikin, was the co-author of *A dictionary of chemistry and mineralogy*; the other, Yelloly, was physician to the General Dispensary in Aldersgate Street at the time of the Society's foundation. This was London's premier dispensary, founded by Lettsom in 1770 and a training ground for young physicians. The Society's Foreign Secretary, Dr Marcet, owed his appointment as physician to Guy's in 1804 to the influence of Saunders with whom he shared an interest in chemistry.

Several of the founders of the Medical and Chirurgical Society had been supporters of the Medical Society of London: these included Yelloly, Abernethy, Saunders, Blane,

Dr Matthew Baillie, founder-member and second President of the Society (1808–10). He was the nephew of William and John Hunter and the author of *Morbid anatomy of some of the most important parts of the human body* (1793), the first systematic atlas of pathology. Baillie presented a copy to the Society's Library in 1805.

Blizard, CR Aikin, Cooper, Babington, Marcet, Garthshore, Heaviside and Hart Myers (its former Librarian), while Abernethy remained a member of both societies. The 'Founders' Picture' of members of the Medical Society (Plate 1) features portraits of several of those who later gave their allegiance to the MCS.[19]

Of the officers and Council of the new Society, twelve were Fellows of the Royal Society or shortly to be so; some belonged to the Associated Faculty meeting at Sir Joseph Banks' house in Soho Square, while Marcet, Baillie, Cooper and others formed part of the wider circle of scientists and physicians that Banks entertained at conversaziones.[20] There was also a personal link between Banks and the Yellolys: Banks was related by marriage to Mrs Yelloly (*née* Sarah Tyssen) and had acted as her guardian. When she married Yelloly in 1806 Banks presented the couple with a handsome Japanese cabinet.[21]

The first members of the MCS were socially and professionally connected through their membership of other societies, and many had been taught or influenced by William or John Hunter. They encountered each other at the dinners of the Pow-wow club, at Guy's Physical Society meetings, at the Royal Jennerian Society for the extermination of smallpox or at the Society for the Improvement of Medical and Chirurgical Knowledge. They collaborated at the hospitals (those on the staff of Guy's were particularly active in establishing the Society), at the local dispensaries, in lecturing at the medical schools, at private and hospital laboratories and in consultations over private patients. And from May 1805 onwards they assembled in increasing numbers at meetings of the new Medical and Chirurgical Society. They were attracted by its liberal principles, the benefits that promised to accrue from 'useful intercourse among the different branches of the medical profession', by the prospect of a circulating (i.e. a lending) medical library, and the presentation and publication of papers by renowned physicians and surgeons.[22]

The Society's statutes gave passing recognition to practitioners of pharmacy or apothecaries, but their numbers never exceeded a small fraction of the membership. Similarly, there were only two accoucheurs among the founder-members. The strength of the newly founded Society derived mainly from the staff of Guy's and from those associated with the Great Windmill Street School, and a smaller group was drawn from the London Hospital and its medical school. It was not until the 1840s that a significant number of accoucheurs joined the membership, which had by that time broadened to include medical practitioners holding appointments at hospitals, infirmaries, lunatic asylums, orphanages and penitentiaries throughout the country.

## Favourable reports

The medical press viewed the new Society with approval. The *Medical and Physical Journal* of 1 July 1805 lauded its aim to 'promote a spirit of harmony among the members of the profession' and published a list of the names of the officers and Council, names that 'justify the highest expectations of the advantages to science which are likely to result from this institution'.[23] The *Medical and Chirurgical Review* pointed out that the Society 'comprises a considerable number of professional men of the first character'.[24] Another report claimed that the formation of the Society was due to the fact that the Medical Society of London had become 'too numerous in its members, and it has been alleged not so select at all times. From this cause dissensions some years ago arose, but as good at times issues from apparent evil, it gave rise to the Medical and Chirurgical Society, a more elevated establishment and which was formed purposely with a view to exclude the lower orders of the profession'.[25] On the other hand, JFL Clarke, who later wrote for the *Lancet*, found the MSL (of which he was himself a member) to be 'somewhat under the influence of the cold shade of aristocracy'. He went on to confirm that it was through the strenuous exertions of younger members such as Clutterbuck and Babington that Sims was eventually ousted from the presidential seat in a coup that came too late to prevent the secession of the more progressive members to found the Medical and Chirurgical Society.[26]

## Organization

At the meeting of physicians and surgeons at the Freemasons' Tavern on 22 May 1805, the Medical and Chirurgical Society was given its name and structure while its organization was placed in the hands of a management committee. The name of the new society emphasized the unity of medicine and surgery (chirurgical derived from the Latin *chirurgia* meaning surgery and the Greek words *cheiros* meaning hand and *ergon* meaning work). The first meetings were mainly concerned with membership: Henry Cline, surgeon to St Thomas', applied to join promptly as did Edward Jenner, who had received the Fothergill Gold Medal from the MSL in 1803 having been associated with that Society since the 1790s. Dr George Birkbeck belonged to the MSL but was invited to meetings of the Medical and Chirurgical by his contemporaries at Edinburgh University, and was elected a member in 1807. He continued to participate in the affairs of the older Society until he was defeated in the contest for Secretary in 1811; thenceforward he confined his attention to the MCS, serving successively as a member of its Council, a Vice President and finally President from 1825 to 1827. He is remembered in the name of Birkbeck College, London University, which originated in the London Mechanics' Institute, founded and endowed by him in 1823.

When it came to the drafting of statutes for the Society, the laws of the 'Royal Antiquarian Society' (perhaps the Society of Antiquaries?) and the Linnean Society were perused, and by the end of the year the Society's own statutes were ready for printing and circulation. Other important items on the agenda were the acquisition of 'a proper house'[27] and the purchase of the Obligation Book. Following their election members were required to sign this book as a mark of their promise or obligation to promote the interests of the Society and observe its statutes and orders. Some escaped the procedure and others had their names erased for non-payment of the subscription; nevertheless the book stands as a record of members' signatures. It contains not only the autographs of men famous for their contributions to medicine, but also the signatures of notable scientists, chemists, philanthropists, authors and royalty: Jenner, Birkbeck, Cline, Pitcairn, Roget, Faraday, King

We whose names are hereunto subscribed, do hereby promise, each for himself, that we will, to the utmost of our power, promote the honour and interest of the Medical and Chirurgical Society of London, and observe the statutes and orders of the said Society. Provided that, whensoever any of us shall signify to the President, under his hand, that he desireth to withdraw therefrom, he shall be free from this obligation for the future.

Members of the Society were required to sign the Obligation Book to signify commitment to promote the honour and interests of the Society and to observe its statutes and orders. By the end of 1805, 65 members had signed the book.

The first Council Minutes of the Medical and Chirurgical Society, 2 July 1805.

## THE SANCTUARY OF GRAY'S INN FROM BUSY THEOBALD'S ROAD

This bird's-eye view of Gray's Inn shows it as an oasis in a desert of brick. The Inn itself has been largely rebuilt, but there is a delightful touch of Old London in Staple Inn, at the Holborn end, which has long ceased to be an inn. The entrance to Gray's Inn from Holborn is through a tunnel-like passage leading into South Square, which, in turn, leads into the larger Gray's Inn Square. The buildings on the right in the foreground are known as Raymond's Buildings, and it is here that Mr. Harold Cox, the well-known writer, has his chambers, while beyond, outside the shady garden of the Inn, is Jockey's Fields.

View of Gray's Inn looking south. The Medical and Chirurgical Society's first house at 2 Verulam Buildings was at the south end of the terrace in the left foreground. The Society was based here from 1805 until 1810 when it moved to Lincoln's Inn Fields.

William IV (on the grant of a charter to the Society in 1834), followed by Queen Victoria, Hodgkin, Brande, Brodie, Lister and many others.[28]

The first Council meeting of the Society was convened on 2 July at the Crown and Anchor in the Strand (Plate 2), where the large hall was a favourite rendezvous for meetings of liberals, politicians and reformers.[29] The Council consisted of the officers of the Society with seven physicians and five surgeons bringing the number to 22 originally, 21 after 1813. The main business of the first Council was the appointment of a committee to search for a house for the Society's headquarters, the ordering of Minute Books and the collection of admission fees.

## Verulam Buildings

In August Dr Yelloly was pleased to report that he had inspected and approved of premises at 2 Verulam Buildings, Gray's Inn Road. This was one of a terrace of four-storey houses built as barristers' chambers by Joseph Wigg, surveyor to the Inner Temple, in 1803. The terrace was set back from the main road with pleasant views to the west over Gray's Inn Gardens. The Society arranged to take rooms on the ground floor for its meeting room and Library, with accommodation for the clerk in the basement. A lease was agreed for three years at 90 guineas per annum, and the MCS held its first general meeting there on 18 December 1805 at 9pm. At a second meeting on Christmas Eve further decisions as to membership were made: medical professors at universities were to be encouraged to join the Society without fees or subscriptions. Practitioners in pharmacy were not to exceed

2 Verulam Buildings, where the Society was based from 1805 until 1810. The drawings were executed by Elizabeth Drake for the centenary history of the Society, 1905. From the top: the front room (exterior); the front room (interior), used as the Library; the back room was used as the Library and meeting room.

one-third of the total membership and foreign members were to be admitted without payment, a concession designed to encourage contact with medical men and scientists abroad. In conclusion, it was with some pride that Yelloly revealed he had received a letter from Humphry Davy 'in which he had expressed the sense of the honour conferred upon him by being elected an Honorary member'.[30]

## The leadership of Dr John Yelloly

Having secured rooms at 2 Verulam Buildings for the Society, Dr Yelloly was chiefly responsible for creating the Society's Library. This he based on the catalogue of the Edinburgh Medical Society. If any single person can be credited with the foundation of the Medical and Chirurgical Society it is Yelloly (Plate 4). He had applied for a post at Guy's Hospital in 1804, only to be thwarted by the influential Treasurer who secured the post for a friend, and three years later he lost another contest for a position at the London Hospital. But with the retirement of Dr John Cooke and support from Sir William Blizard (fellow-members of the MCS), Yelloly eventually obtained the post of physician at the London in 1807, defeating Dr Dale who had not produced his credentials. Yelloly was still in his early thirties and could now reflect upon a successful few years: between 1805 and 1807 he had founded a medical society, married an heiress and secured promotion.

The combination of events meant that Yelloly was less assiduous in attending the Society's meetings than he had been, but he denied that he had 'become luke warm in Society matters'. He commented that 'a Society is somewhat like a female, to be brought forward with great caution and never without a good cause' and, as he explained to Marcet, his absence was for the simple reason that he disliked leaving his new wife alone in the evenings. He reaffirmed the responsibility that he and Marcet shared: 'I really consider the Medical and Chirurgical Society as owing its existence entirely to yourself and me and I moreover perfectly agree with you in thinking that its stability is only to be produced by the continuance of that union of exertion by which it has been so auspiciously commenced'.[31]

The Medical and Chirurgical Society benefited from Yelloly's experience as a former trustee and committee member of the MSL and he introduced many visitors who subsequently became members. He was also a prominent member of the Edinburgh Club, a 'little monthly club of good fellowship' for those who had studied medicine at Edinburgh University and were now in London. Members met at each other's houses from 1800 onwards; after the death of the Secretary Dr Thomas Murray *circa* 1802, Yelloly took over the post and introduced new members including Farre, Roget, Travers, Bateman, Curry and Birkbeck. Yelloly remembered that 'Some years after the formation of the Medical and Chirurgical Society we became acquainted with some very valuable members of that Society whom it was important to have as members of our Club, particularly Lawrence, and I think George Young and others. They, however, had not studied in Edinburgh and in order to obtain their admission among us we changed our name to the Medical and Chirurgical Club'. Presuming that the Medical and Chirurgical Club continued the tradition of the Edinburgh Club, members met for tea and then presented the occasional paper, compared notes, examined preparations and enjoyed friendly discussion; they were all expected to support any professional undertaking of a fellow member. At the conclusion, members adjourned for a cold supper although 'The only stimulating beverage permitted to be drank [*sic*] on these occasions was, strangely enough for a society of medical men, the not very wholesome one of cold punch'. Visitors were welcome. 'Every medical foreigner of distinction used regularly to visit us', Yelloly recalled, Berzelius, Pictet and Frank among them.[32]

There seems to have been a second dining club patronized by members of the MCS, known as the Medical and Chirurgical Society Club, which met at the Freemasons' Tavern for a few years. Cooper and Yelloly were stalwarts of this club while it lasted but shortly before his death in 1842 Yelloly lamented that 'there had not been such festive meetings connected with the Society for many years'.[33] The Pow-wow, to which many members of the MCS belonged, had also ceased to be.

Dr Robert Williams' memoir of Yelloly confirms that the latter was the principal founder of the Society he continued to nurture. Williams was elected to the Society in 1814 (becoming President from 1841 to 1843) so would have had personal knowledge of his subject. 'As the foundation of this Society was mainly due to Dr Yelloly, so its prosperity was always a subject of the deepest interest to him and he often in merriment called it his "eldest son"... he took much personal trouble in procuring our charter... the formation of our library, also, is principally owing to his exertions... [he was] not only its founder, but also its liberal, untiring and firmest friend and whose last aspiration to heaven may be said to have been that it might be permanent and extended'.[34]

## Dr Alexander Marcet

The cultivation of foreign physicians, surgeons and scientists, together with contact with continental libraries and medical schools and with members of the profession serving overseas, was pursued by Dr Alexander Marcet, the first Foreign Secretary of the Society (Plate 5). The MCS had followed the example of the Royal Society in appointing a Foreign Secretary to forge contacts in Paris, Vienna, Stockholm, Geneva and elsewhere. The large Paris hospitals were at this time cradles of research headed by renowned teachers, notably Corvisart, Bichat, his pupil Laënnec (who devised the stethoscope in 1816) and Louis. Their scientific methods and diagnostic techniques attracted admiration, and after the Napoleonic wars British medical students, including Marshall Hall and Thomas Hodgkin, flocked to Paris. The influence of Paris remained dominant throughout the first decades of the 19th century and the Medical and Chirurgical Society of London was determined to keep abreast of the advances in clinical medicine, the methods and the training advocated by the Paris teachers. The research being carried out in the laboratories and universities of Germany was also of great interest; Liebig's laboratory at the University of Giessen opened in 1824, Müller taught physiology and anatomy in Berlin from 1833 and the important work undertaken by both men was recognized by the Society's Council in awarding them Honorary Fellowships.

Alexander John Gaspard Marcet, born in Geneva of Huguenot descent, spoke and wrote fluent French and enjoyed the friendship and confidence of foreign physicians and chemists. He had been banished from Switzerland as a result of the revolutionary disturbances of the late 18th century, finding refuge in medical studies at Edinburgh University. He settled in London in 1799, becoming physician to Guy's Hospital from 1804 and lecturer in chemistry from 1807. His hospital case book (1804–17) survives at the Royal College of Surgeons and reveals that he saw many cases in conjunction with Astley Cooper. Like Yelloly, Marcet married well – Jane Marcet (*née* Haldimand ) was the only daughter of a Swiss banker; her books on chemistry and political economy gained the respect of Jenner and Faraday. Mrs Marcet inherited a fortune on her father's death in 1819, whereupon her husband resigned as physician to Guy's in order to devote himself to chemical studies and the couple purchased a large estate at Geneva.

As a close friend of Jenner, Marcet was instrumental in the introduction of the smallpox vaccine to De Carro in Vienna (and hence to the rest of Europe, the USA and India) and to colleagues in Copenhagen.[35] Another of his friends, Dr JF Berger of Geneva and Paris, was regularly invited to meetings of the Medical and Chirurgical Society in 1810, perhaps sowing the idea that foreign Honorary members – 'eminent men in the sciences connected with medicine and foreign practitioners' – should be invited to join the Society. Consequently in 1812 the first foreign members were elected: Samuel T von Sommering, the most famous German anatomist of the day and the author of treatises on the sense organs, his contemporary JF Blumenbach, Professor of Medicine at the University of Gottingen, along with Dr Benjamin Rush of Philadelphia, Professor Odier of Geneva, Jean Corvisart who was Napoleon's trusted physician, Professor Sabatier, Professor Antonio Scarpa of Padua who described arteriosclerosis, Monsieur Georges Cuvier of Paris and Dr Vieusseux of Geneva.[36] Vieusseux was persuaded to communicate to the Society the particulars of his own case, 'a singular nervous or paralytic affection',[37] of which he died in 1814.

Marcet's friend Jacob Berzelius, Professor of Chemistry at Stockholm, visited London in the summer of 1812 and was entertained by Marcet at a dinner with compatible guests from the Royal Institution and the Medical and Chirurgical Society including Dr WH Wollaston, William Allen and Dr William Babington. Berzelius was also invited to a meeting of the Society on 8 September 1812 to give a paper on 'The composition of animal fluids', later published in the Society's *Transactions*. He enjoyed working in Marcet's private laboratory and Marcet helped Berzelius to achieve recognition in this country (see page 27). Others who accepted Honorary foreign memberships were Dr Albers of Bremen, Anthony Portal, Professor of Medicine at Paris, and Dr JC Spurzheim, the phrenologist from Vienna who in 1814 gave the Society four lectures demonstrating his anatomical discoveries relating to the brain.[38]

There was no person better qualified than Marcet to enlist the support of members, both foreign and resident. He was renowned for the 'persuasive suavity of his manners, the earnestness with which he pursued what he thought was good, and the generous ardour of his disposition, to excite the zeal of others, to overcome their prejudices and to secure their co-operation in every laudable undertaking. These qualities were eminently displayed in the establishment of the Medical and Chirurgical Society of London, an institution of which Dr Marcet and Dr Yelloly, in conjunction, originally conceived the plan and laid the foundations and which has been indebted to them, more than to any other individuals, for its continued and increasing prosperity'.[39]

## The first papers

The reading of original papers at general meetings of the Society was delayed until 15 January 1806, when Sir William Blizard took the chair. Five visitors were invited and several new members were proposed, including Dr John Bostock of Liverpool, one of the many Edinburgh graduates to gravitate towards the Society. The list of books recently presented to the Library was recited, followed by the reading of the first papers: Blizard's 'Observations on morbid inclinations of different parts of the body', illustrated by a case of dissection of diseased prostate, followed by Marcet's cases of dissections which generated earnest discussion. At the next meeting on 29 January Astley Cooper described the first operation for aneurysm of the carotid artery. When there was no paper submitted to a meeting members resorted to discussions of, for instance, the use of purgatives in the treatment of typhus, a topic raised by the recent publication of Dr James Hamilton's *Observations on the utility and administration of purgative medicines* (1806).[40]

Reviewing the first year of the Society's existence, a report told of 'the auspicious beginning of the undertaking ... the public meetings of the Society have already been enriched by several truly valuable communications'. The nucleus of the Library was established, periodicals were available at the Society's rooms for members to consult and the publication of the most important papers read at the meetings was being planned. 'The experience of the last session has shown that the great object for which the Society was instituted has been attained and a bond of liberal union has been established between a considerable number of professional men'.[41]

Contrary to prescribed practice, Dr Saunders retained the office of President for three

The nucleus of the RSM Library, 1805. At the first meeting of the Medical and Chirurgical Society at its house in Verulam Buildings, the first gifts of books for the Library were noted. Dr Baillie and Dr Saunders gave copies of their own works; Mr Hunter was the most generous benefactor, presenting works by Celsus and Hippocrates.

years in the interests of stability, but during the winter of 1807–08 he was frequently absent (he was 65 years old, and was to retire from medical practice in 1814). Humphry Davy and William Allen attended meetings during this session, and among the new names appearing on the membership list stood those of Dr George Birkbeck and Benjamin Travers. Charles Hatchett communicated a case of hydrophobia, Yelloly read his case of dissection of the brain and Bostock's paper on blood engrossed two meetings. Bostock was a regular source of papers, responding to Marcet's requests promptly, for he was eager to see his work in print. 'You send out an order for a paper for your Society, and up one goes; you are saucy, return it, and ask for another and another is sent'.[42] These papers were based on Bostock's chemical experiments, which were breaking new ground in the field of animal chemistry. The originality of his own work contrasted with some of the other papers published by the Society, which he criticized as 'mere cases ... leading to no particular conclusion and not sufficiently curious...'.[43] An outsider, JFL Clarke, confirmed that the early communications were often short and 'not borne down with a weight of learning' but were nonetheless valuable for their 'narration of cases and their thoroughly practical character'.[44]

In March 1808 the Treasurer reported that the Society possessed a healthy balance of £119 14s 10d after expenditure of £264 5s 5d. With the succession of Dr Baillie as President in the same month, attendances at meetings rose. Baillie was supported by Sir Walter Farquhar Bt (physician to Pitt and the Prince of Wales), the surgeon James Wilson (who headed the Great Windmill Street School), Dr Christopher Stanger (physician to the Foundling Hospital and Gresham Professor of Physic) and John Pearson (surgeon to the Lock Hospital) as Vice Presidents. The Council included Henry Cline, Birkbeck,

Everard Home, Dr David Pitcairn (of St Bartholomew's Hospital) and Dr James Franck (physician to HM Forces). The new regime pursued plans for the Society's publication with Messrs Longmans and appointed Thomas Nicholls as clerk in November 1808. By a special arrangement, he was permitted to occupy the Library when it was not in use and to purchase a bedstead at the Society's expense, kept in a corner of the meeting room.[45]

## An overture to union

The Medical and Chirurgical Society was three years old and flourishing when in December 1808 a letter from one of the Secretaries of the Medical Society of London, John Mason Good, proposed that the two societies might unite. The replacement of the militant Dr Saunders by the amiable Dr Baillie as President of the MCS, and the resignation of Dr Sims as President of the MSL in 1808 created an opportunity for reconciliation. The older Society had not recovered from the loss of members to the young Society and when attendances at meetings dropped to less than ten, it was time for an approach to be made to the MCS, which was establishing a Library and planning a regular publication but which lacked a freehold property such as the MSL possessed. JM Good had the reform of the medical profession at heart and the initiative in writing to Yelloly with proposals for a union of the two premier medical societies of London may have been his; the letter hints that preliminary negotiations and the canvassing of opinions had already taken place.[46] The MSL had already appointed a negotiating committee and Good suggested that this committee should meet 'a select committee of the Medical and Chirurgical Society, consisting of the same number, in order to carry into effect the desirable object of an union'. Doctors Shaw, Pearson, Marcet, Birkbeck and Yelloly were duly delegated to confer with their opposite numbers on 24 December 1808 at Verulam Buildings. They reported a week later that 'such union was desirable but that the principles of independence, utility and respectability on which the Medical and Chirurgical Society was formed' must be preserved. The main questions for discussion were whether an altogether new society should be founded, and whether the union would promote communication between the various branches of the profession more effectively than at present. Moreover, would union necessitate a change of name and location?

At an extraordinary meeting of the MCS held on 10 January 1809, the committee to discuss the amalgamation reported on the conference that had been held with representatives of the MSL. While recognizing 'the augmentations of numbers and property which would result from an union' and 'considering the advantages which might arise to the profession from the formation of one great body', insurmountable difficulties had arisen relating to the change of place and name for the proposed united society. The main stumbling block was 3 Bolt Court, a property held in the name of the Medical Society of London, and this could not, apparently, be altered. While the MCS was willing to adopt a completely new name for the united society and to move to a new house, the MSL would not agree to a change of name or place. Legal niceties might have solved the problem of the tenure of Bolt Court but the Society's representatives were adamant that the name of the Medical Society of London must remain unchanged; to members of the younger Society this condition represented the absorption of their institution by the older one, which they would not countenance.[47] The conference reached an impasse and was dissolved, although the possibility of union lingered until February 1809, creating a difficulty for Dr Baillie. He informed Marcet that if a union was 'to take place between the two societies during my Presidentship I should be placed in a situation of the greatest embarrassment. Were I to continue as President under these circumstances I should give great umbrage to my Brethren of the College with whom I should wish to be on good terms – and were I to resign upon such an event it would be very ungracious towards the members of the other Society, many of whom are highly respectable'.[48] Baillie implies that the 'Brethren of the

College' of Physicians did not approve of the proposed union of London's two leading medical societies, which might well have been a factor in the failure of the scheme. With the failure of the amalgamation negotiations Baillie was saved embarrassment and so continued as President for the second year.

Neither Society suffered from the collapse of this, the first of many attempts at amalgamation. The Medical Society of London elected Dr Lettsom as President, which doubtless explained the sudden influx of new candidates for membership, so that by 1817 that Society was reported to be 'very numerous and the influence of apothecaries is predominant in it'. For its part, the Medical and Chirurgical Society forged ahead with the first volume of its *Transactions* and embarked upon the search for a larger, more commodious house, thus earning praise as 'a body which in the course of a few years, has outrivalled in utility and importance, all former associations of a similar kind in this country, and promises to contribute greatly to the improvement and lustre of the medical profession'.[49]

1 Owen, Edmund, 'The Medical Society of London in the eighteenth century', *Lancet* (i) 22 May 1897 pp. 1389–95. Thomson, Sir St Clair, *John Coakley Lettsom and the foundation of the Medical Society* (1918).

2 Letter Bissett to Lettsom 6 September 1788, see Pettigrew, TJ, *Memoirs of the life and writings of the late John Coakley Lettsom* vol 3 pt 2 (1917).

3 Pettigrew, TJ, *Medical Portrait Gallery. Biographical memoirs of the most celebrated Physicians, Surgeons etc etc who have contributed to the advancement of medical science* vol iv (1840) p.9.

4 Letter Wagstaffe to Saunders 13 April 1805, Marcet collection, RCP.

5 The proceedings can be followed in the Council Minutes of the MSL, available on microfilm, WMS/MF/4, Wellcome.

6 *Ibid* 31 August, 7 September 1807, 25 January, 14, 28 March, 19 September, 31 October 1808.

7 *Lancet* (i) 16 November 1833 pp. 307–9.

8 Council Minutes MSL *op cit* 14, 28 November 1808.

9 Clutterbuck, Henry, *A brief memoir of George Birkbeck* (1842) p. 9. Clutterbuck was President of the MSL 1819–21, 1825, 1840. He founded the *Medical and Chirurgical Review* in 1794.

10 *The picture of the present state of the College of Physicians of London* (1817) p. xxii-xxiii. The second edition of 1818 was renamed *Authentic memoirs of the most eminent Physicians and Surgeons of Great Britain* and was attributed to W Nisbet. Yelloly's opinions were given in evidence to the Select Committee on Medical Education (1834). See also the Society's petition for a royal charter (1812–14) for its position *vis à vis* the College of Physicians (chapter 2).

11 The site of the Freemasons' Tavern is now occupied by the Connaught Rooms, Freemasons' Hall, Great Queen Street.

12 GM 22 May 1805, B1.

13 Letter Yelloly to Marcet 8 February 1815, Marcet correspondence (1802–23), Duke.

14 Letters Bostock to Marcet 16 September 1809, 25 February, 16 March 1811, 9 January 1912, Bostock correspondence (1802–22), Duke.

15 Chaldecott, JA, 'Contributions of Fellows of the Royal Society to the fabrication of platinum vessels: some unpublished manuscripts' in *Notes and Records of the Royal Society* vol xxii (1967) pp. 155–72.

16 Collection of the original autograph letters of the early members of the Society and other celebrated professional men relative to the formation of the Society, addressed to Dr Yelloly. Presented by Mrs Yelloly to the RMCS in 1842, Ms 253.

17 Cooper, BB, *The life of Sir Astley Cooper Bart* vol ii (1843) p.40.

18 Baillie, Cline and Farquhar examined Gibbon's swollen testicle in 1793 and punctured it, whereupon four quarts of fluid were discharged; a second time three quarts were discharged, a third time six quarts were drawn off. Gibbon died shortly afterwards.

19 Hunt, Thomas (ed), *The Medical Society of London 1773–1973* (1972). Of the 22 men featured in the picture, Saunders, Haighton, Aikin (an Honorary member), Hart Myers, Jenner, Ware and Babington were later to join the MCS.

20 The Associated Faculty also met at the house of a founder-member of the Society, Dr Maxwell Garthshore, to promote medical reform. Garthshore was a friend and correspondent of Banks. For details of the Faculty see Harrison, Edward, *An Address delivered to the Lincolnshire Benevolent Medical Society in 1809* (1810). Marcet, Wollaston,

Davy, Herschel, Baillie, Cooper, Home, Birkbeck and Lawrence attended Sunday evening conversaziones at Banks' house (1812–13).

21 Suckling, Florence Horatio Nelson, *A forgotten past, being notes of the families of Tyssen, Baker, Hougham and Milles, of five centuries* (1898).

22 *Medical and Chirurgical Review* July 1805 vol lxvii p. lxiv.

23 *Medical and Physical Journal* 1 July 1805 vol xiv p. 191.

24 *Medical and Chirurgical Review op cit.*

25 *Picture of the present state of the College of Physicians of London* (1817) p. 342.

26 Clarke, JFL, *Autobiographical sketches of the medical profession* (1874) p. 229.

27 GM May 1805– May 1811, B1.

28 RMCS Obligation Book 1805–1907, D3/1.

29 The meeting room at the Crown and Anchor saw the birth of the movement for regulation and reform of the medical profession in 1794 when the General Pharmaceutical Association was formed. Reformers met there again in 1812 when an Association of Apothecaries and Surgeon-Apothecaries was founded.

30 GM 1805–06, B1. CM 1805, A1.

31 Letter Yelloly to Marcet 3 December 1806, Marcet correspondence (1802–23), Duke. Letter from Professor JK Crellin, JRSM vol 70 (1977) p.928.

32 Averley, Gwendoline, 'English scientific societies of the early eighteenth and nineteenth centuries', PhD CNAA Teesside Polytechnic 1989. Cooper, BB *op cit* vol i (1843) pp. 284–85. According to James Gray's *History of the Royal Medical Society 1737–1937* (1952) p.181, the Edinburgh Club in London was still active in 1879.

33 Cooper, BB *op cit* vol ii pp.41–42.

34 Williams, Robert, 'Memoirs of De Candolle, Mr Powell and Dr Yelloly' in the *Lancet* (ii) 7 May 1842 pp. 192–95. Dr Williams, physician to St Thomas' Hospital 1817–45, discovered the powers of potassium iodide over secondary syphilis and introduced

potassium bromide into English practice. Clarke, JFL, in *Autobiographical recollections of the medical profession* (1874) p. 215 confirms that Yelloly was the most active of the Society's founders.

35 Garrod, Sir Archibald, 'Alexander John Gaspard Marcet. Physician to Guy's Hospital 1804–19' in *Guy's Hospital Reports* (1925) vol 75 pp. 372–87. Sigerist, Henry E (ed), *Letters of Jean De Carro to Alexander Marcet 1794–1817* (1950). Miller, Genevieve (ed), *Letters of Edward Jenner and other documents concerning the early history of vaccination from the HBJ collection in the Welch Medical Library* (1983). Marcet, A, Collected Papers (1805–22).

36 CM 29 December 1810, 24 December 1811, 29 January, 18 February, 31 March 1812, A1. There were to be no more than 20 foreign members at any one time.

37 Transacs vol ii (1811).

38 GM 8 September 1812, 30 March, 25 May 1813, 29 March, 7 June 1814, B2. CM 22 February 1813, 30 March, 27 April 1814, A1.

39 Obituary of Alexander Marcet in the *Medical and Physical Journal* vol 49 (1823) pp. 85–88.

40 GM 15, 29 January, 12 February 1806, B1.

41 CM 25 August 1806, A1.

42 Letter Bostock to Marcet 18 April 1812, Bostock correspondence (1802–22), Duke.

43 *Ibid* 2 March 1813.

44 Clarke, JFL *op cit* p. 215.

45 CM 26 November 1808, 30 June 1809, A1.

46 JM Good was the founder of the General Pharmaceutical Association. He joined the MCS in 1824. His letter to Yelloly was dated 16 December 1808.

47 CM 16, 30 December 1808, A1. GM 10 January 1809, B1. Excerpts of report, M & P pp.16–17.

48 Letter Baillie to Marcet 17 February 1809, Marcet collection (3), RCP.

49 *Picture of the present state of the College of Physicians of London* (1817) pp. xlv, 173.

# Chapter 2

# The Medical and Chirurgical Society

THE OBJECT OF the Medical and Chirurgical Society was to unite physicians and surgeons in one association so that they might benefit from knowledge shared. The preface to the first volume of the Society's *Transactions* stressed that the 'union of gentlemen in both Branches of the profession affords a greater facility of obtaining accurate information on many points of practice'. The idea was to exchange knowledge and not to engage in controversy, medical politics or disputation: 'it does not at all enter into the plan of this institution to suffer its proceedings to assume the form of debate or discussion'.[1]

Despite this pronouncement it is evident from the General Minutes that discussion did take place at meetings, and from 1831 onwards it was positively encouraged. As to the other point, the Society clung to its apolitical stance; it refrained from medical politics and took no part in the agitation for the reform of the medical profession that absorbed so many associations and members of the profession during the 19th century.

Apart from the routine administration by the officers and Council of a Society whose membership, Library and publication were all expanding, the essential business of the Society centred on the presentation of original papers at its meetings. The initial session of 1805 to 1806 was lean in this respect and there was a problem in the 1820s, but generally the stream of papers flowed freely, reaching a record of 25 published in *Medico-Chirurgical Transactions* for 1850. Members were encouraged to read their own papers at the meetings; alternatively they could communicate them through one of the Secretaries. The Council then selected for publication those it believed the most important.

Initially the papers were straightforward accounts of cases that members judged to be unusual and of interest to colleagues. Astley Cooper's descriptions of his recent feats in the operating theatre at Guy's attracted a large audience at a time when first-hand accounts of operations were rare – the publication of the *Lancet* and *Guy's Hospital Reports* lay in the future. Cooper's 'case of an aneurysm of the carotid artery' in which an operation was performed detailed 'a mode of relief which other Surgeons had never before dared to attempt'. This patient died but Cooper repeated the operation successfully in 1809 and as his nephew reported, 'The practice which he instituted in this instance has been adopted by all surgeons since that time and has been attended with the most beneficial results'.[2] Cooper has been known ever since as the father of arterial surgery. Nearly 20 years later one of his pupils, Charles Aston Key, was the first successfully to ligature the subclavian artery and this too was recorded in the Society's *Transactions* (1827).

Curiosity brought members to listen to Dr James Curry's account of a sailor who had swallowed over 30 clasp knives between 1799 and 1805 but being induced to repeat the performance he became 'the subject of great indisposition' and died.[3] Curry was a founder-member of the Society, one of several Edinburgh graduates working at Guy's Hospital and a believer in the medicinal qualities of calomel. 'With him there was only one organ diseased, the Liver, and only one medicine to be prescribed, Calomel', which he sprinkled on his sandwiches, hence he was known as Calomel Curry.[4]

At another level, members of the MCS who attended the meetings of 20 November and 10 December 1806 heard the first account in English of 'a peculiar disease of the heart' given by David Dundas whose cases were associated with rheumatic fever: he was describing what is now recognized as rheumatic heart disease. At the next meeting the theme continued with the first account of mitral stenosis by John Abernethy.[5]

## Dr Edward Jenner and vaccination

The first years of the Society saw the beginning of free smallpox vaccination for infants in the wake of Edward Jenner's publication of his discovery of the smallpox vaccine in 1798 (Plates 6 and 7). Jenner was a supportive but not very active member of what he called the 'Verulam Socy' (referring to its first address at Verulam Buildings). When Marcet asked him to write a paper for the Society, Jenner doubted that he would be able to oblige: 'I fear it will not be in my power to get a paper ready', he replied. Notwithstanding, he produced two papers, one on 'Observations on the distemper in dogs' and the second reporting 'Cases of small-pox infection communicated to the fetus in utero'. Since Jenner lived in Gloucestershire, his papers were communicated by an Honorary Secretary.[6] The 'dog paper' was the result of researches undertaken on some 20 staghounds of the Earl of Berkeley's hunt in 1801; an anonymous reviewer in the *Medical and Physical Journal* assessed it as 'a truly valuable paper inasmuch as it describes a canine epizootic with great accuracy'.[7] Jenner claimed that the delay in completing this paper was because he awaited details of cases; he was also preoccupied with problems at the National Vaccine Establishment 'which I may say to you is by no means fashion'd to my liking'. Jenner's 'vaccine corps' included several members of the MCS working at the stations for vaccination in London and led by Marcet as Jenner's 'General' in 'the antivariolous army'. Members of the Society – Sir Walter Farquhar, Cline, Blane and Baillie – had given evidence to the House of Commons in 1802, testifying that Jenner's vaccine 'was the greatest discovery that had been made for many years', a discovery for which Jenner received a parliamentary grant of £10,000.[8]

Farquhar, Dr and Mrs Marcet (to whom Jenner sent 'a little game and a couple of wood-cocks')[9] and Saunders were Jenner's personal friends. Marcet in particular was instrumental in promoting Jenner's vaccine, first obtaining it for use in London, and later in distributing it across the world through his many contacts. He sent Jenner in Gloucestershire 'glasses' for the preservation of vaccine matter 'better constructed for the purpose than any I have yet seen', Jenner thanked him, and it was through the co-opera-tion of Henry Cline that Jenner's vaccine first reached the London public. 'The virus for the first patient ever inoculated in the Metropolis was used at my request by Mr Cline', he reminded Marcet,[10] and in 1807 Jenner personally vaccinated the Yellolys' firstborn, 'inflicting a scar on the baby's arm the size of a guinea'.[11]

Marcet sent news of the Society to Jenner in Gloucestershire, receiving the reply, 'I am happy to hear the Medical Society is in so flourishing a state and tho' I have done so little yet I never lose sight of sending contributions': he intended to submit a paper on inflam-mation of the liver, but no trace of it survives.[12] He did attend a meeting of the Society on 18 June 1811 in the company of Wollaston, the main attraction being a paper from Dr Vieusseux of Geneva. Jenner visited London for the last time in 1814 and although he had been invited to stay at Marcet's villa in Swizerland, his health prevented this and he died in 1823. Guy's Physical Society must be credited with first providing a London audience for Jenner; there is no doubt, however, that the distribution of the smallpox vaccine was largely due to the co-operation and support of members of the Medical and Chirurgical Society which also published two of his papers.

## Wartime experience

The presentation of papers by well-known names such as Cooper and Jenner doubtless drew members and potential members to meetings of the Society at Verulam Buildings.

William Fergusson, Inspector of military hospitals, also attracted a large audience, for his papers reflected the current preoccupation with the war against France. The health of the troops fighting Napoleon's army was of immediate importance and the wartime experiences of surgeons provided papers of interest well beyond 1815. Fergusson spoke about the dysenteric diseases suffered by soldiers in the campaigns in Spain and Portugal; on a second occasion he told members that the widespread ophthalmia in the army was a myth, 'artificially excited by the men themselves with a view to escaping military duties and obtaining a discharge' – their trick was to apply a corrosive substance to the eye. In 1812 Fergusson read another paper on venereal disease in the army, a longstanding problem.[13]

A paper from Dr Gilpin describing the fever at the military hospital in Gibraltar prompted a response from the Duke of Kent who told the Society that during his year of command at Gibraltar (1802–03) there had been only 39 deaths attributed to the fever, compared with a previous average of 200 a year.[14]

Daniel Quarrier, serving aboard HMS *Leander* as flag-surgeon to Rear Admiral Milne, sent a copy of his report on the surgical treatment of sailors in action off Algiers in August 1816, when he had laboured in the ship's cockpit for 13 hours treating 65 wounded sailors in conditions he compared to the black hole of Calcutta. 'Under these disadvantages and difficulties our operations were performed and the poor patients afterwards exposed to the double danger of being trampled on'. He took pride in the fact that all amputations had been performed immediately, often at the hip joint after the manner of Larrey (chief surgeon on Napoleon's campaigns, later Baron Larrey and an Honorary member of the Society).[15] The exigencies of war surgery forced surgeons to attempt operations that had previously been regarded as unjustifiable, leading to the pioneering work for which London surgeons became renowned.

The Antwerp expedition of 1809 when Flushing and Walcheren were taken captured the attention of medical authorities on account of the so-called Walcheren fever. The lack of medical stores and personnel needed to combat the sickness created a scandal, exacerbated by the refusal of Sir Lucas Pepys (President of the Royal College of Physicians and Physician General to the army) to take command of the situation. Sir Gilbert Blane was therefore sent on a special mission to investigate the sickness of the troops at Walcheren, where he found more than half the army incapacitated. He presented his observations on the Walcheren fever to the MCS in 1812, and followed them three years later with another paper summarizing the medical reforms he had introduced, which had vastly improved the health of the navy. His paper 'On the comparative health of the British Navy' emphasized the beneficial effects of a general supply of lemon juice as a preventative against scurvy.[16]

Meanwhile, Marcet offered his services to the emergency military hospital where troops with Walcheren fever were sent. The experience of working at Haslar was 'extremely favourable to professional improvement', even so, Dr Bostock thought that however 'honourable, profitable and improving it must certainly have been very disagreeable'.[17] The experience certainly had one disagreeable aspect in that Marcet contracted the fever and was severely ill. The sickness and mortality of the British forces in the Napoleonic wars was subsequently the subject of an enquiry by the Army Medical Board and William Fergusson's answers to some of the questions raised by the official enquiry were conveyed to the Society in 1817, telling of the appalling conditions exacerbated by yellow fever and dysentery on the ships carrying recruits to the West Indies in 1815.[18]

## Chemistry

While a proportion of the papers from 1806 to 1817 reflected the fact that the country was or recently had been at war, several testified to the strong interest in chemistry among members of the Medical and Chirurgical Society. The wonders of chemistry promised miracles and many London physicians, apothecaries and amateurs were fascinated by the potential. Their desire to pursue the subject gave birth to several chemical societies and clubs founded in the early years of the 19th century, none of which survived for long. The Chemical Club of *circa* 1807–26 relied heavily on members of the MCS (Marcet, Bostock, Bright, Babington) before it disappeared at around the same time as the Society for the Improvement of Animal Chemistry (see opposite) ceased to exist. It was not until the 1840s that the Chemical Society of London and the College of Chemistry were founded, with a clutch of periodicals devoted to chemistry appearing in the same decade.

Earlier in the century Humphry Davy's lectures in chemistry at the Royal Institution proved popular, some papers on chemistry were published by the Royal Society and members of the MCS lectured on chemistry at Guy's Hospital and presented papers to the Society highlighting the value of chemical analysis to medicine. At the united hospitals of St Thomas' and Guy's anatomical and surgical lectures were allocated to St Thomas', while the teaching of medicine, chemistry, botany, physiology and natural philosophy was the responsibility of Guy's; the latter thus became the focus of scientific activity, with a particularly strong school of chemistry under the direction of Dr William Saunders.

Lecturing in chemistry at Guy's from the 1770s, Saunders directed the attention of his protégé Marcet to the chemical analysis of mineral waters, and Marcet contributed to Saunders' treatise on the subject (1805). Marcet was soon recognized by his contemporaries as an expert, and a letter to him from Yelloly conveys something of the reverence for chemistry in the early 19th century. 'I cannot help viewing great chemists (like yourself) as placed at a very awful distance on the Parnassus of Chemistry and myself a pilgrim trudging the plains below and very glad to catch hold of any kind of support to raise him but a humble distance'.[19]

Marcet was associated with William Allen in the lecturership of chemistry at Guy's Hospital between 1807 and 1819. Allen, the Quaker pharmacist whose business was known from 1856 as Allen & Hanbury's, was also involved with Davy in lecturing at the Royal Institution; he regularly socialized with members of the MCS (Wollaston, Babington, Marcet and his cousin George Birkbeck) and he attended meetings of the Society as a visitor in 1821. Allen relied on the opinion of Marcet, 'My dear Friend', to whom he sent specimens of leaves and bark from correspondents in Africa. Allen explained the possible medical qualities of the specimens and wanted Marcet to evaluate their potential. 'It is highly probable that Africa contains many useful medicines hitherto unknown', he surmised, 'and if among much rubbish we find a few good things we shall benefit the science of medicine and assist in the efforts to promote the civilization of Africa'.[20]

Dr John Bostock and Arthur Aikin succeeded Marcet as lecturers in chemistry at Guy's; Aikin collaborated with his brother Charles, Honorary Secretary to the MCS, in compiling *A dictionary of chemistry and mineralogy* (1807), which they dedicated to Charles Hatchett. With the exception of Allen and Arthur Aikin (who both had connections with the Society) the medical chemists of Guy's were all prominent in the MCS. Here they found encouragement from fellow-members, an outlet for their papers and a means of publication, thereby making a significant contribution to the development of scientific medicine in the early 19th century.[21]

## Marcet, Berzelius, Bostock and Prout

Marcet was at the forefront of what is now called clinical chemistry. He used to carry his own portable laboratory with him on weekend visits to Cooper's country house, arriving 'as punctually as if at a London party, having given himself just time sufficient to permit him to arrange himself with his accustomed elegant neatness for the dinner table'.[22] He initiated dietary reforms for patients at Guy's Hospital where he also introduced demonstrations to his chemistry lectures, a novelty adopted by the Swedish chemist, Jacob

Berzelius, who was seen as the doyen of European chemistry. Berzelius reported that 'Marcet took me to his chemical lectures at Guy's Hospital and there I had the opportunity to observe how chemical lectures were accompanied by demonstrations and saw a number of beautiful experiments planned expressly to illustrate the lecture. I had opportunity to copy Marcet's plan of lectures and the experiments which accompanied each lecture'.[23] Once Berzelius followed Marcet's example, this method of teaching became a model for the chemical schools of Europe.[24] After Berzelius' visit to London in 1812 he and Marcet corresponded regularly. Marcet proposed Berzelius as a foreign member of the MCS and urged him to submit papers for the Society's meetings. Berzelius obliged by giving one paper, which was published in volume iii of the *Transactions* and which represented the only part of his great treatise to appear in English.[25] Marcet searched for a English publisher for Berzelius, sent the *Transactions* to him in Stockholm and in a letter of January 1816 he described and sketched the miner's lamp recently devised by Humphry Davy.[26]

Inspired by Astley Cooper, Marcet made a number of chemical analyses of the fluid secreted in conditions such as spina bifida. Cooper's interest in spina bifida had been communicated to the Society on 21 May 1811 when he reported on his 'new mode of treatment' by an operation to puncture the tumour – he was the first surgeon to do this. Marcet followed up with his paper of 18 June, which stands as 'the earliest analysis of cerebro-spinal fluid as obtained from cases of spina bifida'.[27] When the paper appeared in the *Transactions* for 1811 it gave Dr John Bostock 'almost more pleasure than I ever before experienced (I mean philosophical pleasure) to find that you had confirmed my experiments – on the two points on which I may be considered as having staked my chemical reputation, on the non-existence of jelly in the blood and on the existence of an animal matter in the blood'.[28]

Bostock and Marcet carried out experiments in animal chemistry in their laboratories, and Marcet introduced animal chemistry into his lectures at Guy's from 1807; the Society for the Improvement of Animal Chemistry was supported by some members of the MCS until it lapsed in 1825. Animal chemistry was a subject in its infancy and Bostock made a

Dr John Bostock, a keen contributor to the Society's *Transactions*. His paper of 1819 on summer catarrh was the first description of hay-fever.

plea to a meeting of the Society for the adoption of more precise terms to define the subject.[29] Bostock assisted Dr Richard Bright at Guy's before taking over Marcet's lecturing duties there jointly with Aikin, when Marcet went to Geneva. Bostock's work on the chemical properties of urine formed the foundation of clinical biochemistry in renal medicine and his 20 papers to the MCS included his researches on diabetes, serum of the blood and on the nature and analysis of animal fluids – he regarded the last-named as his 'grand paper'.[30]

The correspondence between Bostock and Marcet while the former was in Liverpool contains news of their work, shared friends and the MCS. Bostock felt isolated in the provinces; he hungered for news of the London medical milieu, longed to meet Berzelius and relied on the *Transactions* to provide food for the intellect. He moved to London in 1817, tempted by the prospect of lecturing in chemistry and by his need of the Society's Library in order to complete his piece on Medicine for Dr Brewster's *Encyclopaedia*. Another topic of correspondence was Bostock's summer catarrh, an affliction which he found 'extremely disagreeable and harrassing' for it rendered him 'totally unfit for any exertion for almost three months in every year'.[31] Bostock later described his symptoms, 'a periodical affection of the eyes and chest', in a paper to the Society. The remedies he resorted to varied from leeches applied to the chest to the use of opium, mercury and digitalis – none was efficacious. Dr John Sims was able to shed some light on the affliction, deducing that it was caused by 'some irritating substance widely diffused in the atmosphere during the period of hay-making'. Although Bostock called the condition summer catarrh, he is credited with the first description of hay-fever, as disclosed to the Medical and Chirurgical Society in 1819.[32]

Marcet's knowledge of chemistry led to the publication of his major work, *An essay on the chemical history and medical treatment of calculous disorders* (1817), which was dedicated to an Honorary member of the MCS who was Marcet's own mentor, WH Wollaston ('the Pope' as Marcet called him). In this work Marcet distinguished a substance in urinary calculi which he called xanthic oxide (xanthine) and the book as a whole was acclaimed as 'the first systematic attempt to present all the available information in a form suitable for the use of medical students and physicians'.[33] His reputation was made, and colleagues referred to him for his opinion in rare cases: Dr J Abercrombie, for instance, wrote of 'the zeal and ability with which you have cultivated animal chemistry' when sending a specimen of a cyst to Marcet for analysis.[34]

In May 1819 Marcet narrated to his Society one of the cases on which his publication was based, a case of nephritis calculosa, with an account of the operation of lithotomy in bladder stone given by the patient himself, a man of 40. Mr Cline had performed the 'severe' operation in 1811 applying great force to withdraw the stone – according to the patient 'it seemed as if the whole organ was about to be torn out'.[35] The operation was modified by the Norwich surgeon Philip M Martineau, who explained his technique to members of the MCS in 1821 and this method became known as 'the Norwich operation for stone'.[36]

Marcet's last paper to the Society, read in March 1822, presented his researches on 'a singular variety of urine with some particulars respecting its chemical properties' and was the earliest description of alkaptonuria, a disorder which turns the urine black (the substance was named 'alkapton' by Boedeker in 1859). Marcet had sent the sample for analysis to Dr William Prout, a fellow-member of the Society well known for his skill in the analysis of urine. Prout gave papers on the subject to the Society on three occasions between 1817 and 1819, culminating in a communication to the Royal Society that led directly to his Fellowship (his proposer being Marcet).[37] In reporting to Marcet on his analysis, Prout distinguished 'a new substance ... melanic acid' (homogentisic acid). He is better known for his hypothesis that the atomic weights of all elements must be simple multiples of the atomic weight of hydrogen. He discovered hydrochloric acid in stomach secretions, analysed milk, and was the first to classify foods into carbohydrates, fats and proteins; his work on the chemical relationships between bodily substances pre-dated Liebig's.[38]

Marcet's paper of 1822 also noted a case he had come across of a woman subject to paroxysms during which her urine turned black and her limbs tingled – a case of paroxysmal haemoglobinuria with Raynaud's disease, as it was later known. Marcet's contemporary, William Nisbet, thought highly of all Marcet's papers 'marked by originality, precision and clear thinking, impressing unknown or unobserved truths'. Sir Archibald Garrod, writing in the 1920s, echoed Nisbet: 'Although no great discovery stands to his credit, nor is any wide generalization associated with his name, almost every paper he wrote brought forward some new method or unknown facts, not a few of which we attribute to much more recent investigators'[39] (Garrod recognized Marcet's earliest description of alkaptonuria but overlooked his discovery of xanthine). Marcet died suddenly in October 1822 aged 52, having recently enjoyed a holiday in Scotland where he shot blackcock with Sir Humphry Davy. In his last moments he was attended by fellow-members of the Society – Babington, Roget and Bright. His chemistry lectures, his papers to the MCS and his book on calculous disorders established him not only as an experimental chemist but one of the first to perceive that physiological processes could be explained in chemical terms.[40]

## Dr Richard Bright

When the 21-year-old Richard Bright arrived at Guy's Hospital in 1810 he found the place dominated by members of the Medical and Chirurgical Society – Cooper, Babington, Curry, Marcet, Cline, Travers and Haighton. The tradition was to be upheld by the younger generation: Bright himself, Thomas Addison, Joseph Toynbee, John Bostock, James Blundell, William Prout, George Johnson and Thomas Hodgkin.

One of Bright's little-known unpublished papers, 'On the contagious nature of erysipelas', was read to the Society on 21 January 1812 and formed the basis of his MD thesis at Edinburgh, *De erysipelate contagioso* (1813).[41] The nature and treatment of erysipelas was also dealt with by William Lawrence, surgeon to St Bartholomew's, in two papers read to the Society in 1827: 'the most complete account of erysipelas we possess', as

Dr Richard Bright, President of the Society 1837–39. In *Reports of medical cases* (1827–30) he described diseases of the kidney including Bright's disease.

it was judged in 1840.[42] In the early 19th century erysipelas was almost an epidemic among surgical and medical hospital patients and its treatment was controversial. 'We had four practitioners of the highest eminence and skill treating the disease in four different ways!' Clarke recalled. Elliotson (President of the Society 1833–35) painted the patient with nitrate of silver, Dr A Todd Thomson of the North London Hospital preferred mercurial ointment, Astley Cooper attempted to isolate the disease with lines of lunar caustic and Robert Liston preferred fomentations and the application of flour.[43]

Addison, Hodgkin and Bright all proceeded from Edinburgh University to Guy's Hospital and membership of the MCS. Bright joined the Society in 1814 and was to be its President from 1837 to 1839. His team of assistants at Guy's lay behind his work on diseases of the kidney, culminating in his description of chronic non-suppurative nephritis, known eponymously as Bright's disease (Plates 9, 69). His major publication *Reports of medical cases* (1827–30) generated articles on the disease by George Johnson, Joseph Toynbee and AB Garrod in the *Transactions*; Sir Samuel Wilks considered Johnson to be the first physician to add anything to existing knowledge of Bright's disease.[44] Bright contributed four papers to *Medico-Chirurgical Transactions* including an account of pancreatic diabetes in 1833, 'his most original paper among his many on abdominal diseases', followed by one on peritoneal adhesions in 1835, since recognized as the first description of chronic proliferative peritonitis.[45]

## Papers from abroad

A high proportion of the early members of the Society pursued chemistry and were associated with Guy's Hospital; some had been pupils of John Hunter and many were graduates from Edinburgh. The membership also included a generous scattering of royal appointees (David Dundas, serjeant-surgeon to George III, presented one of the first papers in November 1806). There were a few apothecaries and a few practitioners in the provinces among the members but most were cosmopolitan physicians and surgeons with contacts abroad.

Yelloly regarded the Society as a centre of professional communication in the British Empire, and as Foreign Secretary Marcet solicited papers from teachers, scientists and practitioners working in Paris, Geneva, Lucca, Hamburg, Madras, Bengal, Haiti and North America. Surgeons with the East India Company and the British Army in India sent communications telling of the epidemics there; Signor Babantini of Lucca sent a letter to the President describing a new operation for stone, and a surgeon with the 3rd Regiment of Guards in America detailed the complicated pneumonia afflicting troops.[46] Some of the papers were specially commissioned by Dr Roget from medical officers in India, and by Astley Cooper, who managed to transmit to Mr JS Birt in 'Hayti' some queries about the conduct of surgical operations there. Birt replied, 'I am almost inclined to say better than in England!! The blacks are peculiarly unirritable, they suffer the knife almost without a groan'.[47]

## Papers from James Parkinson and Sir Benjamin Brodie

Dr Yelloly's friend James Parkinson and his son John were responsible for the first paper describing acute appendicitis, read to the Society on 21 January 1812. James Parkinson, who was to publish his *Essay on the shaking palsy* five years later, read the paper on behalf of his son. It described a case of diseased appendix, which had caused the death of a five-year-old boy in the Parkinsons' care.[48] This paper claims a place in the annals of British medical literature, as do those received from the surgeon Benjamin Brodie. Several disorders were named after him and he is perhaps best known for his legendary case involving Isambard Kingdom Brunel and a gold coin (see pages 48–49) and for his book *Pathological and surgical observations on the diseases of the joints* (1818), which went into five editions. This developed from three papers read to the Medical and Chirurgical Society between 1813 and 1815.[49] Many of Brodie's papers to the Society, such as those on varicose veins, injuries of the brain, trephining the bone for chronic inflammation of the tibia (describing the chronic bone abscess called after him) and lithotrity, were to become standard authorities on those subjects.[50]

Sir Benjamin Brodie was to prove one of the most successful Presidents of the Society as well as a wise elder statesman, but at the time of his introduction to the MCS he was regarded with suspicion. 'Pray what do you think of Brodie's experiments and opinions?' Bostock asked Marcet, 'Are we to give up all our beautiful hypotheses and renowned Black, Crawford and all the old worthies in favour of this upstart nobody-knows-who chap?'.[51]

Brodie personified the rise of the surgeon in the 19th century, a rise assisted by patronage, dedication, membership of societies and dining clubs and attendance on three monarchs, which brought him a baronetcy in 1834. Perhaps most remarkable among his successes was his election as President of the Royal Society in 1858, the first surgeon to be so honoured. His last public appearance before his death in 1862 was at a meeting of the RMCS when he proposed the vote on the address of condolence to Queen Victoria on the death of Prince Albert.

## Dr James Blundell and the first transfusion of human blood

Two of the most important papers in terms of lives saved were given by Dr James Blundell, joint lecturer on physiology and midwifery at Guy's with his uncle, Dr John Haighton.[52] Blundell's concern about loss of blood, especially postpartum haemorrhage, led him to attempt the first transfusions of blood from human to human.

Experiments in transfusing blood from dog to dog and from sheep to human had taken place in the late 17th century. In this country Dr Richard Lower (one of the Oxford group of natural philosophers associated with Dr Thomas Willis and Robert Boyle) demonstrated a transfusion of sheep's blood to Arthur Coga before members of the Royal Society

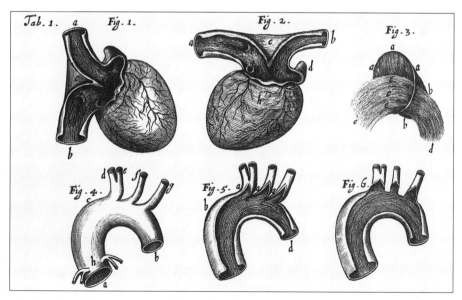

A plate from *Tractatus de corde* by Richard Lower (1669) whose name is remembered in the tubercle of Lower. His treatise presented important observations on the arrangement of muscular fibres in the heart and the coagulation of the blood. It also referred to his experiment in transfusing sheep's blood to Arthur Coga at the Royal Society in 1667.

James Blundell, who reported the first human-to-human blood transfusion to a meeting of the Medical and Chirurgical Society in December 1818. Blundell lectured on midwifery at Guy's Hospital (1814–36).

in 1667. Any further experimentation was discouraged by the authorities, and it was not until the early 19th century that the work of Blundell marked the dawn of human blood transfusion.

Blundell's first paper to the MCS, communicated to a meeting in February 1818 by the surgeon Henry Cline, described 'experiments on the transfusion of blood by the syringe'. Blundell had first experimented on dogs and he had devised a syringe 'capable of receiving blood immediately from the bottom of a cup'. A dog was bled until all signs of life were extinguished, then 'completely restored by infusing 6 ounces of arterial blood from another dog by syringe'. Blundell inferred that a similar operation might be safely carried out on a human subject and in December 1818 he gave a paper entitled 'Some account of obstinate vomiting' in which an attempt was made to prolong life by the injection of blood into the veins. Blundell told how, assisted by Cline, he had met with success in treating a desperate patient named Brazier. Some gentlemen present at the operation volunteered to give a few ounces of blood each and this was immediately infused into the vein of the patient in a gradual stream. 'This operation was repeated ten times so that between 12 to 14 ounces of blood were introduced, in this manner, in the course of 30 or 40 minutes'. Despite an initial recovery the patient died 56 hours later (the autopsy revealed he had suffered from scirrhosity of the pylorus). Blundell was not discouraged: 'the operation is very easy… the infusion of human blood by syringe is unattended with danger. Who can tell the various diseases in the management of which it might perhaps be applied?'.[53]

Blundell performed further transfusions on 10 patients over the next decade, of whom five survived. Inspired by his example others experimented with blood transfusion, using various crude instruments – Blundell's own inventions were called the Gravitator and the Impellor (see opposite). In 1823 Blundell again stood before a meeting of the Society, this time as the advocate of operations for the removal of ovarian cysts, ruptured and cancerous uteri and the repair of ruptured bladders: his experiments on rabbits convinced him that opening the human peritoneum would not usually prove fatal. It seems this paper was too innovative for publication in the Society's *Transactions*, so Blundell published it privately later that year.

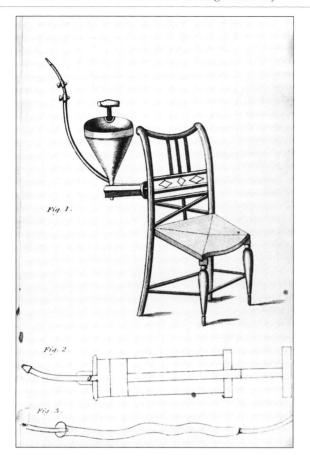

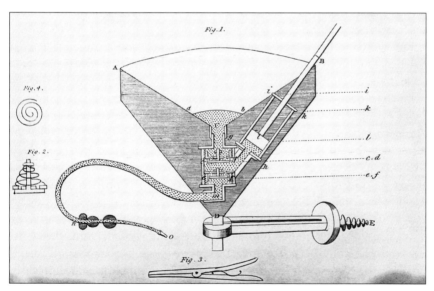

Apparatus devised by Blundell for blood transfusions, as illustrated in his book, *Researches physiological and pathological* (1824). Top, the Impellor mounted, with (Figures 2 and 3) the injecting syringe and tube for transfusion from arteries to veins direct.

Below, a perpendicular section of the Impellor. The outer cup (shaded with lines) was filled with warm water. The blood went into the inner cup (the dots represent the portion filled with blood). When the piston was raised the blood was drawn from the cup down the pipe, through the upper valve into the syringe. When the piston was depressed blood was expelled through the lower valve and along the pipe m,n,o.

Blundell's influence on the development of blood transfusion has barely been acknowledged yet it is clear that after a gap of some 150 years his experiments and publications opened a door that had long been shut. Not only did his example encourage others, but he was one of the first to establish that only blood of the same species should be used and that venous blood was as satisfactory as arterial blood.[54]

## Officers and administration

The founder-members had deliberately shaped the Society's statutes to ensure the replacement of the President every two years and to allow the annual election of Vice Presidents, officers and Council members. The first President, Dr Saunders, commanded a large following and his successor, Dr Baillie, was well liked. The number attending meetings depended not only on the submission of interesting papers but also on the presence and charisma (or lack of it) of the President, rival attractions and probably the weather. Council meetings, on the other hand, relied on the consistent dedication of a handful of members to administer the routine business of the Society. All the officers of the Society and members of Council were summoned to regular Council meetings but in the early years few attended, leaving the administration of the Society's business in the hands of the Secretaries. Sir Henry Halford failed to chair a single Council meeting during the years of his presidency, at which time the Society was run by Yelloly, Marcet and Roget, with occasional assistance from Bateman, Lawrence and other Council members. As Treasurer, Astley Cooper was seldom seen at Council meetings, and after 1810 Yelloly took joint responsibility.

### Fees and subscriptions

Members' fees and subscriptions formed the backbone of the Society's finances and their collection required diligence. There were inevitably some members in arrears with annual subscriptions (22 in 1817) and library fines. Non-resident or country members paid the admission fee of six guineas and were exempt from the annual subscription paid by resident members who lived locally and were more likely to use the Society's house and Library. The definition of a non-resident member was subject to review, being defined in 1813 as one who lived more than seven miles from the Society's house and after 1846 anyone who lived over seven miles from the General Post Office in St Martin le Grand.

The name of a member who failed to pay his subscription was reported to the Council, and if payment was not forthcoming a line was drawn through his signature in the Obligation Book. In 1817 Dr George Birkbeck, Mr Charles Bell, Dr James Curry and Mr James Wilson were in arrears – Wilson had not paid his subscription for three years before it came to the Council's notice. In June 1833 the Council hardened its policy, threatening eight members with expulsion for non-payment of subscriptions; in the event, however, only one was ejected.[55]

Charles Bell, a surgeon of Soho Square who was later knighted, became a member of the Society in 1813 and duly signed the Obligation Book, only to have his signature erased in 1837 for the non-payment of his subscription. Since coming to London in 1804 Bell had written two books and attended the wounded from the battle of Corunna; in 1815 he went to Waterloo where he is said to have operated on 300 soldiers. His paper on muscles of the uterus and the anatomy of the bladder was published in the Society's *Transactions* even before he was elected a member of the MCS. He presented the Library with a copy of his *Engravings from specimens of morbid parts* (he was a talented draughtsman) and a rare copy of his privately printed pamphlet, *A new anatomy of the brain* (1811). His famous description of Bell's palsy, as it was to be known, appeared in the Royal Society's *Philosophical Transactions*; his own copy of *The nervous system of the human body* is to be found in the RSM Library. In all, Bell delivered four papers to the Medical and

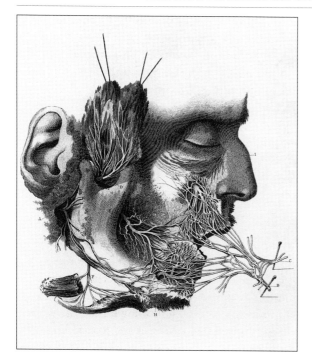

Drawing by Sir Charles Bell to illustrate the nerves of the face from *The nervous system of the human body* (1830); the author's personal copy was presented to the Library by Dr Henry Barnes in 1890. Bell was a member of the Society and served on the Council before going to Edinburgh in 1836.

Chirurgical Society and served on the Council in 1832–33, before moving to Edinburgh in 1836 to take the chair of surgery at the University.

## Fraudulent clerks

The Society's finances were overseen by the Treasurer; Yelloly pressed Astley Cooper to be the first to accept the office in 1810.[56] The collection of subscriptions was the clerk's responsibility, however, and one that Mr Yeoman found too tempting. Yeoman had petitioned for a rise in salary in 1818 because his attendance was required in the Library: he obtained five shillings, topped by a more generous honorarium of £8 15s for his help in moving and arranging books at the Society's new premises at 30 Lincoln's Inn Fields where he and his family were accommodated from 1819. Three months later Yeoman was summoned before the Council to be questioned on the number of members' subscriptions he had received so that those who were in debt could be circulated. He produced a list of those in arrears and some figures, but contrary to his statement at least two members proved by the production of receipts that they had indeed paid their subscriptions. In the course of the enquiry Yeoman's misdemeanours were uncovered and he confessed that he had not accounted for subscriptions amounting to some £140. On further investigation it was revealed that he owed the Society £252 4s in subscriptions, fees and sales of the Library catalogue. Yeoman was dismissed and the Society's solicitor put the sale of his property in hand, with the proceeds (about £230) going to the Society which was still out of pocket – Dr Bostock calculated that Yeoman's debt to the Society amounted to over £335.

Yeoman's misconduct caused Marcet 'very great pain. To be sure, Yelloly was the person who recommended Yeoman, but then he watched him very closely and so long as he was watched everything went on right'. Latterly, however, Yeoman had not only defrauded the Society; he had also neglected his duties and left the books and Minutes in a condition of 'illiterate slovenliness'.[57] The experience led the Society to insist that the next clerk, Mr Law, provided security of £300 deposited with the trustees. He was requested to settle his accounts with the Treasurer weekly and his salary was to be 100 guineas per annum including provision for a servant.[58]

Law, who 'turned out to be still more stupid than Yeoman', was not content with his salary and resigned in 1821, whereupon he was succeeded by Mr Raven; Roget thought he would be more suitable, being an artist and without children.[59] The collection of subscriptions had been taken out of the clerk's hands and Raven was praised for his work on a *catalogue raisonné* of the Society's Library in 1823, for which he was rewarded with 30 guineas. Then history repeated itself. Raven disappeared having overdrawn his salary and left his maid unpaid – the Council estimated that the 'total deficiency' amounted to £120 14s 3d. A small portion of that sum was recovered by the sale of some silver spoons belonging to the ex-clerk, and the Council tightened up the financial management of the Society by the introduction of a members' subscription book and a cash book (1825).[60] Raven's catalogue was a failure; remaining copies were given away in 1826 and members who had purchased one were given a refund.

## The growth of the Society

The growth of the Society in its first decade can be attributed to the leadership of the founders and first Presidents and to interesting meetings; it may also have been related to the demise in 1805 of the Lyceum Medicum Londinense, a society that had had a large membership. Similarly, the dissolution of the exclusive Society for the Improvement of Medical and Chirurgical Knowledge in 1818 allowed its former members to focus on the Medical and Chirurgical Society. Of course there were the counter-attractions of the Westminster Medical Society (founded in 1809) and the Hunterian Society (founded in 1819), while Guy's Physical Society continued to flourish and the Medical Society of London soldiered on.

One of the strengths of the Medical and Chirurgical Society was its distinguished membership; the founders had taken care to recruit the leading physicians, surgeons and scientists. The patronage of Sir Humphry Davy and Sir Joseph Banks inspired confidence and the Presidents elected by the Society were at the head of their profession, men with influence and often royal connections.

As the first surgeon to be elected President, Henry Cline broke new ground in 1815. He was criticized for being diverted by politics and agriculture; nevertheless his period of office saw rising attendances at the Society's meetings at 3 Holborn Row, Lincoln's Inn Fields, next door to his own house. Council's decision that henceforward the office of President should be held alternately by a physician and a surgeon was surely a mark of Cline's success.[61]

Dr William Babington, Cline's successor, had been Apothecary to Guy's Hospital; as a co-founder of the Geological Society he may have initiated the joint tenancy with that Society (see pages 58–60). He was also a keen member of the Athletae, he featured in the 'Founders' Picture' of members of the Medical Society of London and he was by all accounts 'the most delightful of men'... 'amiable as a good Christian; mild as mother's milk... a most industrious, scientific and worthy man'.[62] His popularity attracted as many as 41 members and 10 visitors to meetings of the MCS in 1818. Sir Benjamin Brodie remembered the apprehensive moments that preceded a meeting, as those assembled wondered if Dr Babington might have been required elsewhere until 'the sound of the carriage wheels would instantly dispel the gloom'.[63]

## Yelloly leaves London

At the close of Babington's term of office in March 1819 the Council Minutes record a tribute to Dr Yelloly, who had resigned from the London Hospital in June 1818 and moved to Carrow Abbey, Norwich, so could no longer attend the Society's meetings. Yelloly was not yet retired: he was appointed physician to the Duke of Gloucester in 1819 and to the Norfolk and Norwich Hospital from 1821. His move out of London was said to be on account of 'the health of his numerous family' (Mrs Yelloly had been ill in 1818 and in 1820 gave birth to their tenth child) and his reason for choosing Norwich rested on his wife's associations with Norfolk, connections through Astley Cooper and the local hospital's reputation for 'stones and bones'. Norfolk had the highest incidence of bladder stone of any county, and preserved at the Norfolk and Norwich Hospital was a collection of all bladder stones removed at that hospital since 1771. Yelloly had contributed a paper on an exceptional calculus to volume vi of the *Transactions* and he was especially interested in the chemistry of urinary calculi. His appointment at the Norfolk and Norwich Hospital gave him access to the hospital's collection and provided him with a rich resource for research.

Bostock suspected that Yelloly was 'disappointed in the reception he has met with at Norwich' and had heard 'that they thought him a *meddlesome* man; you will understand this provincial term and I can easily imagine that those who *only see a little* of him might form some such idea. His real worth, however, I know so well that I wish most heartily he was among us again'.[64] At Norwich Yelloly was in the company of the surgeon John G Crosse (a fellow-member of the MCS) and together they studied the epidemiology and chemical analysis of bladder stones. Yelloly's analysis of 663 specimens has been cited as his main chemical achievement[65] and the results formed the subject of two papers in the Royal Society's *Philosophical Transactions* (1829, 1830). Crosse's notebooks, including 13 volumes on *calculus vesicae*, found their way to the RSM Library.[66]

The Council expressed its grateful sense of Yelloly's 'zeal and persevering exertions on its behalf both at the period of its formation and during its gradual tho' rapid progress to the present prosperous state of the society'. Yelloly was anxious that the name of Marcet should be united 'in the acknowledgement of our services', so in thanking the Council for those kind words, he gave 'due credit to a most particular and respected friend whose energy and talents, whose honourable, independent and manly feelings, and whose amiable and conciliatory manner cannot be too highly valued. To both Dr Marcet and myself the rapid and gigantic strides of the Society to the lofty position which it holds in the country and in Europe, have been, and ever will be, a source of most sincere gratification'.[67]

Yelloly resigned as the Society's Treasurer but at his own request continued to be a subscribing member and he remained on the Council for the time being. He was the first member to be given permission to have Library books sent to him in the country and he contributed the occasional paper, but otherwise kept a low profile until 1834 when he proposed and secured a royal charter for the Society (see pages 68–70).[68]

## Sir Astley Cooper

Had he not moved to Norwich, Yelloly would have been an obvious candidate for President. As it was, Astley Cooper was elected to that office in March 1819; given that he was an original member, the first Treasurer and widely known, he appeared eminently suited to the post (Plate 8). His pupil Benjamin Travers described Cooper as 'the handsomest, that is, the most intelligent and finely-formed countenance and person of any man … He wore his hair powdered, with a queue, then the custom, and having dark hair, and always a fine healthy glow of colour in his cheeks, the fashion became him well.' In summer he rode daily on horseback wearing a blue coat and yellow buckskin breeches and top-boots, then much in vogue. 'Nor was he altogether unconscious of the fine proportions of his frame, for he would not infrequently throw his well-shaped leg upon the table'.[69]

Astley Cooper was given a baronetcy during his term of office following his removal of a sebaceous cyst from the head of King George IV[70] and he celebrated in characteristic fashion by giving a dinner for his cronies. Cooper belonged to several societies and dining clubs, and he liked to cut a dash – which may have been why he failed to impress Roget and Yelloly. Bostock, on the other hand, thought Cooper promised to make an excellent President and he refuted Yelloly's claim that the Society was 'going down hill very fast' during Cooper's term in office.[71] Cooper himself declared that 'the good opinion of the Medical Chirurgical Society will be my proudest boast and its welfare will ever be near my heart'.[72]

## Dr Peter Roget

The inner core of officers upon whom the continued existence of the Society relied worked hard, especially in the event of an ineffective President. Surviving correspondence makes it clear that the personal exertions of Roget, with some assistance from Bostock, kept the Society alive during the difficult period of Cooper's Presidency.[73] Bostock was a conscientious Treasurer, apart from an episode when he disappeared to Liverpool for two months leaving all the Society's papers and accounts locked up and inaccessible. Bostock and Roget had graduated from Edinburgh on the same day and in 1815 Bostock joined Roget and Marcet as a neighbour in Bloomsbury.

Like Marcet, Dr Peter Roget was of Huguenot descent, and after practising in Manchester he came to London in 1808 and was elected to the MCS the following year (his father was a member before him). He was already planning his *Thesaurus of English words and phrases*, first published in 1852 and running to 25 editions in his lifetime, and he invented a logarithmic slide rule in 1814. His early devotion to the MCS was plain to see – when in 1811 he was proposed as a member of the Society for the Improvement of Medical and Chirurgical Knowledge the ballot was not proceeded with because it was obvious that all his exertions were concentrated on promoting the *Transactions* of the MCS.[74] Roget participated wholeheartedly in the affairs of the Society until the death of his friend Marcet in 1822 – his biographer describes their relationship as 'the nearest thing to an intimate friendship that Roget had'.[75] After Marcet's death other interests claimed Roget's time, although a few years later he was to return to the Society as President (1829–31).

Dr Peter Roget, President 1829–31 and author of the *Thesaurus of English words and phrases* (1852). Roget was the Society's Treasurer and its Secretary for 12 years, and was responsible for classifying and arranging the Library at 3 Lincoln's Inn Fields.

Roget set about classifying and arranging the Society's Library, having been on the committee that organized the move from Verulam Buildings to Lincoln's Inn Fields. With Bostock he investigated the clerk's fraudulent behaviour, kept an eye on the finances and undertook the unenviable task of editing and preparing the *Transactions* for the printer.

Correspondence between Roget and Marcet reveals their concern about the Society's 'unsettled state' and the difficulties experienced between 1818 and 1820. Roget was ill in October 1818 and Marcet urged him to transfer some of his duties to Henry Earle (surgeon to the Foundling Hospital and joint Treasurer to the Society) 'otherwise great delays will take place and it will be said that when Dr Yelloly, Dr Roget and Dr Marcet are out of the way the Society ceases to thrive'. This was evidently the case, for almost a year later Marcet expressed dismay at the state of 'our darling child in Lincoln's Inn Fields'. He was concerned about the lack of a publication for 1820 and the uncertainty surrounding the Society's future accommodation. 'It would almost seem now as if the Society was going to pieces, without a house and without its volume', he wrote to Roget. 'And I am more alarmed at the present state of affairs as I know that, in point of fact, you have done, personally, all that you could possibly do for the Society'.[76] Yelloly and Marcet agreed that the problems lay with Cooper, who lacked diligence and failed to excite or even animate 'our lukewarm members' (although he did give a dinner for the Council in January 1820).[77] The founders of the Society were at a loss to know how to proceed: Marcet was in Geneva, Yelloly in Norwich, and Roget wrote to both telling of the problems that beset the Society. By contrast, 'Bolt Court is making a great burst' (this referred to the Medical Society of London under the presidency of Clutterbuck), and the Hunterian Society had recently been established and was proving an attraction. At the MCS, however, 'The worthy President [Cooper] is complained of as not encouraging conversation. The meetings I fear are attended mostly by junior members' and Yelloly reported 'that the Society has reached its acme, for there is no individual of sufficient consequence and strength of character to keep matters together'.[78] Bostock was more confident, informing Marcet that neither the Chemical Club nor the Medical and Chirurgical Society were asleep, or even drowsy, as he supposed. Moreover the Society had just found very good accommodation on the west side of Lincoln's Inn Fields.[79]

Sir Astley Cooper had not 'answered our expectations... I long to hear that he has a more zealous substitute', Marcet wrote, looking forward to a more diligent successor, [80] and with the election of the new President in March 1821 optimism returned. Roget reported that the Society was 'going on rather better than for some time – we had resolved upon electing Sir James MacGrigor to the chair but after hesitating some time he declined the honour, chiefly on the score of health'. Dr John Cooke, Roget's former associate at the Great Windmill Street School, a classical scholar and physician to the London Hospital for over 20 years, was elected instead; Yelloly described him as 'a man of great wit and good temper... I think he will exert himself in [sic] behalf of the Society, and I expect that he will take more pains to invite conversation at the meetings than his predecessor and will at any rate do it in better taste'.[81] This was a reference to Cooper's deficiencies – he was no orator, 'had not any large choice of words' and his pronunciation was strongly Norfolk.[82]

Dr Cooke's presidency saw the Society settled in a 'most excellent house' on the west side of Lincoln's Inn Fields. It looked as though income was likely to exceed expenditure by £300, and Roget was more content: 'I think I shall continue as I am in the Society [as Secretary] a year or two longer although I feel it is a serious encroachment on my time which nothing but my attachment to the interests of the society could have made me so long submit to'.[83] Bostock found 'the trouble was very irksome' and resigned as Treasurer, while Henry Earle (a future President) became joint Secretary with Roget.[84]

Roget's dedication to the affairs of the MCS evaporated as his work in other spheres increased. He was involved with, and criticized for, an investigation into an epidemic at the

Millbank Penitentiary in 1823; he completed a pioneer study of the metropolitan water supply in 1828 and was from 1827 Secretary to the Royal Society, a post he clung to for 20 years.[85] His election as President of the MCS in 1829 came at a time when he was immersed in the business of the Royal Society, the committees, meetings and publications of which were time-consuming and took precedence. Roget's reputation took a tumble over alleged irregularities at the Royal Society, where he was accused of blackballing papers by Dr Marshall Hall. Eventually, denunciation by the *Lancet* forced him to relinquish the Secretaryship and soon afterwards he applied his mind to the completion of his *Thesaurus*.

## The liberal mood of the 1830s

The popularity of meetings of the Medical and Chirurgical Society rose with the election of the masterful William Lawrence as President in 1831. He was a lecturer at St Bartholomew's Hospital for 40 years, and with his friend Wakley he pushed for reforms at the Royal College of Surgeons. The 1830s was a decade of political reform and the prospect of medical reform as a result of the tireless enquiries of the Warburton committee. Although the Society took no part in politics the liberal mood was evident in a series of changes in the way the Society was run, beginning with the encouragement of discussion at meetings and the publication of the proceedings in the medical press (1831).[86] The office of clerk was abolished in 1832 on the resignation of Courtland, whereupon an assistant or sub-Librarian, Thomas Williams, was appointed instead. Tea and coffee added conviviality to meetings after 1832, and they were further enlivened by the exhibition of drawings, models and medical instruments. And in 1834 it was conceded that Thomas Wakley's mouthpiece for medical reform, the *Lancet*, should be available in the Library.[87]

### *Medico-Chirurgical Transactions*

In publishing the most important papers given at the Society's meetings, the Council fed the demand for a serious medical journal containing the researches, cases, discoveries and original work of the leaders of the profession. Few authors could aspire to publication in the pages of the Royal Society's *Philosophical Transactions*, and the *Medical Transactions* of the Royal College of Physicians came to a halt between 1786 and 1813, ceasing altogether after 1820. The *Transactions of the Society for the Improvement of Medical and Chirurgical Knowledge* were discontinued after 1800 apart from a single volume in 1812; similarly, the Medical Society of London had been dilatory in publishing papers – volume v of its *Memoirs* (1799) was not followed by volume vi until 1805, with another gap until its *Transactions* appeared (1810–17). The *London Medical Journal* changed its name and faded after 1800; Henry Clutterbuck's *Medical and Chirurgical Review* collapsed after 1808 and the *London Medical Review* lapsed between 1802 and 1808.

The *London Medical Gazette*, the *Medical Times*, the *Lancet*, the *British Medical Journal* and the *Quarterly Review*, together with *Guy's Hospital Reports* and similar reports from other London hospitals, were to swell the torrent of medical journalism in due course. But when the Society's *Transactions* were first published in 1809 the only comparable medical periodicals were the *Medical and Physical Journal* and the *Edinburgh Medical and Surgical Journal*. The former featured original communications and critical analyses covering a wide range of subjects – medicine, surgery, midwifery, chemistry, botany and natural history – while the Edinburgh publication aimed to provide 'a concise view of the latest and most important discoveries in medicine, surgery and pharmacy'.

Clearly there was still room for a publication like the *Medico-Chirurgical Transactions*, containing original papers by physicians and surgeons working in London and the provinces, as well as communications from abroad. As Yelloly pointed out in 1834, commercial periodicals and the transactions of societies fulfilled different purposes:

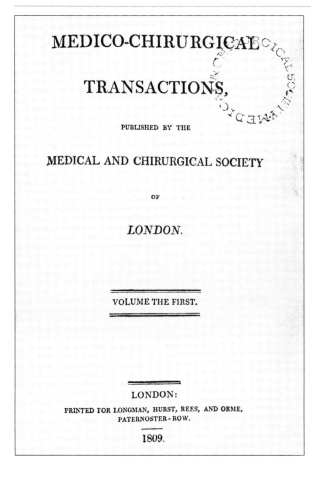

# MEDICO-CHIRURGICAL

# TRANSACTIONS,

PUBLISHED BY THE

## MEDICAL AND CHIRURGICAL SOCIETY

OF

## *LONDON.*

VOLUME THE FIRST.

LONDON:

PRINTED FOR LONGMAN, HURST, REES, AND ORME,
PATERNOSTER-ROW.

1809.

The first volume of *Medico-Chirurgical Transactions* was published in 1809. It contained papers by Astley Cooper on aneurysm of the carotid artery, by John Abernethy on heart disease and two by Dr Edward Jenner.

periodicals were 'works of the moment' containing current news, book reviews, obituaries and correspondence, whereas the publications of medical societies 'are generally more worked up, as they are to form part of the general medical literature of the country'.[88]

The value of the *Transactions* to those eager to keep abreast of the advances in 19th-century medicine and surgery was recognized by contemporary authors and readers; the fact that the first volume (1809) was reprinted for the third time in 1815 indicated its worth. Dr Bostock, a prolific contributor to its pages, stressed the importance of such publications: 'a circumstance which has materially contributed to the improvement of the knowledge of practical medicine is the publication of periodical works, whether in the form of journals or of transactions of societies'. Despite criticizing the early volumes of *Medico-Chirurgical Transactions* on the grounds that they published too many 'mere cases', Bostock later wrote of their sound reputation: 'these in the short space of about 24 years, have amounted to 18 volumes and have acquired a character which is too well-established to require recommendation or sanction'.[89]

The publication of papers was the corollary to the presentation of important communications at the Society's meetings. The first papers had been presented in January 1806 and by August the Council was looking forward 'with great expectation' to seeing them in print.[90] But a year elapsed before it was agreed which papers should be published, and negotiations were opened with Longman, Hurst, Rees and Orme of Paternoster Row to do so on the understanding that the Society took half the profits of sale and a number of copies at 'booksellers' price'. As Secretaries, Yelloly and CR Aikin were responsible for editing and organizing the early volumes of the Society's *Transactions*, reporting that volume i was 'in the press' by November 1807.[91] The possibility of union with another society, at least one author's tardiness with the manuscript and the need for careful proof-reading and editing caused delay, so it was not until February 1809 that a committee was appointed to prepare a preface and select a title for the Society's publication. The President Dr Baillie, the Secretaries and Dr George Birkbeck collaborated on the preface and Baillie chose the title *Medico-Chirurgical Transactions*. It was to be distributed free to every member of the Society, to the Royal Society, the Royal College of Physicians and the Medical Society of London, while others might purchase it.[92]

It was still several months before the volume appeared. Urged on by Marcet, Jenner had obliged by contributing two papers and he began to wonder why there was a delay over the printing: 'the Press seems to have had a lingering labour', he commented to Marcet.[93] Bostock encouraged Marcet to publish as soon as possible: 'So far as the credit of the Society is concerned, out of doors, the sooner the better, when you have got the material. I should be sorry if you were to degenerate into a mere social meeting, however pleasant the members. The volumes published by the old medical society are certainly respectable and useful and I should be sorry if you were not to equal, or indeed surpass it in this, as much as you do in the character and talents of those who are the most interested in its support'.[94] Two years later Bostock despaired about the delay in publishing the *Transactions*: 'I must confess that I have lost all patience and indeed begin to doubt whether they will ever see the light. My poor paper will be quite antiquated I fear'.[95]

When it appeared in the autumn of 1809 the first volume contained 21 papers that had been read at the Society's meetings between January 1806 and April 1809, amounting to 289 pages with 10 plates. The names and occupations of the 98 members of the Society appeared at the front of the volume, and at the back was a list of the books that had been given to the Library. The membership list reveals that there were nine Honorary members, a dozen members held royal appointments, and of the ordinary membership over a half were physicians, a quarter were surgeons, there was one veterinary surgeon and the rest consisted of apothecaries, surgeon-apothecaries and esquires whose occupations were not specified.

The preface told how the Society had been founded on 'liberal and independent principles and conducted with the propriety and dignity which are worthy of the medical profession'. Readers were encouraged to communicate to the Secretaries 'researches in anatomy, physiology and that part of chemistry which is immediately connected with some of the branches of medicine', also descriptions of deviations from healthy structures, curious facts in the natural history of the human body, and surgery. 'The operative part of surgery opens a field of considerable interest and extent, and the number of gentlemen connected with hospitals in London who are members of the Society gives the prospect of being able to communicate to the public some valuable observations and improvements in this branch of the profession'.

*Acceptances and rejections*
The decision whether or not to publish a paper in the Society's *Transactions* was the prerogative of the Council and the reasons for publication or rejection were not given; those assembled at the Council meeting were balloted and the outcome was final.

Dr Martin Wall's paper in Latin, included in volume ii of the *Transactions*, was an experiment that was never repeated, and the Council's decision not to publish Dr Doucet's cases of tetanus cured by regularly pouring between 15 and 26 buckets of cold water over the patient was justifiable. In 1824, however, a paper that was later judged to be 'of the utmost importance' went unpublished; it had been submitted by Valentine Mott, Professor of Surgery at the University of New York, and concerned cases of osteosarcoma in which the right side of the jaw was removed (amends were made in 1853 when Professor Mott was made an Honorary Fellow of the Society). Similarly, Thomas Hodgkin could not understand why a paper by the Demonstrator of Anatomy at Guy's, John Hilton, which was read in January 1833 and which included drawings of what was later known as *Trichina spiralis* was not given more attention: 'its publication was suppressed by the Council' (it was published instead in the *London Medical Gazette*).[96] Two years later James Paget submitted a paper describing and illustrating his discovery of a microscopic entozoon infesting the muscles, and the Council rejected this too (see page 144). Professional applause for the discovery of *Trichina spiralis* was to go to Richard Owen, Conservator of the museum at the Royal College of Surgeons, who devised the name for the worm.[97]

Sometimes it seemed that the unpublished papers were more noteworthy than the published. Dr Forbes' contribution urging the use of the stethoscope in the diagnosis of heart disease, Mr Tyrell's account of an operation for a fractured spine and Dr James Blundell's experiments that led him to surmise as early as 1823 that the womb, spleen and ovaries could be removed without necessarily destroying life, were among those rejected.[98]

Except for a pause in the 1820s, papers were submitted in increasing numbers, and when their quantity and specialized nature threatened to overwhelm the Council a publication committee was formed (1839). The selection process became more rigorous after 1843, when eminent Fellows were nominated as referees who assisted the Council by reading and judging the value of papers on particular subjects – 36 referees were required for the task by 1859. Nevertheless, the system remained open to criticism and was complicated by the publication of the *Proceedings* from 1856.

## Dr Thomas Addison

For reasons unspecified the Council decided not to publish Dr Thomas Addison's paper describing the disease that was named after him (Plates 10 and 11). Sir Samuel Wilks recounted how Addison, President of the Society from 1849 to 1851, wished that there should be some notice of his paper in the *Transactions* 'but not only is nothing to be found about it in them but it is not generally known that he tried three times to get this done and three times failed. He felt much annoyance at their thinking'. As Addison's pupil, Wilks had helped in the preparation of drawings and models to illustrate the paper, so was personally vexed by the refusal to accept the work and he vowed 'never to go to the Society again'.[99]

Addison was the first lecturer on cutaneous diseases at Guy's Hospital and with Bright and Hodgkin was largely responsible for building up the reputation of the medical school there. He proved a popular President of the Society, inviting journalists to meet the élite of the profession, and he was congratulated on the distinguished manner in which he had discharged his duties 'done not only with great ability and impartiality but also with gentleman-like feeling and marked delicacy'.[100] Ironically, Addison's paper – since recognized as the foundation stone of endocrinology – was read to the South London Medical Society and reported in the *London Medical Gazette* in the same month that Addison was elected President of the Royal Medical and Chirurgical Society, March 1849. Two of his papers were in fact published in *Medico-Chirurgical Transactions* (1841,1854) and the earlier one on the anatomy of the lungs was highly praised.

A possible reason for the Council's repeated rejection of Addison's important paper may have been a previous paper by Dr James Johnson (one of the Society's Honorary Librarians) on 'Particulars of a remarkable disease of the heart attended with partial discoloration of the skin', read in 1825 and published in 1827; Sir Jonathan Hutchinson later described this as a pre-Addison description of Addison's disease.[101] Even Addison's defender, Samuel Wilks, admitted later that in his first paper to the Society Addison 'had somewhat overstepped his own boundaries by including among his cases some which did not present the true features of the disease'.[102]

Addison's slender monograph, *On the constitutional and local effects of disease of the supra-renal capsules*, which also described pernicious anaemia, was eventually published in 1855 when the author was 62.

## Dr Thomas Hodgkin

Dr Thomas Hodgkin's paper describing the disease that was to take his name was read to the Society in 1832: 'On some morbid appearances of the absorbent glands and spleen' took two meetings to read and aroused little enthusiasm.[103] Hodgkin was not yet a member of the Society but was already known for his radical views, which made him unacceptable in some quarters. In particular, he alienated the influential Treasurer of Guy's, Benjamin Harrison, who is said to have remarked that he would not have an officer on the staff who drove about with a North American Indian (Hodgkin was a founder of the Aborigines Society). Thus Hodgkin failed to secure the post of assistant physician at Guy's in 1837 in competition with Dr Benjamin Babington. The selection caused a rumpus, and supporters of the two candidates were sharply divided.[104] When the acrimony had subsided Hodgkin was elected a Fellow of the RMCS (1840), and served on the Council for 1842–43 and as a Vice President 1862–64.

Hodgkin's paper of 1832 contained post-mortem descriptions of seven cases characterized by the simultaneous enlargement of the spleen and lymph nodes; of these seven, there were at most four cases of the condition that bears Hodgkin's name.[105] The paper reached the pages of *Transactions* volume xvii, only to lie forgotten until it was read some years later by Sir Samuel Wilks and heralded as the first description of lymphadenoma, known thenceforward as Hodgkin's disease. 'I take credit for having unearthed Hodgkin's paper and introduced it to the profession', Wilks wrote. He might have given his own name to the disease, but in lighting upon Hodgkin's essay and naming the disease after him Wilks 'saved the profession from a name even more uncouth than *morbus Hodgkini*'.[106] Another article by Hodgkin in the *Transactions* for 1843 drew attention to the value of the microscope in medical investigations and ultimately his notes on post mortem examinations (1846–49) came to rest in the Library.

## Difficulties with the Transactions

The first volume of *Medico-Chirurgical Transactions* was long overdue when it finally saw the light of day; the second volume contained papers read between 1809 and 1811 and was well received, and volume iii was eagerly anticipated by Dr Bostock. He wrote, 'I am led to expect great things from it; we shall have no reason to be ashamed of our Society if the third volume be equal to the two former. They certainly contain too many *mere* cases (I do not call mine *mere* cases) and there are one or two long-winded and tedious physiologico-metaphysical discussions... but on the whole they far exceed any similar collection of medical papers that are now publishing, or have been published for a long time'.[107] The first volumes of *Medico-Chirurgical Transactions* were thus valued for their intrinsic merit and they filled a gap left by the discontinuance of the Royal College of Physicians' *Medical Transactions*.

Unfortunately volume iii of the Society's *Transactions* suffered from careless proofreading and failed to fulfil expectations. Bostock found many of the papers valuable but he had one serious charge to bring against this volume, 'that is the great inaccuracy of the printing. In my paper on diabetes there are two shocking errors'. These were infuriating typographical mistakes: in one instance Bostock was 'made to talk about solid water instead of solid matter', which must have stretched the reader's credulity. He threatened to demand that proofs be sent to him in Liverpool, in order to avoid his compositions being 'so terribly mauled'.[108]

The expense of printing the *Transactions* led the Council to restrict the number of free copies in 1811 and by January 1816 the profits from the first four volumes amounted to

£85 19s 1d.[109] Outsiders were beginning to appreciate that the publication contained 'papers of great ingenuity and interest on some of the most important subjects of medicine and its collateral branches' and to purchase copies.[110] That verdict was given in 1817, yet only two years later the *Transactions* ran into difficulties. The volume for 1819 was 'sadly delayed by the unpardonable dilatoriness of the engraver of Howship's plates'.[111] Problems with the engraver and engravings were recurrent: Yelloly reported that 'Stuart [J Stewart] behaved abominably as to the plates and was the sole cause of the delay in publishing' volume iv,[112] and Marcet hoped that John Howship 'will give us no more of his plates for they have always plagued us in the engraving and have excited but little interest' (whatever Marcet thought of them, however, Howship's papers in the *Transactions* established his reputation). 'In the meantime I entreat you to attend more diligently than ever to the collection and printing of *good* papers and the regular publication of our *Transactions*. Depend upon it, those volumes are the true per valum of our existence, and the regular income of a batch of medical news which the Society has hitherto afforded to its members has been the true cause of our extraordinary success'.[113]

Dr Roget edited the *Transactions* for twelve years (1811–23) at the expense of much labour and frustration. In September 1819 he told Marcet how unfortunate it was 'that our Press, should for the first time, have been wanting in diligence'.[114] Even worse, there was no volume for 1820. Marcet, writing from Geneva, urged Roget on: 'I believe there is hardly any option between publication and death'.[115] Some blamed the lack of a publication for 1820 on the removal of the Society from 30 Lincoln's Inn Fields to number 57; others attributed it to the apathy of members, the lack of leadership from the President and 'a total want of materials'. When volume xi did appear, a year late, it made a favourable impression on Dr Fitton. 'So much better than some of its predecessors. The knife case will give it popularity' (this referred to Marcet's paper on the sailor who swallowed clasp knives, based on a previous paper).[116] Another reader, Edward Jenner, relished the *Transactions* when they reached him in Gloucestershire but thought little of George Langstaff's paper in volume ix. 'Have you read the last volumes of the Medico-Chirurgical Transactions?' he wrote to Dr Baron. 'What sad work they make of encysted tumours'.[117]

There was no volume for 1822. Roget resigned as Secretary to the Society in March 1823; there followed a serious hiatus in the submission of papers, so no *Transactions* were published for 1824. The irregular conduct of the Secretaries in selecting papers for publication forced the resignations of both in 1825 (see page 58), with the result that the *Transactions* were suspended. No volumes were published for 1824, 1825 or 1826 and when the volume for 1827 appeared it contained two papers read three years previously and some that had not been read at all.

## Illustrations

The publication of engravings and woodcuts to illustrate papers in the *Transactions* was highly desirable but it required expertise and organization and was expensive. The first volume had set a high standard with 10 plates, some drawn by William Clift, Conservator of the Hunterian Museum and a skilled artist. He had been responsible for the copperplates in Dr Baillie's *Morbid anatomy* and he illustrated anatomical papers in the Royal Society's *Philosophical Transactions*. In 1818 Yelloly arranged for Clift to have access to the Society's Library to facilitate his task, and he was made an Honorary Fellow of the Royal Medical and Chirurgical Society (RMCS) in 1835.[118]

By way of contrast, the engraver J Stewart behaved 'abominably' and caused delay in publication of the *Transactions*;[119] nevertheless the illustrations gradually increased in number and sophistication and were sometimes coloured. The volume for 1821 ran to a fold-out plate showing a vast tumour (37lb 10oz). In 1839 the Society obtained the services of George Scharf as lithographer. Scharf worked for several scientific journals,

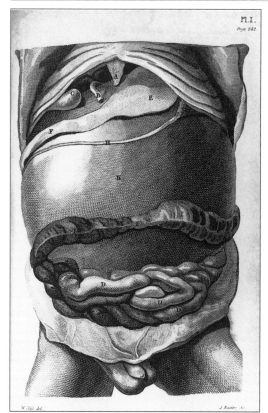
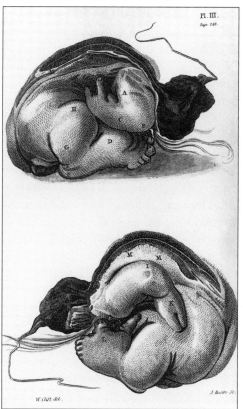

William Clift, the first Conservator of the Hunterian Museum, drew many of the illustrations in the early volumes of *Medico-Chirurgical Transactions* and was made an Honorary Fellow of the Society in 1835. These engravings accompanied a paper by GW Young on a case of a fetus in the abdomen of a boy (1809). The infant boy died within a year of his birth, whereupon Mr Young and Dr Birkbeck examined the body and found a dead fetus 'as rosy and as healthy as if it had been alive' with stout limbs. Left, the appearance of the body on opening, and right, side views of the fetus.

made topographical paintings and detailed sketches of London,[120] and his work for the Society first appeared in volume xxii of the *Transactions*. The illustrations became lavish in the prosperous 1850s and the volume for 1867 extended to 648 pages, by which time the Society was also publishing its *Proceedings*.

## Classic papers

Reviewing the volumes of *Medico-Chirurgical Transactions* between 1809 and 1860, the President FC Skey spoke of their value as 'rich stores of knowledge contributed by the greatest masters of our art and science'. He claimed that the papers were subjected to 'a severe scrutiny without favour or affection' and if accepted for publication they were 'destined to a high place in the archives of medical literature'.[121] He singled out the article on aneurysm by Astley Cooper in the first volume, followed up by papers by Mr Benjamin Travers and Dr James Wardrop in subsequent volumes, Dr Prout on urine, Dr Blundell on the transfusion of blood, Mr T Rose on the treatment of venereal disease without mercury in volume viii, the early papers of Brodie on diseases of the joints, the work on organic chemistry by Berzelius, Bostock and Marcet; Sir Gilbert Blane on the health of the navy, Dr Davis and Dr Robert Lee on phlegmasis dolens and Dr Marshall Hall's first essay on the effects of loss of blood. 'We are all familiar with the influence of these papers on the mind of the profession and every day's experience tests and confirms their value'.[122]

Plate drawn by Samuel Solly (President of the RMCS 1867–69) to illustrate his paper of 1839 on a case of 'dry gangrene'; George Scharf was the lithographer. Solly reported that nature amputated the three extremities leaving stumps 'which might shame many formed by the operator's knife'. Once the extremities had fallen off the child's health improved.

At the turn of the century, Timothy Holmes, editor of *Gray's Anatomy* and President of the Royal Medical and Chirurgical Society from 1890 to 1892, echoed Skey when he testified to the lasting value of 'that great storehouse of medical knowledge, the *Medico-Chirurgical Transactions...* that grand series' containing some of the standard works on disease and surgery.[123]

### The medical journalists

Initially the publication of the Society's papers was jealously guarded, implying a degree of exclusivity. Reporters from medical journals were denied access to meetings and papers printed by the Society were not for publication elsewhere. When a member called John Want (a colleague of Roget at the Northern Dispensary) applied in 1814 for permission to publish a monthly report of the Society's proceedings in the *Medical and Physical Journal*, the Council refused.[124] The temptation proved irresistible to Want, who revealed the contents of a paper that had been read at a meeting on 22 November in the columns of the *Medical and Physical Journal* for December 1814. Want was already in disgrace for refusing to pay Library fines of five shillings; accordingly the Council ejected him from the Society and passed a statute banning members or visitors from publishing any of the Society's proceedings, oral or written, without permission.[125]

This ruling did not prevent Dr James Johnson from committing the same crime as Want in 1828. As editor of the *Medico-Chirurgical Review*, Johnson inserted an account of the proceedings at the MCS, an invasion of privacy which the Council judged to be 'very injurious ... very improper' and forced Johnson's resignation as Honorary Librarian.[126]

The Society's suspicious attitude to medical journalists was not without justification –

the meetings were private, restricted to subscription-paying members and invited guests, and with a publication of its own, the Society felt no need for publicity or the duplication of papers in other journals, least of all in Thomas Wakley's journal, the *Lancet*. The very first issue of that journal in 1823 reported a lecture given by Astley Cooper without the latter's permission, a liberty that was not readily forgiven. John Abernethy obtained an injunction against Wakley on similar grounds in 1824, leading to Wakley's exclusion from St Thomas', and another incident culminated in a trial for libel (1828).

Wakley was incorrigible and his use of the pages of the *Lancet* to urge the reform of the medical profession and to ridicule the establishment alienated members of the Medical and Chirurgical Society, among others. His initial application to report the proceedings of the Society was strenuously opposed by the Council and it was not until the 1830s that copies of the *Lancet* were placed in the Library. Occasionally a paper was leaked to the hungry medical press, much 'to the astonishment and dismay of the Society; the Fellows of which, on assembling at the following meeting, would look anxiously around to see if they could detect the traitor who must have been one amongst the dozen then assembled'.[127]

In October 1831 the Council relaxed the rules by repealing the statute forbidding the publication of reports of the meetings. 'Yes, it is come to this!' exclaimed the *Lancet*. 'The Council of the Medico-Chirurgical Society in Lincoln's Inn Fields has, after eight years of resistance to, eight years of abuse of, *The Lancet*, resolved that Reports of their discussions shall be published ... After outpouring the full phials of their wrath upon *The Lancet* for attempting to give publicity to their debates, after excluding *The Lancet* from their library for the same cause, this beaten society have "resolved" that the same *Lancet* may now, if it pleases, give publicity to their discussions and thus carry them to the remotest corners of the globe. Well it is not in our nature to entertain hostile feelings towards our enemies, and never will we turn aside from the hand of repentance. We shall, therefore, devote a portion of our pages to the discussions of the Medico-Chirurgical, though neglect, pointed and continued neglect, would be no more than a just return for the illiberality, blindness and obstinacy of the council'. It was over a year before reports of the meetings at Lincoln's Inn Fields were given space in the *Lancet*.[128] The *London Medical Gazette*, on the other hand, had included accounts of the meetings of the MCS since its first volume of 1827–28. One of those who implemented this was the young James Paget (the celebrated surgical pathologist) who served as a sub-editor on that journal from 1837 to 1842: 'For about two years I reported the debates at the Medical and Chirurgical Society, not by taking notes but by listening attentively and writing down at home'.[129] This paved the way for a reporter from the *Provincial Medical Gazette* who was allowed to take notes of the proceedings of the RMCS in the 1840s and the door was soon opened to others. The concession was 'effected after great perseverance and difficulty and at first hampered and interfered with as to discourage and annoy the reporter'.[130] Undeterred, JFL Clarke 'ventured to disobey the mandates of the Council, and reported the case and discussion pretty fully – the first time of my so doing being the case of Mr Brunel brought before the Society by Sir B Brodie. On this occasion the meeting was very crowded, and as such general interest was excited by the case, I took full notes of the whole proceedings, and published a long report in the ensuing number of *The Lancet*'[131] (pre-dating the publication of Brodie's paper in *Medico-Chirurgical Transactions*).

## Surgical cases

The paper referred to by Clarke, above, was given by Sir Benjamin Brodie and it involved Isambard Kingdom Brunel, the brilliant engineer of the Great Western Railway and steamships. Brunel had been amusing children after dinner when he swallowed a half-sovereign, which lodged in his throat. He went about his usual business in London and the country but as the coin refused to move, he consulted Sir Benjamin Brodie who was unable to ease Brunel's predicament. Brunel's inventive streak then came into play with his design and construction of a movable platform with hinges to assist the removal of the coin. He was strapped to the platform while his head was lowered until his body made an angle of 80 degrees with the horizon and his back was struck repeatedly, prompting violent coughing. No coin was forthcoming. Brodie then decided that as the half-sovereign had now been inside Brunel for three weeks, he would make an 'artificial opening' into the trachea to extract it with forceps, but several attempts proved unsuccessful. When six weeks had passed the movable platform was brought out once again and Brunel was strapped to it and lowered, and Brodie kept open an incision in the windpipe while Brunel was struck on the back. This time 'the patient felt the coin quit the chest sticking almost immediately against the incisor of the upper jaw and then dropping out of the mouth'.[132] Brodie personally recounted the case to a meeting of the Society and the story was reported elsewhere, becoming legendary, but the version in the *Transactions* stands as the most reliable.

Brodie had a good opinion of the Society's *Transactions*. 'I do not mean to say that all the papers they contain are of great value; but they form, on the whole, by far the best collection of their kind which has been published in England; and indeed, they have a considerable reputation throughout Europe'. He told the Select Committee on Medical Education in 1834 that the first 17 volumes of *Transactions* contained 406 papers, of which 31 had been communicated from abroad and 375 had been contributed by surgeons to institutions, teachers, licentiates of the Royal College of Physicians, general practitioners, surgeon-apothecaries, medical officers of the army and navy and hospital surgeons in London and the provinces. 'Of the 375, 183 are merely relations of remarkable cases and 192 are essays (many of which contain elaborate investigations) intended to illustrate particular subjects in pathology, medicine and surgery'.[133]

As the preface to the first volume had indicated, surgery aroused great interest in the early 19th century and the Society's *Transactions* contained a high proportion of surgical papers, beginning with the excitement of Astley Cooper's novel operations and approaching tedium with Spencer Wells' numerous cases of ovariotomy (see pages 132–34).

Sir Benjamin Brodie, President 1839–41. His work on *Diseases of the joints* (1818) became a medical classic

Some papers gave an insight into 19th-century social conditions; one such was John Dunn's account of the amputation of part of the tarsus and metatarsus on a boy in 1816. The 14-year-old was accustomed to hard labour in a coal pit under conditions that kept his feet wet and cold, causing his diseased foot and subsequent fever. In a 'formidable dissection' a serious degree of haemorrhage ensued but the operation was extended. Deluged with blood the boy fainted and the surgeon's assistants (two 14-year-old apprentices, a woman and two labouring men) 'were so sick and alarmed as to desert the room'. The surgeon was gratified to conclude that the boy recovered well enough to be able to be bound as an apprentice, to walk nine miles a day and was once again equal to several hours daily labour in the coal pit.[134]

Another piece highlighting the hardships of Victorian Britain came from Henry Earle, surgeon to St Bartholomew's and the Foundling Hospital, on the subject of chimney-sweep's cancer or sootwart (1823). The article described several cases, concluding that 'even if it were possible to substitute machinery... the master sweeps and those who were engaged in the removal of the soot would still be liable to the destructive malady', which affected the scrotum.[135]

## Petition for a royal charter

The *Medico-Chirurgical Transactions* were judged to be 'favourable to the advancement of the Society. The number of its members has increased; its meetings have been better attended; and above all, a more abundant supply of communications has been received'. The Library was 'improving', the arrangement of sharing a house with the Geological Society was mutually satisfactory 'and, in short, the Society has assumed a position which augurs most favourably for its permanent and increasing utility'.[136] On this basis, and with the King's physician Sir Henry Halford as President, the MCS petitioned for a royal charter of incorporation.

In February 1812 Dr Yelloly was optimistic, reporting to the Council that Sir Henry Halford had been given an audience with the Prince Regent and that the Prince had responded to the application graciously. Mr Ryder, Secretary of State for the Home Department, was also reported to be favourably disposed to the Society.

The petition put forward the reasons for granting the charter: that the Society's exertions might be carried on with more stability and effect so as to advance the improvement of physic and surgery by affording a ready means of professional communication and a respectable centre for the reception of valuable facts and observations. The examples of the Royal Society, the Society of Antiquaries, the Linnean Society and the Royal Medical Society of Edinburgh were cited, and it was specifically stated that the incorporated society would not seek further powers or interfere with the Royal College of Physicians or the Royal College of Surgeons.[137] Dr Yelloly later told the Warburton committee (1834) that having witnessed the fate of other medical societies, many of which became inert or ceased to exist, the MCS recognized that the sanction of a royal charter would avert the risk of the Society running into decay.[138]

The petition was signed and presented in the names of Sir Henry Halford as President, Saunders and Baillie (past Presidents), Sir Walter Farquhar, Doctors Marcet and Yelloly and Messrs Cline, Abernethy and Cooper. A fund was organized to pay the expenses – Cooper alone contributed £50, and in just one morning over £500 was forthcoming from those eager to acquire the prefix Royal for their Society.[139]

### Opposition from the Royal College of Physicians

On the face of it, the prospects seemed good. But the Society had reckoned without the Royal College of Physicians. The College was averse to change and was at this time threatened by the swelling movement for the reform of the medical profession. Its President,

Sir Francis Milman, had refused Honorary membership of the MCS and in 1812 he suspected that something hostile to the College was intended in the Society's application for a charter. Halford assured him this was not the case; nevertheless at a '*comitus majoribus extra-ordinarius*' of the College summoned in March to consider the petition of the MCS, a committee was authorized 'to take such measures as may seem meet to them, with the approbation of the College, of obstructing whatever may interfere with the Privileges of the College of Physicians'.[140] The committee endorsed counsel's opinion that 'the charter must be opposed *in toto*' and a memorial was sent to the Privy Council opposing the Medical and Chirurgical's petition as 'injurious to the said College... and altogether unnecessary'.[141]

The memorial recited the College's incorporation by Henry VIII, its history and contribution to the advancement of physic; it stressed the importance of keeping the practice of physic separate and distinct from surgery, and its defensive tone suggested that the august physicians feared a challenge from a 'Royal' Medical and Chirurgical Society. Yelloly thought that the College's particular objection was 'that the Medical and Chirurgical Society on obtaining a charter and a consequent increase in favour with the public, might set themselves on a level with the College and elect as members of its body and grant marks of distinction to persons who were not connected with the College, nor qualified to become so ... and thus create a very detrimental rivalship'.[142]

Weighing up the argument, Sir Vicary Gibbs (Attorney General) and Sir Thomas Plumer (Solicitor General) advised against the grant of a charter; in their opinion the objects of the Society could be attained without one. Thus by the end of May 1812 the Society's bid had been rejected by the law officers of the Crown, and the College of Physicians had taken steps to prevent individual Fellows from supporting any such petition in future – this was aimed at Sir Henry Halford, Dr Saunders and Dr Baillie.[143]

## A supplementary petition

The Medical and Chirurgical Society did not accept defeat. 'You must persevere and push the point to the utmost', Bostock urged Marcet, 'so that if you do not gain your cause, at least the world may be acquainted with the spirit of the College. It is something to *expose* an opponent'.[144]

Yelloly and Marcet did persevere. A supplementary petition was sent to the Privy Council in June 1812, emphasizing the public good that arose from the association of physicians and surgeons within the Society; 'in many cases of disease it gives an opportunity of consultation that is extremely advantageous to the public and favourable to the improvement of both Physic and Surgery'. It pointed to the lethargy and exclusivity of the College of Physicians which had not printed a Library catalogue for 55 years and which restricted the use of its Library to a small number of Fellows (43, according to Sir Samuel Romilly's evidence of 1814). It alleged that the College held no useful meetings, that the lectures deriving from bequests numbered no more than five a year and that the College's publication had not appeared since 1786 (stung by the criticism, the College promptly appointed a committee to read medical papers for the first volume of *Medical Transactions* to be published for 27 years). It reaffirmed the Society's vow of non-interference with the privileges of the Royal College and offered concessions; in particular it reassured the College that the Society would not elect as resident members any physician not licensed by the College.

Unfortunately, the petition 'lay on the table' at the Privy Council Office for nearly twelve months. When the College was at last informed of the supplementary petition in May 1813, it launched new objections on the grounds that the document bore the names of three of its Fellows (Halford, Baillie and Saunders) who had not been consulted a second time. This was to be a strong argument in the College's continuing opposition: it was imputed by the College that the MCS was practising a fraud upon the Privy Council by putting forward those three names without authority.[145]

The Registrar circulated every Fellow of the College who was a member of the MCS asking 'whether it is with your knowledge and approbation that there is a renewal of the application from the Medical and Chirurgical Society to the Privy Council, which the late Attorney General and Solicitor General thought unnecessary'.[146] The three Fellows whose names accompanied the original and the supplementary petitions responded promptly. Saunders replied that he imagined the matter had been laid to rest in 1812. Baillie knew that the Society was planning to make a further effort to obtain a charter and he had no solid objection providing it did not interfere with the privileges of the College, but because the charter 'was very disagreeable to the College I have thought it right for a long time past not to mix any further in this business'.[147] Halford claimed that he had not attended a Council meeting of the MCS nor participated in the Society's pursuance of a charter: 'no proceedings have been submitted to me as President of the Society officially for my approbation or disapprobation'.[148] While it is true that Halford was no more than a figurehead as President and had not attended a Council meeting since his election in 1810, he *had* approached the Prince Regent in the first place, had signed the original petition and had subscribed to the fund for charter expenses. When giving evidence to the Select Committee on Medical Education in 1834 he claimed to have forgotten.

On being questioned by the College Registrar, Baillie, Saunders and Halford stated, correctly, that they had not signed the Society's supplementary petition.[149] Halford, having finished his term as President of the MCS, was nursing aspirations to be President of the College, so found himself in a difficult position. In an ambiguous statement he assured the College that he had not signed the second petition, nor did he know of this application. In another letter to Yelloly and Marcet, Halford made it clear that although he wished the Society well, 'the declared opposition of the College precluded him from making any further attempt to promote the Medical and Chirurgical Society'.[150] Embarrassed, perhaps, Saunders resigned as a Censor of the College and Baillie resigned his position as an Elect (the College's equivalent of a Councillor) in October 1813. Halford, on the other hand,

Sir Henry Halford, President 1810–13. During his term as President the Society petitioned for a royal charter – unsuccessfully.

went from strength to strength, leading the committee to organize the removal of the College to a splendid new building in Trafalgar Square and becoming its President in 1820.

Sir Henry Halford was wealthy and influential, reportedly vain, cringing to his superiors and haughty to his inferiors; he was dubbed 'the eel-backed baronet'. He was publicly charged with unprofessional conduct on one occasion, and on another it was claimed he had purloined a vertebra from the corpse of Charles I as a souvenir.[151] In the judgement of the historian of the College of Physicians, he made just one 'false step' in his career and that was in applying for a charter for the Medical and Chirurgical Society, 'but we have seen that he righted himself in good time. Except for that one slip he seems never to have paused in his advance'.[152] He was the longest-serving President of the College to date (1820–44) and he healed the rift with the RMCS by presenting a clock. He was President of the College when the Society lodged its second petition for a royal charter in 1834 and this time the College offered no opposition.

As to the question of the signatures of Halford, Baillie and Saunders on the supplementary petition, officers of the MCS had been advised by the solicitor of the Privy Council that the renewal of permission from signatories was not necessary. The original document, regularly signed, was the basis of the proceedings, therefore there had been no need to consult Halford, Baillie and Saunders a second time.

## *The appeal fails*

The Society appealed to the Lords of the Committee of the Privy Council to overturn the decision of the law officers against the grant of a charter for the MCS. On this occasion the Society was legally represented by Sir Samuel Romilly (former Solicitor General and uncle to Roget, whose son married Marcet's daughter). Romilly was a skilful lawyer and his argument in favour of a royal charter of incorporation for the Society was based on the public good, the advancement of medical knowledge, the importance of the Society's Library and its regular publication. For its part, the College secured the legal representation of Mr Adam, who was senior to Romilly, and even Yelloly had to admit that Adam 'conducted the argument with considerable judgement and ability. I never knew an argument more complete than ours; but I think the decision will be against us just because there will be a disinclination to disoblige an existing Body when it may be considered that there is no urgent need for creating a new one'.[153] Lawyers for the Medical and Chirurgical Society and the College of Physicians presented their opposing views in the Cockpit at Whitehall on 22 February 1814. The following month the Privy Council reported to the Prince Regent that their lordships did not see sufficient grounds for recommending the grant of a royal charter to the Medical and Chirurgical Society.

The Society's ambitions had been successfully thwarted by the Royal College of Physicians, but apart from having to meet its legal fees the Society did not suffer through lack of a charter and other means were found to add dignity to its standing. A motto was devised: *non est vivere sed valere vita* (from Martial's *Epigrammata* Lib.vi Ep.70), which loosely translates as 'it is important to enjoy good health to live fully', and Thomas Wyon, chief engraver of the seals, was commissioned to design a seal for the Society. This represents Salus raising a kneeling figure and was believed to have been inspired by a medal of the Roman Emperor Caracalla in the British Museum (the Museum later expressed 'the very greatest doubt whether there is any antique original on which the design of the seal is modelled').[154] Diplomas were printed and adorned with the seal, to be presented to members as a mark of distinction.[155]

Some resentment towards the College of Physicians lingered. A party in the MCS wanted a narrative of the events to be brought to public notice through the pages of the *Edinburgh Review*. Dr Saunders suggested that Aikin might write an article comparing the Society's *Transactions* with those of the College, with a 'short history of the origin and progress of your society – and the opposition it met with from certain members of another society. You might then force into notice of B [Baillie] and Sir Henry, if I am not mistaken against their wishes, especially the latter who has so shamefully betrayed you and deserted you'. Another guarded remark referred to 'our animated old friend [Halford?] taking care that there should be no sparring between him and 'the old walls of Warwick Castle' (the College of Physicians in Warwick Lane).[156] On the whole, Yelloly decided it was unwise 'to promote a discussion of the charter business in the *Edinburgh Review*. We are going on so well, acting with such general dignity and conciliation that I should be sorry if there should be anything of party feeling ascribed to our side of the Question. If the *Edinburgh Review* were to take up the cudgels for us… the *Quarterly* would take them up against us – we should gain nothing and should get the character of discontented Whigs'.[157] Nevertheless, Yelloly thought Marcet showed a lack of courage in being cordial to 'B and H [Baillie and Halford], the two great constellations in the western hemisphere… you do not abuse them wherever they are spoken of and yet you do not by any means approve of their conduct in a certain business'.[158]

## The Library

At the meeting of physicians and surgeons at the Freemasons' Tavern on 22 May 1805 the creation of a Library was cited as one of the principal objects of the new Society. By the time the MCS was established with apartments at Verulam Buildings in December of the same year, the Library comprised 36 volumes. Dr Baillie had presented two books by his uncle, John Hunter, and his own *Morbid anatomy* (1793) in which the pathological changes caused by diseases were described for the first time. Dr Saunders had given his own works on the liver and on mineral waters, and Dr Yelloly gave a work in French by Sabatier. Dr Robert Willan showed his goodwill by donating the works of Hippocrates, and other gifts included Peter Shaw's *Essays on chemistry* (1731) from Dr Cooke and

¶ The protestation and oath of denyne *Hyppocrates.*

*Hyppocrates* vow, promise and protest to the great God *Appollo* and his twoo Daughters *Higine* and *Panadie*, and also to all the gods and goddesses to obserue all the contents of this oath, or tables wherin this oath is carued, written or ingraued, so far as I can possible, and so farre as my wit or vnderstanding shall be able to direct me viz..that I yeild my my selfe tributarie and debtor to the Maister & Doctor who hath instructed mee and shewed mee this scie̅ce and Doctrine, euen as much or rather more then to my Father who hath begotten me, and that I shal liue and communicate with him and follow him in all necessities, which I shall know him to haue so far as my power shall permit, and my goods shall extend. Also that I shall loue and cherish his children as my brothers, and his progeny as mine own. Further that I shall teach, shew & demonstrate the sayde scyence gratis without rewarde or couenant, and that I shall giue all the Cannons rules and precepts, freely, truely, and faithfully to my Maister his children as to myne owne, without hyding or concealing any thing, and to all other Schollers who shall make the same oth or protestation and to no others. Also that in practising and vsing my science towardes the sicke I shall vse onelye thinges necessarye so farre as I am able and as my spirit and good vnderstanding shall giue vnto mee and

A 3                                     that

In *The whole course of chirurgerie* (1597), Peter Lowe was the first to translate the work of Hippocrates into English. This page shows the Hippocratic oath by which the apprentice vows loyalty to his Master and Doctor 'who hath instructed mee and shewed mee this science and Doctrine (lines 9/10). The apprentice promises to 'teach, shew & demonstrate the sayde scyence gratis' (lines 16/17). Professing the oath was the basis of the concept of a profession.

volumes of the *Edinburgh Medical and Surgical Journal* from Dr Bateman, one of its editors.[159] The most generous donation, of 19 works including *De medicina* by Celsus (Plate 36), came from Mr John Hunter of Mincing Lane. This was the nucleus of the Library of the Royal Society of Medicine, the largest medical library in the British Empire in 1949 and now world-famous.

Initially the Library was in the care of the clerk, who also collected members' subscriptions, attended all meetings and looked after the Society's house.[160] Selected periodicals were ordered from the beginning and were placed on the Library table – the *Medical and Chirurgical Review*, the *Medical and Surgical Journal*, the *Medical and Physical Journal*, *Nicholson's Journal* and the *Monthly Review* were available and might be borrowed.[161]

The expansion of the collection relied on donations and purchases recommended by the Library committee, first appointed in March 1806 with authorization to spend £100 on books.[162] The whole was master-minded by Dr Yelloly, who used as a model the catalogue of the Royal Society of Medicine of Edinburgh, 'a small volume which for many years he had always lying on his table'.[163] Yelloly also had the benefit of his experience as a member of the Library committee of the Medical Society of London to draw upon (that Society possessed some 16,000 books by 1802).

The first regulations of November 1808 ruled that the Library was to be open for two hours a week from noon to 2pm on Tuesdays when each member was entitled to borrow two books for a fortnight, after which time he was liable to be fined sixpence a day. Borrowers' names were recorded in a book and members could register their requests in a 'book of desiderata'.[164] The first volume of *Medico-Chirurgical Transactions* records that there had been 89 donations to the Library between 1806 and 1809: recent acquisitions included Humphry Davy's *Researches, chemical and philosophical* (1800) and Astley Cooper's *Anatomy and surgical treatment of inguinal and congenital hernia* (1804–07). Most of the books were in the English language (there were 36 in Latin, four in French and none in German) and the arrangement of the whole was entrusted in 1809 to Dr Roget.[165] Roget's talent for arrangement and classification found its ultimate expression in his *Thesaurus* of 1852; his biographer suggests that his chief skill was organizational and that his interest in the classification and arrangement of books for the Society led naturally to the classification of ideas and language in the *Thesaurus*.[166] He was responsible for the removal of the books from Verulam Buildings to 3 Holborn Row, Lincoln's Inn Fields in 1810, where the library hours were extended to two afternoons a week and members were allowed to borrow four books each. All books were to be recalled once a year and if not returned a fine of five shillings would be incurred.

## Dr Thomas Bateman, Honorary Librarian

When Roget took the post of Honorary Secretary to the Society in 1811, the Council was persuaded to create the new post of Honorary Librarian. Dr Thomas Bateman, a member of Council and physician to the London Fever Hospital, accepted the offer.[167] He was the chief authority on diseases of the skin in succession to Dr Willan, whom he had assisted at the Carey Street Dispensary. Bateman had co-edited the *Edinburgh Medical and Surgical Journal* and written articles for Rees's *Encyclopaedia*. He was one of the seceders from the Medical Society of London and a founder-member of the MCS, where 'the character which he had established for a profound knowledge of medical literature led to his being appointed its librarian, a post not of mere distinction but attended with considerable labour in assisting to form the valuable collection of books which that very respectable society possesses; and to arrange its catalogue for publication'.[168] Bateman published the *Practical synopsis of cutaneous diseases according to the arrangement of Dr Willan* in 1813, followed by an expanded version of 1817 which included several of Willan's exceptional colour plates. A copy was presented to the Society's Library (Plate 20).

## The purchase of books

Once the rent, the clerk's salary, printing and housekeeping expenses had been paid, the Society's income from members' fees, subscriptions and the sale of *Medico-Chirurgical Transactions* was devoted to books – their purchase, binding, cataloguing and storage. The Library committee received regular injections of cash for the purchase of books and in some years there were exceptional bouts of book-buying, creating the need for more shelving. In 1814 the Library invaded the clerk's sitting-room, where bookcases were installed, probably to accommodate the purchases made by Yelloly and Bateman on a visit to Paris.[169] Another 163 volumes including *Memoires de l'Académie des Sciences* were acquired in 1816 at a cost of £159 11s, through Monsieur Thiébaut de Bernaux, Librarian to the King of France; he was given a copy of Dr Withering's book on botany for his trouble.[170] Additional books in French were presented by Marcet and Dr JA Albers of Bremen, and the Society negotiated two boxes of German books through customs in 1819.[171] These acquisitions were given space in the rooms that became available when the Geological Society moved out of the house it shared with the Society at 3 Holborn Row, Lincoln's Inn Fields.[172]

Dr Yelloly had been pleading for a Library catalogue since 1812. Eventually, in December 1816, 250 copies of the first printed catalogue were published for sale to members at 14 shillings, 1 guinea to outsiders. Bateman was warmly thanked for 'a work to which he has devoted very considerable attention and labour' and Yelloly was praised 'for the great and able assistance he has given to the Librarian in the making and printing of the catalogue in every stage of the work' and for the 'indefatigable zeal he has ever shown in the selection and purchase of books for the Library'; Roget and Lawrence had also helped in completing the catalogue, which needed a supplement in 1818.[173]

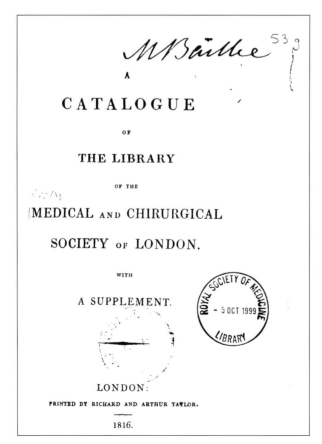

The Society's first Library catalogue
was issued in 1816.
© Royal College of Physicians 2001.

Bateman was ill in early 1817 when Dr William Prout assumed his duties temporarily (Bateman described his malady, mercurial erethism, in a paper to the Society published in volume ix of the *Transactions*). As his health deteriorated he appeared 'a spare, oblique, marasmoid figure, labouring much under disease, and a cornucopia of whims and self-possessions, or conceits; but of a very irritable kind'.[174] In view of Bateman's illness, Samuel Cooper was appointed joint Librarian in 1818.[175] This was at a time when the use of the Library was increasing, members being allowed eight books at once and opening hours having been extended to three afternoons a week between 1pm and 4pm.

The expansion of the Library is a consistent theme in the Society's history and a main reason for the succession of moves to larger premises. After five years at Verulam Buildings the Society moved to 3 Holborn Row, Lincoln's Inn Fields, where the Library occupied one room on the ground floor. The decision to move again, in 1819, was due to the 'increase of their library, the dilapidation of the present house and the approaching expiry of the lease'.[176]

The availability of space when the Geological Society vacated 3 Holborn Row in 1815 prompted a surge of book-collecting that continued into the 1820s when the Council liked to see all the English medical books as soon as they were published, on approval from booksellers. This was at Yelloly's insistence: 'Every English medical book which issues from the press should be procured, whether valuable or not', he wrote from Norwich.[177] This system became impractical, so in 1826 it was decided that the Honorary Librarians should first select books for purchase and then submit the list to the Council for approval.

### *Professor Samuel Cooper and his successors*

Bateman left London on account of his ill-health and died in Whitby in 1821, leaving Samuel Cooper to supervise the removal of the Library to 57 Lincoln's Inn Fields where shelving and fitments for the collection cost £126 18s.[178] Cooper was known as 'the Johnson of medical literature. His great Dictionary (*A Dictionary of practical surgery*, 1809, which went into many editions and translations) was to surgery what Johnson's great work was to English literature'.[179] He had been a surgeon with the army in the

Samuel Cooper, Professor of Surgery at University College, London and the Society's Honorary Librarian 1821–25. He was known as the Johnson of medical literature following the publication of his *Dictionary of practical surgery* (1809).

Peninsular war and at Waterloo, and was later President of the Royal College of Surgeons. Strangely it was the clerk, Mr Raven, and not the Honorary Librarian who was responsible for compiling the *catalogue raisonné* of 1823.[180] Raven absconded the following year and was not heard of again (see page 36).

Samuel Cooper resigned as Librarian in 1825 along with the Secretaries, Dr JA Gordon and Mr Edward Stanley (who was to be President from 1843 to 1845). The exact reason goes unrecorded, although it can be deduced that there was some irregularity over the reading (or not) and publication of papers, and a general laxity in the conduct of procedures following Roget's resignation as Secretary in 1823. The simultaneous resignations implied culpability and at an extraordinary general meeting called in April 1825 a resolution was passed that the Secretaries must give notice of papers at least a week in advance – a measure designed to stimulate interest and to tighten the organization.[181]

Dr John Sims and Dr James M Arnott were the new Honorary Librarians; Dr James Johnson replaced Sims in 1827 but was forced to resign the following year over his publication of the Society's proceedings in the press.[182] Dr Marshall Hall, elected to the Society in 1826, was Honorary Librarian for 1828 and 1829, and in 1832 the task of the Honorary Librarians was eased by the appointment of Thomas Williams as assistant or sub-Librarian, a paid servant of the Society.[183] He oversaw the removal of the Library in 1834 to 53 Berners Street, where the first priority was to prepare a room for the Society's books.

## Lincoln's Inn Fields

The first home of the Society at 2 Verulam Buildings provided modest accommodation which needed refurbishing at a cost of nearly £250 in December 1805. The ground floor room at the front housed the Library, although books overflowed into the meeting room. Mr Egerton, the landlord, gave the Society notice to quit in January 1810 because he planned to sell the property. Faced with eviction, Council members immediately recalled that the Geological Society was in need of larger premises. Cohabitation with the Geological Society was considered to be highly desirable by the MCS while the trustees of the Geological Society saw the advantages in sharing a house as giving a greater degree of respectability, more space for cabinets and for persons visiting the collection, and the convenience of a shared clerk and a place for general meetings.[184]

### *The Geological Society shares 3 Holborn Row*

The Geological Society had originated as a dining club, becoming a fully fledged scientific society in November 1807 under the patronage of Babington, Davy, Banks and the wealthy and urbane GB Greenough MP.[185] Dr William Babington, whose name was given to a mineral, was a founder-member of the MCS and with Dr James Laird, a Council member of that Society and the first Secretary of the Geological, may have prepared the ground before formal negotiations to share a house were opened by Cooper, Yelloly, Aikin and Marcet. They reported in March 1810 that they had found a house belonging to Mr Edward Hughes at 3 Holborn Row, Lincoln's Inn Fields, offered on a 14-year lease. Number 3, situated in the north-west corner of the square, was next door to the house of the surgeon Henry Cline. The architect of the Bank of England, Sir John Soane, was establishing his museum at numbers 12 to 14, and on the south side of the square the Royal College of Surgeons was being rebuilt to designs by George Dance the younger.

The annual rent for 3 Holborn Row (£115 10s) was no more than the Society had been paying at Verulam Buildings, although there were additional expenses for fittings and a £50 premium. Mr Greenough was willing to lend both societies capital to be repaid with interest, so on this understanding an agreement was reached whereby the first room on the ground floor was for the Library of the MCS, the whole of the second floor was allocated

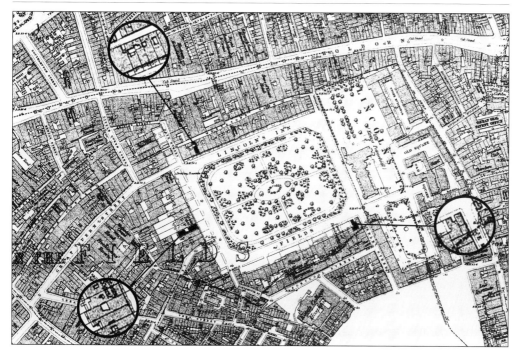

The Ordnance Survey map of 1873 indicates the location of the Society's premises in Lincoln's Inn Fields: 3 Holborn Row on the north side, where the Society was based from 1810 to 1819; number 30 in the south-east corner of the square was a temporary home from 1819 to 1820, and number 57 on the west side of Lincoln's Inn Fields was occupied by the Society from 1820 to 1834.

to the Geological Society for their cabinets and collections; the first floor meeting room and other rooms were shared. The societies were also to share the services of a clerk, briefly Mr JR Jones, succeeded by Mr Yeoman, whose salary was paid jointly by the two societies. The terms of the agreement were drawn up by Doctors Curry, Marcet, Yelloly and Roget and Mr Young on behalf of the MCS, with Greenough, Sir Abraham Hume Bt MP, Mr Francis Horner MP, Dr Babington, Mr Robert Ferguson, Mr David Ricardo and Mr Samuel Woods representing the Geological Society. [186] The relationship between the societies was close, fostered by shared scientific interests and by the participation of many members in both societies. Leading members of the MCS (Marcet, Yelloly, Roget, Bostock, Babington, James Parkinson, Franck, Holland, Tennant and Wollaston) all served on the Council of the Geological Society, which doubtless explains why the organization of that Society had much in common with its medical counterpart.

The Geological Society held its first meeting in the house at Lincoln's Inn Fields on 1 June 1810, and the first Council meeting of the Medical and Chirurgical Society at that address took place on 28 September when the joint expense of purchasing the lease, repairs and furniture (£330) was divided between the two societies, Greenough having agreed to lend the MCS £165 (repaid in 1819). The 17th-century building had been redecorated and the improvement in the Society's accommodation encouraged members to bring guests to meetings there – Dr Sylvanus Bevan, Arthur Aikin who was Secretary of the Royal Society of Arts, TJ Pettigrew (who included biographies of several members of the Society in his *Medical portrait gallery*), Jacob Berzelius and Dr Berger were among the distinguished visitors.[187]

The Geological Society's collection of minerals and fossils spilled into the meeting-room, where they were displayed in two cabinets on either side of the fireplace. More space was needed, however, and the Geological Society gave notice that it was moving in July 1815.

This raised the possibility that the Medical and Chirurgical Society might move with the geologists to a larger house in Russell Square. The building was surveyed and pronounced unsuitable; the joint plan was abandoned, whereupon the Geological Society found a new home at 20 Bedford Street, Covent Garden in 1816.[188] Despite its move into larger premises, Marcet was not confident about its future, and his correspondent Leonard Horner compared it unfavourably to the MCS: 'medical friends here [Edinburgh] speak in the highest terms of the usefulness of the Medical and Chirurgical Society... I wish, however, that the Geological Society would communicate their papers to the public with the same despatch that the Medical Society does ... for God's sake do not allow the Council of the Geological Society to disintegrate', Horner wrote in 1816.[189]

*30 Lincoln's Inn Fields*
In 1819 the MCS was given notice by the landlord who wanted the remainder of the lease. The Council investigated the house next door, but this was in need of extensive repairs and within a few months its front was demolished leaving the Society's premises in a very dangerous state. The Council then took the bold decision to acquire a freehold house belonging to Mr Justice Best and valued at £5,000: this set in motion a round of negotiations and wrangles that distracted the Society for some while. Roget, Secretary at the time, despaired. 'I can give you but a general and imperfect outline of the difficulties and embarrassments in which the unlucky demolition of the adjoining house to ours in Lincoln's Inn Fields has involved our Society', he wrote to Marcet in August 1819. He told of endless meetings and plans without number proposed, considered, debated upon and ultimately discarded as being impracticable or inexpedient. 'We were a long time occupied about Justice Best's house and indeed had agreed to take it. But £4,000 was wanted as the purchase money'. Justice Best, Chief Justice of the King's Bench and later Baron Wynford, had evidently lowered his price, which still posed a problem to the Society. The suggestion that members might subscribe towards the purchase fell on deaf ears. 'Not one was to be found who would stir even a finger in the business. All eyes were naturally turned on our President: but he was not to be moved'.

A second plan invited members to advance 60 guineas each as a loan at 5% but only 17 accepted the proposition. A special appeal was then launched at a general meeting, with Astley Cooper presiding. 'The business could not have been in worse hands than those of our President. His manner gave no encouragement to whatever latent spirit there might have been: his example threw a fatal damp upon all generosity that might otherwise have been excited. Lawrence was the only rich man possessed of any public spirit; he offered to lend the Society 4 or £500 if the whole sum could by this means be made up'. Dr Granville, who founded the Obstetric Society in 1825, opposed the scheme vehemently and nothing came of it. Therefore the Society took a temporary house 'on the opposite side and corner of Lincoln's Inn Fields. It has only one drawing room which will do very well for the meetings – and one parlour which I fear will not hold our books'.[190] This temporary house, number 30 Lincoln's Inn Fields, was taken for one year from September 1819 for £200.[191]

*57 Lincoln's Inn Fields*
In the spring of 1820 the Society received a letter from Mr Richard Debarry offering to let 57 Lincoln's Inn Fields for £150 per annum, later reduced to £140, an offer that was accepted in July. Number 57, on the west side of the square, was built by Henry Joynes for Lord Talbot, the Solicitor General 'in the most refined Palladian taste' of 1730 (Plate 13).[192] The large house was later divided into numbers 57 and 58 (now reunited), with a twin porch and staircase designed by Sir John Soane in 1795. By Articles of Agreement of 1 September 1820 Debarry kept one floor, a back bedroom and use of the kitchen, while the Medical and Chirurgical Society occupied the ground floor, the basement except for

Debarry's wine and beer cellars, and shared the kitchen, on a seven-year lease with the option of renewal for 14 and 21 years thereafter.

In November the Astronomical Society, founded in 1820 by John Herschel among others, applied for the use of the meeting room, ante-room and Council room and the exclusive use of the attic for observations of the sky. The MCS welcomed the Astronomical Society as tenants who yielded a rent of 50 guineas a year.[193] Roget was satisfied: 'We have a most excellent house on the west side of the square', he reported, 'one large room serves as library and meeting room'. Debarry soon vacated his portion of the house, whereupon the Society took it and let it to a Mr Cuthbert for the satisfactory sum of £140 per annum.[194]

## The Society moves west

For the first few years at 57 Lincoln's Inn Fields, the Society was euphoric. An anniversary dinner was held at the Freemasons' Tavern in 1822, plans were made to institute a prize in the form of a gold medal for the best paper read to the Society and the clerk was set to work on a new Library catalogue. By 1825, however, the *Transactions* had lapsed, three officers had resigned over the misconduct of procedures (see page 58) and a proposal that meetings should be enlivened by *viva voce* discussion and questions suggests that they had become tedious. There was also some discontent expressed about the inconvenient location of Lincoln's Inn Fields, prompting consideration of a move westwards.[195] The College of Physicians had moved to Trafalgar Square in 1825, plans were afoot for a new St George's Hospital at Hyde Park Corner and another new hospital at Charing Cross. Physicians and surgeons were colonizing Savile Row and Mayfair and spilling north into the area around Cavendish Square: the medical profession was moving west, along with fashionable society.

The first members of the profession to favour the area around Harley Street were disreputable. Dr William Rowley, an accoucheur and superintendent of the Marylebone Infirmary and workhouse, was established in Harley Street before the end of the 18th century and from 1828 John St John Long, 'the king of quacks', attracted a stream of gullible females to his rooms there. More respectable physicians moved into the area from the 1840s onwards, establishing it as the medical quarter of London.

The Medical and Chirurgical Society struggled through the last years at Lincoln's Inn Fields. Marcet and Baillie were dead, Yelloly was in Norfolk, Roget had resigned as Secretary, and the clerk had defrauded the Society of some £240. There was also the counter-attraction of the Westminster Medical Society, said to have 1,000 members in 1824 and meeting at the Great Windmill Street School. Meetings of the MCS held in the spring of 1826 attracted only nine members and the occasional guest to listen to just one paper or to converse. Several members resigned in 1830 and the question of moving west was revived in the hope of improving attendances at meetings. The Council 'having taken into consideration the present state of the Society are of opinion that such state may be attributed in good measure to the present situation of the Society's house'. Therefore it was resolved 'that the Society should be moved to some more convenient part of the Metropolis westward'. The opinion of members was canvassed, eliciting 31 replies of which 21 were in favour of moving west, and in 1832 Dr James Copland's resolution that 'the Society should remove further westward to a situation more convenient to the majority of members' was passed.[196]

Agents in Wimpole Street were alerted to search for a suitable property but when the Society heard that the Royal Astronomical Society, having been granted a royal charter in 1831, was moving into Somerset House, where the Royal Society, the Royal Academy and the Society of Antiquaries were already ensconced, it was proposed to follow suit. Moreover, the Society had just launched its own petition for a royal charter. 'We should be enabled to procure a charter before long, and subsequently, as a chartered body, to obtain apartments in Somerset House or some other public building'.[197]

The matter assumed urgency when the landlord informed the Society that he no longer wished to let 57 Lincoln's Inn Fields as apartments, so with the possibility of being homeless while the application for a charter was pending, the Society advertised for a house. At a special general meeting held on 23 July 1834 the President reported that he had seen several houses in different parts of town and had decided upon 53 Berners Street. He had agreed with the proposal by the landlord, Mr Scott, to build and finish by Michaelmas a Library and ante-room in the rear of the house and to let these, together with the ground floor of the house and the basement, on an annual tenancy at £210.[198] The draft agreement was completed in August and in the same month Yelloly was pleased to inform the President that the royal charter of incorporation had at last been sanctioned; this, perhaps his greatest service to the Society, is described in Chapter 3.[199]

1 Transacs vol i (1809) pp. iv–vi.

2 Cooper, Bransby B, *The life of Sir Astley Cooper Bart* vol ii (1843) pp. 42–46.

3 GM 29 January 1806, 21 February 1809, 21 March, 4 April 1809, B1. Marcet later enlarged on the case of the sailor, Transacs vol xiii (1823) pp. 52–75.

4 Cooper, BB *op cit*, pp. 309–11.

5 GM 26 November 1806 (Dundas), 10 December 1806 (Abernethy), B1.

6 GM 21 March, 4 April 1809. Both were published in *Medico-Chirurgical Transactions* vol i (1809). The oldest surviving text on Jenner's vaccine, 'An Enquiry into the natural history of a disease known in Gloucestershire under the name of Cow-pox', signed and dated by Jenner 29 March 1797 is Western Ms 3019, Wellcome. The RSM Library has a printed version (1798), Plate 64. Jenner had himself founded a medical society in Gloucestershire, which he referred to as the Medico-Convivial Society.

7 Fisher, Richard B, *Edward Jenner 1749–1823* (1991) p. 213.

8 For Jenner's correspondence with Marcet see Miller, Genevieve (ed), *Letters of Edward Jenner and other documents concerning the early history of vaccination from the HBJ Collection in the Welch Medical Library* (1983) and note 10 below. Jenner received an additional £10,000 voted by Parliament in 1807. Baron, John, *The life of Edward Jenner* (1827). Credit is also due to Benjamin Jesty, a Dorsetshire farmer, who introduced cowpox by vaccination in 1774.

9 Letter Jenner to Marcet April 1803, Fisher, Richard B *op cit* pp. 84–85. Jane Marcet's book *Conversations on chemistry* (1806) first interested Faraday in chemistry, see *DNB*.

10 Eighteen autograph letters from Jenner to Marcet 1801–14. Presented to the RSM in 1923 by Marcet's grandson, Dr William Pasteur, Ms 514.

11 Suckling, Florence Horatio Nelson, *A forgotten past, being notes of the families of Tyssen, Baker, Hougham and Milles, of five centuries* (1898).

12 Letter Jenner to Marcet 26 March 1812, Miller, Genevieve *op cit* pp. 74–75, 78–79.

13 GM 16 January, 4 June 1811, 9 June 1812, B2. William Fergusson, surgeon and Inspector of military hospitals, should not be confused with Sir William Fergusson (1808–77) the pioneer of conservative surgery.

14 GM 8 November 1814, B2.

15 GM 12 November 1816, B3. Quarrier was proposed as a member 26 November 1816.

16 GM 3 March 1812, B2. GM 20 June 1815, B3. Blane was created a baronet in 1812, midway through his term of office as President of the Society.

17 Letter Bostock to Marcet 15 January 1810, Bostock correspondence (1802–22), Duke.

18 GM 18 March 1817, B3.

19 Letter Yelloly to Marcet 2 October 1805, Marcet correspondence (1802–23), Duke.

20 Letter Allen to Marcet 13 November 1812 in Marcet's 'Hospital and Practice Casebook 1804–17', RCS.

21 Coley, NG, 'Medical chemistry at Guy's Hospital 1770–1850' in *Ambix* vol xxxv pt 3 November 1988 pp. 155–68.

22 Cooper, BB *op cit* vol ii p. 264.

23 Berzelius, JJ, trans. Larsell, Olaf, *Autobiographical notes* (1934) p. 81.

24 Garrod, Sir Archibald, 'Alexander Gaspard Marcet. Physician to Guy's Hospital 1804–19' in *Guy's Hospital Reports* vol 75 (1925) pp. 373–81.

25 Transacs vol iii (1812) pp. 198–276. Coley, NG, 'The Animal Chemistry Club; an

Assistant Society to the Royal Society' in *Notes and Records of the Royal Society* vol xxii (1967) pp. 173–85.

26 Marcet, Alexander, *Correspondence with JJ Berzelius 1812–22* (1913).

27 GM 18 June 1811, B2. Garrod, Sir Archibald *op cit*.

28 Letter Bostock to Marcet 2 January 1812, Bostock correspondence (1802–22), Duke.

29 GM 16 March 1813, B2.

30 GM 23 April 1811, 28 April 1812, B1. GM 13 March 1814, B2. For Bostock's papers see the Index to vols i-liii of the *Transactions* (1871). His 'grand paper' on animal fluids in vol iv was referred to Marcet in January 1813, see Letter Bostock to Marcet 31 January 1813, Bostock correspondence (1802–22), Duke.

31 Letters Bostock to Marcet 8 September 1813, 6 July 1816, *ibid*.

32 GM 16 March 1819, B3. GM 6 June 1820, B4. GM 22 April 1828, B5.

33 Coley, NG, 'Animal chemistry and urinary stone' in *Ambix* vol xviii no 2 July 1971 pp. 69–93.

34 Letter Abercrombie (senior) to Marcet 12 February 1817 in Marcet's ' Hospital and Practice Casebook 1804–17', RCS.

35 GM 11 May 1819, B4.

36 Transacs vol xi (1821) pp. 402–13. Shaw, Anthony Batty, 'East Anglian bladder stone' in JRSM vol 72 (1979) pp. 222–28.

37 GM 24 June 1817, B3. Prout's discovery of hydrochloric acid was also announced to the Royal Society (1823). Much of Prout's research foreshadowed Liebig and his school, see Brock, WH, 'The life and work of William Prout' in *Medical History* vol ix (1965) pp. 101–26.

38 Copeman, WSC, 'William Prout MD FRS physician and chemist (1785–1850)' in *Notes and Records of the Royal Society* vol 24 (1970) pp. 273–80.

39 GM 5 March 1822, B4. *Picture of the present state of the College of Physicians* (1817). Coley, NG, 'Alexander Marcet 1770–1822. Physician and animal chemist' in *Medical History* vol xii (1968) pp. 394–402. Jorpes, J Erik, *Jac. Berzelius. His life and work* (1970) p. 83. Garrod, Sir Archibald *op cit*.

40 Marcet, Alexander, *Collected papers* (1805–22). Marcet's son, William was also interested in chemistry and was a Fellow of the Royal Society and of the RMCS. His grandson, Dr William Pasteur, was a member of the RMCS.

41 GM 21 January 1812, B2.

42 Pettigrew,TJ, *Medical Portrait Gallery. Biographical memoirs of the most celebrated Physicians, Surgeons etc etc who have contributed to the advancement of medical science* vol ii (1840) p. 15.

43 Clarke, JFL, *Autobiographical sketches of the medical profession* (1874) p. 312.

44 *A memoir by Sir Samuel Wilks* (1911) p. 76.

45 Hale-White, Sir William, *Great doctors of the 19th century* (1935) p. 80. 2 March 1863, PRSM vol iv (1861–64).

46 GM 12 June 1821, B4 (Paris), 9 January 1816 B3 (Geneva), 25 April 1820 B4 (Lucca), 22 November 1814, B2 (Hamburg), 2 March 1819, B3 (Madras), 14 March 1820, B4 (Bengal), 22 June 1819, B4 (Haiti), 20 March 1821, B2 (North America ).

47 GM 22 June 1819, B4.

48 GM 21 January 1812, B2. Transacs vol iii (1812) pp. 57–58. Critchley, Macdonald (ed), *James Parkinson 1755–1824* (1955).

49 GM 13, 27 April, 22 June 1813, B2. Transacs vol iv (1813) pp. 210–77, vol v (1814) pp. 239–54, vol vi (1815) pp. 318–74.

50 Holmes, Timothy, *Sir Benjamin Collins Brodie* (1898) p.160. Le Fanu, William, 'Sir Benjamin Brodie FRS (1783–1862)' in *Notes and Records of the Royal Society* vol xix (1964) pp. 42–52. Hawkins, Caesar, *The works of Sir Benjamin Brodie* 3 vols (1865).

51 Letter Bostock to Marcet 18 September 1813, Bostock correspondence (1802–22), Duke.

52 The RSM inherited Haighton's lectures on midwifery (1809–10, 1811), annotated by Blundell, Mss 160, 161.

53 GM 3 February, 5 January 1819, B3. His paper on the first human blood transfusion was published in the *Transactions* for 1819, having been read on 22 December 1818. For Blundell's further cases on blood transfusion with illustrations, see Blundell, James, 'Some remarks on the operation of transfusion' in *Researches Physiological and Pathological* (1824) pp. 63–146.

54 Jones, Harold W and Mackmull, Gulden, 'The influence of James Blundell on the development of blood transfusion' in *Annals of Medical History* vol 10 (1928) pp. 242–47.

55 CM 13 January 1813, 26 November 1817, A1. CM 20 June, 11 October, 12 November 1833, A2.

56 Cooper, BB *op cit* vol ii (1843) p.40. CM 29 December 1810, A1.

57 Letter Marcet to Roget 5 January 1820, Marcet collection, RCP.

58 CM 28 January 1818, 31 August, 24 November to 29 December 1819, 10 February 1820, A2.

59 Letter Roget to Marcet 25 January 1820, Marcet collection, RCP.

60 CM 26 July 1823, 1 November 1824, 12 January 1825, A2.

61 CM 12 February 1817, A1.

62 Atkinson, James, *Medical Biography A and B* (1834) p. 334. Cooper, BB *op cit* vol i (1843) p. 303, vol ii pp. 135, 265, 386. The 'Founders' Picture' by Samuel Medley, depicting members of the Medical Society of London (1800) in fact showed only four founder-members, see Abraham, JJ, *Lettsom. His life, times, friends and descendants* (1933).

63 Bright, Pamela, *Dr Richard Bright 1789–1858* (1983) p. 127.

64 Letter Bostock to Marcet 29 October 1819, Bostock correspondence (1802–22), Duke.

65 Shaw, Anthony Batty, *Norfolk and Norwich medicine. A retrospect* (1992). Spring, Robin J, 'The development of chemistry in London in the 19th century', PhD London University 1979. Williams, Robert, 'Memoirs of De Candolle, Mr Powell and Dr Yelloly' in the *Lancet* (ii) 7 May 1842 pp. 193–95. Yelloly's papers in *Philosophical Transactions* (1829, 1830) refer to the work of Marcet, Prout and the assistance of Faraday.

66 Crosse, V Mary, *A surgeon in the early 19th century. The life and times of John Green Crosse* (1968).

67 Letter Yelloly to Marcet 8 March 1819, Marcet correspondence (1802–23), Duke. CM 24 June 1818, 24 February, 24 March 1819, A2. GM 2, 16 March 1819, B3.

68 GM 7 May 1834, B6.

69 Cooper, BB *op cit* vol i (1843) p. 318.

70 Power, Sir D'Arcy, 'The removal of a sebaceous cyst from King George IV' in *British Journal of Surgery* vol xx January 1933 pp. 361–65.

71 Letter Bostock to Marcet 22 April 1821, Bostock correspondence (1802–22), Duke.

72 GM 20 March, 3 April 1821, B4.

73 Letters of Marcet, Roget, Saunders 1799–1822, Marcet collection, RCP.

74 Letter Hawkins to President RMCS 13 February 1882, Western Ms 5282, Wellcome.

75 Emblen, DL, *Peter Mark Roget, The word and the man* (1970) p. 46. Roget initiated the correspondence with Marcet in 1799; Marcet attended Roget when he was ill and Roget referred to their friendship as 'one of the greatest blessings of my life', 25 January 1820, Marcet collection, RCP.

76 Letter Marcet to Roget 30 September 1819, Marcet collection RCP.

77 Letter Roget to Marcet 25 January 1820, *ibid*.

78 Letter Yelloly to Marcet 14 May 1820, Marcet correspondence (1802–23), Duke.

79 Letter Bostock to Marcet 23 July 1820, Bostock correspondence (1802–22), Duke.

80 Letter Marcet to Roget 16 November 1820, Marcet correspondence (1802–23), Duke..

81 Cooper, BB *op cit* vol ii p. 240.

82 Feltoe, Charles Lett (ed), *Memorials of John Flint South* (1884) pp. 83–84.

83 Letter Roget to Marcet 19 March 1821, Marcet collection, RCP.

84 *Ibid*. GM 1 March 1821, B4.

85 Emblen, DL *op cit* p. 212.

86 CM 20 September 1831, A2.

87 GM 25 October 1831, B5. CM 10 April 1832, 13 November 1832, 22 January 1833, 8 May 1832, 17 April 1834, A2.

88 *Report from the Select Committee on Medical Education* (1834) part I pp. 290–304.

89 Bostock, John, *A sketch of the history of medicine* (1835) pp. 234–35. The book was dedicated to Dr Richard Bright.

90 CM 25 August 1806, A1.

91 CM 7 November 1807, A1.

92 CM 17, 28 February, 5 May, 30 June 1809, A1.

93 Letter Jenner to Marcet, 12 June 1809, Ms 515.

94 Letter Bostock to Marcet 15 October 1806, Bostock correspondence (1802–22), Duke.

95 *Ibid* 18 September 1808.

96 Wilks, Samuel, 'An account of some unpublished papers of the late Dr Hodgkin' in *Pamphlets by Thomas Hodgkin MD* n.d., Hodgkin collection PP/HO/D/D285, Box 24, Wellcome.

97 Bett, WR, 'The Discovery of the Trichina Spiralis' in *St Bartholomew's Hospital Journal* vol xxxvi (1928) pp. 39–42.

98 For excerpts from these unpublished papers and comments, see M & P pp. 52–56, 58–59, 61–63, 67.

99 Letter Wilks to MacAlister, 12 February 1906, G1–5/Box 21. This letter cites the Council's refusal to accept Addison's paper as one reason why Sir Samuel Wilks was reluctant to accept Honorary Fellowship. Wilks, Samuel and Bettany, GT, *A biographical history of Guy's Hospital* (1892) p. 228. Bishop, PMF, 'Dr Addison and his work' in PRSM vol 48 (1955) pp. 1032–38.

100 Clarke, JFL *op cit* pp. 215–16. GM 1 March 1851, B8.

101 9 February 1858, PRSM vol i (1856–58).

102 Wilks, Samuel, 'On disease of the supra-renal capsules or morbus Addisonii', offprint from *Guy's Hospital Reports* (1862). The copy in the RSM Library contains an autograph letter (and typescript) from Wilks to Rolleston (1895) on the Society's treatment of Addison which

made Wilks 'rather unfriendly to the Society, although I was prejudiced before when Hilton told me that they would not publish his original paper on Trichina Spiralis'.

103 GM 24 January 1832, B5.
104 Wilks, Samuel and Bettany, GT *op cit* p. 384.
105 Rosenfeld, Louis, *Thomas Hodgkin. Morbid anatomist and social activist* (1993) p. 76.
106 Wilks, Samuel, 'An account of some unpublished papers of the late Dr Hodgkin' in *Pamphlets by Thomas Hodgkin MD* n.d., Hodgkin collection PP/HO/D/D285, Wellcome.
107 Letter Bostock to Marcet 12 November 1812, Bostock correspondence (1802–22), Duke.
108 Letter Bostock to Marcet 2 February 1813, Bostock correspondence (1802–22), Duke.
109 CM 24 December 1811, 19 January 1816, A1.
110 *Picture of the present state of the College of Physicians* (1817) p. xiv.
111 Letter Roget to Marcet 27 August 1819, Marcet collection, RCP. John Howship's paper on 'The morbid appearances and structure of bones' (the sequel to his paper in vol viii) was illustrated with three detailed plates drawn by the author.
112 Letter Yelloly to Marcet 13 January 1814, Marcet correspondence (1802–23), Duke.
113 Letter Marcet to Roget, 30 September 1819, Marcet collection, RCP.
114 *Ibid.*
115 *Ibid* 2 August 1820.
116 Letters Roget to Marcet 19 March 1821, 9 August 1822, *ibid.*
117 Letter Jenner to Baron 30 January 1819, Autograph Letters Series J22, letter 27, RCS.
118 Note, Yelloly to Yeoman, 9 March 1818.
119 Letter Yelloly to Marcet 5 January 1811, Marcet correspondence (1802–23), Duke.
120 Jackson, Peter, *George Scharf's London sketchbook. Watercolours of a changing city 1820–50* (1987).
121 Presidential address, 1 March 1860, PRSM vol iii (1858–61).
122 *Ibid* 1 March 1861.
123 Holmes, Timothy *op cit* pp. 65, 160.
124 CM 13 March 1814, A1.
125 CM 13 March, 16, 26 December 1814, 1 February 1815, A1.
126 CM 12, 18 February 1828, A2.
127 Clarke, JFL *op cit* p. 217.
128 *Lancet* (i) 3 December 1831 pp. 335–36, (i) 22 December 1832 pp. 396–97.
129 Paget, Stephen, *Memoirs and letters of Sir James Paget* (1901) p. 73.
130 GM 25 October 1831, B5. CM 10 November 1835, A2. Clarke, JFL *op cit* pp. 148, 216–17.
131 Clarke, JFL *op cit* p. 219.
132 A brief notice of the case appeared first in the *Morning Chronicle*, see *Lancet* (ii) 20 May 1843 pp. 279–80. Brodie read his paper to the Society on 27 June, it was published in the *Lancet* (ii) 1 July 1843 pp. 481–83 and in the Society's *Transactions* vol xxvi (1843) pp. 286–97. Conacher, ID, 'Brodie's tracheostomy' in JRSM vol 85 September 1992 pp. 570–72.
133 *Report from the Select Committee on Medical Education* (1834) part 1 p. 120.
134 Transacs vol xi (1821) pp. 337–45.
135 *Ibid* vol xii (1823) pp. 297–307.
136 Transacs vol ii (1811) p. iv.
137 CM 14 February 1812, A1. For the sequence of events and correspondence, see Papers relative to an Application to His Royal Highness the Prince Regent in Council, for a Charter of Incorporation 1812–14, signed by Roget and Lawrence 26 December 1814, Ms 521.
138 *Report from the Select Committee on Medical Education* (1834) part 1 pp. 290–304.
139 The subscribers were thanked in March 1815: Halford, Baillie, Marcet, Yelloly, A Cooper, Cline, Farquhar, Curry, Young, Farre, Birkbeck, J Pearson, Abernethy, Stanger, GM 14 March 1815, B2.
140 Annals RCP, 6 March 1812.
141 *Ibid* 13 March 1812.
142 *Report from the Select Committee op cit.*
143 Annals RCP 25 June 1812.
144 Letter Bostock to Marcet 14 May 1812, Bostock correspondence (1802–22), Duke.
145 *Report from the Select Committee op cit.*
146 Annals RCP 24 November 1812.
147 Draft letter Baillie to Marcet and Yelloly, 2 August 1813; see also draft letter Yelloly and Marcet to Baillie 1 August, Hunter-Baillie Papers vol viii, RCS.
148 Correspondence of Saunders, Baillie, Halford and others to the Registrar November 1812, Envelope 37, legal documents, RCP.
149 Annals RCP 15 June 1813.
150 Letter Halford to Hervey 30 May 1813, CM 16 August 1813. Letter Saunders to Yelloly and Marcet 2 June 1813, letter Baillie to Yelloly and Marcet 2 August 1813, letter Halford to Yelloly and Marcet 3 August 1813. Ms 521.
151 Clarke, JFL *op cit* pp. 349–53.
152 Clark, Sir George, *A history of the Royal College of Physicians of London* vol ii (1966) p. 654.

153 Letter Yelloly to Marcet 22 February 1814, Marcet correspondence (1802–23), Duke.

154 Letter Hill (Department of coins and medals, British Museum) to MacAlister 8 June 1920, M15/Box 53.

155 CM 29 November 1815. Wyon was paid £21 5s, CM 24 July 1816, 8 January 1817, A1.

156 Saunders offered to assist with the article so long as his name was not mentioned and he asked Marcet to destroy this letter, letter Saunders to Marcet 22 April circa 1815–17, Marcet collection (54). Letter Yelloly to Marcet 2 May 1816, Marcet collection, RCP.

157 Letter Yelloly to Marcet 2 February 1816, Marcet correspondence (1802–23), Duke.

158 Ibid 5 February 1816.

159 GM 18 December 1805, B1.

160 GM 28 June 1805, B1.

161 CM 11 December 1805, 29 December 1810, A1.

162 CM 8 March 1806, A1. The Library committee was formed in 1806 but there are no surviving Minutes until 1836.

163 Williams, Robert, 'Memoirs of De Candolle, Mr Powell and Dr Yelloly' in the Lancet (ii) 7 May 1842 pp. 192–95.

164 CM 17 November 1808, A1.

165 CM 9 November 1809, A1.

166 Emblen, DL, Peter Mark Roget. The word and the man (1970).

167 CM 28 October 1812, A1.

168 Rumsey, J, Some account of the life and character of the late Thomas Bateman MD FLS (1826) p. 214. Bateman's Clinical Notebook or Commonplace Book 1799–1814, Western Ms 7057, Wellcome.

169 They were assisted by Professor Thomson, CM 28 September 1814, A1.

170 CM 22 May 1816, A1.

171 GM 16 April 1816, B3. CM 14 August 1816, A1. 24 November 1818, 15 June 1819, A2.

172 CM 22 May, 12 June 1816, A1

173 GM 24 December 1816, B3. CM 30 December 1818, A2. An original copy of the Bateman/Yelloly catalogue of 1816 was bequeathed to the Society by Yelloly but it cannot be traced at the RSM. A facsimile has been acquired. Original copies survive at the BL and another bearing Matthew Baillie's signature at the RCP. I am grateful to Dr G Storey for supplying a copy of Yelloly's will.

174 Atkinson, James, Medical Biography A and B (1834) p. 351.

175 CM 26 March 1818, A2.

176 CM 29 June 1819, A2.

177 Letter Yelloly to Marcet 20 March 1822, Marcet correspondence (1802–23), Duke.

178 GM 23 June 1821, B4.

179 Clark, JFL op cit p. 323.

180 The printing cost £44 13s 4d, CM 26 July, 29 October 1823, A2. It seems likely that this catalogue is the three-volume Catalogus Bibliothecae Societatis Med. Chirurg., undated apart from a page water-marked 1819, M.8.b.26–28.

181 GM 26 April, 6 May 1825, B5. CM 30 March 1825, A2.

182 CM 12,18 February 1828, A2. See page 47.

183 CM 10 April, 8 May 1832, A2. Courtland is also spelt Cortlandt.

184 Woodward, Horace B, The history of the Geological Society of London (1907).

185 CM 25 January 1810, A1. Rudwick, MJS, 'The foundation of the Geological Society of London' in British Journal for the History of Science vol i pts 1 to 4 (1962–63) pp. 325–55.

186 CM 7 March, 14 May 1810, A1.

187 Their names are recorded in the Court Minutes 1811–1813.

188 CM 26 July 1815, 9 January, 22 May, 12 June 1816, A1. GM 1 March 1819, B3.

189 Letter Horner to Marcet 14 March 1816, Lyell, Katharine M, Memoir of Leonard Horner (1890) vol i p. 89.

190 Letter Roget to Marcet 27 August 1819, Marcet collection (37), RCP.

191 CM July-September 1819, A2, gives the plans and changes of plans, the possible move to 36 Bedford Row and the final agreement to move to 30 Lincoln's Inn Fields.

192 Pevsner, Nikolaus, and Cherry, Bridget, The buildings of England. London 1. The Cities of London and Westminster (1973) p. 369. Cherry, Bridget, and Pevsner, Nikolaus, The buildings of England. London 4: North (1998) p. 308. Joynes had been comptroller and conductor of building at Blenheim Palace (1705–15) and was clerk of the works at Kensington Palace from 1715 to 1754. Numbers 57–58 Lincoln's Inn Fields survive.

193 CM 15 June, 26 July, 27 September, 29 November 1820, A2.

194 Letter Roget to Marcet 19 March 1821, Marcet collection, RCP. CM 27 December 1820, 28 March 1821, A2.

195 CM 27 April, 29 November 1825, A2.

196 CM 15 February, 12 April 1831, 27 March 1832, A2. GM 11 February 1834, B6.

197 CM 17 April 1834, A2.

198 GM 23 July 1834, B6.

199 CM 27 August 1834, A2.

# Chapter 3

# The Royal Medical and Chirurgical Society

UNDER ITS NEW name of the *Royal* Medical and Chirurgical Society of London, the Society achieved status and maturity during the reign of Queen Victoria. The security bestowed by the charter of 1834 coupled with the acquisition of premises in the West End created the climate in which the RMCS flourished as an academic institution. As the Society matured, so the medical profession settled into a period of stability and progress that followed the agitation of the first half of the 19th century. The medical corporations had not crumbled under pressure from discontented practitioners and the demands of the expanding population of industrial Britain, as some had feared. The Apothecaries Act, the Anatomy Act, the Public Health Act, the formation of the British Medical Association and the Medical Act of 1858 establishing the General Medical Council brought a new structure and a measure of reform and self-regulation to the profession that put it in a stronger position than ever before. The supremacy of the Royal College of Physicians had been challenged, the Royal College of Surgeons gained a new charter and an army of qualified general practitioners provided an effective force for the medical care of the burgeoning population of Victorian London.

By the middle years of the century the medical schools and licensing authorities were overseeing the systematic education and examination of students. The general and specialist hospitals afforded new opportunities for research and training, and a vigorous medical press and an abundance of medical societies fortified the profession. The scene was set for the advance of surgery and medicine at a time when philanthropy, industry and confidence in human progress motivated the professional classes of Victorian Britain.

The expansion, prosperity and optimism of the Victorian era epitomized by the Great Exhibition of 1851 was reflected in the increasing numbers of Fellows gathering at the RMCS to present their work and to debate the medical issues of the day. With a strong membership, a valuable Library and a record number of papers read and published, the Society was able to survive a skirmish with the *Lancet*, the secession of some Fellows to the Pathological Society and the competing attractions of other medical societies. The foundation of the new Pathological, Epidemiological, Obstetrical and Clinical Societies signalled the specialization of the profession, a tendency that was deplored by many. The RMCS, founded in 1805 specifically to embrace the several branches of medicine and surgery, earnestly sought to unite the specialist offshoots in one large society, an aim that proved elusive until the amalgamation of 1907.

When the amalgamation scheme of 1860–61 failed, the RMCS found a new and useful role through its scientific committees. The first of these embarked upon an investigation into the resuscitation of the apparently dead in 1861. Another enquired into the safety of one of the greatest medical innovations of the 19th century, the use of chloroform as an anaesthetic, while other committees investigated diphtheria and croup, and the effectiveness of the hypodermic method of administering medicines.

The papers presented at the Society's meetings showed that Fellows were often ahead of current practice, breaking new ground in ovariotomy, for instance, and in the use of the clinical thermometer, and leading the way in specialties such as diseases of the eye and ear.

In other respects the Society was inflexible: anything that savoured of quackery was unacceptable and the Council's refusal to publish a paper on mesmerism forced a past President to resign his Fellowship.

In 1881 the International Medical Congress was held in London for the first time, giving publicity to the revolutionary work of Professor Koch, stimulus to the profession generally and prompting a demonstration of bacteriology at the RMCS. At this time London's most famous physicians and surgeons were to be found at the Society's house: Dr Thomas Barlow, Sir Henry Thompson, Sir James Paget, Sir Jonathan Hutchinson and Dr John Hughlings Jackson were among those present at meetings, taking part in discussions and encouraging colleagues to explore new avenues. The same decade heralded the formation of a second batch of specialist medical societies, bringing renewed calls for amalgamation.

## The royal charter of incorporation

The Reform Act of 1832, the Anatomy Act of the same year and the searching enquiries of the Warburton committee into all aspects of the medical profession (1834) created a climate that was favourable to the incorporation of the Medical and Chirurgical Society by royal charter. Circumstances had altered since the Society's first, unsuccessful petition for a charter: medical education had been regulated in 1815 and by the 1830s the ranks of the medical profession were being swollen by 300 to 400 general practitioners a year. New hospitals, dispensaries and medical schools had been founded during the last 20 years, the increasing population of the towns and cities created a heavy demand for medical care and the cholera epidemic of 1832–33 focused attention on public health. Even the Royal College of Physicians, which had effectively blocked the Society's first bid for a charter, was being driven towards reform, pushed in that direction by Dr JA Wilson and the medical press. Wilson, the son of a founder-member of the MCS and himself a Fellow from 1839, was strongly supported in his campaign by Dr John Elliotson, the President of the Society whose name headed the petition for a royal charter in May 1834 (Plate 65). Elliotson had recently been appointed the first Professor of Medicine at University College, where he was recognized as 'one of the most popular teachers that ever existed',[1] and he was at the height of his fame during the years of his presidency of the Society (1833–35), not yet seduced by the mesmerism that was to be his downfall. Elliotson gave the first paper to the first meeting of the Society in Berners Street: it concerned the medicinal properties of creosote. He had experimented with this new drug by administering it to patients suffering from phthisis, epilepsy, neuralgia, cholera, vomiting and diabetes and he claimed to have met with some success.[2]

Elliotson's professional reputation, the influence of Sir Astley Cooper and Sir Benjamin Brodie and the initiative of Dr John Yelloly formed a powerful combination. Yelloly had never given up hope that the Society would eventually be incorporated by royal charter: 'We failed in getting a charter in the first instance but I felt sure that, sooner or later, we should succeed ... In 1833 or 1834 an opportunity occurred to me of pressing on the business and nothing could be more kind or friendly than the conduct of Sir Astley on this occasion. He readily went with Sir Benjamin Brodie and myself, to Lord Normanby [later Home Secretary] on an important matter of society business'.[3]

This second attempt to obtain a royal charter was initiated by Yelloly at a special general meeting of the MCS on 7 May 1834. The resolution was passed unanimously.[4] Therefore a 'humble petition' was addressed to King William IV in the names of Dr John Elliotson, Sir Astley Cooper who was serjeant-surgeon to the King, and Dr John Yelloly, formerly physician to the Duke of Gloucester. As founder-members of the Society Cooper and Yelloly stood for its continuity and achievements over the past 30 years, and with Brodie they had contacts at court and in the government. Sir Benjamin Brodie had been the constant attendant on George IV prior to his death in 1830 and was serjeant-surgeon to

William IV from 1832. Cooper had also served the late King and attended William IV before he came to the throne. This all augured well for the Society's petition.

The petition stressed the Society's achievements, notably 'the purchase and collection of a large and valuable library' and the publication of 18 volumes of *Transactions* 'which have had a very extensive circulation'. The petitioners pleaded for a royal charter on the grounds that it would 'materially contribute to the stability and efficiency of this Society' of which, it was hoped, His Majesty and his successors would be Patrons.

The Whig government of Earl Grey was committed to sweeping changes when it came to power in 1830, Viscount Normanby was well known for his liberalism and the King was affable and eager to please, so doubtless he concurred with the advice of his ministers on the subject of a new incorporation. The one body that might have objected, as it had done some 20 years previously, was the Royal College of Physicians. Its President, Sir Henry Halford, had however recently stated in evidence given to the Warburton committee on medical education that he thought there could be no objection to the incorporation of the Medical and Chirurgical Society.[5] The College was in a vulnerable position in the 1830s: its privileged status had been undermined by the emergence of a large body of qualified general practitioners, by widespread criticism and by the enquiries of the Warburton committee. Those providing evidence to this committee were critical of the 'supineness' of the College, composed of an élite 'reposed on their dignities', out of touch with both the public and the medical profession as a whole. It was generally agreed that the ancient demarcation between the three branches of the medical profession – physicians, surgeons and apothecaries – had broken down by 1834. This favoured the MCS, dedicated as it was to the unity of medicine and surgery.

The Society's petition progressed unopposed and swiftly in spite of a change of government in the summer of 1834. It had evidently been approved by Lord Melbourne as Home Secretary and when he succeeded as Prime Minister in July he was in a position to advance the Society's interests. Grey and Melbourne promoted a baronetcy for Brodie in August, and in the same month Yelloly announced to the Council of the MCS that 'the charter had received the sanction of the law officers of the Crown' (Plate 15). Dr Elliotson volunteered to bear the legal expenses until subscriptions could be raised and at the same triumphant Council meeting it was announced that the draft agreement to rent 53 Berners Street was complete.[6]

The only hitch came with the request from the Home Office that the future title of the Society should be the Royal Society of Medicine and Surgery. Yelloly and Bostock objected

The seal of the Royal Medical and Chirurgical Society. The motto *non est vivere sed valere vita* (it is important to enjoy good health to live fully) was inherited from the Medical and Chirurgical Society. The image depicts Salus raising a kneeling figure.

strongly, insisting that the only changes should be the prefix Royal and the title of Fellows for members.[7] The Home Office conceded, contributions amounting to £346 9s towards the cost of the charter were collected from 134 members of the Society, and Yelloly set to work amending the statutes and by-laws. The new statutes re-affirmed the aims of the Society with emphasis on the importance of science: 'The Royal Medical and Chirurgical Society is instituted for the cultivation of Physic and Surgery, and the branches of science connected therewith'. The duties of the officers of the Society were defined and the Library hours, membership fees and subscriptions were laid down, and were all circulated to Fellows in the *Transactions* for 1835, complete with details of the petition and charter.

## Yelloly's last years

Once again, the Council paid tribute to the leading role taken by Dr Yelloly, this time in relation to the royal charter. The document, dated 30 September, was laid before a special general meeting of the Society held on 11 November 1834 at Elliotson's house in Conduit Street. Sir Astley Cooper superintended the affixing of the Society's seal to a grateful response to King William IV in February 1835 and on 4 March Elliotson, Yelloly and Brodie presented the address at St James's (Cooper was indisposed); on the following Monday the King's signature was inserted in the Society's Obligation Book, signifying his patronage (Plate 14). Queen Victoria was persuaded to follow her uncle's example in 1840, encouraged by an obsequious address from the Society congratulating her on her marriage. This too was initiated by Yelloly, who 'had intercourse with persons of influence in the government' to whom he made application 'with a view of gaining high patronage for the Society'. The satisfactory result was that Queen Victoria agreed to be the Society's Patroness, and at a cost of £1 3s Yelloly procured her signature for the Obligation Book.[8] This was his last service to the Society, for as the result of a fall from a phaeton he succumbed to paralysis on his right side. He died two years later in 1842, having contributed more than any of his contemporaries to the success of the Society he founded. He had also been active in founding the Geological Society (1807) and was one of the orig-inators of the British Association for the Advancement of Science (1831), becoming President of its Section of Medical Science in 1839. He was called upon to give evidence to the Warburton committee in 1834, and in retirement he wrote treatises connected with the sick poor (1837) and spade husbandry in Norfolk (1838).[9] Shortly before his death, Yelloly recounted his reminiscences to Dr Bransby Cooper for inclusion in *The life of Sir Astley Cooper Bart* (1843). In the second volume of that work Yelloly is described as 'a man of considerable observation, extensive literary attainments and one who uniformly throughout life exhibited that integrity of purpose and delicacy of behaviour in his profes-sional conduct'.[10]

## A contentious election

The first Council of the new Royal Medical and Chirurgical Society, elected in March 1835, boasted four baronets (Cooper, MacGrigor, Brodie and Tierny) and the membership was soon to include Dr Michael Faraday of the Royal Institution, Sir William Hooker, botanist and the first Director of Kew Gardens, Sir David Brewster, editor of scientific journals and experimenter in optics, and Mr William Clift of the Hunterian Museum. The choice of President in 1835 was contentious, as the *Lancet* pointed out in a scathing piece: 'This learned body, having for some years past been acquiring the character of a subscrip-tion library rather than that of a scientific society, its managers, in order to increase the number of its subscribers, obtained a royal charter, in consequence of the security which a royal charter gives to a joint-stock company. As soon, however, as the society obtained this mark of royal favour, it became and it has since continued to be, the seat of internal discord and intrigue'.

This discord centred on the election of Henry Earle, surgeon to St Bartholomew's and to the Foundling Hospital, as President. According to the *Lancet*, 'it was proposed by some of the menials of the Society that Mr Earle should be passed over, and that the eminent Sir Benjamin Brodie should be elected in his place' so as to adorn the chair with a title. When Earle heard of the plot he threatened resignation. The Council then persuaded 'the flexible baronet' [Brodie] to withdraw, and Earle took the chair.

A letter from 'A Spectator' to the editor of the *Lancet* confirmed that the Society had indeed degenerated into 'a mere library society' and that 'Sir Benjamin Brodie's friends endeavoured to turn out poor Mr Earle. This was a scheme of Dr Yelloly, who thought that Sir Benjamin, an eminent surgeon from St George's, would keep up the respectability of the chair better than a sparrow from St Bartholomew's, but when that little bird heard what was going on, he instantly took wing, and flew about in great anger until he perched on the chair where he now roosts'.[11] Earle was duly elected in 1835 and Brodie had his turn as President from 1839 to 1841. The Society was not impervious to this public criticism of the conduct of its affairs and appointed a committee to investigate 'the best means of selecting candidates for offices', which concluded that fitness for office rather than seniority was the best qualification for all officers of the Society.[12]

As Yelloly had foreseen, Sir Benjamin Brodie proved to be an inspiring President. He never missed a meeting and he encouraged the discussion of papers. 'It was after the reading of a paper that he was particularly great. Acting up to his axiom, that the debates in the Society constituted its most important and interesting feature, he always encouraged discussion.' Even the *Lancet* acknowledged that Brodie breathed new life into the meetings: 'from the period of his presidency may be dated the remarkable prosperity of the Medical and Chirurgical Society and this is mainly attributable, we believe, to the mode in which he fostered and protected discussion'.[13] He was the first President 'who had the courage and ability to foster discussion and commend reporting... he stimulated Fellows to speak and if he found that discussion was flagging, or altogether avoided, he would himself continue or open the debate'.[14] Brodie's presidency heralded a period of prosperity that reached a zenith in the middle years of the century.

## 53 Berners Street

The Society having reached the decision to move its base to the West End and having failed to find a suitable house in the neighbourhood of either Charing Cross or Wimpole Street, the availability of an 18th-century house in Berners Street was brought to its notice. This was a convenient location, being close to the residences of middle-class and aristocratic patients of Cavendish Square, to the practices and homes of Fellows of the Society and to several hospitals. The Middlesex Hospital stood at the north end of the street and University College Hospital was being built not far away in Gower Street. The College of Physicians, Charing Cross Hospital, the new St George's at Hyde Park Corner and Westminster Hospital in Broad Sanctuary were likewise easily accessible. Fellows who worked at Guy's, St Thomas' and in the City had a longer journey to meetings at Berners Street, but travel across London was soon to be eased by the extensive Victorian street improvements.

Berners Street had first been developed by William Chambers and Thomas Collins who purchased leasehold land from William Berners in 1764. Chambers was enjoying royal favour and public recognition for his work at Goodwood House and Buckingham House, and he was knighted in 1769. His friend Thomas Collins was one of London's finest plasterers, so they formed a business partnership for the speculative development of Berners Street. Chambers designed between 19 and 26 houses for the street, all ornamented with Collins' craftsmanship. The first house to be built was number 13 on the east side of the street, and Chambers and his family lived there for nearly 30 years.[15] The west side of the street, including number 53 which was to house the RMCS from 1834 to 1889, was completed the following year. All the houses were dignified by the fine doorcases and plasterwork characteristic of Chambers: 'even in their smallest details his houses revealed the best of craftsmanship and materials'.[16]

Number 53 Berners Street, now swamped by the Sanderson Hotel, was first occupied by Philip Stevens Esq in 1775. One James Stephens is mentioned in a lease of 1784; these two may possibly have been relatives of Chambers' principal assistant, Edward Stevens. In 1805 Charles Berners of Woolverstone in Suffolk leased the property to Sir William Bensley Bt, when it was described as a brick messuage on the west side of Berners Street

Horwood's map (1813 edition) shows the locations of (a) 53 Berners Street, the Society's house from 1834 to 1889, (b) 20 Hanover Square where the Society was based from 1889 until 1910, (c) 15 Cavendish Square, a temporary home from 1910 to 1912, and (d) 2–5 Henrietta Street, the site where 1 Wimpole Street was built.

having a street frontage of 30 feet 4 inches, flanked by the properties of Thomas Parry Esq and Thomas Collins and with a mews at the far end of the garden. The lease was assigned to Edward Rankin Esq in 1830, from whom it passed to Messrs Scott and Parsons who let the house to the RMCS from 1834 at an annual rent of £210.[17] Before the Society moved in, Mr Scott agreed to build and finish a Library and ante-room at the rear of the house, which with three rooms and a closet on the ground floor and the basement comprised the Society's accommodation.[18]

When the RMCS held its first Council meeting at Berners Street in February 1835 the original chimneypieces, doorcases and plasterwork were still in place, as was an ornamental circular gesso relief depicting Aeneas carrying his father from burning Troy (Plate 16). This was the work of the sculptor John Bacon RA and had earned him the first Gold Medal ever awarded by the Royal Academy for sculpture (1769). Bacon was living in Wardour Street at the time that Berners Street was being completed, and he was later commissioned to execute the bronze statue of George III and the River Thames for the courtyard at Somerset House, Sir William Chambers' masterpiece in the Strand. Possibly Bacon presented Chambers with his prize-winning medallion of Aeneas, or Chambers, his assistant or an occupant of the house purchased it as a good match to the late-18th-century chimneypiece (Plate 17) it surmounted. Both the medallion and the chimneypiece were greatly prized by the RMCS and were removed to Hanover Square in 1889, eventually coming to rest at 1 Wimpole Street where the medallion can be seen at the entrance to the Domus Medica, and the chimneypiece adorns the Marcus Beck Library.

The structure of 53 Berners Street was sound so that apart from removing the Drapers' doorplate (the building was previously occupied by the Drapers' Institution) and

53 Berners Street, London W1, the Society's house from 1835 to 1889. Drawn by Elizabeth Drake in 1905. Clockwise from left: exterior; Library and meeting room; Resident Librarian's room.

equipping the Library with bookcases, seats and tables, expenditure on the Society's house was small. The main improvement was the installation of gas lighting by means of chandeliers, gas lamps and brackets, and for the first time attention was given to the archives which with the charter were placed in a safe.[19] Two years later Fellows demanded heating as well as light, complaining of the cold and discomfort of the Library. Stoves 'on Dr Arnott's principle' were ordered, 'genuine thermometer stoves with copper boilers' – these were the invention of a Fellow of the Society, Dr Neil Arnott. Physician, natural philosopher and one of the original members of the senate of London University, Arnott was also an inventor; he had devised a water-bed for one of Henry Earle's patients in 1832 and he was the author of *On warming and ventilating* (1838). His invention of a stove with a chimney-valve and smokeless grate gained him the Rumford Medal of the Royal Society, but the version that was installed in the Library at 53 Berners Street proved inadequate. Fellows reported that in December 1840 the temperature in the room never rose above 55° Fahrenheit and for two days fell to 46°. A larger version was then installed at a cost of £30.[20]

## Tenants

The Society was pleased to grant the use of 53 Berners Street to congenial societies for their meetings. A longstanding tenant at Lincoln's Inn Fields, the Royal Astronomical Society, had hoped to continue the arrangement in the new location, and indicated that there was a larger plan afoot in 1834 'that several societies should unite to take a house for their meetings'. This was not to be: the Royal Astronomical Society found accommodation in Somerset House and the RMCS moved to Berners Street alone.[21]

The Council of the Zoological Society was given permission to meet at the Society's house in Berners Street in 1836 – a Fellow named Thomas Bell, the naturalist/dental surgeon who had instigated the scientific meetings of the Zoological Society, may have been instrumental in this arrangement. The Society for the Relief of Widows and Orphans of Medical Men, with Sir Henry Halford as its President and Sir Astley Cooper as a Vice President, was granted the use of the Council room for quarterly meetings of its Court of Directors in 1839, and in 1843 Dr BG Babington and Dr John Clendinning requested the use of the Library for meetings of the Sydenham Society for three months. The Widows and Orphans Society remained a tenant at Berners Street for many years, whereas the Sydenham Society moved to 45 Frith Street within two years. The Sydenham Society, named after the 17th-century physician Thomas Sydenham, had been founded at Dr James Copland's house in 1843 with the aim of publishing reprints of rare English medical literature (Copland was a literary figure, author of the *Dictionary of medical practice* and President of the RMCS 1853–55).[22]

Generally the Council agreed to accommodate like-minded societies for a small rent but when Mr Oscar Byrne applied to take the upper floors of 53 Berners Street and use the front room for dancing classes, the application was rejected 'decidedly'.[23] For different reasons the Council refused to allow the Pathological Society use of rooms. The recently established Pathological Society made its polite introduction in June 1846, sending a prospectus and pointing out that many of its members were Fellows of the RMCS. The Council of the Pathological Society denied any wish 'to interfere with the province, or detract from the usefulness' of the older society; on the contrary it was 'desirous of securing its countenance and co-operation' and the use of rooms in its house for meetings between October and June.[24] After some deliberation, the application was refused on the grounds that the meetings of the energetic Pathological Society would lure Fellows away from meetings of the RMCS. Rebuffed as a tenant in 1846, the Pathological Society made advances again in 1850 with proposals for a conference to discuss a joint tenancy and/or the possibility of the union of the two societies. Again, the RMCS refused to have the rival organization in the same house because that might diminish attendances at its own meetings; furthermore, 'the exhibition of many specimens by the Pathological Society would probably create a nuisance'. The suggestion for the union of the two societies was ignored and it was not until 1857 that the Pathological Society gained an entrée to Berners Street at an annual rent of £30. The application of the Royal College of Veterinary Surgeons to use the rooms was rejected, whereas the Epidemiological Society was welcomed and with Dr Benjamin Babington as its President it held its first meeting at Berners Street on 2 December 1850.[25]

*Expansion and renovation*

By 1847 it was already clear that the Society needed more space, either the whole of 53 Berners Street or larger premises elsewhere. The architect George Pownall of Wigg and Pownall, the successor to Joseph Wigg who had built the Society's first house at Verulam Buildings, was called in to advise; his firm had recently been responsible for the design of an Italianate library at Gray's Inn and for the Jacobean Staple Inn building of 1842–43. Pownall's estimate to put the building in a good state amounted to £1,200, with another £600 required for the enlargement of the meeting room. These costs were prohibitive and the Society negotiated instead for the use of an additional room on the second floor where 1,500 books could be stored.[26] Expansion into all floors of 53 Berners Street was the simplest solution and was master-minded in 1849 by the Society's Treasurer, Benjamin Phillips. A new 54-year lease was promptly acquired at £160 per annum and the Society appeared settled. A programme of repairs was then undertaken according to plans by Wigg and Pownall, chiefly renovations to the Library, the lobby leading to it, the roof, drains and fittings, whereby 'considerable improvement has been effected' by 1850.[27]

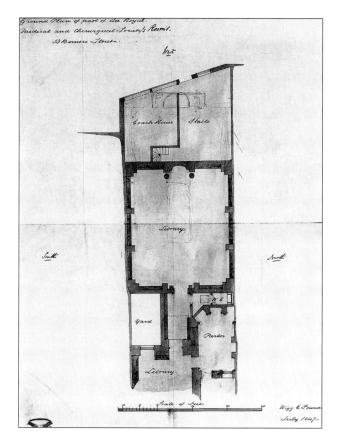

Plan of 53 Berners Street by the architects Wigg and Pownall showing the Library, parlour and other ground floor rooms occupied by the Society, 1847.

## The Library at Berners Street

The grant of the royal charter brought an influx of new Fellows, placing the Society's finances on a firm footing and warranting large purchases for the Library. This in turn called for more shelves, a new catalogue, better facilities for readers, a Library committee and the appointment of Benjamin Wheatley as Librarian. In 1832, before the move to Berners Street, it had become necessary to employ a paid sub-Librarian, Mr Thomas Williams, who acted as assistant to the two Honorary Librarians; he bore an increasing work load and made repeated requests for a larger salary.[28]

Honorary Librarians followed each other in rapid succession in the 1830s: FC Skey resigned in 1831, Dr William Gairdner did so the next year, and Dr John Burn in 1834. This lack of continuity and the disruption of the move from Lincoln's Inn Fields to Berners Street meant that the Library grew more by chance than direction. The arrangement of the collection in the room that doubled as the meeting room at Berners Street was achieved without difficulty, but before the Society could settle into complacency a vituperative article in the *Lancet* of 23 April 1836 drew attention to the deficiencies of its Library. The anonymous reporter calculated that Fellows' annual subscriptions 'must be at least £1,200' and that taking into account the Society's expenses 'a large surplus must be left over for supplying the library'. These calculations were based on a membership of 400, including Honorary and non-resident Fellows; the truth was that only 137 Fellows actually paid their subscriptions for 1835–36. The author went on to criticize the lack of foreign publications in the Library: 'Will the Managers inform us how many volumes have been added to the shelves within the last three years? It is only lately that any French journals have been taken in; no German or Italian, or any other continental medical periodical journals besides the French is now received. None of the many excellent scholars connected with the Society appear to concern themselves about it or surely they would immediately obtain every new publication … The utmost ignorance of Foreign medical literature evidently prevails among the managers. Such a fatal disregard for the true purposes of the institution should induce every zealous member to inquire into its efficiency and endeavour to place it on a proper footing'.[29]

Whatever the criticisms levelled by the *Lancet*, the Society's Library was famous and to many it was the chief advantage of membership. Dr William Baly told his father in 1836: 'Dr Burrows will propose me a member at the next meeting of the Royal Medical and Chirurgical Society, the Medical Library of which is the best in London' (Baly was to be an Honorary Librarian in due course).[30] Furthermore, a Library committee of 11 members was appointed in April 1836 with the aim of selecting books for purchase. It set about obtaining back numbers of the *Lancet* and appointed Mr Churchill of Princes Street as bookseller to the Society on the understanding that he would give 5% discount on purchases. It took a personal memoir from Dr Yelloly to galvanize the committee into consideration of a new Library catalogue, which Mr Spilsbury undertook to compile in 1837 (he was later responsible for cataloguing the Lincoln's Inn Library, assisted by Wheatley). Spilsbury presented his work to the Council in 1838, yet the Society did not publish it until 1844; by then the cost of printing amounted to £137 12s – more than the sub-Librarian's annual salary (which probably explained the delay).

Members of Council were urged to donate copies of books they had written to the Library, and busts of past Presidents were placed around the room. New bookcases and the prospect of occupation of the whole of the building encouraged the Library committee to expand the collection. The selection of appropriate works was entrusted to sub-committees composed of experts in the various subjects. Richard Owen, Hunterian Professor of Comparative Anatomy, led the team recommending books on that subject; he had given a paper to the Society in 1830 and was made an Honorary Fellow in 1847. James Paget, William Bowman, James Dixon and Dr William Sharpey advised on anatomical and physiological works; Jonathan Pereira, author of *Elements of materia medica* (1839–40) and the first Professor in *materia medica* to the Pharmaceutical Society, contributed his expertise; Dr Benjamin Babington, Dr Henry Lee, Dr Henry Bence-Jones, John Erichsen, Dr Charles West and Dr Arthur Farre gave advice. They also studied the catalogues of the Royal College of Surgeons and the Royal Medical Society of Edinburgh before making their recommendations to Council. As a result, 432 books were purchased for the Library in 1848 at a cost of £253 10s 9d: 175 were in German, 153 in French, 57 in English, 42 in Latin, five in Italian. The purchase of so many foreign books suggests a belated response to the criticism made 12 years previously in the *Lancet*, although it was another 10 years before foreign dictionaries were provided for readers.[31] The scope of the collection widened with the acquisition of the *Report from the Select Committee on Medical Education*; the *Reports of the Sanitary Commissioners* were presented by Edwin Chadwick, who was elected an Honorary Fellow in 1849 in recognition of his efforts in advancing the Poor Law Amendment Act (1834) and the Public Health Act (1848).

The Library of the RMCS was well used, to the extent that Fellows were sometimes kept waiting at the door, so a boy was engaged to act as door-keeper and messenger in 1846. He earned six shillings a week and was given a livery that cost a disproportionate £8 4s 6d. Additional bookcases were installed early in 1847; even so the congestion of books and readers posed the question of a move to larger premises or the enlargement of the room.[32]

## *Benjamin Wheatley, Librarian*

By March 1849 there were 13,926 monographs in the Library (about 20,000 volumes) and the great increase of acquisitions since the catalogue of 1844 persuaded the Library committee that the compilation of a new general catalogue was necessary and that this was to be supervised by James Dixon as Honorary Librarian.[33] Dixon was surgeon to the Royal London Ophthalmic Hospital and to St Thomas' but had no cataloguing experience, and he must soon have realized that the task was beyond him. Benjamin Wheatley then came to the rescue. He had first worked in the Society's Library at the age of 17 in 1841 and again in 1848, when he was described as a copier. He went on to catalogue the libraries of the Travellers' and Oxford and Cambridge Clubs, and he completed an index for the Statistical Society in 1854. The Library committee of the RMCS approached him in 1852, obtaining his estimate for the compilation of a new Library catalogue and on this basis the Council commissioned him. Wheatley's labour involved re-cataloguing the entire Library, which was growing by 500 to 800 volumes each year. Wheatley disregarded previous catalogues and supplements, choosing to work 'from the books themselves'. The timing was perfect, for on Williams' resignation as sub-Librarian due to ill-health in November 1854, Wheatley, 'whose experience in the management of libraries most of the Fellows will appreciate' was appointed Resident Librarian. Before he resigned Williams had made some headway with a manuscript catalogue of the most important works in the collection, but Wheatley preferred his own system.[34]

Wheatley's manuscript catalogue was pronounced 'perfectly complete' in April 1855 and 500 copies were printed in March 1856 at a cost of some £165. Dixon and Dr William Wegg were credited with the supervision of the work, but the achievement was Wheatley's. He was also responsible for subject indexes of 1860, for a three-volume catalogue of 1879 (Plate 18) and for cataloguing the Society's Soden collection of engraved portraits of medical men. In 1873 'the obliging and indefatigable Wheatley' also found himself organizing a conversazione at which the artistic achievements of members were exhibited. The President at the time, Dr Charles Williams, wrote of Wheatley's pivotal role in the Society: 'to him, whom I called our genius loci, I found myself under continual obligations'.[35] His knowledge of the Library was invaluable and having served the Society for nearly 30 years, he died at 53 Berners Street in 1884. His obituary in the *Transactions* refers to his work as 'most original, [he] introduced novelties both of general plan and detail. His system has been admired and imitated'. As a tribute to Wheatley a subscription was opened so that Fellows could contribute to a fund to benefit the late Librarian's dependants.[36]

Cataloguing and indexing extended to the *Transactions*: if papers (as many as 25 in one volume) were to be of permanent value, a comprehensive index was necessary. John Flint South, a Fellow who was twice to be President of the Royal College of Surgeons, volunteered to compile an index of the first 18 volumes in 1836, and this the Council intended to distribute free.[37] John Erichsen (who was to be President of the Society 1879–81) produced a manuscript index to 27 volumes in 1845, passing the next stage to Dr John Hennen, Honorary Librarian from 1848 to 1850 and an experienced editor. Dr Edward Hall made a contribution but soon withdrew, leaving Hennen to take the credit for the first index to the *Transactions*, published in 1850.[38] Its sequel was completed by Wheatley in 1871.

The volumes of the *Transactions* became increasingly expensive to print and profits diminished. An investigation in 1839 found that Longmans owed the Society £80, rather than the £25 they had claimed (in error) from the sale of copies. Even so it was decided to sell back-numbers whenever possible, authors were asked to pay for their own colour plates, a smaller typeface was adopted from 1846 and volumes were advertised for sale to the public at £20 apiece.[39]

## Innovations

From the 1830s fresh ideas circulated within the Society; some took root, others were vetoed by the Council and a few bore fruit later in the century. A liberal mood could be detected in the decisions of the Council to repeal restrictions on the reporting of meetings (1831), the provision of abstracts by the Secretaries from 1836 onwards, and in 1842 the first reporter from a medical journal was authorized to attend meetings – the point was broadly conceded in 1850 with the provision of a table for them in the meeting room. Discussion of written communications was formally sanctioned by Council in 1831 and positively fostered during Sir Benjamin Brodie's presidency (1839–41). At the same time an initiative was launched by Doctors Charles Williams, James M Arnott and others to establish a pathological branch of the Society with meetings devoted exclusively to the study of pathological specimens, 'recent or prepared, drawings or casts of morbid structure'. A few meetings were held at which specimens were exhibited and interest was shown in the proceedings but not sufficient to secure its continuance 'in opposition to the red tape and lethargy of the old Society', as Dr Williams put it.[40]

Although the pathological meetings soon ceased, the general meetings were enlivened when Fellows brought 'objects of interest connected with medicine and the auxiliary sciences'.[41] The new instruments and apparatus signified progress and promise in the detection and treatment of disease and were eagerly viewed. Dr John Sims of the Marylebone Infirmary showed a model and drawings to illustrate his paper on malignant tumours of the lungs in January 1833, and the surgeon William Beaumont described and exhibited the instruments he used in 1837. In 1843 a newly elected Fellow, Dr John Snow, requested permission to exhibit a pessary he had invented;[42] he was soon to turn his attention to chloroform anaesthesia and cholera. Dr Protheroe Smith, who was largely responsible for founding the Hospital for Diseases of Women in Red Lion Square, gave an account of a newly invented speculum uteri in 1844,[43] and a similar instrument was exhibited two years later by William Fergusson, Professor of Surgery at King's College.[44] Dr Robert Lee was outraged and his paper told of the horror and shame women had suffered by its use: 'the speculum emanates from the syphilitic wards of Paris', he fumed.[45] Dr Ridge's model of an invalid carriage, on the other hand, was greeted as an improvement of humane and practical value. So too was the invention of collodion by William Acton (1848): Mr Quekett of the Microscopical Society had examined Acton's solutions and found them entirely satisfactory and perfectly elastic (Quekett was later elected an Honorary Fellow). John Hutchinson introduced his spirometer to the Society in 1846 as a precise and easy mechanical method of detecting lung disease by measuring the capacity of the lungs, and in 1850 Joseph Toynbee demonstrated how to use his osteope, which consisted of an elastic tube with a piece of ivory or ebony at each extremity.[46]

## The laryngoscope

Dr Benjamin Babington was President of the Society from 1861 to 1863; reflecting on the fact that the Society's first President had been his godfather and the sixth his father, he pointed out that nine out of the 27 Presidents who preceded him had been alumni of the Borough schools (St Thomas' and Guy's). [47]

Babington is credited with inventing a 'glottiscope' in 1829; Thomas Hodgkin described it as a '*speculum laryngis* or *laryngiscope* invented by my friend Dr Babington'. This elementary tool with an oblong mirror was refined by the surgeon Robert Liston and by Manuel Garcia, a singing teacher. In 1905 the 100th birthday of the latter was celebrated in the meeting room of the Society's house at 20 Hanover Square: Garcia was hailed as the father of laryngology and showered with medical doctorates and medals. Credit must also be given to Professor Johann Czermak of Prague, who had persuaded physicians of the potential of the laryngoscope and demonstrated its use to hospitals and medical societies all over Europe: in May 1862 he exhibited his instrument to a meeting of the RMCS. The catalogue published by the instrument-maker John Weiss in 1863 illustrated a laryngeal mirror and the following year Morell Mackenzie showed and described Babington's laryngoscope to Fellows, giving Babington due credit for his inventive genius in 'perceiving the essential requisites of a laryngoscope'. Within a few years Fellows of the Society, including GD Gibb, Dr George Johnson and AE Durham, were reporting their successful use of the instrument in operations (1863, 1865, 1868).[48]

Babington's contributions to the *Transactions* revealed an aptitude for chemistry and provided the first analysis of the blood into red corpuscles and *liquor sanguinis*, and 'the latter term being quite original at once came into use'. He also described multiple hereditary telangiectasia, which became known as Babington's disease.

Dr Benjamin Guy Babington, President 1861–63. He invented a laryngeal mirror or 'glottiscope' in 1829.

Professor J Czermak (on the right) demonstrating laryngoscopy. Czermak exhibited his equipment and showed its usefulness 'in examining the physiological and pathological conditions of the interior of the larynx' at a meeting of the Society in 1862.

### The thermometer and the microscope

Members' presentations revealed that they were keeping pace with the development of new instruments, notably the thermometer and the microscope as well as the laryngoscope. The use of the mercury thermometer to measure temperature in fevers had been recognized in the 18th century, but it was not until the 1830s that physicians in this country began to use it as a tool in diagnosis and research. In 1832 Dr Marshall Hall made use of a thermometer to measure the effects of the loss of blood in experiments that formed part of his campaign against indiscriminate blood-letting.[49] And Sir Benjamin Brodie's 1837 paper on injuries of the spinal cord was bolstered by evidence of the temperature of 111° in a dying man. The President of the Society in 1905, Sir Richard Douglas Powell, claimed that this was 'the earliest use of clinical thermometry, fully to be established 25 years later by the careful labours of Wunderlich in Germany and Professor Ringer in this country'.[50]

A longstanding Fellow of the Society, Dr Thomas Clifford Allbutt, physician to Leeds Infirmary and later Regius Professor at Cambridge University, introduced his clinical thermometer in 1866. At scarcely six inches long (later reduced to three) and taking five minutes to register, it was a considerable improvement on the previous device, which was almost a foot long and required a 25-minute wait before it could be read. Allbutt's modification, combined with Wunderlich's book on the Temperature in Diseases (1868) provided the practical tool and the textbook but the medical profession was slow to realize the importance of the thermometer in diagnosis: it was still regarded as a curiosity in 1870.

Allbutt's observations on optic nerves and retinae in the insane were read to the RMCS in 1868 and his paper on the rise in blood pressure in later life (1903) was the source of the phrase quoted by Sir Berkeley Moynihan, 'with the pathology of the dead we have made great way, the pathology of the living is hardly begun'. Allbutt was still active in the

Society at the age of 87 when he was elected the first President of the Section of Comparative Medicine (see pages 365–66).

The first instrument that could be regarded as a microscope was constructed *circa* 1600, and its development and use were quintessential to the new scientific medicine; Robert Hooke, stalwart of the Royal Society, published his microscopical studies as early as 1665. In the 1820s and 1830s Joseph Jackson Lister improved the instrument dramatically, devoting himself to investigations with its aid. Working with Dr Thomas Hodgkin, Lister provided a new description of human red blood cells and introduced histology to the medical profession, and his more famous son drew special attention to this achievement when he wrote his father's entry for the *DNB*. The surgeon John Howship, whose contributions to the Society's *Transactions* caused the editors to despair, was an expert in the use of the microscope, hence the 'lacunae of Howship'. Yet good instruments were still hard to come by in the 1830s and the young James Paget had to borrow one from a botanist in order to study *Trichina spiralis* in human muscle (see page 43).

The Microscopical Society, founded in 1839, was dominated for 20 years by John Quekett, who initiated histology courses at the Royal College of Surgeons. Quekett's society was strongly supported by Fellows of the RMCS and he was elected an Honorary Fellow in 1859. As the profession became acquainted with the instrument and its uses, the results of microscopic examinations became a regular feature of papers. In 1843, when microscopic examination was still in its infancy, Dr Thomas Hodgkin communicated to a meeting the discovery by George Gulliver of fatty globules of the arteries. Hodgkin also reported his own microscopic investigations of adventitious structures, thanking several Fellows of the Society for the use of their 'excellent instruments'.[51] Dr John Davy (brother of Sir Humphry) looked at the composition of meconium and vernix under the microscope in 1844, and one Fellow claimed that a case of acute retinitis had been caused by the use of a microscope.[52]

Microscopic examination of urine was still an unusual practice when in 1852 Charles Moore told his colleagues that it 'might have the effect of determining the nature of a doubtful case'.[53] Another Fellow, T Wharton Jones, was using the microscope for his observations on blood and blood vessels in 1853, by which time the instrument was beginning to revolutionize the study of physiology in this country. With further refinements, more sophisticated techniques, preparations, textbooks, the work of Virchow and the introduction of microscopy to the curriculum of medical students, the microscope was to become an essential tool of medical research.

## Restricted initiatives

Many papers presented to the Society in the first decades of its existence were short, clear narrations of cases, descriptions of surgical advances, wartime experiences or the results of chemical research. In the 1830s and 1840s the instruments and tools of medicine and surgery aroused special interest. Other papers reflected concern with matters of public health and social conditions, as the conscience of the professional classes awoke to the problems and diseases of the crowded, insanitary and polluted towns of Britain. At the RMCS the desire to investigate the causes, symptoms and treatment of the common diseases of the 19th century generated an initiative to establish investigative committees – for example, into dysentery and scarlatina. It was proposed in 1831 that Fellows should pool their experience, collect information and report on such subjects but unfortunately the idea foundered on a technicality, possibly connected with the presumed authority of the Royal College of Physicians in such matters.[54] The proposal was revived in 1849 following the experience of the most severe cholera epidemic ever suffered in this country and a recent outbreak of scarlatina. The Council then toyed with a proposal for committees to investigate fever, cholera, hernia and erysipelas. Another suggestion, that a prize should be awarded for the best account of the recent influenza epidemic or for an essay on a subject specified by the Council, found no support; it was not until 1878 that the Society awarded its first prize, and this was in memory of Dr Marshall Hall (see page 117).[55]

In 1838 Dr Merriman, physician-accoucheur to the Middlesex Hospital, proposed that a committee should examine and report on mesmerism, a practice that was exciting much interest and controversy.[56] Dr John Elliotson, who in 1831 had identified 'the flower of grass' as the cause of hay-fever, was President of the Society from 1833 to 1835 and he later became the leading exponent of mesmerism in this country (see page 422 and Plate 65). The Council of the RMCS was not prepared to dabble in mesmerism, or even to investigate its claims, and Merriman's suggestion was vetoed. Furthermore, a paper communicated by two non-members describing an amputation of the thigh carried out while the patient was in a mesmeric coma was deliberately not recorded in the Minutes, even though it had aroused the interest of 169 Fellows and guests when it was read by Edward Stanley in November 1842. Elliotson resigned his Fellowship in protest at the Council's blinkered attitude.[57]

Nor would the Council condone unconventional or fringe practitioners. When William Lawrence, a past President, proposed that the membership might be extended to those eminent in any branch of the profession who were distinguished for scientific attainments or practical proficiency even if they possessed no legal qualification, there was an outcry. Dr Wilson objected that this would make a 'homeopathist' or a 'water-doctor' eligible for Fellowship. 'A very irregular discussion now took place between the President [Mr Edward Stanley] who seemed to be quite bewildered as to how he was to act... all was confusion', the *Lancet* reported with relish. The motion was lost.[58] Sir Samuel Wilks confirmed that the Society was inaccessible to many: 'whenever any approach was made by midwifery men or anyone outside their august body they were expelled', he recalled.[59] Apothecaries (general practitioners) were of course eligible for membership, although only a handful joined, and it was only in 1872 that a second general practitioner was given a seat on the Council.

## Fevers, cholera and public health

The Society failed to establish the proposed committees to investigate common diseases, relying instead on the work of individual Fellows conveyed to the membership at meetings. A severe fever epidemic of 1817 cost many lives and a Select Committee of the House of Commons subsequently conducted an enquiry, taking evidence from three members of the MCS, James Parkinson, Dr Marcet and Dr Yelloly. Parkinson was alone in stressing the importance of isolating fever patients and he had personally instituted a fever ward at the St Leonard's Workhouse in Kingsland Road. As medical practitioners struggled to understand the nature and treatment of fevers and epidemics there were regular papers and discussions at the RMCS on dysentery, consumption (known as phthisis), scarlatina, smallpox and cholera and an account of a diphtheria epidemic in Haverfordwest (1849–50). Diphtheria, first described by Dr John Fothergill in 1748, reappeared in epidemic proportions between 1855 and 1858; scarlatina nearly doubled its mortality rate in 1840 and continued to be a major cause of death in children, with a serious outbreak in London in 1848 prompting James Miller's paper on the subject in 1849.

An epidemic of Asiatic cholera broke out in Sunderland, spread to Newcastle, and reached London in February 1832. Widespread fear of infection activated preventive measures and investigations that culminated in the Public Health Act of 1848. The outbreak of 1848–49 was the most severe ever suffered in Britain and caused 13,584 deaths in London alone between June 1848 and November 1849. There was a less severe outbreak in 1853–54, another bout in 1865–66 with 5,596 deaths in London, and a last occurrence of the epidemic in this country in 1893.[60]

Two Fellows with personal experience of cholera, Dr George Budd and George Busk, reported their findings to the Society. They concentrated on cases at the seamen's hospital ship HMS *Dreadnought* where Busk was the resident surgeon and Budd the visiting physician.[61] The main medical interest of the cholera outbreaks of 1848–49 and 1853–54 centred on the mode of its communication, and credit for the discovery that the disease was waterborne belongs to Dr John Snow. Snow was elected a Fellow of the Society in 1843 and one of his last appearances before his death in June 1858 was at a meeting of the Society. Snow's one article in the *Transactions* (1851) was on the administration of chloroform (which he gave to Queen Victoria in childbirth). His essay *On the mode of communication of cholera* (1849) and his identification of the Broad Street pump as a source of contamination in 1854 did not prevent later outbreaks of the disease. Its recurrence in 1865–66 gave rise to two papers and a full discussion of its nature and treatment at the Society's meetings in 1867. Dr George Johnson, President of the RMCS 1884–86, made cholera and the kidney his special subjects; following Robert Koch's discovery of the cholera bacillus in 1883 he ensured that Fellows were given the opportunity of viewing specimens of the cholera bacilli under the microscope.

Dr George Budd's younger brother, Dr William Budd of Bristol, was an epidemiologist who wrote on the causes of fever, malignant cholera and typhoid. But it was his paper on diseases which affect corresponding parts of the body in a symmetrical manner that commanded the respect of the 27-year-old James Paget. The papers by Budd and Paget on this subject were read at the same meeting of the Society on 14 December 1841 and both were published in the volume of *Transactions* for 1842. Budd's, in particular, attracted much attention: 'My "symmetry" paper is just published in the Medico-Chirurgical Transactions', wrote Paget. 'Budd's rather overwhelms it, but I am fortunate, I think, in getting even a share of the credit for the discovery, for he had certainly begun to work it out before I did. It will do me some good; for these papers are abstracted in almost every journal, and are profusely advertized'.[62]

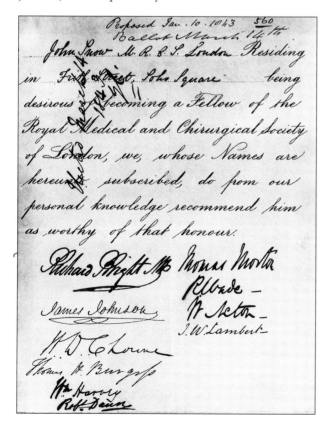

Dr John Snow's proposal form for membership of the RMCS, signed by Dr Richard Bright and others. Snow was duly elected a Fellow in March 1843.

## Typhus and typhoid

Typhus and typhoid were the other Victorian diseases that claimed many lives and about which the medical profession was confused. There was an epidemic of typhus in England from 1837 to 1839, and Dr Bostock applied his analytical mind to the subject in a paper of 1842. Dr William Budd had first suggested that typhoid and typhus were different diseases, but this was only firmly established when Dr William Jenner revealed the results of his careful investigations to the Society in December 1849. Jenner was not yet a Fellow, so his paper was communicated by Dr William Sharpey in advance of Jenner's monograph on the same subject, *On the identity or non identity of typhoid and typhus fevers* (1850). The paper analysed cases in which two or more fever patients came from one house. Jenner found that scarcely a single instance occurred where typhoid and typhus came at the same period from the same house. His researches led him to conclude that 'the specific causes of typhoid and typhus fevers are absolutely different from each other'.[63] Jenner's differentiation of typhus from typhoid did not save Prince Albert from dying of typhoid fever in 1861, but Dr William Gull and Jenner successfully treated the Prince of Wales for typhoid ten years later. Jenner was appointed physician to the Queen in 1861 and was made a baronet in 1868.

Jenner's work on typhus and typhoid enabled Dr Charles Murchison to distinguish between the different fevers in his survey of 6,628 cases at the London Fever Hospital between 1848 and 1858. He believed that typhoid fever was caused by emanations from putrefying matter or by organic impurities in drinking water, and he called for action: 'the origins that have been adduced call for the serious attention of those instructed with the care of public health'.[64] Murchison's researches, first revealed to a meeting of the RMCS, led to his publication of *A treatise on the continued fevers of Great Britain* in 1862. One of those who responded to his call for public health measures was John Simon, a Fellow of the RMCS from 1842 and a Vice President in 1865. His work as the first Medical Officer of Health for the City of London, his crusade for better sanitation and his report on cholera resulted in the improved health of the population and gained him a knighthood. His one contribution to the Society's *Transactions* was on inflammation of the kidney (1847) – he later referred to it apologetically as one of his youthful papers; at the time it elicited some remarks respecting its lack of originality.[65]

## Smallpox

Edward Jenner's smallpox vaccine was available at stations in London from 1803, and a National Vaccine Establishment was formed in 1808. The disease was by no means eradicated, however. There was an epidemic in London in 1825, and the 'present increased prevalence' of smallpox in 1838 caused Fellows to devote an evening to its discussion in December.[66] Dr George Gregory of the Smallpox and Vaccine Hospital told the Society in January 1845 that admissions to that hospital in the previous year reached 647, which with the exception of 1838 was the greatest number for any year since 1746. Of the 647 admissions, 312 were vaccinated and mortality was 23.5%. On the basis of these figures he urged legislation to establish a system of infantile vaccination 'made doubly sure' by adult inoculation for 10- to 20-year-olds. Gregory was well in advance of current thinking – smallpox vaccination was not made compulsory for infants in England until 1853 (rescinded in 1909).[67]

## Tuberculosis

Pulmonary tuberculosis, known as phthisis or consumption, was the disease of the industrial towns, and Dr Addison's paper of April 1841 on the anatomy of the lungs called for new investigations into its pathology. He pressed for a modification of Laënnec's teaching on lung disease; Sir Samuel Wilks, for one, thought very highly of this paper.[68] Dr Robert

Williams, physician to St Thomas' and the immediate past President of the Society, conducted a series of experiments on possible remedies for phthisis which he reported in 1843. He had tried preparations of platina, palladium, titanium, chromium, osmium, iridium and cerium. He then resorted to all the seeds he could obtain from a firm in Covent Garden and tried every available wood, bark and gum, 'none of which appeared beneficially to influence the disease, ye result was as usual uniformly fatal'.[69]

One paper of 1856 hinted at the beneficial treatment of consumption by sunlight, and a new approach was launched with Villemin's inoculation of animals with the blood and sputum of tuberculosis sufferers (1865). Samuel Fenwick's paper on the microscopical examination of the sputum (1866) and Dr William Marcet's on the inoculation of animals as a means of tubercular diagnosis took up Villemin's work. The way forward did not however become clear until Koch's discovery of the bacillus that caused tuberculosis in 1882, although the premature announcement of a cure in 1890 proved a false dawn (see pages 149–50).

## Lunatic asylums and prisons

Papers from Fellows of the Society expressed their concern with the common diseases of Victorian Britain and with the need to improve public health and social conditions. In the 1840s several Fellows held appointments in prisons, lunatic asylums and charitable foundations so were able to throw light on the treatment of inmates, the effects of the treadmill and causes of mortality at these institutions. Bethlehem Hospital ('Bedlam') provided fertile ground for research into the unexplored field of insanity and Dr John Webster, physician to St George's Hospital, analysed the historical statistics of those confined to Bethlehem. He deduced that insanity was more prevalent among women than men, more curable in women and more common in summer than winter. Webster also undertook 175 post mortems at Bethlehem as part of his pursuit of statistics (the tabulation of figures was a relatively new and convincing method taught by Louis in Paris, which became a feature of papers in the *Transactions*).[70]

In 1868 Dr Clifford Allbutt told the Society about his researches on the state of the optic nerves and retinas in the insane, based on the results of his own examinations of inmates at two Yorkshire asylums. 'Allbutt of Leeds' as he was known, was later to be appointed Commissioner for Lunacy in London, Regius Professor of Physic at Cambridge and was a strong supporter of the new specialty of comparative medicine (see pages 365–66).

Dr William Baly, who translated Müller's *Elements of physiology* into English in 1838, was Honorary Librarian to the Society from 1847 to 1848 and physician to the Millbank Penitentiary. His paper of February 1845 acknowledged the recent improvement of conditions for prisoners while emphasizing the continuing evils that contributed to their illness – solitary confinement, sedentary occupations, cold and poor diet. Baly's definitive work on *Diseases of prisons* was published later that year and he became a leading government adviser on prison hygiene – his recommendations that prisoners be fed liberally on lightly cooked potato was found to be effective in eliminating scurvy.

## The ascendancy of surgery

The number of papers reporting successful operations and encouraging Fellows to reconsider the viability of surgery multiplied towards the middle of the 19th century. The passing of the Anatomy Act in 1832 and the award of the charter of the Royal College of Surgeons (1843), combined with the College's regulations for examination and the facilities afforded by the new hospitals and medical schools, tended to encourage surgical teaching, practice and specialism. There was also the example of Sir Astley Cooper and his successors in the field, notably Benjamin Brodie, Robert Liston and William Fergusson, who were all Fellows of the Society eager to share their expertise with colleagues.

Sir Benjamin Brodie was probably the most versatile surgeon of his generation, as his papers on lithotrity, aneurysm, injuries of the spinal cord and varicose veins suggest. Amputation was still the most common operation and JP Potter's statistics on those carried out at University College Hospital between 1835 and 1841 showed that 56 out of 66 amputations were successful, without anaesthesia or antiseptics.[71] Dr JM Arnott, who was to be President of the Society from 1847 to 1849, was one of the surgeons who carried out rare operations in the 1830s. In 1832 he performed an oesophagotomy on a boy who had swallowed a piece of mutton bone. The operation was only undertaken because breathing had become laborious and the piece of bone was easily removed, but the child died. Arnott claimed that he knew of only three recorded cases of oesophagotomy, all carried out in France, two of which had taken place over a century before. He was satisfied that the operation could be performed with facility and without danger.[72]

Robert Liston established his reputation as the flamboyant, speedy surgeon of Edinburgh. He was known to plug a haemorrhage with a piece of wood hewn from the operating table and in the heat of the moment he would clasp the knife in his teeth in order to free both hands. He was invited to take the post of lecturer in clinical surgery at the newly founded University College Hospital in 1834 and in the following year he joined the RMCS. He 'went to Med. Chir. Society [sic] last evening for the first time' on 14 April 1835 to hear a paper on fractures, to which he responded in characteristically forthright manner, 'could have told them what they do not seem to know'.[73] Liston presented his own first paper on 'Tumours of the mouth and jaw' to the Society in June 1836. 'I think there will in all probability be a full meeting of the Society when the paper is read and there will be some fun', he wrote to his former assistant in Edinburgh. 'My friends among the

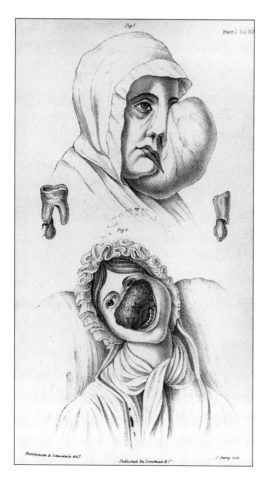

Illustration from a paper on 'Tumours of the mouth and jaw' read to the Society by Robert Liston in June 1836. He operated successfully on both patients without anaesthetic.

dentists will muster strong, they are delighted at the subject being taken up … I can assure you there is much interest excited about the paper'. In the event, 'the Secretary read the paper badly', nevertheless Liston thought the Society could hardly avoid publishing it (as predicted, it appeared in volume xx of the *Transactions*).

Liston found Sir Astley Cooper, 'the old Bart', 'exceedingly pleasant … We had a dinner with the excellent Bart a day or two before [seeing Bransby Cooper cut for stone]. He is a most magnificent old chap and well deserves to be where he now is'. (Cooper was elected President of the Royal College of Surgeons for the second time in 1836.) Liston also enjoyed the company of a former Librarian to the Society, Samuel Cooper, whom he referred to as 'Old Sam, a straight-forward, honest fellow – oldish – a perfect Nathaniel', and he arranged another rendezvous with JY Simpson, the Edinburgh obstetrician, at one of the Society's meetings in April 1840.[74] He gave several papers to the Society and was a Vice President in 1846, the year that he performed the first major operation in London on an anaesthetized patient (see page 128).

William Fergusson of King's College Hospital was the pioneer of conservative surgery in that he advised the excision of a joint rather than the amputation of a limb. He described to the Society his two entirely satisfactory operations for cleft palate in 1844 – he knew of one precedent in this country in 1821, since when there had been no progress. In the same year Dr JA Wilson of St George's provided the example of a successful tracheotomy to urge his colleagues not to neglect the means surgery provided to save life.[75]

Benjamin Phillips, surgeon to St Marylebone Infirmary and Westminster Hospital, compiled 81 recorded cases of extractions of ovarian tumours and in 1844, on the basis that 35 had been successful 'notwithstanding the magnitude and apparent danger of the operation', he urged Fellows to give it serious consideration.[76] Colleagues must have been encouraged by the success of HE Burd of Shropshire who told of his removal of an ovarian tumour complicated by pregnancy (the whole mass weighed about 50 pounds),[77] but it was another ten years before Spencer Wells' consistent successes began to convince the medical profession that ovariotomy was a justifiable operation (see pages 132–33).

Dr Golding Bird and John Hilton presented a meeting of the RMCS with the first recorded instance 'of any surgeon in this country having succeeded in his attempts to relieve internal strangulation by an operation' in 1847. Hilton was an accomplished dissector and Golding Bird lectured in natural philosophy and specialized in chemistry. The operation lasted about an hour, the patient was 'somewhat collapsed', became delirious and died nine hours later. Hilton was far from discouraged, concluding that the direct results were very satisfactory.[78] Innovative operations such as these, combined with the use of anaesthesia after 1846 and surgeons' experiences in the Crimea, accounted for London's pre-eminence in surgery from the 1840s to the 1870s.

## New specialties

### Eyes

Among the rare books in the RSM Library is a late-16th-century *Treatise of the eyes* by Jacques Guillemeau 'contayning the knowledge and cure of one hundred and thirteene diseases incident unto them'. This was reprinted with similar studies by Richard Banister who described himself as a master in surgery, oculist and practitioner in physic in 1622 (this treatise is also on the shelves). During the 18th century diseases of the eye attracted as much interest from charlatans as from regular medical practitioners. The return home of troops suffering from 'Egyptian ophthalmia' contracted during the campaign against Napoleon in Egypt (1798–99) commanded the attention of the profession in the early years of the 19th century because the disbanded men spread the disease to the inhabitants of towns and villages throughout Britain. Those afflicted usually resorted to quacks or

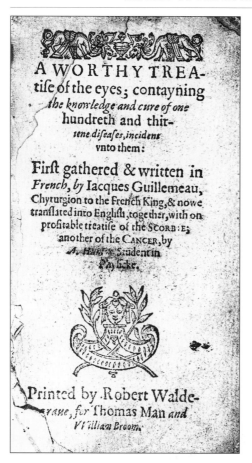

A WORTHY TREA-
tife of the eyes; contayning
the knowledge and cure of one
hundreth and thir-
tene difeafes, incident
vnto them:

Firft gathered & written in
*French*, by Iacques Guillemeau,
Chyrurgion to the French King, & nowe
tranflated into Englifh, together, with on
profitable treatife of the Scorb:e;
another of the Cancer, by
A. Hum. Student in
Phyficke.

Printed by Robert Walde-
raue, for Thomas Man and
William Broom.

Title page of a rare treatise on diseases of the eyes by Jacques Guillemeau, printed and translated into English between 1585 and 1589. This copy, also a translation of 1622 by Richard Banister entitled *A Treatise of one hundred and thirteene diseases of the eyes and eyeliddes*, form part of the Library's historical collection.

oculists, sometimes suffering the loss of one or both eyes. Dr James Curry, a founder-member of the Society, thought that the experience of treating his own ophthalmia might 'shed light on the disease that committed such ravages among the soldiers and seamen on the expedition to Egypt'. He described his extreme pain and extreme remedies (leeches, saline purgatives, calomel, blood-letting, antimonal powder, tincture of opium), none of which brought relief. In desperation, Curry, who was senior physician to Guy's Hospital, consulted a surgeon-oculist who advised scarification, fomenting the eye with a decoction of poppy-heads, blood-letting, head-shaving and dosing with muriate of quicksilver dissolved in spirit of nutmeg to induce vomiting. The only effective treatment proved to be two grains of opium at hourly intervals, and on a second occasion, three grains a day for ten days.[79]

Another Fellow deplored the extravagant use of opium and wanted the Society to discourage it. Julius Jeffreys based his case on the custom-house returns of imported opium, which had increased from 16,196 pounds in 1820 to 131,204 pounds in 1838. He hoped to solicit from the Society a declaration condemning 'the improper use of opium in England'[80] – this was not forthcoming. Dr Clendinning, however, suggested an alternative to the use of opium in acute and chronic disease: Indian hemp, which he had found a most useful narcotic in trials.[81] As it was, the use of opium in the form of morphine increased following the introduction of the hypodermic syringe in the 1850s; Florence Nightingale was one of many who found it a great comfort.

The study of diseases of the eye took a step forward with the foundation of the first public eye hospital in the world by John Cunningham Saunders in 1805. Originally known as the London Dispensary for the Relief of the Poor Afflicted with Diseases of the Eye and Ear, later as the Royal London Ophthalmic Hospital and Moorfields, its foundation was an act of courage that would not have been practical without the support of Sir Astley Cooper and other influential members of the Medical and Chirurgical Society.

Members of the MCS who were prominent in this field were Benjamin Travers, James Wardrop, William Lawrence, William Bowman, John Dalrymple, Frederick Tyrell and James Ware, who founded the School for the Indigent Blind. Travers was the first general hospital surgeon to concentrate on eye disease and he gave two papers on cataracts (Plate 19) to the Society (1813, 1814), prior to the publication of his *Synopsis of the diseases of the eye*. James Wardrop, surgeon extraordinary to King George IV, had 13 papers published in the Society's *Transactions* including two that were peripheral to his *Morbid anatomy of the human eye* (1818–19). As his obituary in the Society's *Proceedings* recognized, the operation for relieving tension of the eye by puncturing the cornea was first suggested and practised by Wardrop.[82] He was not a popular member of the Society: as early as 1811 he was in disgrace with Marcet and Yelloly on account of his ill-bred and impolite behaviour. Yelloly thought that Marcet should give him 'a very good lecture ... he ought to incur all the penalties of medical excommunication'.[83] The exact nature of Wardrop's offence is not revealed; he was an unscrupulous reporter on the *Lancet* for 10 years, and he alienated leading members of the profession and the Royal Colleges as much as he offended Marcet and Yelloly. One contemporary described him as 'vain, self-opinionated and scurrilous' and he found himself dismissed from Court during King George IV's last illness.[84]

John Dalrymple, author of *The anatomy of the human eye* (1834) and *The pathology of the human eye* (1845–52), was surgeon to the Royal London Ophthalmic Hospital, where he was succeeded by William Bowman in 1851. Dalrymple gave several general papers to the Society but strangely none dealing with his specialty. Bowman's papers, on the other hand, told of his pioneering work in treating epiphora and operating on the eye. Bowman joined the Society in 1841, was a Vice President 20 years later and enjoyed a reputation as the most distinguished ophthalmic surgeon of the mid-Victorian era.

RA Stafford, surgeon to the Duke of Cambridge, reported to the Society on a successful operation for cataract in 1842 and the number of papers on diseases of the eye increased, with contributions from Dr Edward O Hocken and Dr William Cumming's observations on retinal disease (1846). Cumming was Professor of Botany at the Glasgow Institution but his work, like that of his contemporaries, was hindered by the lack of the ophthalmoscope, an invention of 1851. The introduction of the ophthalmometer followed soon afterwards and these instruments transformed ophthalmology in the hands of Sir William Bowman and Sir Jonathan Hutchinson, who were both Presidents of the newly founded Ophthalmological Society in the 1880s.

*Ears*

Bartolomeo Eustachi's description of the auditory (Eustachian) tube and the cochlea were important contributions to the knowledge of the ear, illustrated by exceptional plates (see page 90). Further studies on the teeth and ears emerged from France in the 18th century, but there was little interest in these subjects among members of the Medical and Chirurgical Society while they remained the province of toothdrawers, aurists and unqualified practitioners. Astley Cooper had made a rare foray into ear surgery in the early years of the 19th century but there was no follow-up. The founding of a hospital for ear diseases in 1816 and the opening of the Metropolitan Ear and Throat Institute in 1838 created new opportunities, and the first dissections of the internal ear in congenital deafness were brought to the notice of a meeting of the Society in December 1834 by Edward Cock, Cooper's nephew, Demonstrator in Anatomy at Guy's Hospital and surgeon to the Deaf and Dumb Asylum. He summarized the situation at that time: 'Perhaps there is no part of the human body which has so little engaged the attention of the pathologist or which has

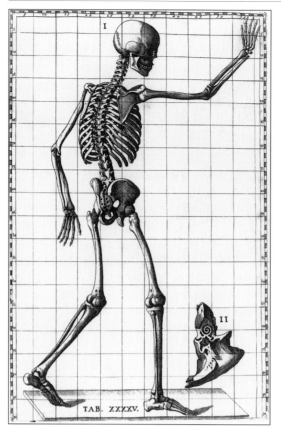

Bartolomeo Eustachi described the auditory (Eustachian) tube, the thoracic duct, the adrenals and the cochlea in the 16th century but his plates lay forgotten in the Vatican Library until their rediscovery in the early 18th century (this edition is dated 1728). Shown here is a skeletal figure and a section through the temporal bone revealing the open bony cochlea and semicircular canals. The grid along the borders of the illustration allowed easy reference.

afforded such slender encouragement to research as the ear'. Cock's paper, followed by one from the surgeon J Thurnham, did something to rectify current ignorance.[85]

In the 1840s Joseph Toynbee's pathological and surgical observations on diseases of the ear appeared regularly in the *Transactions*, culminating in his report on 915 dissections in 1849.[86] Toynbee was surgeon to St James' and St George's Dispensary at the time and he gained his Fellowship of the Royal Society at the age of 27 on the merit of his dissections, which resulted in his book on *Diseases of the ear: their nature, diagnosis and treatment* (1860). The respect he commanded from those not generally sympathetic to the specialty was marked by his appointment as the first surgeon and lecturer on diseases of the ear at St Mary's Hospital in 1852. His obituary (Toynbee died as the result of an overdose of chloroform in an experiment aimed at reducing tinnitus) testified that he had 'the merit of being almost the first to wrest the practice of aural surgery from the possession of empirics'.[87]

Toynbee's assistant, James Hinton, the first aural surgeon appointed to Guy's Hospital, described his successful performance of mastoidectomy in the *Transactions* for 1868 – he was the first in Britain to master the cortical mastoidectomy. Contemporaries gave him little credit: scientifically minded colleagues regarded Hinton's popular publication, *The mystery of pain,* with suspicion and his writings were thought to be 'speculative in the highest degree'. Sir Samuel Wilks recognized Hinton as 'one of the most remarkable men in our profession'; that said, the emphasis was on the term 'remarkable': 'I feel astonished that he was ever *in* it but being in it he was not of it'.[88]

Toynbee, Hinton and Sir William Wilde (father of Oscar) have been named as the founders of modern otology: the historian Dr Douglas Guthrie identified them as 'the three men who raised otology out of random empiricism and established it as a worthy science'.[89]

Joseph Toynbee, whose papers on diseases of the ear appeared regularly in the *Transactions* during the 1840s. Toynbee made a valuable contribution to the treatment of deafness by inventing an artificial tympanic membrane.

## Teeth

The famous John Hunter wrote on the *Natural history of the human teeth* (1771) and published his *Practical treatise of the diseases of the teeth* in 1778; both books are in the Society's Library. Even so, knowledge of diseases of the teeth was still elementary in 1819 when Thomas Bell gave a paper 'to prove the vitality of the teeth' to the Society.[90] Bell lectured in anatomy and diseases of the teeth at Guy's Hospital and was later Professor of Zoology at King's College and Secretary to the Royal Society.

Alexander Nasmyth, who was Prince Albert's surgeon-dentist and after whom Nasmyth's membrane is named, expanded on the structure, physiology and pathology of the teeth in 1839, and Alexander Shaw, surgeon at the Middlesex Hospital, presented two papers in the 1840s, by which time the London Institution for the Diseases of the Teeth had been opened. Efforts to found a dental society and the campaign for a dental faculty were also under way in the 1840s, although the first British dental journals were short-lived. Samuel Cartwright, Edwin Saunders and T Arnold Rogers, who took the lead in establishing the first Dental Hospital of London and in the foundation of the Odontological Society in 1856, were all Fellows of the RMCS (see Plate 42 and page 238).

## Skin

The Society's first Librarian, Dr Thomas Bateman, specialized in diseases of the skin and having worked with the famous Dr Robert Willan for 10 years he published *A practical synopsis of cutaneous diseases according to the arrangement of Dr Willan* in 1813, a year after Willan's death. He followed this by *Delineations of cutaneous diseases* (1815–17), completing the series of Willan's engravings and containing 70 colour plates in all. Bateman's name is linked with molluscum contagiosum (Bateman's disease), among other skin afflictions (Plate 20).

Bateman's colleague at the City Dispensary, Dr Thomas Addison, was also 'a great authority on the subject before it was made a specialty', according to one pupil. [91] Their successor in the study of skin disease was Erasmus Wilson, later Sir William Wilson, elected a Fellow of the RMCS in 1839 when he was on the verge of deciding to devote himself to the subject, and as Plarr's *Lives* phrases it 'he found the field of dermatology almost virgin'. Wilson contributed two papers to the Society's *Transactions* (1844, 1845), conciding with his book *Healthy skin*. The descriptions of lichen planus, exfoliative dermatitis and naevus araneous are linked with his name and he was the founder editor of the *Journal of Cutaneous Medicine and Diseases of the Skin*. He achieved wide recognition as a philanthropist and for importing Cleopatra's Needle – the ancient obelisk reached London in 1878.

The infirmary for skin diseases was established at London Wall in 1841, expanding into the Hospital for Diseases of the Skin at Blackfriars, where Jonathan Hutchinson worked in the 1850s. He was to become an authority on skin disease as in other subjects, and President of the RMCS from 1894 to 1896. Willan, Bateman, Wilson and Hutchinson all advanced dermatology, yet the specialty did not emerge as such until the 1880s, under the auspices of the Dermatological Society of London and the Dermatological Society of Great Britain and Ireland.

## Children

The education and welfare of children was brought to public notice by the social reformer Lord Ashley (later the Earl of Shaftesbury) who led a campaign to improve the working conditions and health of women and children. His efforts gained public sympathy and drew attention to the plight of poor, sick children who lacked any significant hospital provision. A dispensary for the infant poor had opened in 1769 but it closed before the end of the century, and few children were brought to the general dispensaries and hospitals owing to the danger of infection and lack of facilities. In the first half of the 19th century Guy's Hospital showed the way by setting apart a ward for children, which was used for teaching purposes as well as serving the poor of the neighbourhood.

A founder-member of the Medical and Chirurgical Society, Dr John Clarke, made an early study on the diseases of children in 1815, and Patrick Macgregor, surgeon to the Royal Military Asylum in Chelsea, reported to the Society the results of his survey of the diseases of 1,200 children there between 1804 and 1814: measles was particularly severe and often fatal.[92]

A dispensary for children was established in Waterloo Road in 1816. This was where Dr Charles West worked: West was a Fellow of the RMCS from 1842, and was the author

Dr Charles West, founder of
the Hospital for the Diseases of Children
(Great Ormond Street) in 1852, was President
of the RMCS 1877–79.

of *Diseases of infancy and childhood* (1848) and two papers in the *Transactions*. He was determined to establish better medical care for children and with the help of three other Fellows of the Society, Dr Henry Bence-Jones, Dr Robert Lee and Dr William Jenner, he founded the Hospital for the Diseases of Children in 1852, later known as the Hospital for Sick Children, Great Ormond Street. West was senior physician to the hospital for 23 years, after which he was elected President of the RMCS.

The benefits of colostrum to infants was given a scientific basis by John Davy, Inspector of Hospitals, who had researched its effect on calves (1845). But the methods of treating children for diarrhoea were still primitive, as illustrated by a paper from JS Allen of the St Marylebone Infirmary in 1846. He recommended the abstraction of blood from the head; if this was not sufficient, it should be followed by doses of mercury with chalk, occasionally magnesia, possibly calomel and jalap so as to purge freely.[93]

## Dr Marshall Hall

The meetings and *Transactions* of the RMCS revealed the part Fellows were playing in the hospitals and dispensaries of London in promoting the health of the sick poor, of children and of prisoners and in the developing specialties such as eye surgery and the diseases of the teeth and ears. Other Fellows pursued their individual interests and research projects in private laboratories, and for them too the Society provided an invaluable means of communicating and publishing their work. Dr Marshall Hall, for instance, failed to secure a permanent hospital appointment and sought an outlet for his work by lecturing and by publication in the Royal Society's *Philosophical Transactions* and the *Medico-Chirurgical Transactions*. Hall's papers in the latter on the effects of the loss of blood (1824, 1828, 1832) marked the beginning of the end of blood-letting in this country, and his discovery of the reflex action was the basis of four Memoirs in the Society's *Transactions* (1839, 1840, 1841).

Hall had first revealed his observations of the reflex function of the spinal cord in the separated tail of a triton (newt) at a lecture given to the Zoological Society in November 1832 and his findings were published in the following year. The originality of Hall's work

Dr Marshall Hall, whose papers on blood-letting and the reflex function of the nervous system were controversial. He devised a 'ready method' of resuscitation of the apparently drowned, illustrated on page 111.

aroused suspicion: both the Royal Society and the RMCS refused to publish his most controversial papers. For example, his work on the hydrencephaloid affection of infants arising from exhaustion was read to the RMCS in 1828 but was rejected for publication, although Dr Gooch and the surgeon TJ Pettigrew found the cases extremely interesting (Hall later published the paper as a tract).[94] Hall found the Society's reaction to his papers 'rather singular. When my paper was read before the Medico-Chirurgical Society there was some demur about its publication, and some proceedings to which I did not choose to submit. Now that Dr Gooch has confirmed my observations, and that fresh evidence of their correctness is added daily, the merit of originality has been, not claimed by, but given to, another! As to the conduct of the Society, Dr Gooch has characterized it as "foolish". But when the Council of such societies is, in fact, one person, its decisions may well be partial and its members driven away in disgust', he wrote to the editor of the *London Medical Gazette*.[95]

The Royal Society refused to publish Hall's paper on the circulation of the blood in 1831, and another on spinal marrow met with the same response in 1837. Hall and his defendant Wakley blamed Dr Roget, then Secretary to the Royal Society, who was accused of blackballing Hall's work.

With the exception of the *Lancet*, which habitually championed the underdog, the medical press denigrated Hall's discoveries. The *London Medical Gazette* claimed that the discovery of the reflex function, which Hall paraded as his own, should be attributed to George Prochaska, whose book on the nervous system Hall had borrowed from the Library of the RMCS on several occasions. In order to refute this charge of plagiarism, Hall produced correspondence with the Society's Librarian as evidence that he had studied Prochaska three years *after* his significant lecture to the Zoological Society.[96] The *Lancet*'s reporter, JFL Clarke, recalled that the 'Prochaska controversy' embittered Hall for several years.

On the other hand, the evening on which Hall presented his 'Memoir on some principles of the nervous system' to the RMCS was clearly a personal triumph. 'Dr Marshall Hall never appeared to greater advantage than at the memorable discussion on his system at the Medical and Chirurgical Society, nearly twenty years ago. Arrayed against him were some of the ablest men of the day, men accustomed to speak and "well up" in the subject. He was attacked by a host, certainly with great ability, and not in a bitter spirit. He was thought to be overwhelmed; this was a mistake. He rose to reply; the audience listened with profound attention. In his quiet unobtrusive manner, with his subdued voice, he seemed no equal match for his great opponents; but he soon displayed his real power. In a speech of unsurpassable clearness and true eloquence he quickly grappled with the arguments that had been advanced against him. In sentences almost epigrammatic in their brevity and style, he demonstrated the truth of his theory. He met with great applause at the conclusion of his address; but there were still many who maintained that he was in error'.[97]

## Dr Henry Bence-Jones

A paper presented to the RMCS in 1844 by Samuel Solly, assistant surgeon at St Thomas' Hospital and to the General Dispensary, contained remarks on the pathology of mollities ossium, then known as soft bones and now as myeloma.[98] Its publication was soon followed by the work of three Fellows involved with one patient suffering from the disease: Dr Henry Bence-Jones, physician to St George's, John Dalrymple, consulting surgeon to the Royal London Ophthalmic Hospital, and Dr William MacIntyre of the Western General Dispensary. Bence-Jones was the chemist among the three, working along the lines of Dr William Prout and Dr Golding Bird in biochemistry. In 1845 he received samples for analysis from MacIntyre and the results of his work identified an unusual urinary protein, later known as Bence-Jones protein. He revealed his findings to the Royal College of Physicians in 1846 and to the Royal Society the next year. Dalrymple also produced a paper describing the case, and this was published in the *Dublin Quarterly Journal of Medical Science*.[99] Dr MacIntyre chose to give his report of the case to the RMCS in April 1850. He described how the patient with mollities ossium had been in his care since 1845; he gave the main clinical features and described the urinary discovery of Bence-Jones.[100] The latter received little notice until the mid-20th century when studies of Bence-Jones protein in America produced valuable information about multiple myeloma.[101]

Bence-Jones's first publication had been in the Society's *Transactions* for 1840, giving his analysis of a very large cystine calculus. On the merit of this he was requested by the Governors of St George's Hospital to analyse and catalogue all the calculi in the hospital museum, the results of which appeared in the *Transactions* for 1843. He contributed further papers including those on the presence of uric acid in urine (1844) and on diabetes in the elderly (1853). Bence-Jones had studied chemistry under Liebig at Giessen and this had launched him on his studies of pathological chemistry; he was one of the first to insist on the use of the microscope and the importance of urinary analysis in diagnosing disease. He attended Charles Darwin during his illness of 1865, putting him on a diet that 'half-starved him to death', and he was a close friend of Florence Nightingale, who thought he was the best chemical doctor in London. Bence-Jones's letter to her in the Crimea first planted the seed of an idea for a training school for nurses.[102]

## Sir Richard Quain

Richard Quain, assistant physician to the Hospital for Consumptive Diseases at the time, is remembered for his bequest of awards and prizes to University College, London and his classic *Anatomy of the arteries of the human body* (1844). He was an Honorary Librarian to the RMCS in 1846 and four years later he presented a new aspect of heart disease to a meeting of the Society. He apologized to Fellows for the length of his paper (presenting 83 cases of coronary obstruction), which was due to the importance of the subject. Quain's main thesis was that fatty degeneration of the heart, 'a disease which has hitherto escaped observation', was brought about by obstruction of the coronary arteries and not, as was

Sir Richard Quain, author of an important paper on the fatty degeneration of the heart and its relation to coronary disease (1850).

generally supposed, by inflammation. Of these cases, 52 were later identified as likely to be ischaemic heart disease.[103]

Quain's work was immediately recognized as important and was 'listened to throughout with the greatest attention; at its close the Fellows, who formed a very large meeting, expressed their high opinion of its merits by the unusual compliment of warm applause. Many felt that the meeting might have been prolonged with advantage, so as to have afforded an opportunity for discussing this new and important subject'.[104]

Quain devoted seven years to his *Dictionary of medicine* (1882), editing it and contributing articles on heart diseases. He was appointed physician to the Queen in 1890 and received a baronetcy the next year.

## Mid-19th-century prosperity

The Great Exhibition opened in May 1851 as a celebration of the prosperity of Victorian Britain. It exhibited recent achievements in the art, science and industry of all nations and heralded a golden age of progress. Compared with the sections on industry, manufacture and the arts, medicine was modestly represented at the Crystal Palace. Nevertheless the French surgical and ophthalmic instruments commanded attention, as did the numerous items exhibited by dentists, including the best apparatus yet invented for 'artificial masticating', devised by Mr Tomes, which received a medal. Many varieties of stethoscope could be inspected, together with the most up-to-date chloroform inhalers, a device for restoring the club foot to its natural position, artificial limbs and Dr Gray's medical walking stick containing medicines and articles that might be required in an emergency. Several inventions of Dr Neil Arnott, a Fellow of the RMCS, were on view – a new truss, contrivances for obtaining a loss of feeling by intense cold and his pneumatic dilator. Hutchinson's spirometers, which he had demonstrated to a meeting of the RMCS in 1846, were exhibited, and there were chemical and pharmaceutical products of interest to the medical profession.[105] The Society celebrated the exhibition by opening its rooms at 53 Berners Street to foreign medical men and visitors from the provinces, a hospitable gesture that was repeated during the Great Exhibition of 1861.

By the year of the 1851 Exhibition London University boasted two teaching hospitals, Charing Cross Hospital had been rebuilt with a medical school attached, St George's was rebuilt, Westminster Hospital was erected in Broad Sanctuary with a medical school in Dean Street, an enlarged Royal Free Hospital stood in Gray's Inn Road, and the Middlesex had also been enlarged. St Mary's opened in Paddington in the same year as the Great Exhibition, its medical school three years later. The specialist hospitals had also multiplied since 1805 when the first hospital devoted to diseases of the eye was founded. The Hospital for Diseases of the Chest was established in 1814, St Mark's Hospital for Fistula opened in 1835, the Samaritan Hospital for Women in 1847 and William Marsden's cancer hospital in 1851, and there were many others. In addition there were 35 local dispensaries in London by 1830, as well as many asylums, prisons, institutions and parishes where medical attendance was required.

The expansion of medical care, improvements in surgical techniques and the extension of medical education made for a crowded medical profession hungry for knowledge. The medical schools and licensing authorities, societies, periodicals and journals fed the demand with considerable success. The reform of the profession, however, was ponderous and slow. The Apothecaries Act of 1815 regulating the education of medical students and the Anatomy Act of 1832 legalizing the supply of corpses for dissection benefited the profession, but unlicensed practitioners, chemists and druggists continued to threaten the integrity of medicine. A reforming element could at last be detected in the Royal College of Physicians during the 1830s, and in 1843 the Royal College of Surgeons obtained a new charter and regulations. Several associations pushed for reform and independence: the

Provincial Medical and Surgical Association of 1832 gathered strength to become the British Medical Association in 1856, and the National Association of General Practitioners was founded in 1844 (and was served by two Fellows of the RMCS as Secretaries). After a plethora of proposals, inquiries and Bills, a measure of reform was achieved by the Medical Act of 1858. It failed to penalize unlicensed practitioners or to standardize medical qualifications in the United Kingdom, but it did regulate medical education in England and Wales; it also established the registration of qualified practitioners and the General Medical Council.

In these encouraging circumstances the physicians and surgeons of mid-19th-century London pursued scientific medicine, studied and gained experience abroad, made use of new instruments and embarked upon specialties. They attended meetings of scientific societies such as the RMCS and subscribed to and wrote for the numerous periodicals, hospital reports and journals. The activities of medical societies and medical periodicals reached a peak in the mid-19th century: the Medical Society of London was fortified by the absorption of the Westminster Medical Society in 1850; the Pathological Society attracted 106 members to its first meeting in 1846 and new societies devoted to epidemiology, odontology and obstetrics were founded in the 1850s, with their attendant publications.

Initially the RMCS lost Fellows to the Pathological Society but some were to return. The Council reported in March 1850 that the total number of ordinary Fellows stood at 557 (308 resident, 249 non-resident) and there were 12 Honorary Fellows, including WT Brande, Professor of Chemistry at the Royal Institution, Professor Richard Owen, Curator to the Royal College of Surgeons, Edwin Chadwick, Commissioner to the Board of Health, Michael Faraday of the Royal Institution and Sir John Herschel, the President of the Royal Astronomical Society. Among 24 Foreign Honorary Fellows were Baron Justus von Liebig of the University of Giessen, Monsieur Louis and Professor Magendie of Paris, Dr Carl Rokitansky of Vienna and Dr Johannes Müller of Berlin.

*Annus mirabilis*

The Society's finances were reported to be 'highly satisfactory' in 1850, allowing Fellows to opt for a composition fee in lieu of further subscriptions,[106] and prosperity continued into 1851, the year that has been described as an *annus mirabilis* for the RMCS.[107] With a large membership, a fine house, a Library that was open every weekday and a plump volume appearing annually, the Council congratulated itself on the easy state of the finances and rejoiced in the Society's reputation. 'Whether they regard the addition made to the number of Fellows; the return of valuable Fellows who had seceded; the crowded state of the meeting-room; the number and character of the papers presented or the interesting discussions to which they give rise, the past Session has been, so far one of the most important in the history of the Society'. The RMCS had secured the lease of 53 Berners Street and made improvements to the building, significant purchases had been added to the Library; an index to the *Transactions* had been compiled and the volumes themselves expanded to 360 pages in 1850 and 1851.[108]

The flourishing state of the Society was in part due to the influence of Dr Thomas Addison, President from 1849 to 1851 (see page 43). Although retiring by nature, Addison made a special effort to improve relations between the medical profession and the press by inviting reporters to meet the leading physicians and surgeons of London at the RMCS, with evident success as one of those present reported: 'One of his objects [was] to show that we were not "the ruffians" that some professed to think us. The evening was one of the most delightful I ever spent. I was astonished at his bonhommie [*sic*], his hospitality and his powers of conversation. All honour to his memory! say I, for this mark of his independence and liberality'.[109]

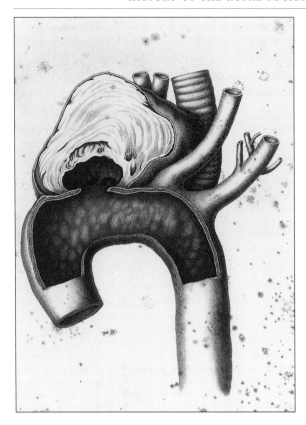

Joseph Hodgson, President of the Society 1851–53, was the author of *A treatise on the diseases of the arteries and veins* (1815), which gave the first description of non-sacculated dilation of the aortic arch (Hodgson's disease). He drew the plates, which were acclaimed as the best illustrations of aneurysms and aortic valvular endo-carditis to date. This plate represents an aneurysm of the arch of the aorta 'to illustrate the mode by which a spontaneous cure of aneurysm is some-times accomplished in consequence of the sac being filled with lamellated coagulum'.

## Joseph Hodgson

Addison's successor as President, Joseph Hodgson, was described by the same author as 'one of the most urbane and dignified persons who ever filled that post, but less decided and suggestive than had been expected'.[110] Hodgson was known in Birmingham for founding the Eye Infirmary and for lithotrity: he had cut 86 patients for stone and lost only four. His most important study was on wounds and diseases of the arteries and veins, which won him the Jacksonian Prize in 1811 and formed the basis of his *Treatise on the diseases of the arteries and veins* (1815). Herein Hodgson gave the first description of non-saccular dilatation of the aortic arch (Hodgson's disease); he drew the illustrations himself.

At the time of his death in 1869 Hodgson was the most senior Fellow of the Society, having belonged to it for 56 years.

## Popular meetings

The popularity of the President combined with the intrinsic interest of the papers and the reputations of their authors guaranteed audiences of over 100 with almost the same number of guests at several meetings in 1850, prompting plans to enlarge the meeting-room. A series of papers on ovariotomies, Caesarian sections and the diseases of women aroused considerable interest at this time.

The debate had been opened by Benjamin Phillips' survey, published in the *Transactions* for 1844, giving the encouraging results of 81 operations for ovarian disease. The proce-dure was still controversial, as was shown by papers given at the first meeting of the session in November 1850 when EW Duffin and Dr Robert Lee presented opposing views. Duffin described a single successful operation by a new method in a case of ovarian tumour; Lee gave his analysis of 108 ovariotomies in Great Britain since 1822. Lee was physician to the British Lying In Hospital and physician-accoucheur to St Marylebone Infirmary, and was known for his forthright views. He contributed twice as many papers as any of his contemporaries to the Society's *Transactions* and attracted the largest audiences to meetings: 'this rare conflux was due not only to the importance of the debate; for Dr Robert Lee always felt strongly that he was in the right ... and was a severe cross-examiner in trials of novelties'.[111] True to form, Lee expressed his doubts about ovariotomy and his views were echoed by Caesar Hawkins, surgeon to St George's Hospital. Nor was William Lawrence convinced. He had not witnessed an ovariotomy and had no intention of doing so, much less of performing one. He hoped that 'the discussion of this evening, excited by the important communication of Dr Lee will at least serve the useful purpose of admonishing us to pause in the attempts at treating diseased ovaries by surgical operation'.[112] The majority of the profession agreed with Lawrence, and few ovariotomies were performed until Thomas Spencer Wells reported his successes, beginning in 1857 (see pages 132–33). Lee remained obdurate, set against ovariotomy and against the use of chloroform in labour (see page 112).

Retrogressive by nature, Lee was one of the first medical historians in the Society, seizing on the Chamberlen obstetrical instruments (see overleaf) as items worthy of research. The instruments had been presented to the Society by Mr H Carwardine in 1818, following their discovery at a property in Essex where Dr Peter Chamberlen had died in 1683. Lee was able to verify that the instruments originated in the mid-17th century, having visited the house where they were found and consulted Dr William Munk before presenting his paper to the Society in November 1861.[113]

It has been calculated that 30% of the membership attended meetings of the Society in 1851 at which a total of 41 papers were read.[114] At a single meeting on 24 June 12 papers were presented, the main attraction being Faraday's reading of a communication from Schonbein, Professor of Chemistry at Basle, on the physiological effects produced by atmospheric electricity (ozone). This had the advantage of some advance publicity, having been preceded by a general paper 'On Schonbein's ozone' delivered by Faraday to the Royal Institution on 13 June. Both Schonbein and Faraday had given much thought to the communication of the discovery, Faraday being particularly anxious to 'make your subject interesting... I hope I shall not discredit you or fail in using all the matter you have given me'. Schonbein was in no doubt about the poisonous nature of 'certain gaseous bodies or vapours' in the atmosphere and he warned Fellows of the RMCS that 'their accumulation would render the air unfit for the support of animal life'.[115]

In November 1851 the industrious Dr Lee resumed his reporting of cases of ovarian disease, attracting a record number of 145 Fellows and 70 guests to one meeting. The next week Fellows heard Dr Edward Meryon's case of a family with granular and fatty degeneration of the voluntary muscles, later assessed as 'the first recorded examples of pseudo-hypertrophic paralysis'.[116] Meryon was Honorary Librarian to the Society (1859–60), on the Council for 1864–65 and became well known for his work on muscular dystrophy (sometimes known as Meryon's disease).

## Criticism from the *Lancet*

The large attendances at the Society's meetings for 1850 and 1851 were not sustained to the end of the decade, by which time new groups such as the Epidemiological, Odontological and Obstetrical Societies were providing counter-attractions. The creation of the British Medical Association in 1856, the lead-up to and consequences of the Medical Act of 1858 and the Crimean War were other major distractions claiming the time and energy of members of the medical profession. Furthermore, in 1854 the Society came under fire from the *Lancet*, enduring unwelcome publicity as the journal launched missiles against the exclusive and censorious nature of the Society's Council. The first volley centred on the Council's rejection of Dr Ransom of Nottingham as a candidate for membership on the grounds that his only professional qualification was a degree from

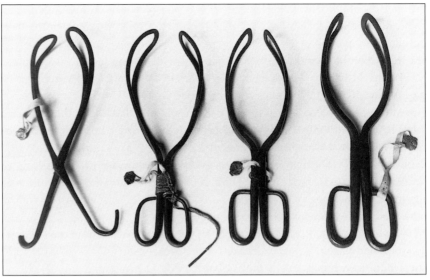

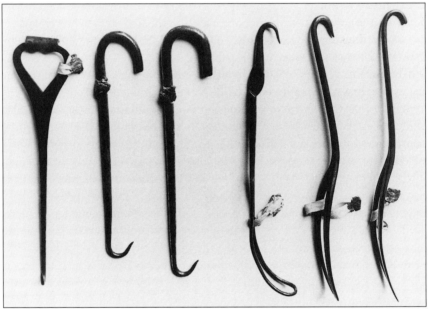

The Chamberlen obstetrical instruments were discovered in 1813 at Woodham Mortimer Hall, Essex, presented to the Medical and Chirurgical Society in 1818 and provided the subject of Robert Lee's paper of 1861. The instruments are now at the Royal College of Obstetricians and Gynaecologists.

London University. The *Lancet* took up his cause and the Society was forced to respond by altering a by-law. Whereas previously candidates for the Fellowship had been loosely described as physicians, surgeons and general practitioners, from 1854 those eligible for membership had to fall into one of the following categories: 'Fellows or Members of the Colleges of Physicians or Surgeons of Great Britain or Ireland, Doctors and Bachelors of Medicine of the universities of Great Britain and Ireland, Members of the Faculty of Physicians and Surgeons of Glasgow, Licentiates of the Apothecaries of London and Dublin and Foreigners whose qualifications are satisfactory to Council'.[117]

The second blast from the *Lancet* originated with the case of John Gay, a Fellow of the Society and surgeon to the Royal Free Hospital. He had rashly referred to the Royal Free in offensive terms in a biography. The *Lancet* seized on Gay's indiscretion and as a result of the unfavourable publicity Gay found himself dismissed from his post. Campbell de Morgan, surgeon and lecturer in anatomy at the Middlesex Hospital, objected strongly to the influence the *Lancet* had wielded in this affair and at the anniversary meeting of the RMCS he declared that 'the tone and spirit of the *Lancet* did not entitle it to a place in the Society's library … the journal was exercising an improper influence and one that was degrading to the profession (Cheers)'. Dr Meryon seconded the motion; Dr Theophilus Thompson thought the Society should not be so hasty; Dr Snow maintained that if the *Lancet* was to be banned the *Medical Circular* must go also ('hear, hear'), and Mr Henry Ancell took the opportunity to deride the *Lancet* as 'the medium for the exercise of private and personal influence, the interests of science and of our noble profession occupying only a secondary position' in its pages.

Thomas Wakley, who continued to edit the *Lancet*, revelled in the fray. He alleged that banning the journal from the Library amounted to interference with the medical press and 104 Fellows of the Society agreed, insisting that the *Lancet* be available. A special general meeting was called on 24 March 1854 to resolve the issue, attended by 189 Fellows. The President, Dr James Copland, said he wished he had nipped de Morgan's original motion in the bud. Copland disliked controversy and the public expression of feelings – he had put an end to the custom of cheering, laughing or clapping at the conclusion of papers presented to meetings, reminding Fellows that they were not actors but men of science.[118]

The special meeting proved to be a stormy one. Sir Benjamin Brodie, who justly described himself as 'an old member of the Society' (he was 71) came forward as a mediator, urging Fellows to abstain from medical politics and to refrain from disagreeable disputes and dissensions. He stressed the honour of the Society 'obtained because men met on friendly and amicable terms' and the importance of its *Transactions*, 'there was nothing to be compared to them', with the exception, perhaps, of the volumes published by the French Academy of Surgery. Brodie's conciliatory skills calmed the meeting and were to stand him in good stead as the first President of the General Medical Council on its foundation in 1858, the same year that saw him elected President of the Royal Society. De Morgan had his say, among others, before the proceedings were 'abruptly brought to a close, many of the gentlemen protesting in very loud and angry tones'.

After all the fuss, no medical periodicals were excluded from the Library, which the *Lancet* proclaimed as a victory for the press: 'It was an act of tyranny savouring of trades' combinations, or exclusive dealing, for a powerful Society like the Medico-Chirurgical to attempt to interfere with the independence of the press'. The editorial went on to question why the Society continued to honour Dr Elliotson, whose bust stood in the Library – 'he who in an evil hour fell away from the ranks of the profession and devoted his talents to the furtherance of Mesmerism' – and criticized the Council for refusing to be responsible for the papers published in the *Transactions* (this referred to the note inserted in each volume disclaiming responsibility for statements, reasonings or opinions expressed by the authors of papers).[119]

## Publication of the *Proceedings*

The influence of the medical press persuaded the Council to grant reporters from the journals admission to the general meetings. The *Provincial Medical Gazette* was the first to be given the privilege in 1842, and before long JFL Clarke was reporting the proceedings on behalf of the *Lancet*, Dr Alexander Henry for the *British Medical Journal* and in 1867 the editor of the *Medical Times and Gazette* nominated Dr Hughlings Jackson as its representative at the Society's meetings. Editors were at liberty to print all or part of the proceedings and accuracy could not be guaranteed. Therefore the Council of the RMCS embarked on the official publication of the *Proceedings* of the Society in 1856. They were to be printed every two months, providing 'notices of proceedings of the society to include longer or shorter abstracts of all papers' and papers considered too brief for the *Transactions*. Thus for the first time the President's address, obituaries of Fellows, the financial accounts and the Report of the President and Council presented at the Annual General Meeting saw the light of day; and from 1882 discussions generated by the papers was also included.[120] The *Proceedings* were modelled on those of the Royal Society and although their discontinuation was proposed periodically, they appeared regularly, expanding to door-stop proportions after the amalgamation of 1907 when they replaced *Medico-Chirurgical Transactions*.

Initially authors submitting papers could specify whether they wished their work to be published in the *Proceedings* only or in the *Transactions* with an abstract in the *Proceedings* (the Council later reserved this decision to itself). Resident Fellows received copies of the *Proceedings* free, in addition to the annual volume of *Transactions*; others could purchase them for five shillings per annum. The commercial medical periodicals were provided with the *Proceedings* in lieu of the abstracts of papers formerly supplied by the Secretaries, and might also report the meetings directly, with permission of the Council. The arrangement rendered the recording of abstracts in the General Minutes unnecessary, gave wider publicity to the Society's business and did not detract from the prestige of the *Transactions*, which remained the authoritative source of important papers until the last volume was published in 1907.

## Specialist societies

Tangible evidence of the specialization of the medical profession lay in the increasing number of specialist hospitals and dispensaries of 19th-century London. Whereas in 1800 there were 12 specialist charity hospitals and dispensaries, by 1859 there were 53 and by 1890 a hundred. The leaders of the profession and the general practitioners were united in deploring the proliferation of specialist institutions because they diverted funds, consultants and research opportunities from the general hospitals; over 400 members of the profession petitioned against the foundation of St Peter's Hospital for the Stone in 1860 for these reasons.[121]

The trend towards specialization could also be seen in the foundation of new medical societies: the Pathological Society (1846), the Epidemiological Society (1850), the Odontological Society (1856), the Obstetrical Society (1858) and the Clinical Society (1867), with another clutch appearing in the last two decades of the century. Sir Henry Holland, a Fellow of the RMCS, was one of many who condemned 'the extravagant multiplication of societies and institutions of every kind, dividing and subdividing all the concerns of human life' – and this was before the foundations of the late 19th century.[122] Another contemporary observer thought 'that it would have been far better for the Profession and for the public too, if the new Societies had not been established. Whatever may be the advantages of the division of labour – and these are many – I contend that whatever conduces to the union of Medicine has far more advantages'.[123] There was an element of antagonism as the various societies competed for members and papers, not to mention the potential for duplication and exclusiveness and, moreover, the expense incurred by those who found it necessary to belong to more than one society. Nevertheless, new specialist medical societies multiplied and defied amalgamation until the creation of the Royal Society of Medicine in 1907 drew many of them into one institution (see Chapter 7).

### Pathological Society

The foundation of the Pathological Society in 1846 was attributed to deficiencies in the RMCS (which itself owed its birth to perceived deficiencies in the Medical Society of London). Dissatisfaction with the conduct of elections, the almost entire exclusion of general practitioners from office, the mode of selection of papers for publication and the failure of the pathological meetings 'were amongst some of the more prominent causes which tended to the establishment of the Pathological Society ... a most useful institution, unquestionably, and one that has rendered good service to the Profession, but which would have been still more useful had it remained a part of the Medical and Chirurgical. To some extent and to similar causes to those mentioned above, the Obstetrical and Clinical Societies derived their origin'.[124] Sir Samuel Wilks went further, alleging that the Medical and Chirurgical Society was opposed to all that was progressive, 'an example being at the time when pathology was advancing, but as this was founded on morbid anatomy the rising men wanted to show their histological and microscopical work – this was far beyond the vision of the old fogies and so the Pathological Society was founded – and a Clinical Society where new ideas were welcome'.[125] Many years later as he reflected on the meetings at Berners Street, Sir Rickman J Godlee remembered the RMCS as being 'old fashioned, very serious and rather dull', in contrast to the Pathological Society which was 'excitedly ploughing the virgin soil of rudimentary pathology'.[126]

According to a reporter who gained access to the meetings of the RMCS at this time, 'the attempt of some of the more energetic of the Fellows to introduce pathological specimens of cases for the purpose of discussion was not cordially received by the Council', and this led directly to the foundation of the Pathological Society.[127] Dr Charles Williams, the first President of the Pathological Society and President of the RMCS 1873–75, attributed the idea of establishing the former to Dr Edward Bentley of Guy's Hospital. Bentley and Nathaniel Ward were the new Society's first Secretaries, and preliminary meetings were held at the houses of Dr Babington and Dr Williams. The founder-members included many Fellows of the RMCS: Williams, Babington, Bright, Hawkins, Arnott, Liston, Quain and others. 'Of the Pathological Society it is not too much to say that it has attained and preserved to the present time, an amount of popularity, utility, and eminence, equal, if not superior, to that of any medical society in this or in any country', Dr Williams wrote in 1884. 'In the attendance of its members, in the supply of interesting objects, and in the animation and searching character of its discussions, there never seems to have been any material falling off; so that its whole career of 37 years has been one of uninterrupted success'.[128]

Perhaps the most astonishing case ever reported in the *Transactions of the Pathological Society* was that of the 'Elephant Man', Joseph Merrick, deformed in body, head, face and limbs and with skin that hung in folds like the hide of an elephant.[129] His appearance was described in 1885 by Frederick Treves in a paper entitled 'A case of congenital deformity'; Merrick was subsequently given accommodation at the London Hospital, where he attracted curious visitors.

The seal of the
Pathological Society of
London, founded in 1846.

The seal of the Epidemiological Society of
London, founded in 1850.

## Epidemiological Society

The Council of the RMCS harboured reservations about the Pathological Society for several years. Not so with regard to the Epidemiological Society, founded in the wake of the cholera epidemic of 1848, when a correspondent to the *Lancet* proposed 'the formation of a new society, which might be styled the Asiatic-Cholera Society, or the Epidemic Medical Society, the object of which would be to investigate epidemics ... A paid librarian, secretary and managing director would be required and rooms at first, as a matter of course; if established a house'.[130]

The correspondent, later identified as Mr JH Tucker, became the first Honorary Secretary of the Society. As he pointed out, there was a degree of urgency: 'Can it be said that the cholera has left us? Where is it now? Even when it is no longer heard of, may it not be lying in ambush, awaiting a fitting opportunity to attack us again? After having lost so many thousands of our countrymen by the devastating foe, we must first learn with what weapons we have been beaten before we can well prepare ourselves for another attack'. His fears were justified, for cholera was to strike again in 1854.[131]

The Epidemiological Society was formally founded in July 1850 at a meeting chaired by Lord Ashley, the social reformer better known as the Earl of Shaftesbury, at which Dr Benjamin Babington was elected the first President, a position he retained for 16 years (he had been a Fellow of the RMCS for 25 years and was to be its President in 1861). The new Society held its first ordinary meeting at 53 Berners Street later in the same year, attended by several members of the RMCS as Vice Presidents and office-holders, including Dr John Snow and Dr John Simon.[132] The Epidemiological Society's committee on smallpox and vaccination submitted a report to the Home Office in 1853, and further important reports were to follow.

## Obstetrical Society

The Obstetrical Society of London was granted the use of 53 Berners Street for its first meeting in January 1859, and was to be a tenant until 1868, rejoining the RMCS in Hanover Square in 1889.[133] The Obstetrical Society had a precursor, founded in 1825 by Dr AB Granville, which fought for the recognition of practitioners in midwifery by the Royal Colleges. After three years Granville's Society made some headway with the institution of examinations in midwifery at Apothecaries' Hall but the arrogant attitude towards accoucheurs or man-midwives proved hard to dispel – the occupation was regarded as unsuitable for gentlemen.

Another obstetrical society existed at Guy's Hospital briefly in 1836, having been founded by Doctors Ashwell, Tweedie and Lever. Dr Granville, whose own Society had been shortlived, had the satisfaction of being present at the inaugural meeting of the Obstetrical Society of London at the Freemasons' Tavern in December 1858, when its

The seal of the Obstetrical
Society of London.

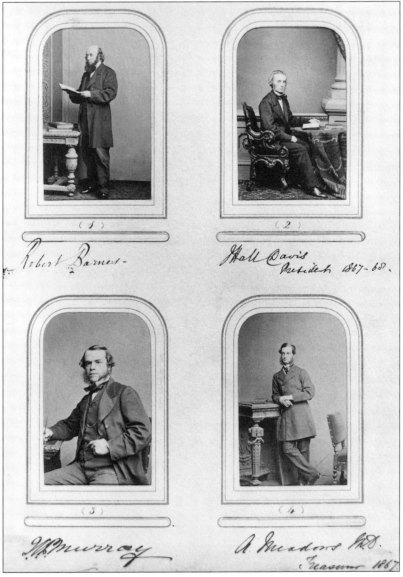

Fellows of the Obstetrical Society *c.*1867. Dr Robert Barnes is commemorated
in the Barnes Hall at 1 Wimpole Street.

object was established: 'to advance knowledge of obstetrics and the diseases of women and children'. Dr Edward Rigby was the first President and within the year over 300 ordinary members, many of them in the provinces, had joined.[134] The Society was to be incorporated in the Royal Society of Medicine on its formation in 1907 (see pages 244–45).

## Odontological Society

The Odontological Society of London was founded in 1856 by Samuel Cartwright, John Tomes and T Arnold Rogers, all of them except Tomes being Fellows of the RMCS. By founding this scientific society and establishing the first London School of Dental Surgery and Dental Hospital at Soho Square (1858–60), this group virtually created the dental profession. In 1863 the Odontological Society amalgamated with a rival association to become the Odontological Society of Great Britain. It met at the premises of the Medical Society of London until 1901, when it joined that 'perfect hive of societies' at 20 Hanover Square (see pages 238–39).[135]

## Clinical Society

The Clinical Society was inaugurated at Sir John Burdon Sanderson's house, Queen Anne Street, in October 1867 (it was also to be the birthplace of the Physiological Society in 1876). The initiative lay with Dr Edward Headlam Greenhow of the Middlesex Hospital who felt that clinical medicine, almost a new development of the healing art, ought to have its proper avenue of debate and publication.[136] The Clinical Society attracted the younger members of the profession and was regarded as a sister to the Pathological Society, which Burdon Sanderson, for one, thought was too exclusively occupied with the examination of post mortem results.[137] The clinicians were strongly opposed to academic discourses on general topics: ten minutes was the time allowed for their communications of cases, in contrast to the prosy nature of the papers at the RMCS.[138] 'The venerable Royal Medical and Chirurgical Society was already fully occupied with its sundry profound and elaborate subjects; and valuable as both its proceedings and Transactions are, they must be admitted to be somewhat of the slow-coach character, and hardly fit for the quick and ready reports of clinical practice', wrote Dr Williams. With 127 founder-members under the presidency of 'the venerated and beloved Sir Thomas Watson ... it became at once as popular as the Pathological Society had been at its foundation'.[139] Its work was to be continued by the Clinical Section of the RSM (see page 254).

The seal of the Odontological Society of Great Britain, founded in 1863.

The seal of the Clinical Society, founded in 1867.

## Amalgamation proposals

By 1850 the Pathological Society was ready to unite with the RMCS but the latter was unreceptive to the proposal: its Council did not wish to have the Pathological Society as tenants, let alone partners. Ten years later, however, the Council appointed a committee to confer with the other societies based at 53 Berners Street on the possibility 'of uniting in one comprehensive body the different societies which are engaged in prosecuting distinct departments of Medical Science'.[140] The prospect of a larger, unified society retaining the title of the Royal Medical and Chirurgical Society encouraged pretensions to grandeur and the Council cast an eye on Burlington House, Piccadilly, which had been purchased by the government in 1854. Plans for rebuilding Burlington House to accommodate the country's learned societies were circulating in 1859 and the Royal Medical and Chirurgical was keen to apply for rooms; Dr Edward Meryon contacted Lord Granville 'relative to the Society being permitted rooms in Burlington House' in July 1860. On consultation, the Royal Society objected; apparently there was a 'want of accommodation at present'. At a second attempt, when Burlington House was on the verge of a drastic remodelling in 1866, the Society again applied for a tenancy, claiming that with 640 members it was the largest society for the advancement of medical science in the United Kingdom and in possession of a Library of 25,000 volumes. Again the application failed. The enlarged Burlington House was reserved for the Royal Society, the Society of Antiquaries, the Linnean, the Geological, the Chemical and the Royal Astronomical Societies.[141]

Four Honorary Fellows of the RMCS in 1863: top: Sir John Herschel, President of the Royal Astronomical Society; right: Sir William Hooker, Director of the Royal Botanic Gardens, Kew; left: Reverend William Whewell, Master of Trinity College, Cambridge; below: Michael Faraday, Professor of Chemistry at the Royal Institution. A note indicates that Herschel presented his photograph to the Society.

Unsuccessful in its bid for accommodation at Burlington House, the Council of the RMCS began to search for a building with 'a more public aspect … a more imposing appearance' where affiliated institutions could be gathered under one roof. Dr Hare, President of the Medical Society of London, supported the proposition, indicating that he would like to see the medical societies of London housed in 'some building of architectural character which might serve them all'.[142] Before plans could be advanced, Thomas Warren offered the Council of the RMCS a ground lease of 53 Berners Street for 38 years at £2,000. As this represented an overall reduction in the Society's annual expenditure on rent for the foreseeable future, the deal was agreed in 1866. The RMCS remained at 53 Berners Street for another 20 years.[143]

### The amalgamation scheme of 1860–61

The question of accommodation was settled but the question of the union of the medical societies persisted. The President between 1859 and 1861, Frederick C Skey, assistant surgeon to St Bartholomew's Hospital, surgeon to the Northern Dispensary and a lecturer at the Aldersgate School, promoted the union of the societies meeting at Berners Street: the RMCS and the Pathological, Epidemiological and Obstetrical Societies, and in 1860 a scheme was drawn up for a united society with seven sections. Difficulties arose when the Society's solicitor pointed out that unless a new charter was obtained the expenditure of the sections would have to be under the control of the Council of the RMCS.

The Obstetrical Society, with a membership of over 300 led by Dr W Tyler-Smith, who was also a Fellow of the RMCS, was the first to decline the terms. It had recently launched a campaign urging the GMC to enforce the examination and registration of obstetricians and was in no mood to accept relegation to a mere section of the RMCS, for it was perceived that this would submerge the specialty. The Epidemiological Society remained in favour of the union under a new charter; the Pathological was apathetic; and Dr Robert Lee of the RMCS wanted to see the Society's house reserved exclusively for the use of the RMCS. The issue was shelved.[144]

This lost opportunity to unite the profession in one large London society 'so as to form, as it were, a Royal Academy of Medicine' was a disappointment to those who valued the unity of medicine above specialism, such as Skey and Babington. The latter reported that the proposed amalgamation of 1860–61 had been unpalatable to two of the societies (the Obstetrical Society and a majority of the RMCS members voted against it). Personally, he regretted the failure of the scheme, chiefly because the other medical societies were syphoning much valuable material away from the RMCS.[145] He warned Fellows not to indulge in 'unpleasant animadversions', probably referring to their habit of showing displeasure at an unsatisfactory paper – 'a gentle tapping with the heels… designed to drown the voice or overcome the resolution of the boldest or most persistent speaker'.[146] 'Some of the most distinguished and most experienced of our Fellows are actually deterred from attending our meetings and giving us their opinions … by a dread that they might, possibly, subject themselves to unpleasant animadversions … one of the oldest and most revered members if our profession I know to have avoided joining our Society from a similar feeling'. Babington was progressive; he wanted the Society to institute medals for individuals who had promoted the science of medicine or surgery, or to award funds for research, experiments and publication. He thought foreign corresponding Fellows would be an asset and it was during his presidency that the first scientific committee was appointed (see page 110).[147]

### Amalgamation proposals of 1868–70

The advantages of amalgamation were equally obvious to Samuel Solly (President 1869–70) and to his successor, Sir George Burrows. Solly was aware of 'the deficiencies of this Association' and tried to persuade members to do more to foster industry and research and to encourage younger Fellows: 'Many an ardent devotee of science has been discouraged by the rejection of his first paper from the *Transactions*'. He spoke poetically of 'the darling dream of Presidential longings', i.e. the formation of a Royal Academy or Royal Society of Medicine by 'the amalgamation of the societies of London and the occupation of a building worthy of our noble profession'.[148]

This plea for unity was fuelled by applications from the Clinical Society and the Medico-Psychological Association to make Berners Street their headquarters, and by a letter received early in 1868 from Dr Horace Dobell, physician to the Royal Hospital for Diseases of the Chest. He conveyed the news that a Therapeutical Society was being planned – unless of course the RMCS would institute a therapeutical section (the Therapeutical Society was eventually founded in 1902, becoming a Section of the RSM five years later).[149] Faced with the prospect of another new medical society, a committee of the RMCS was formed to report on the possibility of the union of several or any societies. For two years discussions on the number of sections (between seven and nine) and the title of the new society (Royal Academy of Medicine, Royal Society of Medicine or Royal Society of Medicine and Surgery) were held. The argument hinged on the separation of medicine from surgery to form two sections, or alternatively the institution of one medico-chirurgical section. The Council, led by Sir George Burrows as President, stood true to the principle on which the Society had been founded in 1805, viz. the union of medicine and surgery. The Obstetrical Society, which now boasted a membership of 600, a library and museum, remained opposed to the union. 'We were invited to become a *section*', its President Dr Graily Hewitt reported in 1871, 'asked to sink our independence, to give up our hardly-earned savings, to subject ourselves to the control of a central council in which the obstetrical interest would have been represented by three out of twenty-eight. Moreover, we were to have been placed apart from medicine and surgery, these two branches constituting one compact section to themselves'.[150]

The Medico-Psychological Association, essentially an occupational society that had little in common with any of the Berners Street societies, decided not to co-operate and the enthusiasm of the Pathological Society for amalgamation had waned. Dr C Theodore Williams believed the scheme collapsed because Sir James Paget and Sir Richard Quain, Presidents of the Clinical and Pathological Societies respectively, opposed it,[151] and a vote at a special general meeting of the RMCS on 8 November 1870 revealed that the majority of that Society was against the union.[152]

### Sir George Burrows

The failure to achieve union left the RMCS divided and weakened. Sir George Burrows' valedictory address described the depleted and struggling Society he handed over to Thomas Curling of the London Hospital, noted for his papers on acute ulceration of the duodenum (Curling's ulcer) and the absence of the thyroid gland in mentally deficient children with fat pads (1842,1850). The recent agitation over the question of amalgamation had diverted Fellows from scientific work and discouraged admissions. The Society had also suffered by the expansion of the medical press, which continued 'to withdraw from our cognizance much that would otherwise have been thrown into papers to be read and discussed at our ordinary meetings', while the younger physicians and surgeons preferred to enrich the reports now published by their respective hospitals. According to one commentator, the quality of papers given at the Society had deteriorated – in former times 'we had none of the windy reports that characterize those of the present day. The evil had begun to exhibit itself in the time of Sir Astley, who once naively remarked "Sir, the writers are becoming like seamen who neglect the prominent landmarks for taking useless soundings, and make absurd calculations of no use to anyone, and liable to run the unlucky ship on a rock"'.[153] Lastly, but not least in the influences detrimental to the Society, Burrows blamed 'the rapid successive formation of new societies, offshoots from this parent-stock, devoted to special branches of medical and surgical knowledge formerly within the orbit of the parent Society and now withdrawn from it'.[154]

In this respect, Burrows was a disappointed man, although from birth to death he was immersed in the medical profession and he worked for its advancement. His father had been instrumental in securing the Apothecaries Act of 1815; Burrows junior married John Abernethy's daughter; his cousin Sir Charles Hastings founded the British Medical Association. Whilst he was President of the RMCS Burrows was appointed physician-extraordinary to Queen Victoria and in the year that he vacated the presidential chair at Berners Street he was elected President of the Royal College of Physicians, receiving a baronetcy in 1874.

## Scientific committees

When the attempts of 1860–61 to amalgamate the Berners Street medical societies failed, the Society took a fresh appraisal of its role and embarked in a new direction. Over a hundred Fellows signed a memorial urging the Council to carry out 'certain propositions recently discussed by sections of the Society'. This referred to proposals from Dr Charles Williams, Professor of Medicine at University College, and Mr James Paget, surgeon-extraordinary to Queen Victoria, that from time to time the Council should appoint committees to investigate and report on questions of scientific medical interest. The memorialists expressed a strong desire to extend the usefulness and sphere of operation of the Society and as the scheme for amalgamation had collapsed, it was suggested that 'with a view to the advancement of science and to the development of the strength of the Society, committees should investigate questions of scientific and practical interest'.[155]

### Suspended animation

As soon as the proposal for scientific committees was ratified by the Council in July 1861, Dr Williams suggested a subject that deserved investigation: suspended animation and the best methods of restoration from it. He was duly made Chairman of the Society's first scientific committee which consisted of Dr CE Brown-Séquard, JE Erichsen, Dr J Burdon Sanderson, Dr John Harley, Dr WS Kirkes, Dr H Hyde Salter, WS Savory and D Handfield-Jones. The term 'suspended animation' had been coined by Dr Henry Hickman in 1824 to describe the state induced in animals by giving them carbon dioxide. The Society's committee defined suspended animation as the apparent extinction of life produced by drowning, mechanical suffocation and suffocation by irrespirable air.[156]

The subject of suspended animation and recovery from it after drowning had been raised by a paper from James S Christian, surgeon to the Royal Humane Society, communicated to the RMCS by William Sharpey in January 1861. Christian was bemused that the Royal Humane Society and the Royal National Life Boat Institution issued conflicting instructions for the resuscitation of persons apparently drowned. The Royal Humane Society with nearly 90 years' experience to draw from, used the method recommended by Dr Henry Silvester in 1858 – this treatment aimed to imitate the natural respiratory movements and included placing ammonia under the patient's nose and a hot bath. The Royal National Life Boat Institution, on the other hand, issued instructions based on Dr Marshall Hall's 'ready method', devised by Hall after reading the annual report of the Royal Humane Society for 1855, which had made him despair. He set to work on an alternative method that was effective in stillborn infants and drowning, published in the *Lancet* (1856). Hall's 'rules' involved placing the patient on his face, then raising him to a sitting posture and endeavouring to excite respiration with snuff, hartshorn, tickling the throat with a feather or dashing cold water on the face and chest. If this was not successful he

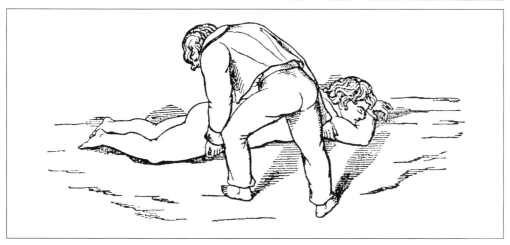

In 1856 Dr Marshall Hall wrote to the *Lancet* promoting his new method of restoring respiration in asphyxia. He recommended the body be placed in the prone position and turned gently.

should be placed face down with his arms under his head and the body turned from the side to the front alternately, with pressure applied along the back and ribs to induce expiration and inspiration repeated 16 times a minute. Rubbing the limbs and covering with clothes were also recommended.[157]

Previous experiments to revive the apparently drowned had included the use of bellows to inflate the chest (one Fellow reported this had proved effective in averting death from opium poisoning in 1836), the use of electricity, bleeding, the introduction of tobacco smoke into the rectum, the injection of terebinth and a bandage method. Mouth-to-mouth resuscitation had also been tried but was rejected on account of the 'impure' air transferred.

As Medical Officer at the Royal Humane Society's receiving station near the Serpentine in Hyde Park, Christian had recorded 443 cases of submersion in 12 years. Of these, 181 were rescued and recovered without treatment, 165 were given treatment and recovered, and 97 died. Christian favoured Dr Silvester's method, and Sir Benjamin Brodie shared his opinion. The opposite view was voiced by ATH Waters, lecturer in anatomy at the Liverpool Royal Infirmary, who stressed the danger of the hot bath treatment recommended by Dr Silvester.[158]

The committee entrusted with the task of investigating the most effective method of resuscitation secured the co-operation of University College, the Royal Humane Society and the Life Boat Institution in conducting experiments on living animals and dead humans. Within a month of its first meeting on 27 September 1861, Dr J Burdon Sanderson had designed an instrument capable of measuring the quantity of air passed into and out of the chest. After evaluating their experiments and considering whether drowned lungs contained water or not, the committee reported in July 1862 in favour of Dr Silvester's method. Dr Marshall Hall being dead, his defendants were dismissive of the report: 'an unworthy attempt has been made at the Medical and Chirurgical to "burk" the Marshall Hall method, which signally failed'.[159] Following the publication of the Report, the Royal Humane Society continued to recommend Silvester's method while the Royal National Life Boat Institution adopted a system that was a combination of Hall's and Silvester's methods.

There the matter rested until Dr Bain requested that the RMCS investigate his method of resuscitation in 1869. A committee was organized with WS Savory in the chair, with Burdon Sanderson and his measuring device again playing an important part. This time the committee investigated Bain's and Silvester's methods, and also a third technique advocated by an Italian, Professor Pacini. Experiments on the dead human body were carried out at St George's Hospital and the committee recorded 83 different observations. Its findings were that Bain's, Pacini's and Silvester's methods were all satisfactory if properly carried out.[160]

Another method was promoted by Dr Benjamin Howard of New York and, at the request of the Royal Humane Society, this too was investigated by a committee of the RMCS in 1879. The committee judged that Howard's method derived largely from Marshall Hall, although Professor EA Schäfer later condemned Howard's method as dangerous. Schäfer, better known as Sir Edward Sharpey-Schäfer, Jodrell Professor of Physiology at University College Hospital, was to emerge as the authority on the subject. He chaired the Society's committee appointed in June 1889 to investigate the new theory of Dr RL Bowles of Folkestone, who in a paper to the Society the previous month had insisted that the patient must be kept on his side while being treated, not supine and not rolled. The committee carried out a series of experiments in 1891 and 1892 but was hampered by defective apparatus. Schäfer alone persisted and eventually presented his 'simple and efficient method of performing artificial respiration' in a paper of December 1903. This required one man to perform it and Dr Bowles, who had collaborated with Schäfer, demonstrated the technique on a living subject. The report describing Schäfer's method was published in 1904.[161]

It was still not clear to the life-saving societies whether or not the RMCS endorsed Schäfer's method, much to his annoyance. He complained to the President to that effect: 'In four years many lives have been lost owing to the fact that such societies have been induced to ignore [his method] of resuscitation, in consequence of the note which your Council appended to my paper'.[162] This referred to the standard disclaimer in the *Transactions* that the Society did not hold itself responsible for the statements and views put forward in papers.

Thus it was that in 1908 the Chief Medical Officer to the Metropolitan Police requested guidance from the RSM about the correct treatment of the apparently drowned. This led to the appointment of yet another committee, which reported promptly in favour of Professor Schäfer's method. Therefore this was adopted by the Royal National Life Boat Institution, the Metropolitan Police, the Royal Humane Society, the Royal Life Saving Society and the Board of Trade, and Sir Edward Sharpey-Schäfer was awarded the Distinguished Service Medal of the Royal Life Saving Society for devising the method (1909).[163] It was not until 1966 that an international symposium endorsed the mouth-to-mouth method of inflating the lungs that has been practised ever since.

*The chloroform committee*

The range of subjects investigated by the Society broadened with the appointment of committees on the uses and effects of chloroform, the remedial effects of electricity and on the hypodermic method of administering drugs. A suggestion for a committee to investigate ovariotomy was not taken up, possibly because Spencer Wells was fulfilling this role.

The use of ether as an anaesthetic in operations was pioneered in this country by Robert Liston at University College Hospital in December 1846 when he is alleged to have exclaimed 'This Yankee dodge, gentlemen, beats mesmerism hollow'. Ether was soon superseded by a preference for chloroform. Queen Victoria gave chloroform anaesthesia the royal stamp of approval in the 1850s, although clergymen continued to denounce it, and over 100 deaths were attributed to its use. Dr Robert Lee claimed that 'Conceited and ignorant women of fashion made a past time of this, as of other quackeries... It was not wonderful that women, doomed to bring forth their offspring in pain and sorrow should seek to escape from the troubles of our race by means of this treacherous gift of science'.[164] A paper presented to the RMCS in 1848 by Francis Sibson pointed out the effects of chloroform on respiratory movements and in the next few years several other surgeons recounted operations they had carried out while the patient was under the influence of chloroform.

Once the work of the Society's committee on suspended animation concluded, Caesar Hawkins called for a committee to investigate the uses and the physiological, therapeutical and toxicological effects of chloroform, as well as the best means of administration and of obviating ill consequences.[165] The surgeon Thomas Curling chaired the inquiry, which investigated the evidence of 2,586 major operations performed before the introduction of anaesthetics and 1,847 after. The results showed that the use of anaesthesia during operations did not increase the mortality rate, although to date 123 deaths were assigned to the inhalation of chloroform. The committee had the advice of two practising anaesthetists and conducted experiments with the help of Mr JT Clover, a Fellow of the Society for 29 years and London's premier anaesthetist in succession to Dr Snow.

The committee concluded in its report of 1864 that ether was safer than chloroform, the danger of which increased with the degree of stupor induced. On the other hand, chloroform was a more convenient anaesthetic to administer than ether. More important as far as the long-term development of anaesthesia was concerned was the suggestion that a mixture of chloroform, ether and ethyl alcohol was the best form of anaesthetic. This endorsed the opinion expressed in 1860 by Dr George Harley, a Fellow of the Society, and had the effect of dimming the popularity of chloroform alone.

The findings of the Society's committee were still valid 30 years later: 'The Commission [committee] drew up certain valuable rules relating to the administration of chloroform, rules which we may venture to say might be more studied and more frequently carried into effect with advantage to the community', the *BMJ* commented in 1896. The guidelines were evidently useful yet there was a lingering suspicion that the Society's committee had been 'rather afraid of chloroform, and, not knowing how to use ether with advantage, adopted the suggestion made before the Royal Society by Dr Harley that these substances be employed as a mixture together with alcohol'.[166] The debate as to the best anaesthetic continued: the BMA appointed a committee of investigation in the 1870s, followed by the Glasgow committee of 1880.

## Medical electricity

Medical electricity remained within the realm of quackery until a department for electrical treatment was established at Guy's Hospital with Dr Cuthbert Golding Bird in charge (1836).

John Marshall, an assistant surgeon at University College Hospital, who was to be President of the RCMS from 1882 to 1884, hoped to draw the attention of the profession to the use of electrical heat in surgery by means of his paper on the subject in 1851. He described his invention of the galvano-cautery, an apparatus with a galvanic battery fitted with flexible poles, wires and copper holders, and he gave instructions for its use in operations for fistula.[167]

Some practitioners alleged that electrotherapy was successful in the treatment of nervous disorders, chorea and local paralysis, but most of the medical profession remained sceptical. Therefore in 1865 the RMCS appointed a committee to investigate the subject, with Dr Charles Radcliffe, physician and lecturer on *materia medica* at Westminster Hospital and physician to the National Hospital for the Paralysed and Epileptic, as chairman. Members met at the 'electrical room' of the National Hospital, Queen Square, where experiments were carried out using an electrical machine and an insulated couch. Dr Radcliffe and Dr Meryon were quick to volunteer for treatment: Radcliffe's headache was cured by an electrical charge from the positive pole of the machine and Meryon was surprised to find, on rising from the 'electrical couch', that the rheumatic pain in his hip

had disappeared. More extensive investigations were hampered by the lack of co-operation from hospitals where letters went unanswered and apparatus varied, so that after 16
meetings the committee was dissolved, having issued a statement on the clinical application and best modes of applying electricity.[168]

## The hypodermic committee
The same Council that appointed the committee to investigate electricity as a remedial agent
appointed a second committee to inquire into the physiological and therapeutical effects of
different substances introduced hypodermically (1865). Hypodermic medication had been
introduced in 1844 on the invention of the syringe, and in 1855 Dr Alexander Wood was the
first to show that morphine could be administered with the hypodermic needle.
Unfortunately he was unable to attend the Society's committee, which included WS Savory as
chairman, Bostock, Dickinson, and Holmes. Charles Hunter, surgeon at the Royal Pimlico
Dispensary, who had read a paper to the Society on 23 May 1865 about the hypodermic
administration of certain medicines, volunteered to assist, claiming that his method constituted an important discovery. The Council of the RMCS judged otherwise and declined to
publish Hunter's paper in the Transactions on the grounds that it was not original.[169]

The Society's hypodermic committee reported in 1867, having conducted experiments
to assess the rapidity of absorption, intensity and duration of the effects of the hypodermic
method. The committee was in no doubt about the advantages in terms of rapidity, facility
and economy, particularly in the administration of morphine: 'To confirmed opium eaters
the method has been found of much service; and patients suffering from cancer derived
much benefit from the use of subcutaneous injections'.[170]

## Vaccino-syphilis
The committee on vaccino-syphilis arose out of cases brought to the Society's notice by
Jonathan Hutchinson, surgeon to the London, the Royal London Ophthalmic and the
Hospital for Skin Diseases. Two meetings were devoted to his paper presenting cases in
which syphilis was communicated by vaccination, and 16 Fellows participated in the
ensuing discussion on 9 May 1871. Hutchinson had long been working on the pathology
of syphilis and in 1876 he publicized his discovery of a malformation of the teeth associated with hereditary syphilis (Hutchinson's teeth, see page 142).

Members of the Society's scientific committee personally inspected Hutchinson's cases of
vaccino-syphilis and were able to confirm that they provided 'unequivocal evidence of
constitutional syphilis' conveyed by vaccination. Hutchinson's observations and the
findings of the committee, composed of Wilks, Savory, Gascoyen and Smith, confronted
the medical profession with a problem, for many were incredulous: 'it is probable that no
communication ever made to our Society had a more profound effect on the profession
and on the country'.[171] In 1873 Hutchinson presented further cases to persuade the profession that syphilis vaccination was possible. The President, Thomas Curling, recognized the
importance of Hutchinson's findings and encouraged the authorities to enforce preventive
measures.[172]

## Diphtheria and croup
A paper by Dr Henry Sutton and Sir William Gull on chronic Bright's disease with
contracted kidney was contradicted by one from Dr George Johnson in 1872. The discussion gave rise to calls for the RMCS to appoint committees to research heart disease in
relation to Bright's disease and to investigate the evidence suggested by specimens
submitted by Gull, Sutton and Johnson. The spirit of enquiry was strongly voiced but it
was not possible to secure the co-operation of Fellows 'with sufficient weight' to make up
the committees.[173]

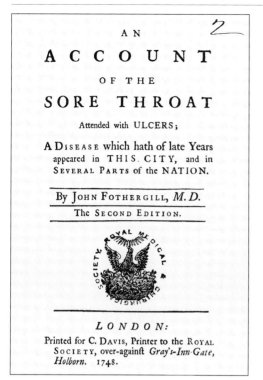

AN   2

# A C C O U N T

OF THE

## SORE THROAT

Attended with ULCERS;

A DISEASE which hath of late Years
appeared in THIS. CITY, and in
SEVERAL PARTS of the NATION.

By JOHN FOTHERGILL, *M. D.*

The SECOND EDITION.

*L O N D O N:*

Printed for C. DAVIS, Printer to the ROYAL
SOCIETY, over-againſt *Gray's-Inn-Gate,*
*Holborn.* 1748.

Title page from Dr John Fothergill's *Account of the sore throat attended with ulcers* (1748), which gives a model clinical description of diphtheria. This copy is in the Society's Library.

Diphtheria and croup were subjects of more general interest and gave rise to a controversial debate on the relation between the two in November 1875: the problem was that Fellows could not agree on a definition of diphtheria.[174] Dr Charles West and WH Dickinson, who both worked at the Hospital for Sick Children, pressed for a committee to investigate the diseases commonly known as membranous croup and diphtheria.[175]

This committee drafted a questionnaire for circulation to Fellows and other medical men: 700 copies were printed but only 90 replies were forthcoming. They were digested and the committee reported in 1878, publishing tables of cases, government reports and appendices that lacked a firm conclusion. The President, Dr West, was nevertheless satisfied that the committee he had instigated had contributed much towards greater accuracy in the diagnosis of croup and diphtheria. The investigation was pursued at three meetings in the spring of 1879, when Sir William Jenner was one of those who aired his views.[176]

## Climates and baths

The most laborious of the Society's scientific committees investigated 'the medical climatology and balneology of Great Britain and Ireland' at the suggestion of Dr E Symes Thompson, Gresham Professor of Medicine and physician to the Hospital for Consumption.

Water-cures at the Victorian spas had long been popular, although a scientific basis for cures was questionable and this was the aspect the committee addressed in 1889. Charles Darwin was one of many convinced of the benefits of hydrotherapy, undergoing treatment several times at Malvern following the advice of Dr Henry Holland, a Fellow of the RMCS whose patients were invariably eminent, aristocratic or royal. By the 1870s many thousands were visiting the spas and health resorts of Great Britain seeking cures for a wide variety of ailments.

The investigation of the scientific basis for water-cures was entrusted to the committee under the chairmanship of Dr William Ord, senior physician to Guy's Hospital. Ord, AE Garrod, who became an expert on rheumatism and gout, and other members of the 13-strong committee visited health spas and springs to evaluate the water and climate of

Dr William Turner's *Booke of the natures and properties as well of the bathes in England as of other bathes in Germany and Italy* (1562), an early treatise on the virtues of baths.

each. They also obtained information from medical men practising in the resorts, enabling them to produce the first volume of their report in 1895.

The second phase of the investigation was conducted under the chairmanship of Dr C Theodore Williams, physician to St George's and a leading authority on pulmonary tuberculosis, whose name was attached to a second volume of 1902. Each resort in Great Britain and Ireland had been researched, with analyses of the waters, meteorological reports, maps and the committee's opinion of the beneficial results that might be expected where, which diseases were likely to respond to treatment in a particular place and the therapeutical indications of the climate. It was hoped that this vast compilation would be useful to local medical practitioners and officers of health, civil engineers, agriculturalists, horticulturalists, municipal bodies and councils interested in the health of the community.[177]

The Society's two-volume report cost over £1,000 to publish and it was claimed that the enormous popularity of health resorts in the early 20th century followed from it.[178] The British Balneological and Climatological Society was founded in the year that the first part of the RMCS report was published and in 1909 became part of Royal Society of Medicine (see pages 316–17).

The Secretary, JYW MacAlister, liked to boast of the achievements of the scientific committees of the RMCS, particularly the reports on the resuscitation of the drowned and on climates and baths. He also drew attention to reports on spina bifida (1885), myxoedema (1888) and the incubation and contagiousness of certain infectious diseases (1892); these and others, however, were the work of the Clinical Society of London, not the RMCS.[179]

## Last years at Berners Street

At Berners Street the 1870s saw the construction on the site of some dilapidated stables of a new reading room and an upper room, fitted with bookcases for 27,000 volumes. The main rooms of the house were littered with the busts of past Presidents; ten were placed on scagliola pedestals in front of the pillars around the meeting-room and four surveyed the Council room, while others were now placed on mantelpieces in the committee room and new reading room. The new building and renovations were carried out by Colonel RW Edis as architect and Messrs Adamson, builders, at a cost of £1,216.[180] Edis was later responsible for the new ballroom at Sandringham for the Prince of Wales and for the extension of the Great Eastern Hotel at Liverpool Street Station.

## Marshall Hall Prize

The Society honoured its past Presidents in the form of life-sized busts and in 1872 it undertook to honour the memory of a Fellow who had failed to achieve due recognition during his lifetime, Dr Marshall Hall. Friends and supporters of Hall had contributed to a fund in his memory and in 1871 the Council of the RMCS was persuaded to take on the responsibility for administering the Marshall Hall Memorial Fund. The capital was invested in a government security (the original amount was £566 10s 3d) and the interest from the investment was to provide for a prize every five years for the best original work in English in anatomical, physiological or pathological research relative to the nervous system.

The first award, made in 1878, amounted to a little over £83 and with a Diploma it was given to Dr John Hughlings Jackson. His contribution to the knowledge of aphasia, his observations on epilepsy and researches with the ophthalmoscope were specially mentioned by the President at the award ceremony. Dr David Ferrier became the second Marshall Hall Prizeman in 1883 for his investigations into the physiology and pathology of the nervous system and he was invited to deliver an account of his work to a meeting of the Society. Dr Walter Gaskell (1889), Dr William Gowers (1892), Dr Charles Sherrington (1898) and Dr Henry Head (1903) were successive Marshall Hall Prizemen – Gowers being chosen from a record number of 45 candidates.

The Marshall Hall bookplate depicts his method of resuscitation (top). The Marshall Hall Memorial Fund originally sponsored prizes but in 1911 the capital was transferred to the building fund for 1 Wimpole Street where a room was named after Marshall Hall. The bookplates were for neurological works added to the Library.

The prize was not awarded after 1903. In 1908 a new arrangement was mooted for the distribution of the fund's income in grants, and a Marshall Hall Medal was suggested. Both ideas appear to have been overridden by the building of the Society's new house in Wimpole Street. The Secretary, MacAlister, who was seeking contributions to the building fund from all and sundry, found a new application for the Marshall Hall Memorial Fund. As the award had been in abeyance for some while and as the fund was entirely at the disposal of the Council, he suggested that it should be redirected to the building fund. Marshall Hall would then be remembered in the name of a room and by specially designed bookplates for neurological works in the Library.[181]

## William Harvey memorial

In 1878 the construction of a memorial statue to the physician William Harvey (1578–1657) was planned in Folkestone, Harvey's birthplace, to commemorate the tercentenary of his birth. Sir Edward Sieveking proposed that the Society should contribute 50 guineas towards the proposed statue, but the Council's unanimous vote in favour was halted by an objection from one of the Secretaries, Dr John Harley, 'who was obstreperous'. Harley questioned whether it was legal within the terms of the Society's charter to apply the Society's funds to a memorial statue. He insisted on taking legal advice: two of the three lawyers consulted gave the opinion that the subscription was not within the scope of the Society's charter. Accordingly individual Fellows were obliged to dig into their own pockets for the donation, and Harvey's statue by AB Joy was eventually erected in 1881.[182]

## Hospitality and honours

Having failed to secure the amalgamation of medical societies so earnestly sought from 1860 to 1861, and again by Sir George Burrows between 1869 and 1871, the RMCS took heart in the improvements to its house; it extended hospitality and privileges to medical officers of the army and navy and held conversaziones for Fellows and guests. The first conversazione held in June 1872 was judged a success, so was followed by a second in 1874 with the added attraction of an exhibition of vases, busts, ancient cinerary urns and works of art by Fellows in addition to scientific objects.[183] The summer conversazione then became an annual event at which Fellows were revived by strawberries and cream and claret cup.

Morale was further boosted by the election of distinguished Honorary Fellows: Claude Bernard of Paris, Hermann von Helmholtz, Charcot, Pasteur and Charles Darwin among

Charles Darwin wrote from the Isle of Wight accepting Honorary Fellowship of the Society, 25 July 1868. Darwin's book *The origin of species* was published in 1859.

them. Bernard had written to the Council in 1871, enclosing details of a nostrum that would cure cholera – or so he claimed. The Council would have nothing to do with secret remedies; nevertheless it was pleased to confer a Foreign Honorary Fellowship on Bernard in acknowledgement of the brilliance of his experimental medicine.

## Revival of the 1880s

Following an article in the *BMJ* of August 1879 by WS Savory attacking the antiseptic methods advocated by Professor Lister, who had recently been appointed to King's College Hospital, 'Listerism' became the topic of the day. It reverberated around the corridors of Berners Street and gave rise to a forceful debate in which the supporters of Lister ranged behind T Spencer Wells in opposing the arguments of Robert Lawson Tait (see page 136). The debate revived interest in the meetings of the RMCS and at the same time the presidency of Sir John Erichsen brought fresh inspiration to the proceedings. He was remembered as 'stout and tall, gentlemanly and impressive',[184] a man of great charm and an eloquent speaker; he was then at the peak of his career as President of the Royal College of Surgeons (1880) and President of the Surgical Section of the International Medical Congress (1881). Erichsen urged the RMCS to enlarge its sphere of action as a tribunal 'before which might be discussed those great scientific problems which underlie the practice of medicine and surgery'. He thought the Society should provide leadership in such matters to the public, the profession and if need be to the government. [185]

Erichsen was succeeded in 1881 by Dr Andrew Whyte Barclay, Harveian Orator in the same year, consulting physician to St George's and the first Medical Officer to Chelsea. He lacked his predecessor's vision and 'had not the superfluous vitality necessary for a wide popularity', being 'modest and retiring almost to a fault'.[186] Possibly it was for these reasons that Barclay resigned after one year as President, causing a hiatus. Mr Prescott Hewitt declined to succeed him and 20 names were put to the ballot before Mr John Marshall, a Fellow of the Royal Society, was nominated, taking the presidential chair in 1882.

Marshall brought constructive leadership to the RMCS. He was elected President of the Royal College of Surgeons in 1883 and a few years later he fulfilled the same role for the GMC. He possessed an original mind, and as President of the RMCS he instigated innovations to render meetings more interesting and useful. Abstracts of papers were to be circulated a few days before meetings to give Fellows ample notice and time to prepare questions for discussion, which were to be printed in full giving the names of those participating. Fellows were asked to read their own papers rather than delegate this to a Secretary and to bring objects of interest – apparatus, instruments, novelties and preparations – to meetings.[187]

These changes to the conduct of meetings, continuing controversy over Listerism and ovariotomy, and the exciting discoveries of Koch, drew a large number of Fellows to the Society in the 1880s. The Seventh International Medical Congress, the first to be held in London, took place in August 1881 and this, with its 15 specialist sessions, undoubtedly had a stimulating effect on the profession. Around 3,000 delegates from some 70 countries converged on London, where the proceedings were master-minded by Sir William MacCormac, a Fellow of the RMCS since 1867, and Sir James Paget, a past President of the RMCS, was elected President of the Congress. Speakers included Virchow, Huxley, Osler and Simon, and the Congress brought together the pioneers of medical bacteriology (Pasteur, Koch and Lister), a great attraction being Koch's demonstration of new bacteriological techniques. The Society threw open its rooms and Library to visiting delegates, receiving a commemorative medal in return; the Royal Colleges hosted entertainments and individual Fellows held receptions. The philanthropist Baroness Burdett-Coutts took it upon herself to hold a garden party at her Highgate home, attended by many Fellows and recorded by the artist AP Tilt (Plate 21).[188]

The President's suggestion that meetings of the RMCS could be made more interesting by the exhibition of specimens and other items received a good response: John Croft showed his method of applying plaster of Paris splints, Clement Lucas brought his patient with syphilis of the tongue to a meeting and thereafter the introduction of patients and the exhibition of apparatus, diagrams and specimens became a regular feature. The publicity the International Medical Congress gave to Professor Koch's work inspired Watson Cheyne, who was the first in London to confirm Koch's work on the tubercle bacillus. With Nelson, Horsley and Dowdeswell he demonstrated specimens of this and other pathogenic bacteria at a meeting of the RMCS in May 1882, and in November another group organized a demonstration of bilharzia, *Trichina* and other parasites. The next year rickets and scurvy proved popular subjects, occupying several evenings: Dr Thomas Barlow (later Sir Thomas) of University College Hospital produced an analysis of 31 recorded cases in German and English medical literature of acute or scurvy-rickets in young children, concluding with his description of the characteristic symptoms of infantile scurvy (Barlow's disease).

Also in 1883, a year of outstanding papers, Jonathan Hutchinson tried to persuade his audience that lives could be saved by high amputation for senile gangrene, and Dr George Thin revealed his researches on the bacillus of leprosy. Cholera was the subject of a special discussion in March 1886, opened by the President and with specimens of the cholera bacillus exhibited. Cholera had been a persistent scourge in England since 1832, and despite the work of Dr John Snow, the investigations of the Epidemiological Society and Koch's isolation of the bacillus, the nature of the disease was still not understood.

A new subject was broached at a meeting in January of 1887: the physiological effects of massage. A one-month course was strongly recommended by Dr A Symons Eccles, who

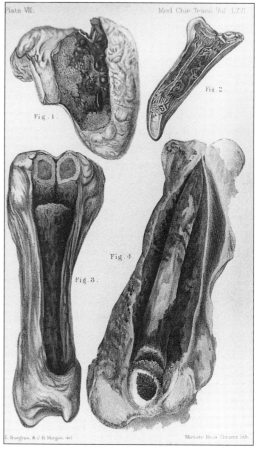

Sir Thomas Barlow and an illustration from his paper presented to the Society in March 1883, 'On cases described as Acute Rickets which are probably a combination of scurvy and rickets'.

alleged this increased body weight, the appetite, muscular strength and the ability to work and sleep well. Fellows were unconvinced by methods that savoured of quackery and Mr Timothy Holmes thought it 'was a great pity we cannot talk English… these rugged names [*effleurage, pétrissage, massage à friction, rapotement*] what do they all mean except rubbing, kneading, tapping?'.[189]

This vitality of the Society during the 1880s was all the more remarkable in view of the competition from other societies. A sudden burst of new foundations (the Ophthalmological Society, the Dermatological Society, the British Gynaecological Society, the Anatomical Society of Great Britain) meant that by 1884 there were 13 medical societies in London, all pursuing scientific and practical work, and several more were founded before the end of the century. In these circumstances the President John Marshall was gratified to reflect that the RMCS 'has held its onward course without serious dissension from within and without exciting hostility from without'. Marshall concluded with the persistent cry of Presidents for amalgamation, promoting 'a combination of certain of the more recently formed metropolitan medical societies, clustered as it were around the Royal Medical and Chirurgical Society as their centre'. His valedictory address bequeathed the union of these societies as a legacy for the future.[190]

The prosperity of the 1880s was marred by the death of the Librarian Benjamin Wheatley in 1884, but three years later the appointment of JYW MacAlister as Resident Librarian opened an era that was to continue until he resigned as Secretary in 1925. MacAlister found a larger house for the Society at 20 Hanover Square, and the move to Mayfair came at a time when the medical profession as a whole was buoyant. Surgical advances, the mastery of anaesthesia and the successes of Pasteur, Lister and Koch generated a sense of achievement and optimism that was matched by improvements in medical education and regulation. Efforts to educate, regulate and reform the expanding medical profession were a persistent theme of the 19th century, and in the 1880s with the report of a Royal Commission into the Medical Acts, the creation of the Conjoint Examining Board of the Royal Colleges and the Medical Act of 1886 the struggle for the education, registration and regulation of the profession was rewarded.

1 Clarke, JFL, *Autobiographical recollections of the medical profession* (1874) p. 180.

2 GM 24 February 1835, B6.

3 Cooper, BB, *The life of Sir Astley Cooper Bart* vol ii (1843) p. 41.

4 GM 7 May 1834, B6.

5 *Report from the Select Committee on Medical Education* (1834) part 1 pp. 3–30.

6 CM 27 August 1834, A2. The petition for the charter, the charter, subscription list and new by-laws were printed in *Transactions* vol xix (1835).

7 CM 8 September, 6 October 1834, A2.

8 CM 14 April 1840, A3. RMCS Obligation Book 1805–1907, D3/1.

9 Suckling, Florence Horatio Nelson, *A forgotten past, being notes of the families of Tyssen, Baker, Hougham and Milles of five centuries* (1898).

10 Cooper, BB *op cit* vol ii p. 38.

11 *Lancet* (i) 21 March 1835 p. 903, 28 March 1835 p. 934, (ii) 25 April 1835 p. 126.

12 CM 10 November 1835, A2.

13 Obituary of Sir Benjamin Brodie, *Lancet* (ii) 25 October 1862 pp. 452–57.

14 Clarke, JFL *op cit* p. 219.

15 It has been claimed that Chambers occupied number 53. This is disproved by the St Marylebone ratebooks which list William Chambers as the occupant and rate payer of number 13, being a house with a coach-house and stables (from 1771), St Marylebone Ratebooks 1771–75, Westminster City Archives.

16 Harris, John, *Sir William Chambers. Knight of the Polar Star* (1970) pp. 73–74, 216–17. Chambers' own house, number 13, had a drawing office at the end of the garden. Harris points out that the doorways at Berners Street foreshadowed the courtyard doorways at Somerset House built to designs by Chambers 1776–96.

17 Berners Street deeds, F2.

18 GM 23 July 1834, B5.

19 Abstract of receipts and expenditure 1835–37, CM 24 March 1835; 11 April 1835, A2. 14 August 1838, A3.

20 CM 28 January, 11 August, 13 October, 22 December 1840, A3. GM 22 February 1842, B7.

21 Letter from Lee of the Astronomical Society, 17 February 1834, Ms 500 f. 60.

22 CM 12 November 1839, 14 February 1843, A3. Taylor, JL, *The Society for Relief of Widows and Orphans of Medical Men 1788–1988* (1988). Meynell, GG, *The two Sydenham societies* (1985).

23 CM 11 March 1845, A3.

24 CM 23 June, 7 July 1846, A3.

25 CM 13 August, 12 November 1850, A4.

26 CM 12 October 1847, A3.

27 CM January (n.d.) 1849, A4. CM 11 June, 13 August, 29 October 1850, A4.

28 GM 10 April 1832, B5. CM 4 April 1839, 23 February 1841, A3.

29 Review of J Forbes' *Manual of select medical bibliography* (1835), *Lancet* (ii) 23 April 1835 p. 152.

30 Letter Baly to Baly senior 28 August 1836, Ms 715/207, RCP.

31 CM 17 April 1834, 27 February, 12 March 1844, A3. CM 11 July 1848, A4. Library committee minutes 7 May 1847, H55. Wade, P, 'The history and development of the Library of the Royal Society of Medicine' in PRSM vol 55 1962, pp. 627–36.

32 CM 28 April, 12 May 1846, 9 March 1847, A3. Library committee minutes 1836–68, H55.

33 Report of President and Council 1848–49, 1 March 1849. CM 26 February 1850, A4.

34 CM 14 November 1854.

35 Williams, Charles JB, *Memoirs of life and work* (1884) pp. 417–18.

36 GM 25 June 1856, B8. Transacs vol lxvii (1884) pp. 21–23. *Biographical notes on the life of the late Benjamin R. Wheatley.* (1884) Tract 337 (i). *Medical Times and Gazette* (i) 1884 pp. 79–80. CM 1 March 1884, A7.

37 CM 12 January 1836, A2. JF South's index is as yet untraced although there is reference to it in the BL catalogue.

38 CM 14 March 1848, 9 April 1850, A4. The 1850 index has not been found.

39 CM 3 July 1847, A3.

40 CM 28 January, 11 February, 14 July 1840, A3. Williams, Charles JB *op cit* p. 216.

41 CM 14 November 1843, A3.

42 CM 13 June 1843, A3.

43 GM 25 June 1844, B7.

44 GM 9 December 1845, B7.

45 Transacs vol xxxiii (1850) pp. 261–78. PRSM vol i (1856–57).

46 CM 10 June 1851, A4 (Ridge). GM 14 November 1848, B7 (Acton). GM 28 April 1846, B7 (Hutchinson). GM 12 February 1850, B8 (Toynbee).

47 Wilks, Samuel, and Bettany, GT, *A biographical history of Guy's Hospital* (1892) p. 235.

48 GM 13 May 1862, B9. 10 November 1863, PRSM vol iv (1861–64). 26 April, 8 November 1864, PRSM vol v (1864–67). For a discussion on the invention of the laryngeal mirror see Harrison, Donald, 'Benjamin Guy Babington and his mirror', *Journal of Laryngology and Otology* vol 112 March 1998 pp. 235–42. Brodnitz, Friedrich S, 'One hundred years of laryngoscopy: to the memory of Garcia, Tuerck and Czermak' in *Transactions of the American Academy of Ophthalmology and Otolaryngology* vol 58 (1954) pp. 663–69.

49 Transacs vol xvii (1832) pp. 250–99.

50 Transacs vol xx (1837) pp. 118–64. Presidential address, 22 May 1905, Transacs vol lxxxviii (1905) p. cxxxviii.

51 GM 28 February 1843, B7. Transacs vol xxvi (1843) pp. 86–99 (Gulliver). *Ibid* vol xxvi (1843) pp. 242–85.

52 GM 12 March, 25 June 1844, B7.

53 GM 22 June 1852, B8.

54 GM 25 October 1831, B5. CM 20 September 1831, A2.

55 CM 18 February, 14 March 1837, A2.

56 CM 24 April 1838, A3.

57 PRSM 1 March 1869 vol vi (1867–71). Ridgway, Elizabeth S, 'John Elliotson 1791–1868: a bitter enemy to legitimate medicine?' in JMB November 1993 pp. 191–98 and February 1994 pp. 1–7. Clark, Sir George, *A history of the Royal College of Physicians of London* vol ii (1966) p.689. GM 22 November 1842, B7.

58 *Lancet* (i) 8 March 1844 pp. 802–3.

59 Letter Wilks to MacAlister 12 February 1906, G1/5.

60 Underwood, E Ashworth, 'The history of cholera in Great Britain' in PRSM vol 41 (1948) pp. 165–73.

61 GM 12 December 1837, 26 February 1839, B6. Cook, GC, 'George Budd FRS (1808–82): pioneer gastroenterologist and hepatologist' in JMB vol 6 no 3 1998 pp. 152–59.

62 Paget, Stephen, *Memoirs and letters of Sir James Paget* (1901) p. 118.

63 GM 11 December 1849, B8. Transacs vol xxxxiii (1850) pp. 23–42. Jenner was elected a Fellow in 1851 and served on the Council 1864–65. He also published a paper on typhoid and typhus fevers in the *Edinburgh Monthly Journal of Medical Science* vol ix (1849) pp. 663–80.

64 27 April 1858 PRSM vol ii (1857–58).

65 CM 3 August 1847, A3. *Personal recollections of Sir John Simon KCB* (1897) p. 11.

66 GM 11 December 1838, B6.

67 GM 28 January 1845, B7.
68 GM 27 April 1841, B7. Transacs vol xxiv (1841) pp. 146–54. Dale, Sir Henry, 'Thomas Addison: pioneer of endocrinology' in BMJ (ii) 13 August 1949 pp. 347–52. Wilks, Samuel, and Bettany, GT, *A biographical history of Guy's Hospital* (1892) pp. 225–26.
69 GM 10 January 1843, B7.
70 GM 27 June 1843, 12 March 1844, B7.
71 Transacs vol xxiv (1841) pp. 155–76.
72 GM 1 March 1833, B5.
73 Letter Liston to Miller 15 April 1835 among Copies and Extracts of Letters from Liston to James Miller 1834–40, Memorials for a life of Robert Liston, Western Ms 6095, Wellcome.
74 Copies and Extracts of Letters *op cit.*
75 Transacs vol xxvii (1844) pp. 134–45.
76 *Ibid* pp. 468–92.
77 GM 23 March 1847, B7.
78 GM 9 February 1847, B7.
79 Transacs vol iii (1812) pp. 348–71.
80 GM 24 November 1840, B7.
81 *Ibid* 9 May 1843, B7.
82 1 March 1869 PRSM vol vi (1867–71).
83 Letter Yelloly to Marcet 5 January 1811, Marcet correspondence (1802–23), Duke.
84 Clarke, JFL *op cit* pp. 336–49.
85 GM 9 December 1834, B6. Transacs vol xix (1835) pp. 152–61, 162–66.
86 GM 22 June 1841, 13 February 1849, B7. Toynbee's series on ears, Transacs vols xxiv-xlix (1841–66).
87 1 March 1867 PRSM vol vi (1867–68).
88 Wilks and Bettany *op cit* p. 403. Hinton was reappraised by Philip Reading in his presidential address to the Section of Otology, PRSM vol 62 (1969).
89 Guthrie, Douglas, 'The Renaissance of otology: Joseph Toynbee and his contemporaries' in *Journal of Laryngology and Otology* vol 52 (1937) pp. 163–76.
90 GM 19 January 1819, B3. Bell was the author of *The anatomy, physiology and diseases of the teeth* (1829).
91 *A memoir by Sir Samuel Wilks* (1911) p. 73.
92 Transacs vol v (1814) pp. 435–47.
93 GM 18 April 1845 (Davy), 13 January 1846 (Allen), B7.
94 Pettigrew, TJ, *Medical Portrait Gallery. Biographical memoirs of the most celebrated physicians, surgeons etc etc who have contributed to the advancement of medical science* vol iv (1840) p. 6.
95 Hall's series on the nervous system, Transacs vols xxii to vol xxiv (1839–41). *London Medical Gazette* vol vii (1830–31) pp. 462–63. Hall, Charlotte, *Memoirs of Marshall Hall* (1861). *Lancet* (ii) August 1857 pp. 172–75.
96 Manuel, Diana E, 'Marshall Hall FRS 1790–1857. A conspectus of his life and work' in *Notes and Records of the Royal Society of London* vol 35 no 2 (1980) pp.135–66. *London Medical Gazette* vol xxii (1838) pp. 72–73. Hall's annotated copy of *Aperçu de système spinal* (1855) is in the Library.
97 Clarke, JFL *op cit* pp. 328–29.
98 Transacs vol xxvii (1844) pp. 435–61.
99 *Dublin Quarterly Journal of Medical Science* vol ii new series (1846) p. 85.
100 Transacs vol xxxiii (1850) pp. 211–32.
101 *Ibid* vol xxxvi (1853) pp. 403–32. *Lancet* (i) 26 April 1873 pp. 614–15. Coley, NG, 'Henry Bence Jones MD FRS (1813–73)' in *Notes and Records of the Royal Society* vol 28 (1973) pp. 1–56. Putnam, Frank W, 'Henry Bence-Jones; the best chemical doctor in London ' in *Perspectives in Biology and Medicine* vol 36 (1993) pp. 565–79. Stone, Marvin J, 'Henry Bence-Jones and his protein' in JMB February 1998 pp. 53–57. *Henry Bence-Jones MD FRS 1813–73. An autobiography* (1929).
102 Darwin, Francis, *Life and letters of Charles Darwin* (1887) vol iii p. 31. Cope, Sir Zachary, *Florence Nightingale and the doctors* (1958) pp. 21–23.
103 GM 12 March 1850, B8. Transacs vol xxxiii (1850) pp. 121–96. *Lancet* (ii) 1 October 1887 pp. 687–88. Morgan, AD, 'Some forms of undiagnosed coronary disease in nineteenth century England' in *Medical History* vol xii no 4 October 1968 pp. 344–58.
104 *Lancet* (i) 23 March 1850 pp. 367–68.
105 *The Crystal Palace and its contents 1851* (1852).
106 GM 1 March 1850, B8.
107 M & P p. 97.
108 Report of Council. Abstract of Receipts and Expenditure 1850–51, CM 5 March 1851, A4.
109 Clarke, JFL *op cit* pp. 281–82.
110 *Ibid* pp. 334–35.
111 1 March 1875, PRSM vol vii (1872–75).
112 GM 12 November 1850, B8. *Lancet* (ii) 23 November 1850 pp. 583–87.
113 Ms 204. Transacs vol ix (1818) and vol xlv (1862). Western Ms 8525, Wellcome. The instruments are now at the Royal College of Obstetricians and Gynaecologists.
114 M & P p. 97.
115 GM 24 June 1851, B8. Transacs vol xxxiv (1851) pp. 205–20. Bence-Jones, Henry, *The life and letters of Faraday* vol ii (1870) pp. 268–88.

116 M & P p. 100. GM 9 December 1851, B8.

117 *Lancet* (i) 1 April 1854, pp.368–70. CM 1 March 1853, 1 March 1854, A4.

118 *Lancet* (i) pt 2 27 May 1905 pp. 1439–40.

119 GM 24 March 1854, B8. *Lancet* (i) 7 January 1854, p. 29; 4 March 1854 pp. 270–76, 18 March 1854 p. 321; 25 March 1854, pp. 346, 362–64; 1 April 1854 pp. 368–70.

120 CM 25 November 1856, A4. GM 2 March 1857, B8. CM 22 January 1867, A5.

121 Peterson, Jeanne, *The medical profession in mid-Victorian London* (1978) pp. 262–3.

122 Holland, Sir Henry, *Recollections of past life* (1872) p. 259.

123 Clarke, JFL *op cit* p. 222.

124 *Ibid* p. 221.

125 Letter Wilks to MacAlister 12 February 1906, G1/5.

126 Presidential address, *Bulletin* 26, 1918.

127 Clarke, JFL *op cit* p.221.

128 Williams, Charles JB, *Memoirs of life and work* (1884) pp. 216–22.

129 *Transactions of the Pathological Society* vol xxxvi (1884–85) pp. 494–98, plate xx.

130 *Lancet* (ii) 1 December 1849 p. 592.

131 *Ibid*.

132 CM 12 November 1850, A4. Ms by E Ashworth Underwood, Section of Epidemiology, Royal Society of Medicine - I am grateful for a copy provided by Dr NS Galbraith. 'The foundation of the Society' in *Index to Transactions of the Epidemiological Society of London 1855–1900* (1900) pp. 3–16.

133 GM 9 November 1858, B8.

134 Report of the Inaugural Meeting of the Obstetrical Society of London, 16 December 1858, *Transactions of the Obstetrical Society of London* vol i (1860) pp. v-xxxv. Wilks and Bettany *op cit* pp. 150, 193. Williams, David Innes, 'The Obstetric Society of 1825' in *Medical History* vol 42 no 2 April 1998 pp. 235–45.

135 Ms 229. Presidential address 1902, *Transactions of the Odontological Society* vol xxxv (1902–03) pp. 1–8. Cartwright, FF, 'The relationship of medicine and dentistry in the nineteenth century' in PRSM vol 59 (1966) pp. 1237–40.

136 Williams, Charles JB *op cit* p. 414.

137 Sanderson, Lady Burdon, *Sir John Burdon Sanderson. A memoir* (1911) pp. 72–73.

138 11 October 1907, PRSM vol i pt 1 (1907–08).

139 Williams, Charles JB *op cit*.

140 CM 8 May 1860, A5.

141 *Ibid* 10 July 1860, 22 January 1861, 22 March 1864, 13 November, 11 December 1866, A5.

142 *Ibid* 8 January 1867, A5. 1 March 1865 PRSM vol v (1864–67).

143 CM 10 April, 26 July 1866, A5.

144 1 March, 23 July 1861 PRSM vol iii (1858–61). CM 9 July 1861, A5.

145 1 March 1862, 2 March 1863 PRSM vol iv (1861–64).

146 *Lancet* (i) pt 2, 27 May 1905 p. 1439.

147 Presidential address, 2 March 1863, PRSM vol iv (1861–64).

148 2 March 1868, 1 March 1869 PRSM vol vi (1867–71).

149 CM 18 December 1867, 1 January 1868, A5.

150 *Transactions of the Obstetrical Society* vol xiii (1871) pp. 10–11.

151 *The Royal Society of Medicine. Record of the events and work which led to the formation of that Society by the amalgamation of the leading medical societies of London with the Royal Medical and Chirurgical Society* (1914) p. 92.

152 2 March 1868, 1 March 1869, 1 March 1870, 14 March 1870 PRSM vol vi (1868–71).

153 Clarke, JFL *op cit* p. 118.

154 1 March 1871 PRSM vol vi (1868–71).

155 GM 14 January, 1 March 1862, B9.

156 CM 28 May, 9 July, 6 August 1861, A5. Scientific Committee Minutes 1861–93, H50.

157 Hall, Charlotte, *Memoirs of Marshall Hall* (1861) p. 360. *Lancet* (i) 12 April 1856 pp. 393–94, (ii) 29 November 1856 pp. 601–2.

158 22 January, 14 May 1861 PRSM vol iii (1858–61).

159 Report on Suspended Animation, Transacs vol xlv (1862) pp. 449–92. Hall, Charlotte *op cit* p. 453.

160 CM 12 January 1869, A6. Report of the committee on Bain's and Pacini's methods of restoring suspended animation, Transacs liii (1870) pp. 291–301.

161 GM 1 March 1879, B9. GM 28 October 1879, B10. Report of the committee on suspended animation, Transacs vol lxxxvii (1904) pp. 609–23. *Report of the committee to investigate the subject of suspended animation in the drowned* (1904).

162 Letter Schäfer to Douglas Powell 31 October 1907, folder 3, G6/Box 22.

163 CM 10 June, 11 November 1890, A7. CM 29 July 1908, A10. GM 8 December 1903, B11. Transacs vol lxxxvii (1904) pp. 609–23. Scientific Committee Minutes 1908, H49. Letter MacAlister to Newton Pitt 29 June 1908, folder 3, G7/Box 22. Letter MacAlister to Latham, 22 November 1909 G21/Box 33.

164 GM 13 December 1853, B8.

165 CM 4 November 1862, A5.

166 Report of the committee to enquire into chloroform, 5 July 1864, Transacs vol xlvii (1864) pp. 321–442. BMJ vol ii (I) 17 October 1896 pp. 1135–50. Scientific Committee Minutes 1862–64, H50. Duncum, Barbara M, *The development of inhalation anaesthesia* (1994) pp. 253–58.

167 Transacs vol xxxiv (1851) pp. 221–32.

168 CM 28 March 1865, A5. Scientific Committee Minutes, 1865–70, H50.

169 Letters Burkett to Hunter 12 July 1865, Hunter to Thompson 20 April 1866, Western Ms 6892, Wellcome.

170 GM 18 June 1867, B9, CM 12 February, 14 March 1867, A6. Report of the Scientific Committee to investigate the physiological and therapeutical effects of the hypodermic method of injection, Transacs vol l (1867) pp. 561–643.

171 M & P pp. 147–48. Transacs vol liv (1871) pp. 317–50.

172 1 March 1873 PRSM vol vii (1872–75).

173 GM 10 December 1872, B9. CM 1 January 1873, A6.

174 Wilks, Samuel, *Biographical reminiscences* (1876) p. 154.

175 GM 27 April, 9 November 1875, B9.

176 Report of the Scientific Committee to investigate the relations of Membranous Croup and Diphtheria, Transacs vol lxii (1879) pp. 1–167. 1 March 1879 PRSM vol viii (1875–80). GM 8 April, 22 April, 13 May 1879, B10.

177 *The climates and baths of Great Britain, being a report of a committee of the Royal Medical and Chirurgical Society* 2 vols (1895, 1902).

178 Letter MacAlister to Latham, 22 October 1909, G21/Box 33.

179 Letter MacAlister to Ruston, 7 May 1912, folder 3, G8/Box 23.

180 This figure includes the architect's fees. 8 May 1871 PRSM vol vi (1867–71). 1 March 1872 PRSM vol vii (1872–75). GM 1 March 1873, B9. CM 20 November 1871, A6.

181 Report of subcommittee, Marshall Hall Memorial Fund, CM 10 October 1871, A6. GM 1 March 1879, B9. MacAlister correspondence, 22 November 1911, folder 6, G20/Box 33.

182 GM 1 March 1879, B9. 1 March 1879 PRSM vol viii (1875–80). CM 14 March 1882, 9 January 1883, A6. Letter MacAlister to Rose Bradford, 9 January 1912, folder 1,G10/Box 25. Counsels' opinions (1879), M16/Box 53.

183 Subcommittee Minutes 1873, H1.

184 Dobson, Jessie and Wakeley, Sir Cecil, *Sir George Buckston Browne* (1957) pp. 43–44.

185 Presidential address, 1 March 1881 PRSM vol ix (1880–82).

186 Obituaries, BMJ (i) 10 May 1884 pp. 932–33, *Lancet* (i) 10 May 1884 p. 872.

187 24 October 1882, PRSM vol i (1882–85).

188 Sakula, Alex, 'Baroness Burdett-Coutts' garden party: the International Medical Congress, London 1881' in *Medical History* vol 26 no 2 (1982) pp. 183–90.

189 11 January 1887 PRSM vol ii (1885–88).

190 Presidential address, Transacs vol lxvii (1884) pp. 1–31.

# Chapter 4

## Advances in medicine and surgery

THE HISTORY OF MEDICINE in Victorian Britain is truly a record of achievement. The 19th-century ethos of self-improvement and progress found expression in medical and surgical innovations and scientific discoveries that absorbed the profession and fuelled the medical societies. By the 1860s there were at least 21 medical societies in London: the Royal Medical and Chirurgical was not the oldest but it was the largest society for the advancement of medical science in the United Kingdom and the only one to boast a royal charter. With a membership of over 600 Fellows who enjoyed the facilities afforded by a Library of approximately 25,000 volumes and the opportunity to publish their work in *Medico-Chirurgical Transactions*, the Society followed an exclusively academic path. It was able to profit from the expansion and regulation of the profession while remaining aloof from the political and professional issues that engaged the medical organizations and corporations.

The major advance of the 1840s was in the use of anaesthetics in surgical operations. According to one account an experiment in anaesthesia took place at the RMCS shortly before the first use of ether in this country during an operation performed by Robert Liston in December 1846. It was within the walls of this Society that Spencer Wells established the validity of ovariotomy, encouraging the development of abdominal surgery generally, and from the debates of the 1880s came the eventual acceptance of Lister's antiseptic methods of surgery. Sir James Paget presented his classic paper on osteitis deformans at a meeting in 1876, Dr William Ord gave his description of myxoedema the following year and in 1899 Dr Archibald Garrod launched the concept of the inborn errors of metabolism at the RMCS. These are just some examples of the achievements Fellows brought to the notice of the Society and which were published in that storehouse of medical knowledge, *Medico-Chirurgical Transactions*.

In the last years of the century the Society moved to 20 Hanover Square and for a while the disruption of the move, combined with the death of the President and straitened financial circumstances, had a negative effect. In a bid to revive interest in meetings of the Society special discussions were promoted, allowing Fellows to air their views on subjects such as enteric fever and the open-air treatment of tuberculosis; demonstrations of specimens were encouraged and a house dinner was instigated to strengthen the social life of the Society. By 1900 the financial management had been tightened and attendances at meetings improved – a record number of 351 Fellows and visitors crowded into the meeting room on one evening to hear Frederick Treves open a debate on the wounded in the Boer War.

### The introduction of anaesthesia
In December 1846 the first ether anaesthetic to be administered in England was given by the dentist James Robinson at Dr Boott's house in Gower Street. Two days later anaesthesia was used in a major surgical operation for the first time in this country, by a Fellow of the RMCS, Robert Liston. Another Fellow, Dr John Snow, was London's best known anaesthetist of the mid-19th century; several others prominent in the specialty – JT Clover,

Francis Sibson, and later Frederic Hewitt and Dudley W Buxton – were also RMCS members. Their individual contributions were recorded in the Society's *Transactions*, which in 1864 had published the Society's report on the physiological, therapeutical and toxicological effects of chloroform and ether (opposite).

## Robert Liston

On 21 December 1846 Robert Liston amputated a diseased thigh in 25 seconds while the patient was anaesthetized with ether; he thus made medical history as the first in this country to carry out a major surgical operation using anaesthetic. The admiring audience in the operating theatre of University College Hospital included Joseph Lister, John Erichsen, JT Clover and Edward Palmer, Liston's dresser, who reported that 'not the slightest groan was heard from the patient nor was the countenance at all expressive of pain'.[1] Liston performed a second operation using ether on the same day with equal success. He was known for his physical strength and speed of operating and he excelled at cutting for stone. Liston's colleagues at the RMCS recognized his ability but, as Dr Charles Williams wrote, they objected to 'the jocular disparagement with which he was in the habit of speaking of medicine and of doctors in general. His skill and manual dexterity in operative surgery and the efficacious simplicity of his methods of treatment had gained for him the highest reputation and success, which surmounted the objectionable qualities of his character, which, if they were obnoxious to others, were quite as damaging to himself'.[2]

When in 1910 Dr FW Cock began researching Liston and the introduction of anaesthesia he advertised in the press in the hope of tracing any living witnesses to Liston's operation of December 1846. One reply, from 88-year-old Dr HM Duncan, claimed that an experiment in the administration of ether had first taken place at the Royal Medical and Chirurgical Society. Duncan gave details of a meeting of the Society to which he had been invited as a friend of Mr Holmes Coote, allegedly in November or December 1846. Over 60 years after the event, Duncan recalled that he had heard George Johnson's paper on the kidney, after which either Dr WT Morton of Boston (who had performed the first surgical operation using ether on 16 October in America) or an assistant had exhibited an inhaling apparatus. There was then a demonstration but 'a patient from University College

The surgeon Robert Liston in May 1847, a few months after he made history by performing the first major operation in this country to be carried out while the patient was anaesthetized with ether.

Hospital who had promised to appear to be tested failed to do so. And as no-one else would submit to the trial, I offered myself'. Duncan described how he had inspired the vapour, lapsed into unconsciousness and awoke in good health to a sea of anxious faces. 'The Boston visitor thanked me heartily and Mr Liston was so convinced of the value of anaesthesia that he – a few days later – engaged the services of Mr P Squire, chemist of Oxford Street and his nephew Dr W Squire in the construction of an apparatus for administration of ether vapour'.[3]

If this account is to be believed, Duncan was anaesthetized at the RMCS in Berners Street prior to Liston's operation on 21 December. Unfortunately there is no record of the occasion in the Society's Minute Books. The last official meeting of the year 1846 took place on 8 December and there is no account of the exhibition of ether apparatus or any trial. Johnson's paper to which Duncan referred had been read in November 1845, not 1846, and Duncan's memory also seems to have deceived him over the presence of Dr Morton or an assistant. On the other hand, Duncan was a pupil of Liston and his references to Holmes Coote and Mr Squire ring true. Furthermore, it was most irregular for the RMCS to have held only one meeting in December, raising the possibility of an unrecorded, informal gathering at Berners Street sometime between 8 and 21 December, when the events described by Dr Duncan may have taken place.

## Fellows experiment with ether and chloroform

Other Fellows soon followed Liston's example. George Pollock of St George's Hospital gave a paper to the RMCS telling how he had used ether in a case of tetanus. His description highlighted the irritation and distress caused by ether 'such as to forbid perseverance in this endeavour to relieve his frightful suffering',[4] and for these reasons ether was soon displaced as an anaesthetic by chloroform. In 1848 William Fergusson reported on 'one of the most formidable and severe [operations] as yet effected under the influence of ether'. This was his case of resection of the scapula 'supposed to be the only case of the kind, as a surgical proceeding, which had occurred in this country and was in every respect successful'.[5]

In the same year Fellows heard that John Hilton preferred to use chloroform rather than ether, while R Druitt and Dr W MacKenzie persisted in operating without anaesthetics. One of the country's first anaesthetists, Francis Sibson, who developed a chloroform inhaler, conveyed to the RMCS his observations on the effects of chloroform on respiratory movements and was promptly elected a Fellow. Sibson collaborated with Dr John Snow, whose book *On chloroform and other anaesthetics* (1858) became the definitive work on the subject. Snow had been a Fellow of the Society since 1843 and made his last public appearance at a meeting in June 1858, shortly before his death. Queen Victoria had consulted him about the use of chloroform in childbirth in 1850 and three years later Snow administered it to her during the birth of her eighth child, Prince Leopold (who proved to be a haemophiliac). The Queen reported that she found the anaesthetic 'soothing, quieting and delightful beyond measure', and repeated the experience at the birth of Princess Beatrice in 1857.

The RMCS took the initiative in investigating the use and safety of chloroform and ether, and the committee charged with the task produced a report of 1864 that has been seen as marking 'the end of a clearly defined phase in the history of inhalation anaesthesia in England – the period of chloroform's supremacy in this country' (see pages 112–13). The committee's suggestion that a cocktail of anaesthetics might be preferable to either chloroform or ether charted the path for the future development of anaesthetics.[6] In 1871, however, J Warrington Haward, chloroformist at St George's and the last President of the RMCS (1906–07), pleaded for the revival of ether as an anaesthetic: 'It is sometimes useful to recall attention to neglected or forgotten remedies or methods of treatment', he

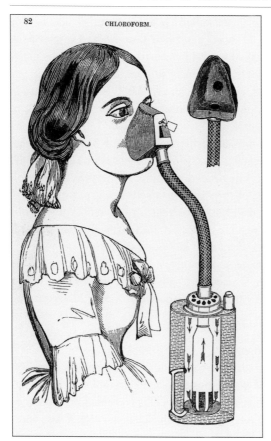

82  CHLOROFORM.

The chloroform inhaler used by Dr John
Snow from 1847, as illustrated in his book
*On chloroform and other anaesthetics: their
action and administration* (1858).

reflected.[7] The matter was discussed by TB Curling, T Spencer Wells, AE Sansom,
T Holmes and JT Clover – all of them experienced yet all holding different opinions. As it
happened, Warrington Haward's paper foreshadowed the revival of the use of ether in this
country, promoted by B Joy Jeffries from Boston.

### Dr FW Hewitt and the continuing debate

After the deaths of Snow in 1858 and Clover in 1882, Frederic W Hewitt and Dudley
W Buxton were London's chief anaesthetists and both were elected Fellows of the RMCS
in the 1880s. Hewitt, who lectured at the London and Charing Cross Hospitals, gave what
was described as 'a very instructive paper' on respiration during anaesthesia to the Society
in December 1890, and his book *Anaesthetics and their administration* came out three
years later. For ten years Hewitt experimented with nitrous oxide, air and oxygen mixtures
as anaesthetics, and his paper reporting the results of 231 cases was published in *Medico-
Chirurgical Transactions* in 1899.[8]

There was justifiable concern in the 1890s about the effects of chloroform on the heart,
a question that engaged the principal of the Hyderabad Medical School, Surgeon
Lt Colonel Lawrie of the Bengal Army Medical Service. Under his leadership the
Hyderabad Commission reported that experiments in administrating chloroform to dogs
showed there were no injurious effects on the heart. The *Lancet* refused to accept the
Commission's 'scanty statements of experiments performed upon dogs' as conclusive,
pointing out that the results 'appear to go in the very teeth of those at which the
Commission appointed by the Royal Medical and Chirurgical Society and by the British
Medical Association arrived'.[9] The RMCS was drawn into the controversy when the
Secretary received a personal communication from Colonel Lawrie, who clung to the belief
that chloroform was perfectly safe in the face of increasing evidence to the contrary. The

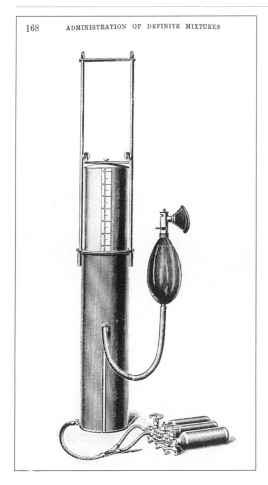

168    ADMINISTRATION OF DEFINITE MIXTURES

The 'gasometer' used by Frederic Hewitt (later Sir Frederic) who performed many experiments with 100% nitrous oxide, nitrous oxide and air, and nitrous oxide and oxygen between 1889 and 1899. His paper giving the results of 231 administrations of anaesthetics at the Royal Dental Hospital was read to the RMCS in February 1899: the best results were obtained with nitrous oxide and oxygen.

question was debated at a special general meeting in July 1894 attended by 63 Fellows and 43 visitors. Dr WH Gaskell, Professor Victor Horsley, Dr Buxton, Dr Shore and Dr Hewitt were all present and spoke at length. The consensus of opinion did not support Lawrie's conclusions: Dr Gaskell condemned the methods and results as 'absolutely worthless' and Professor Horsley stressed the danger of chloroform generally.[10]

There was no end to the debate on anaesthesia: Hewitt and Mr Marmaduke Shield gave the Society their views on posture in relation to operations under anaesthesia in 1895, leading to an altercation between Hewitt and Dr John Silk, the anaesthetist to Guy's Hospital, who had recently founded the Society of Anaesthetists. Silk implied that Hewitt had plagiarized a lecture given by Dr CE Sheppard; Hewitt was incensed and wanted the Council of the RMCS to adjudicate, whereupon Silk withdrew his charge.[11] Hewitt administered anaesthetic to King Edward VII during his operation for appendicitis in 1902 (see page 139) and was knighted in 1911. By this time anaesthetics was a recognized specialty with its own Society and *Transactions*. The Society of Anaesthetists was a tenant of the RMCS at Hanover Square and was to be drawn under the umbrella of the Royal Society of Medicine in 1908 as the Section of Anaesthetics (see pages 301–02).

In 1918 the RSM Library was presented with a small, historically valuable collection of papers relating to the first administration of sulphuric ether by Dr WT Morton at Massachusetts General Hospital in October 1846. The pamphlets, inscribed with notes and quotes written by Osler, had been obtained from Morton's son and Osler presented them at the conclusion of a paper he gave to the History of Medicine Section in May 1918 (see page 331).[12]

## Spencer Wells and ovariotomy

The alleviation of pain by the administration of anaesthetics allowed surgeons to be more adventurous than ever before. Those who had experience with the wounded during the Napoleonic wars, in the European revolutions of 1848 and in the Crimean War realized that the peritoneum was more tolerant to injury and surgery than had been supposed, and the availability of anaesthetics made feasible operations that had hitherto been considered too painful or too dangerous. Thomas Spencer Wells showed the way by proving that ovariotomy could be successful. His cases generated heated discussions at meetings of the RMCS and his papers, published regularly in the Society's *Transactions*, had the effect of persuading the profession and the public that ovariotomy was safe.

Spencer Wells was first a naval surgeon in Malta; then he went to Paris to gain experience of gunshot wounds during the disturbances of 1848. In 1855 he left his post at the Samaritan Free Hospital for Women in London to go to Smyrna and Renkioi during the Crimean War. In December 1857, soon after returning to the Samaritan Hospital, he performed his first ovariotomy. The operation had been undertaken in Britain for the first time in 1824, but it had since fallen into disrepute because of fatalities. Undeterred by the failure of his own first attempt, Spencer Wells achieved success in February 1858 when he was assisted by Isaac Baker Brown. A year later he reported to the RMCS on five cases of ovarian disease, in three of which ovariotomy had been performed successfully, with his observations of the means of diminishing the mortality of the operation.[13] To his disappointment this paper was not published in the *Transactions*; nevertheless it marked the start of Wells' campaign to improve the operation. He experimented with new techniques and 'made his subject scientific', obtaining publicity at meetings of the RMCS (which by then were widely reported), and exhibiting every tumour he removed at meetings of the Pathological Society 'until the operation was thoroughly recognized as legitimate'.[14]

By 1881 Spencer Wells had carried out 1,000 ovariotomies under anaesthesia. Mortality had diminished from 34 in the first hundred to 11 in the last hundred, with a reduction to 10.6% as a result of his adoption of antiseptic methods from 1878. His cases, with their careful figures giving irrefutable evidence of success, were published by the Society (1863,

Sir Thomas Spencer Wells, whose papers and
figures on ovariotomy eventually persuaded the
profession that the operation was safe.

1865, 1867, 1869, 1871, 1873, 1881) giving what is virtually a history of the development of ovariotomy in this country during the second half of the 19th century.

To begin with Spencer Wells met with opposition. A fellow-member of the Society, Dr Robert Lee, castigated ovariotomists as belly-rippers; Spencer Wells' reams of evidence failed to convince him. His own research, which he had presented to the Society in 1850, showed that in 71 removals of cysts or tumours, 24 proved fatal; in 108 operations for ovarian disease 38 had fatal results. Fellows listening to Lee in 1850 had agreed that ovariotomy had been discredited and 'one of the oldest, ablest and most experienced Fellows, Mr Lawrence' had expressed doubt whether surgical treatment for diseased ovaries could 'be encouraged and continued without danger to the character of the profession'.[15]

The tide of opinion began to turn following Spencer Wells' paper of December 1862 in which he traced the history and progress of ovariotomy since William Hunter had suggested that it might be advisable in a desperate case (1762). Wells ended his paper on a patriotic note with the plea that his colleagues should 'no longer oppose or condemn this operation' but should study its history and regard it with pride 'as an offspring of British genius, cultivated by British industry' and so 'aid its future progress by perfecting the means of diagnosis … and thus render ovariotomy in each coming year more honourable to British surgery and more useful to mankind'.[16]

This exciting meeting was attended by 159 Fellows and guests, including Lee, Erichsen, Tyler-Smith and Hutchinson. Lee refused to recognize the statistics and Tyler-Smith criticized Lee for his unreasonable hostility to the operation, especially seeing that Lee had never performed an ovariotomy nor even seen one performed. The meeting was reported in the *Lancet* with the unusually charitable observation that the 'Medical and Chirurgical Society may be fairly considered as occupying the first place among these institutions for the advancement of professional knowledge which we possess in this country. With a little more energy in management and assertion of its claims, it might even take the lead of the foreign Academies. The library is being judiciously nursed, and gives promise of great completeness. The company is of the best; and a moderately interesting subject always ensures a full and attentive meeting. The papers are carefully prepared, and the audience properly impatient of mere verbiage in discussion, although far too tolerant in such cases as we directed attention to in a previous notice; and the arrangements for discussion are not so trying to the nerves as in foreign societies'. The editor thought the Society should have taken a corporate decision in favour (or not) of ovariotomy, 'it would have been of infinite service to the profession in this country who know not how to decide amid such conflicting assertions, and would have given weight and importance to the deliberations of the Medical and Chirurgical Society'.[17]

Stirred by 'one of the classics of medical literature and one of the chief treasures of our Transactions',[18] Erichsen and Hutchinson declared their support for Wells' crusade for ovariotomy. Thomas Bryant and Tyler-Smith followed Wells' example and performed the operation, so that by 1865 it was becoming acceptable. Once antiseptic methods came into use, the principles governing ovariotomy were applied to the uterus, kidneys, liver, spleen and intestines, leading to further advances in abdominal surgery. Wells personally pioneered the removal of the spleen in 1865, performing his last splenectomy in 1888 at the age of 70.

Spencer Wells was also ahead of his contemporaries in his observations on tetanus, foreshadowing the work of Arthur Nicolaier, who discovered the tetanus bacillus in the 1880s having inoculated mice with garden earth. Wells' paper of November 1859 on three cases of tetanus following ovariotomy suggested 'very respectfully to the Fellows of this Society that more accurate observation of what may be called the Natural History of Tetanus is much needed … Much light may be thrown on this interesting question by noting the effects produced on animals by inoculation of the secretions of the wound, or of the blood or juice of muscle, or of the urine and other excretions of tetanic patients'.[19]

Spencer Wells worked for 24 years at the Samaritan Free Hospital perfecting ovari-otomy, and he developed the artery forceps. He was also a co-founder of St Peter's Hospital for the Stone in 1860, which three years later moved to 54 Berners Street, next door to the RMCS.

## 'Listerism'

The leading surgeons of the mid-19th century recognized the importance of cleanliness in surgical procedures in the pre-bacteriology sense, but for all the washing and scrubbing, sepsis or 'the hospital disease' remained a strong deterrent to surgery. The state of affairs in 1859 was illustrated by Thomas Bryant's figures based on 300 amputations at Guy's Hospital of which 224 were successful; of the fatal cases, however, 42% died of pyaemia. Bryant was highly skilled and developed new techniques and instruments to improve his operations; but unlike Spencer Wells, he never adopted the antiseptic methods advocated by Professor Lister. The opposing stance taken by Bryant and Spencer Wells on Listerism was echoed by the profession at large.

### Lord Lister

Joseph Lister, Professor of Surgery at Glasgow University, reported his new method of treating injuries such as compound fractures and abscesses in the *Lancet* of 16 March 1867. He had become aware of the powerful antiseptic effect of carbolic acid three years previ-ously and began to experiment by using it in the treatment of compound fractures. Although his cases presented evidence of success the London hospitals were not convinced. Lister moved south to take the chair of Clinical Surgery at King's College Hospital in 1877; in December of that year he was proposed as a Fellow of the Royal Medical and Chirurgical Society, and was elected in February 1878. Later that year he gave his first address to a London medical society in the Library at 53 Berners Street; this was at a meeting of the Pathological Society to which he was promptly elected. Lister's nephew and assistant, Sir Rickman J Godlee, remembered that his uncle's presence in London 'was a godsend to the secretaries of medical societies anxious to provide attractive programmes'.[20]

Lord Lister was elected a Fellow of the Society in 1878. At a special meeting held in 1901 he proposed the motion for a loyal address to the new sovereign, King Edward VII.

At the time of Lister's arrival in London the medical profession was divided on the subject of antiseptic surgery. Watson Cheyne was Lister's chief apostle and John Wood of King's was soon persuaded, but the majority found the concept of bacteriology difficult to grasp. In May 1873 J Burdon Sanderson, Professor of Physiology at Guy's, had been the first to bring the subject before a meeting of the RMCS, with a paper on the infective products of acute inflammation. He had undertaken an enquiry into secondary inflammation for the medical department of the Privy Council, so his conclusion that bacteria were present in the source of inflammation and in the blood in secondary infections carried weight. Subsequent judgement of the paper gave it pre-eminence: 'in all the long line of our *Transactions* there is no communication of more profound significance'.[21] The subject was to be fully explored at a meeting of the Society in 1882, which was devoted to the demonstration of Koch's specimens of the bacilli of tubercle and other pathological bacteria.

Lister was a Fellow of the RMCS for many years but he seems to have favoured the Medical Society of London (he delivered its oration four times and left it the pick of his medical library) and the Clinical Society of which he was an active President (1881–82). The Secretary of the RMCS, MacAlister, revealed that Lister was considered for the presidency of that Society in the early years of the 20th century, but the proposal was withdrawn because it was usual for Presidents to be 'the best of those who had served longest' and there were others with longer records than Lister's.[22] He was awarded an Honorary Fellowship of the Society in 1905.

Lister did not participate in the debate on antiseptic surgery at the RMCS in December 1880 when it was left to his defendants, J Matthews Duncan, T Spencer Wells and J Knowsley Thornton, to suppress a minor revolt against antiseptic methods spearheaded by Dr George Bantock and Robert Lawson Tait. As Baron Lister he did take part in a special meeting of the RMCS held in February 1901 to consider an address to the new sovereign. Lister proposed the adoption and presentation of the official address and paid tribute to the late Queen's confidence in her medical advisers. 'I believe, sir, that I happen to be the only person who ever exercised upon her sacred body the divine art of surgery', he claimed. This referred to the 'critical and anxious occasion' in 1871 when Sir William Jenner and Lister had treated Queen Victoria for a large abscess in her left armpit. The Queen noted in her journal that Sir William Jenner gave her some whiffs of chloroform, Mr Lister froze the place and the abscess – six inches in diameter – was quickly cut. When the wound was dressed the next day the Queen's physician at Balmoral, Dr Marshall, misdirected the carbolic spray on to Her Majesty's face (she was quick to complain) and Lister devised *ad hoc* rubber tubes to drain the wound.[23]

## Debate on antiseptic methods

The debate at the RMCS on Lister's antiseptic methods was provoked by William Savory of St Bartholomew's Hospital who launched his attack on Lister in the *BMJ* of August 1879. 'Antiseptic surgery! Unhappily there is much confusion in the current employment of this phrase', he began. Personally he recommended clean water as the safest and best antiseptic.[24] Robert Lawson Tait, surgeon to the Birmingham Hospital for Women, shared Savory's views. He had at first been impressed, but having tested Lister's methods in 100 cases of successful ovariotomy he concluded that 'the antiseptic processes of Professor Lister have not facilitated the recovery of my patients'. He criticized the antiseptic spray and argued that the dexterity of the surgeon and condition of the patient counted for more than antiseptic procedures. Not one speaker endorsed Lawson Tait's views, and by the end of the discussion he stood alone. According to Sir John Bland-Sutton, who regularly attended the Society's meetings, 'Tait was a quarrelsome fellow, rough and rude' whose statistics were 'certainly unreliable'.[25] For these reasons Lawson Tait was unpopular, and when in May 1881 he submitted a paper on the removal of uterine appendages, the Council rejected it for publica-

Robert Lawson Tait, a pioneering surgeon who was
not convinced by Lister's antiseptic methods.

tion. According to the slighted author, the paper was received with 'incredulity and that
conservative body did not even think it worthwhile to publish'. Lawson Tait sent it to the
*American Journal of Medical Sciences* instead 'and in the New World it at once received the
attention which I knew the facts merited. I can now speak calmly of the action of the London
Society, but I felt very bitterly about it at the time'.[26]

Knowsley Thornton of the Samaritan Hospital presented the other side of the argument
over Listerism, presenting figures to prove that his use of antiseptic methods had lowered
the rate of mortality in ovariotomy fom 23.94% to 4%. In the following month Spencer
Wells' final tally of 1,000 ovariotomies showed that after he had adopted antiseptic
methods mortality fell dramatically, and Dr Bantock, Frederick Treves and J McCarthy
followed up with papers giving strong and differing views on antiseptic methods at the
meetings of 1880–81.

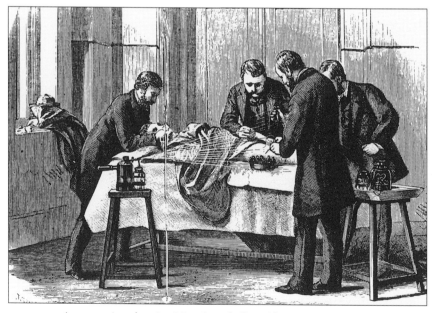

An operation showing Lister's carbolic acid steam spray in use.

A disadvantage of Lister's antiseptic methods was the carbolic spray, which issued from a steam-driven apparatus and soaked those present. AW Mayo Robson, lecturer in pathology at the Leeds School of Medicine, reported to the RMCS in 1882 that he had invented an apparatus for the production of a dry antiseptic spray and he brought his device to a meeting. This ingenious piece of equipment failed to achieve acclamation and within a few years Lister himself had abandoned the use of carbolic spray.

*New operations*
The combination of Spencer Wells' statistics, the use of anaesthetics and the eventual acceptance of antiseptic procedures served to encourage the medical profession to undertake, and their patients to undergo, new operations. James Syme, Professor of Clinical Surgery at Edinburgh University, claimed that he had never had a death under chloroform and of his five papers in the Society's *Transactions*, two reported new operations (1857). Syme returned to Scotland after a brief appointment at University College Hospital and his obituary spoke plainly of 'the susceptible and irritable being who had played such a prominent part in the great arena of professional life'.[27] He took full advantage of the new anaesthetics and was one of the first to welcome the antiseptic methods advocated by his pupil and son-in-law, Joseph Lister.

JW Hulke, who like Spencer Wells had been at Smyrna during the Crimean War, was appointed to the Royal London Ophthalmic Hospital (Moorfields) soon after his return. He was President of several societies and a loyal Fellow of the RMCS, serving as a member of Council, Honorary Secretary, and then Honorary Librarian from 1879 until his death in 1895. He gave two papers on glaucoma (1857, 1860), the second one describing its treatment by iridectomy 'so very successful that the author is desirous of bringing the operation to the notice of the Society'. Von Graefe had found that iridectomy was effective in 1857 and in this country both Bowman and Hulke promoted the new method. Hulke's last paper of 1892 was described by Dr Harley as 'the first case of washing out of the peritoneal cavity after the bursting of the liver into it' and Hulke offered the paper 'as an encouragement to the doing-of-it'.[28]

Charles H Moore, who had been at Brussels after Waterloo and who became a Vice President of the RMCS, was an early advocate of mastectomy. Astley Cooper had

JW Hulke, a Fellow of the Royal Society and Honorary Librarian to the RMCS 1879–95. He was President at different times of the Royal College of Surgeons, the Clinical Society, the Geological Society, the Pathological Society and the Ophthalmological Society.

advocated radical mastectomy in the 1820s although the horrors of the operation without anaesthesia did not commend it. Fanny Burney's personal account of her ordeal at the hands of Napoleon's surgeon, Larrey, describing 'the terrible cutting ... to separate the bottom, the foundation of this dreadful gland' is harrowing and by the 1860s surgeons had almost given up operating for cancer of the breast because patients so often suffered a recurrence.

Moore was in charge of the cancer ward at the Middlesex Hospital for many years and in 1867 he performed a radical mastectomy, described in his paper in *Medico-Chirurgical Transactions* which recommended that 'cancer of the breast required the careful extirpation of the entire organ'. Moore's operation pre-dated William Halsted's radical mastectomy by 27 years and his paper eventually came to the attention of Lister and Mitchell Banks, who adopted his recommendations.[29]

Dr Hans Wilhelm Meyer of Copenhagen sent a paper communicated by John Marshall in 1870, giving news of his operation for 'adenoid vegetations' and showing how he used a ring-knife fitted over a finger. The existence of adenoids had only been acknowledged in 1852 and Meyer had begun operating to remove them in cases of deafness from 1868. Following publication in the *Transactions* Meyer's paper was translated into several languages.

Robert Lawson Tait, the antagonist of Lister, had performed his first ovariotomy in 1868 and in 1879 he carried out the first successful operation in England for the removal of gall stones. 'To my good fortune ' he wrote, 'it has fallen to me to be the first to follow out Dr Handfield Jones' idea and Dr Sims' plan successfully'.[30] Lawson Tait was well aware of the importance of his achievement, yet in the discussion that followed the presentation of his paper at the RMCS there was no enthusiasm from the distinguished audience. It was left to his pupil, AW Mayo Robson, to pursue the surgery and treatment of gall stones and he gave details of his first cholecystenterostomy to the Society in 1889.

In the year of Lawson Tait's operation for the removal of gall stones, Arthur Barker completed a nephrectomy, 'an unusual operation not yet familiar to English surgeons' (it had first been performed in America in 1861). Encouraged by Barker's example, several Fellows including Spencer Wells and John Marshall undertook operations on the kidney and by 1889 Knowsley Thornton was in a position to report on 25 cases.

The 1880s saw remarkable advances in surgery achieved by Frederick Treves, Rickman J Godlee, William Gowers, Victor Horsley, Thomas Smith, Howard Marsh, Spencer Wells, Knowsley Thornton and Mayo Robson. They reported their achievements to colleagues at the RMCS, leading Dr Goodhart to remark that 'surgery was a sort of Russia in the domain of practice – nothing if not aggressive'.[31]

## Sir Frederick Treves

As surgeon to the London Hospital from 1884 to 1898 Frederick Treves was recognized as the leader of British surgery, and he is remembered even today for his humane treatment of the 'Elephant Man'. Treves submitted his new method of intestinal resection to the RMCS in 1883 and he was to become famous for appendectomy (Lawson Tait claimed to have performed the first such operation in 1880). Treves' account of his operation in a case of 'relapsing typhilitis' was published by the Society in 1888 and then sank into oblivion. Treves later described it as 'an unpretending paper which lies buried in the annals of an ancient society', since when the operation has been recognized as 'the first in this country which was undertaken deliberately for the cure of a chronic, relapsing inflammation' of the appendix.[32] On the occasion he described in 1888 Treves did not remove the appendix but he advised colleagues that in the majority of cases it would be wise to do so during a quiescent period. 'Looking back on the discussion which followed that paper it is curious to note how very feebly it was received and how the method advocated therein was scarcely

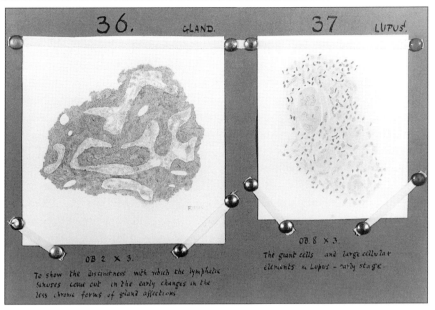

Sir Frederick Treves' album of drawings of changes in scrofulous glands was
presented to the RSM by Dr Sharma in 2000. Number 36 (left) shows the
distinctness with which the lymphatic sinuses come out in the early changes in less
chronic forms of gland affections. Right (37), the giant cells and large cellular
elements in the early stage of lupus.

accepted at all as a reasonable method of treatment. In that particular discussion one
physician of considerable experience said that in the whole of his life he had never seen a
case of typhilitis that could possibly have called for surgical interference of any sort, so
that the reception of that paper was one which, I must confess, condemned me very
much'.[33]

In 1902 Treves was consulted by the Society's Patron, King Edward VII, whereupon he
successfully drained an abscess of the King's appendix. The publicity surrounding the
King's operation, which caused his coronation to be delayed for six weeks, brought appendicitis to public and professional notice and appendectomy soon became a fashionable
nostrum. In 1905 Treves was invited to open a debate at the RMCS with his paper on
appendicitis after operation. He pointed out that he had first mooted the removal of the
appendix before the Society in 1887, since when there had been exactly 1,000 such operations at the London Hospital. No less than 78 Fellows and 63 visitors came to the meeting
to hear Treves, and interest in the subject was such as to occupy two further evenings.

### The heart and brain

Heart surgery belongs to the 20th century. Even attempts to repair wounds to the heart
were rare before this time, and few papers given to the Society in the 19th century explored
diseases of the heart and arteries. A notable exception was one from Dr WS Kirkes of
St Bartholomew's Hospital, communicated by Dr Burrows in 1852. Kirkes' discovery 'of
the principal effects of the detachment of fibrinous deposits from the interior of the heart
and their mixture with the circulating blood' was greeted by laughter and cheers from
those present. It was only later acknowledged as the first English essay on embolism.[34]

In emergency, surgery for the extraction of a sharp object piercing the heart was sometimes attempted but the risks were high. The record of the removal of a sharp needle from
the heart of a pewterer who had been involved in a brawl in a public house was noteworthy because the man lived: GW Callender of St Bartholomew's Hospital gave his paper

on the subject to the Society in 1872 as 'the only instance on record in which a patient has recovered' in such a case.[35]

Interest in brain surgery revived during the 1870s, and in 1879 James West, surgeon to the Queen's Hospital in Birmingham, told the Society about trephinings being carried out by a local surgeon in Cornwall who attributed his success to strict adherence to Lister's instructions. Trephining had not been unusual in the 17th century but it had gone out of practice, supposedly because of the death rate. By the 1880s it was back in fashion and two patients who had undergone the operation were brought to a meeting of the RMCS for inspection.

'The first case recorded in this country in which a cerebral tumour was diagnosed by the symptoms observed, without tangible external signs, and was in consequence operated on and successfully removed' was revealed to a meeting of the RMCS in May 1885. The operation had been performed at the Hospital for Epilepsy and Paralysis in Regent's Park by Rickman J Godlee the previous November in the presence of Dr John Hughes Bennett and Professor David Ferrier. The event was reported in *The Times* of 16 December under the arresting heading 'Brain Surgery'. The correspondent, 'FRS', pointed out that while the Bishop of Oxford and Professor Ruskin were denouncing vivisection, a man who owed his life to animal experiments was recovering from an operation which 'inaugurates a new era in cerebral surgery'. The recent operation demonstrated exemplary co-operation between Ferrier, whose animal experiments enabled him to guide Dr Hughes Bennett who placed 'his divining finger' precisely on the spot where Godlee made the opening to remove the tumour. The somewhat provocative letter to *The Times* generated replies on surgery, vivisection and a claim that Dr William Macewen of Glasgow Infirmary had carried out similar operations. A second missive from 'FRS' conveyed the news that Dr Hughes Bennett's patient had died 28 days after the operation.[36]

Dr Macewen was present at the meeting of the RMCS to hear Bennett and Godlee's news and he contributed to the discussion, describing some operations on the brain he had performed in Glasgow that had been followed by recovery. He tactfully refrained from

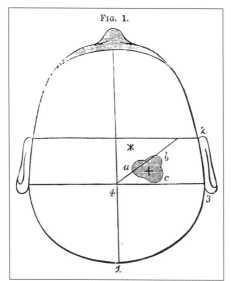

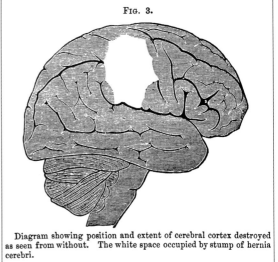

Diagram showing position and extent of cerebral cortex destroyed as seen from without. The white space occupied by stump of hernia cerebri.

Figures illustrating the paper by Hughes Bennett and Godlee describing their operation for the removal of a cerebral tumour. The trephine openings were made at a, b and c; the cross indicates the location of the tumour, and the star marks the tender point on the scalp. A tumour about the size of a walnut was removed and the case received much publicity.

asserting his own claim to have pioneered brain surgery.[37] John Bland-Sutton was also present and he later wrote that he felt sure 'the foundation of the Neurological Society was the outcome of that meeting'.[38]

## Horsley, Gowers and Hughlings Jackson at the National Hospital

Victor Horsley, who joined the RMCS in 1883, also took part in the discussion of the Hughes Bennett/Rickman J Godlee paper on the removal of a cerebral tumour. He returned to the Society some months later with news of his own operation to remove a tumour from the spinal column; in January 1888 he brought his convalescent patient (an army officer whose legs had been completely paralysed) to a meeting to demonstrate the success of the operation, 'an event which takes a great place in the history of surgery'. The paper on the subject by Horsley and William Gowers was read to the Society the following June and published in the *Transactions* for 1888.[39] Horsley was the first neurosurgical specialist in this country and his example encouraged others. He joined the staff of the National Hospital for Paralysis and Epilepsy, Queen Square, in 1886, was elected President of the Neurological Society in 1898 and (as Sir Victor) was still taking part in discussions on brain abscess and thyroidectomy at the RSM in 1912.

The foundation of the National Hospital, Queen Square, in 1860 and the inauguration of the Neurological Society in 1885 with Dr J Hughlings Jackson as its first President, were central events in the development of neurology as a specialty. Hughlings Jackson and HC Bastian were joined at the National Hospital by Gowers, Ferrier and Horsley, forming a brilliant team.

## Sir William Bowman and Sir Jonathan Hutchinson

Hughlings Jackson pioneered the use of the ophthalmoscope in neurology and readily acknowledged the help he had received from Sir William Bowman, founder of the Ophthalmological Society in 1880, and from Sir Jonathan Hutchinson, his lifelong friend.

Sir William Bowman had been a Fellow of the RMCS since 1841, the same year in which he was elected a Fellow of the Royal Society at the age of only 25. He gave papers to the RMCS on his new treatment of epiphora in 1851 and on the use of two needles at once in operations (1853).

Sir Jonathan Hutchinson,
President 1894–96, was an authority on
leprosy and syphilis (see overleaf).

Portrait from Stereograph showing the dwarfed & notched condition of the permanent teeth in
Hereditary Syphilis

Hutchinson's teeth showing the dwarfed and notched condition of the permanent teeth in hereditary syphilis – a case presented to the Pathological Society by Hutchinson in 1858.

Hutchinson worked with Hughlings Jackson on ophthalmoplegia, ophthalmology being just one of Hutchinson's interests. In a memoir he drew attention to their very interesting joint paper on ophthalmoplegia: 'so far as I am aware, this group of cases has not as yet received any notice from English writers' (1879).[40] Hutchinson was a general surgeon, dermatologist, syphilologist and neurologist and his papers covered a variety of subjects from fractures of the patella to the effects of tobacco and the first description of varicella gangrenosa. In the *Transactions* for 1874 he described the first successful operation for intussusception performed on an infant: 'the operation had been an extremely simple one and had not occupied more than two or three minutes' during which he removed the intus-suscepted mass of about six inches long. The child left the hospital in excellent health three weeks later.[41] Hutchinson also described progeria, and in collaboration with Hastings Gilford reported a condition of mixed premature and mature development to the Society in 1897; this rare type of dwarfism was to become known as Hutchinson–Gilford syndrome. Hutchinson first described the notched, peg-shaped incisor teeth in congenital syphilis (Hutchinson's teeth) to the Pathological Society in 1858; he was active in several London medical societies and became President of five, including the RMCS (1894–96). Rickman Godlee remembered him 'presiding at our medical societies and addressing them in precise clear-cut sentences, rather solemn, without much sparkle, but full of meat and made attractive by more than a trace of Yorkshire accent'.[42] Hutchinson was knighted in 1908 and his former house at 15 Cavendish Square was to be the temporary home of the RSM from 1910 to 1912.

### Sir Henry Thompson

The work of Hughlings Jackson, Bowman and Hutchinson fed the new specialties of neurology, ophthalmology, dermatology and syphilology. Urology was also coming to

Sir Henry Thompson gave the first of several papers to the Society in 1854. He is known as the father of British urology.

notice as a special subject largely due to Sir Henry Thompson, who has since been identi-fied as 'the first British urologist'.[43] He had given a preview of his work on the prostate to the RMCS in 1857 and his monograph on the subject was published four years later. Thompson studied in Paris under Civiale, who first practised the removal of stone from the bladder by crushing, a technique Thompson used successfully on the King of the Belgians in 1863. Ten years later he attended Napoleon III and operated for stone, but unfortu-nately his patient died from uraemia before the final operation was completed. As Emeritus Professor of Clinical Surgery at University College, Thompson reported to the RMCS on his operations for stone in 1870 and 1878. The latter paper, an analysis of 500 cases with the entire series of calculi exhibited and catalogued, comprised 'a faithful account of the most important results of my entire personal experience', as the author put it.[44]

Thompson's method of removing bladder stones warranted two papers in 1883 and was fully explained in his book of the following year. At a special meeting of the RMCS in 1886 to discuss supra-pubic lithotomy Thompson opened the discussion, assuring his audience that this operation was safer and easier than the old lateral method. Thomas Bryant, on the other hand, urged caution.[45] Thompson introduced cremation into this country; he was a convivial host and a talented artist, the author of novels and a Vice President of the RMCS in 1888.

## Thomas Bryant

Bryant had given his first paper to the Society in 1859 on the causes of death after amputa-tion – pyaemia was then the scourge of hospitals and a major cause of post-operative death (see page 134). He carried on the tradition of Astley Cooper and Aston Key, never adopted Lister's methods but was a reputable ovariotomist, an early advocate of the electric cautery and one of the first to investigate appendicitis. His name was associated with torsion forceps, a splint and the ilio-femoral triangle as a means of diagnosing injuries of the hip joint, which he explained to a meeting of the RMCS in February 1875. Bryant had already written a standard textbook on surgery, yet his paper of 1875 failed to reach the pages of the *Transactions*, achieving the publicity it deserved in the *Lancet* the following year.[46]

Many other papers by Bryant did appear in the *Transactions*, sustaining his reputation into old age; in 1902, aged 74, he gave a paper on cancer of the breast that aroused a good deal of interest. His main point was early treatment, when a safer, minor operation was sufficient. In opening the discussion Sir William Mitchell Banks, who was largely responsible for the modern operation for the removal of the cancerous breast, agreed with Bryant that 'the great thing now was to encourage the medical profession and the public to look with grave suspicion upon the smallest and most innocent-looking tumour, and to have early recourse to operation'.

Bryant's career had begun at Guy's in 1846, when surgery was still regarded as the mechanical handmaid to medicine. By the time he was surgeon-extraordinary to Queen Victoria and President of the RMCS (1898–1900) surgery had been elevated to one of the greatest sciences the century had seen.

## A plea for papers

The new specialist medical societies syphoned information and knowledge into channels other than the RMCS, and the medical journals had a similar detrimental effect on the Society. The resulting shortage of papers was a cause for concern in the 1860s, although Dr George Burrows found some consolation in the hope 'that if there has been a loss to us as a Society, the domain of science may have been enlarged, and its fertilizing influences may have been more extensively diffused throughout the profession'. James Alderson, President in 1866, thought that many papers given to the Royal Society were more appropriate to the RMCS and he urged Fellows to submit papers on scientific subjects collateral to medicine. Samuel Solly spoke in 1867 of the urgent need for 'papers calculated to sustain the reputation of the Society' which he described as 'an educational institution; or it was a myth, a vanity and a delusion. It is, and I hope it always will be, an evening school for adults'. During the presidency of Burrows (1869–71) the academic pursuits of the Society were neglected due to the prolonged and unsuccessful negotiations for amalgamation. When the scheme failed, Burrows urged Fellows to bury angry feelings engendered by the recent discussions and revert to 'the exclusive objects of the advancement of knowledge and mutual instruction'.[47]

Fellows rallied to the call with the result that the 1870s and 1880s brought a stream of papers from the giants of the London medical world such as Hutchinson, Paget, Thompson, Ord and Garrod. Discussions and debates were fired by important new issues – congenital syphilis, ovariotomy, bacteriology and antiseptic surgery, for example, and the Society was fortunate (or perhaps wise) in electing inspiring Presidents, notably Sir James Paget, John Erichsen and John Marshall – 'one of the best of all our Presidents'[48] – and in appointing JYW MacAlister as Resident Librarian.

### Sir James Paget

Sir James Paget, one of the leaders in medical circles of the 1870s, had known the Society since the 1830s when he reported its meetings for the *London Medical Gazette,* and he was elected a Fellow in 1840. His own early papers on *Trichina spiralis* and on symmetry were overshadowed by the work of others, but his observations on dull white patches on the surface of the heart gained a place in the *Transactions* for 1840. His observations on eczema of the nipple preceding cancer (Paget's disease of the nipple) went to *St Bartholomew's Hospital Reports* in 1874; nevertheless the paper generated subsequent papers in the *Transactions* by HT Butlin and Henry Morris, prompting a special discussion at the RMCS.

While President in 1875–77 Sir James Paget presented the results of a study of a rare disease of bones. After detailing the cases he concluded that the disease was an inflammation of the bones and suggested it should be called osteitis deformans though 'a better name may be given when more is known of it' – it came to be called Paget's disease. The paper, read in November 1876, attracted attention in this country, France, Germany and the USA and was augmented by further cases in 1882.[49] Another paper by Paget on fistulae on the ear (1877) brought a reply from Charles Darwin, who had been elected an Honorary Fellow of the Society in 1868 and therefore received copies of the *Transactions*.

On Paget's retirement as President he drew attention to the 'good history of the progress of all medical science in the papers published in our Transactions. I could see that this

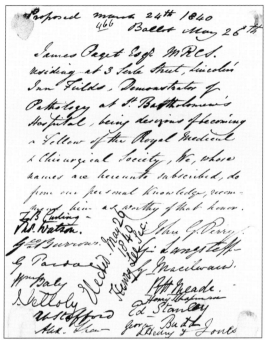

James Paget's proposal form of 1840, with 16 signatures. As Sir James, he was President of the Society 1875–77. His paper of 1876 described osteitis deformans (Paget's disease).

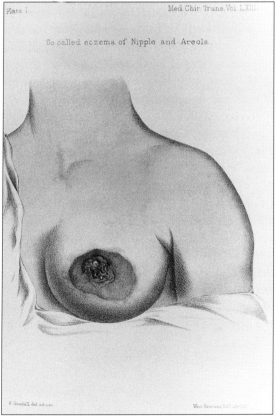

In 1879 Henry Morris, who as Sir Henry was to be President of the Society 1910–12, gave a paper 'On carcinoma of the breast preceded by so-called eczema of the nipple and areola'. He referred to Sir James Paget's work of 1874 and contributions from another Fellow, HT Butlin (Sir Henry Butlin). The association between eczema of the nipple and cancer of the breast was as yet imperfectly understood. In the case described by Morris, he removed the left breast in 1876; the woman had a child but died of a tumour of the abdomen in 1877.

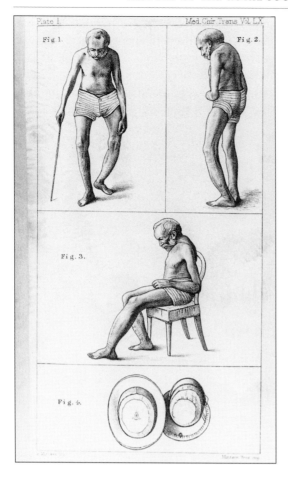

Illustration from Sir James Paget's paper of November 1876 on chronic inflammation of the bones (osteitis deformans or Paget's disease). The patient is shown six months before death. Figure 4 shows his cap, worn in 1844 and a hat worn in 1876, during which period the skull had increased in circumference from 22½ inches to 27½ inches.

Society was always in advance of current knowledge and belief ... with the progress of science the papers have grown more elaborate, the methods of inquiry more various and minute, the investigations more deep and thorough'. He insisted that there was no ground for conflict between the RMCS and 'those younger societies which have grown up around us ... there is more than room for all of us'. He drew a comparison with the Royal Society, which had originally embraced all the natural sciences and which still reigned supreme among the many scientific societies.[50]

The day after he had given this address, Paget wrote wearily to his brother of the relief he felt having 'finished my Presidency of the Medico-Chirurgical Society... and so brought to an end the heaviest work of two years that I have ever done; for besides all the professional-official work I have had in them larger practice than in any former years. Thank god the work does not seem to have hurt me: I feel as if I could (though I would not) do it again'.[51] Paget had served as President of the Royal College of Surgeons in 1875 and was much involved with the antivivisection controversy: with Sir Joseph Lister and Sir William Gull he was called upon to give evidence to the Royal Commission on Vivisection, leading the defence. The RMCS did not become involved in the argument, going only so far as to give an icy reply to a letter from the Secretary of the RSPCA who requested permission for inspectors to be present at operations on living animals. The Council made it clear that the Society was not engaged in such experiments and even if it was, the presence or interference of witnesses would not be permitted.[52]

## Sir Felix Semon

Like many leaders of the profession, Paget did not approve of the increasing number of specialist hospitals. He told Morell Mackenzie that he might as well found a hospital for

Sir Felix Semon, painted by
Sir Hubert von Herkomer in 1906. Semon
founded the Laryngological Society of London
in 1893.

Sir Morell Mackenzie, painted by Sidney
Starr *c.*1892. The portrait was given to the
RSM in 1951 by Dr James Irwin Moore,
Mackenzie's former assistant, after much
persuasion.

diseases of the great toe as one for diseases of the throat.[53] Undeterred, Mackenzie founded the first Dispensary for Diseases of the Throat in 1863 and recruited Felix Semon to its staff. 'Get yourself elected to the Royal Medical and Chirurgical Society before it becomes known that you are attached to our hospital', he advised, for he was well aware of the hostility towards specialist hospitals. Semon was duly elected a Fellow in 1877, but Mackenzie never was. His career was punctuated by unfavourable publicity, most notably criticism of his treatment of Crown Prince Frederick of Prussia, Queen Victoria's son-in-law, who died of laryngeal cancer three months after succeeding as Emperor in 1888. Mackenzie communicated one paper to the RMCS through Dr Copland in 1864, drawing attention to the invention of the laryngoscope by a past President of the Society, Dr Benjamin Babington, in 1829. 'Laryngology is not popular with the medical profession', Mackenzie explained to Semon, 'British medicine is extremely conservative and hates specialism. At present it is our specialty that has to bear the brunt of this antipathy, because it is the youngest. At the beginning of the century it was ophthalmology. Should there ever be a specialty for diseases of the liver, the aversion will turn against it, and we correspondingly, will become less unpopular'.[54]

Semon joined the staff of the Hospital for Diseases of the Throat, Golden Square, in 1877 and by 1882 he had earned the distinction of being the first laryngologist appointed to a general hospital, St Thomas'. He was also associated with Hughlings Jackson, Gowers and Horsley at the National Hospital, Queen Square, from 1888. At the RMCS he served on the Library committee and the Council in the 1890s and he presented papers in 1878, 1882 and 1895. On the last occasion his ideas on the nature of acute septic inflammations of the throat and neck sparked a discussion lasting for two meetings. 'Only a few of the numerous speakers accepted my views', he remembered, 'some others endeavoured to occupy an intermediate position and most of them entirely disagreed. But I foretold the ultimate victory of my cause'. He was gratified when, in 1903, a sequel to his paper was read by Mr PRW de Santi and this time the views expressed by Semon eight years previously were regarded as self-evident.[55]

In 1893 Semon founded the Laryngological Society, which by his own account 'fostered the development of British laryngology, called forth an unprecedented esprit de corps amongst British laryngologists and unearthed and published a collection of most interesting cases'. The Society, described as 'a somewhat vigorous child' in 1905, became a Section of the Royal Society of Medicine in 1907 (see pages 269–75).[56]

## Myxoedema

Several Fellows of the RMCS are identified with myxoedema, a word coined by Dr William Ord in his paper of 1877 describing 'the cretinoid affection occasionally observed in middle aged women'. Ord referred to an 1850 paper by Thomas Curling, which had noted the absence of the thyroid gland in two mentally deficient children with fat pads, and to the work of two colleagues at Guy's Hospital, C Hilton Fagge and Sir William Gull. The latter, a Vice President of the RMCS in 1874, had been created a baronet in 1871 for his part in the Prince of Wales' recovery from typhoid. The following year his joint paper with Henry Sutton on chronic Bright's disease was published in the *Transactions*; it showed that Bright's disease is more than a local renal infection (the pair had also collaborated on a paper on rheumatic fever in 1869). The work by Hilton Fagge that Ord referred to was a paper on sporadic cretinism, given to the RMCS in 1871. Thus developing the work of Curling and Fagge that could be found in the *Transactions*, Gull brought together current knowledge of the condition called cretinism. His recognition of the absence of the thyroid as the cause of cretinism was published by the Clinical Society in 1873.

Building on these foundations, Ord's paper of 1877 gave exact evidence of the microscopical and chemical changes of the condition which he proposed to call myxoedema. Within a few years of its publication further cases were observed and published by JM Charcot of Paris (among others), and myxoedema came to be recognized in men as well as in women. The Clinical Society's report on the subject (1888) was a definitive 215 pages long with contributions from Ord, Halliburton, Semon and Horsley, but it contained no hint of a cure.

Illustration from Dr William Ord's paper on cretinoid affection in middle-aged women, which he called myxoedema. This patient was brought to the Society's meeting for inspection on the occasion Ord's paper was read in 1877.
Figure 1: the woman aged 21, before the beginning of the myxoedematous swelling.
Figure 2: the patient seven years later.

## Tuberculosis

At the centenary meeting of the RMCS in 1905 the President, Sir Richard Douglas Powell, referred to the major achievements of medical science found in the Society's records. He singled out some papers as being of great practical and historical importance: Samuel Fenwick's work on the microscopical examination of the sputum in persons with phthisis (1866), William Marcet's paper on the inoculation of animals as a means of diagnosis in tuberculosis (1867), Jonathan Hutchinson on vaccino-syphilis (1871) and Dr Ord's paper on myxoedema (1877).[57]

While Fenwick and Marcet were thus commended for their research into tuberculosis, the prevention and effective treatment of the single most serious disease of 19th-century industrial towns remained elusive. Dr Henry MacCormac, physician to Belfast Hospital and father of Sir William, presented an exposition on the nature and 'absolute preventability' of tubercular consumption to the RMCS in 1861. His thesis centred on fresh air: 'there can be no immunity from the two-fold scourge of phthisis and scrofula until medical practice and popular conception concur alike as to the indispensableness of fresh, untainted air'. The paper was not well received and was not considered worthy of publication in the *Transactions*. The Council's failure to give credence to MacCormac's views was seized upon by Sir Samuel Wilks, who later wrote to the Secretary criticizing the Society for being 'made up of what is usually called a set of old women... they once had the chance of being the promoters of the open-air treatment of consumption' but their response to MacCormac's paper was 'a storm of indignation ... the Society was a stick in the mud ... so opposed to all that was progressive'.[58] Details about the 'disgraceful scene' that greeted MacCormac's paper reveal the vehemence of its rejection: the Secretary was questioned why it had been allowed, Dr Chambers said it was a waste of time, Dr Tanner thought the author's views were 500 years old and Fellows refused to table a vote of thanks.[59]

Several Fellows of the RMCS nursed their pet theories on the treatment of consumption: Dr Hermann Weber introduced the idea of prolonged residence in elevated regions (1869), Dr James Wynne of Guatemala recommended central America as a suitable climate for consumptive patients (1871) and Dr T Clifford Allbutt advocated Davos as a health resort for those with pulmonary tuberculosis. Dr Charles Williams and his son gave an elaborate paper analysing 1,000 cases of consumption and published a monograph on the subject in the same year (1871). Williams *père* was elected President of the Society, unexpectedly he claimed, in 1873. As a young man he had regarded the RMCS as 'rather old fashioned' and delayed joining it until 1840, compelled by the need to have access to the Library. 'I had always great respect for the Medical and Chirurgical Society', he wrote later, 'viewing it as an outgrowth of the vitality of the science and art of medicine of a past age, springing from independent and individual effort and owing nothing to authority or endowment. It endeavoured to do what the College of Physicians ought to have done, regularly publishing its *Transactions* – and accumulating its library – with Astley Cooper, Brodie, Travers and other distinguished men among its most zealous members, until it grew into a very important and useful institution'.[60]

His son, Dr C Theodore Williams of the Brompton Hospital, became a leading authority on tuberculosis in the last years of the century and an advocate of the high-altitude treatment. He told the RMCS of the improvement this produced in 141 cases of consumption he had monitored, although the precise reasons for the improvement escaped him; Dr Bowles thought the presence of snow had much to do with it.[61] The importance of Dr Weber's paper of 1869 was eventually acknowledged some 20 years later when Weber, in turn, praised Williams for his work which he said was 'likely to aid the treatment of consumption more than any other paper which has been read before this Society'.[62]

When in 1890 Koch announced that he had discovered a cure for tuberculosis, called

Sir William Watson Cheyne. His paper of 1891 on the value of tuberculin in the treatment of surgical tubercular diseases was acclaimed as an important contribution to the subject.

tuberculin, the medical profession was intoxicated by the news. Physicians and their patients clamoured for Koch's 'miracle cure' – until it became apparent that Koch's claims were premature and unrealizable. Meanwhile, London surgeons, physicians and patients flocked to Berlin to obtain the 'cure'. William Watson Cheyne, surgeon to King's College Hospital, visited Koch's laboratory, studied his methods and undertook extensive trials, experimenting with different dosages of tuberculin. In April 1891 he presented the results of his research to the RMCS, reporting that repeated doses in rapid succession often brought an improvement in his patients' condition but very rarely a cure. His paper was immediately recognized as the first important contribution on the subject in this country and it was accompanied by the appearance of patients, keeping his audience of nearly 100 at Hanover Square so late that discussion was postponed until 7 May. Dr Douglas Powell hoped that tuberculin might render some cases quiescent; on the other hand Mr Howard Marsh (who thought Watson Cheyne's paper was one of the best he had ever heard) expressed disappointment with the results, and several other Fellows spoke at length.[63] Watson Cheyne's reputation as a bacteriologist and as a pioneer of abdominal surgery went from strength to strength and he was made a baronet in 1908.

The subject of tuberculosis was again on the agenda at a meeting of the RMCS in 1899 when discussion centred on the value of open-air treatment. This time Fellows took the idea seriously and the debate continued for three evenings. Papers and debates such as these encouraged the fashion for sanatoria where consumptive patients enjoyed fresh air and exercise: the first examples appeared in Germany, and by 1910 there were 41 public sanatoria in England.

## Fin de siècle
In 1889 the Society moved to 20 Hanover Square and for a brief period the labours of the Building committee and domestic arrangements superseded academic proceedings: the major priority was to build a large room for the Society's meetings. Timothy Holmes, who chaired the Building committee, was elected President in 1890 and at his suggestion the social life of the Society was strengthened. A conversazione for some 3,000 Fellows and

guests was held in 1891, the first House Dinner took place in 1892 and the next year the Society entertained guests from Persia. Unfortunately, the President, Sir Andrew Clark, was too ill to be present on that occasion and died later in the year. Clark's obituaries dwell on his industry, his generosity (he donated £10,000 towards the removal of the RMCS to Hanover Square and he gave a set of *Encyclopaedia Britannica* to the Library) and his fame as a practising consultant and friend of the Gladstone family. To students at the London Hospital he was known as 'molecules and granules ... careful, painstaking and terribly prosy; one remembers how well, after a good hour's exordium, he would look around, and with the well known lift of the shoulders, exclaim "Allow me to recapitulate" '.[64]

The amalgamation of London medical societies must have seemed almost achievable in the 1890s. Clark realized that the complete fusion or absorption of the many specialist societies into one was not feasible: the specialists would not tolerate it and the older societies did not want it. He therefore promoted a federation in which each specialty would preserve its autonomy while maintaining the solidarity of the larger institution; every specialty might thus exercise an individual and a corporate life.

This idea of a federation of societies, proclaimed in Clark's inaugural address of 1893, provided the blueprint for the Royal Society of Medicine in 1907. The scheme originated with JYW MacAlister, the Society's Resident Librarian, later its Secretary and the engineer of the amalgamation of 1907. Timothy Holmes had tentatively suggested the revival of amalgamation plans in his presidential address of 1891 and MacAlister drafted a scheme that was ready for launching by Sir Andrew Clark in March 1893 – as President of the Royal College of Physicians Clark was in a good position to foster it. Clark also belonged to the Medical Society of London and the Pathological Society, and had recently been President of the Clinical Society – he evidently set great value on the rôle of medical societies.[65] He held informal meetings at his house to promote the federation of the main London societies and prospects were promising, but the first formal meeting of the organizing committee was scheduled for the very day that Clark died in November 1893, 'struck down by a mortal wound when in the full vigour of his life and at the summit of his fame'.[66] MacAlister later wrote to Sir William Osler that 'since Andrew Clark's death I had never found a single one of the leading men keen enough to take it up or even to encourage it'.[67] It was not until 1905 that MacAlister's persistency persuaded Sir Richard Douglas Powell to pursue the idea.

After Clark's death, gloom overshadowed the Society. Plans for a federation of societies died with him and there seemed no end to the multiplication of specialist societies that tended to detract from the work of the RMCS: half a dozen new foundations of the 1880s were followed by another four new specialist societies in the 1890s. Meetings of the RMCS for the 1894–95 session were sparsely attended and often featured just one paper or a perfunctory discussion. The Council sought to solve the problem by circulating papers before they were read in the hope that this would allow Fellows time to prepare questions for discussion. In practice this had a detrimental effect, as Fellows found it easier to read the papers in their own time rather than to attend the meetings.

Further measures designed to encourage Fellows to submit their work to the Society were adopted from 1900: the *Proceedings* were discontinued for the time being (they had long been regarded as a grave for the burial of abstracts of papers not accepted for the *Transactions*) and henceforth all papers were published in the *Transactions*. More radical was the freedom now given to authors of papers to publish in the medical journals as soon as the paper had been read to the Society.

*Tropical medicine*
A paper on malaria from Dr Patrick Manson, who was a Fellow of the Society from 1890 and later an Honorary Fellow, followed by contributions on leprosy and other diseases in

the new discipline of tropical medicine brought this specialty to the notice of the RMCS. Manson had first published his hypothesis that malaria was spread by mosquitoes in 1894. He convinced Ronald Ross, who conducted tests, and confirmation that malaria was spread by mosquitoes came on 'mosquito day', 20 August 1895.

The development of tropical medicine went hand in hand with British colonialism. It was probably the most comprehensive of specialties, embracing plagues, malaria, venereal disease, myriad fevers and the general health of colonists and the colonized in different climates and countries. Manson's textbook on tropical diseases was published in 1898, a journal was devoted to the subject and the next year schools of tropical medicine were founded at London and Liverpool. The RMCS provided a forum for the presentation of papers and discussions on tropical diseases that were often attended by Manson; in 1901 he brought Fellows up to date with a paper on the recent advances in the knowledge of malaria. The Society of Tropical Medicine and Hygiene was founded in 1907, predating the Section of Tropical Diseases and Parasitology of the RSM, and there was some rivalry between the two bodies (see pages 342–43).

## Syphilis

When syphilis broke out in Italy it was known as the disease of Naples, becoming the French pox or the British disease according to its spread. It reached epidemic proportions in 16th-century Europe and was first given its present name in a poem by Girolamo Fracastoro, *Syphilis sive morbus gallicus* (1530). Fracastoro's poem told of a shepherd called Syphilus who had provoked the anger of Apollo and was punished by disease; the symptoms were described and among many remedies, bleeding and mercury were recommended.

In the mid-19th century the possibility of inoculation to prevent syphilis was raised. Henry Lee of the London Lock Hospital told Fellows of the RMCS about the new method of syphilitic inoculation in 1859, and subsequent papers by Lee and Dr JA Marston of the

Girolamo Fracastoro (or Hieronymus Fracastorius), a physician of Verona, first used the word syphilis in his poem *Syphilis sive morbus gallicus* (1530). It told the story of a shepherd named Syphilus who suffered from the disease previously known as 'morbus gallicus'. The success of the poem and its translation into many languages gave the disease its name.

Royal Artillery enlarged on the subject. A few years later James Lane and George Gascoyen, also of the Lock Hospital, were persuaded by Professor Boeck to carry out trials there, the results of which they reported to the RMCS in 1867. Their exhaustive tables of cases failed to arouse enthusiasm for 'syphilization' although Gascoyen was later acknowledged to have been 'one of the most far and deep-seeing of syphilographers'.[68]

The prevalence and severity of syphilis among troops was a recurrent concern: the surgeon William Acton had conducted a personal investigation that revealed syphilis was rampant among soldiers in London yet quite rare in the garrisons of Paris and Brussels (1875). For instance, 500 Foot Guards in London presented more venereal disease than a French garrison of 3,841 soldiers. Acton could offer no plausible explanation.

Sir Jonathan Hutchinson emerged as the authority on the pathology of syphilis in the 1870s when his paper on vaccino-syphilis prompted the appointment of a scientific committee of the RMCS to examine his cases (see page 114). While President of the Society in 1895 Hutchinson opened a special debate on affections of the nervous system in syphilis, and the subject was raised at several other meetings during his presidency. The breakthrough in the treatment of syphilis was to come from the research laboratories of Frankfurt where Paul Ehrlich synthesized the chemical cure, salvarsan, in 1910.

## Archibald Garrod and alkaptonuria

At a meeting of the RMCS in May 1899 Dr Archibald Garrod 'launched his epoch-making concept of the inborn errors of metabolism'. His paper has since been assessed as 'an intellectual leap forward ... a conceptual breakthrough whose consequences continue to have the greatest theoretical and practical significance for physicians, geneticists and biochemists'.[69] The discussion that ensued was opened by Dr Frederick Pavy of Guy's Hospital and although not everyone present agreed with his findings, Garrod presented a sequel on alkaptonuria in 1901. He took the groundwork of a founder-member of the Society, Alexander Marcet, a step further – he mentioned in his paper that it was 77 years since the first case of the kind had been presented to the Society by Marcet (see page 28). Continuity was thus sometimes maintained from Fellow to Fellow, and occasionally from father to son, as in the case of the Marcets (Alexander and William) and the Garrods (Alfred and Archibald).

Sir Alfred Garrod had contributed a paper to the *Transactions* on conditions of the blood and urine in gout, rheumatism and Bright's disease in 1848, conveying his seminal discovery of the presence of uric acid in the blood of patients with gout that enabled him to make the distinction between gout and rheumatic arthritis. His second paper on 'so-called rheumatic gout' was published in 1854, the year Garrod was elected to the Society. His fourth son, Archibald, followed suit in 1886 and they sometimes attended the meetings together. Sir Archibald was to be fêted by the History of Medicine Section of the RSM in 1932 and awarded the Society's Gold Medal in 1935, a year before his death.

## Old and new topics

The last few years of the 19th century produced an assortment of the old and new at meetings of the Society. The question of the best method of reviving the drowned was raised once more, and for the first time for many years the subject of venesection came before the Society. Dr Pye-Smith called for a re-evaluation of bleeding, having found it beneficial in nearly 50 cases ranging from consumption to epilepsy. Also looking to the past, Sir Joseph Fayrer wanted to see chloroform reinstated as an anaesthetic.

Among the new ventures was a demonstration of actinomyces fungus 'so elaborate, beautiful and complete that it must afford the greatest satisfaction to Fellows' (1889) and Watson Cheyne's paper on the value of tuberculin in the treatment of surgical tubercular cases, which included the exhibition of patients and occupied two meetings in the spring of

1891. Mayo Robson and Knowsley Thornton maintained the tradition of reporting new operations to meetings and John Croft spoke about 'plastic operations' after burns.

Controversy was encouraged by Dr Dickinson's researches into renal dropsy, with which Dr Johnson could not agree: 'the paper raised some of the most important questions in the principles of medicine', he commented. Later in 1892 Archibald Garrod's experience in cases of rheumatic arthritis 'would not allow him to agree with Mr Lane' who based his opinions on experience at the Royal Mineral Water Hospital, Bath. Rickman Godlee's account of an amputation for diabetic gangrene was guaranteed to upset trenchant views on the danger of the operation, and at another meeting Fellows argued about the nature of German measles.

In October 1899 the Boer War broke out. As consulting surgeon to the field force Frederick Treves witnessed the disastrous engagements leading up to the relief of Ladysmith, a story he told in *The tale of a field hospital* (1900). On his return to England he received a hero's welcome, although there was mounting criticism of the inadequacies of the medical services during the campaign. The possibility of obtaining an insight into the scandal doubtless drew the large audience to hear Treves address the RMCS on 'The wounded in the present war' in May 1900. He explained that the type of bullets used in the warfare caused surprisingly little internal damage, so cases of abdominal section in the field were few. And because the fighting was on uncultivated ground there was relatively little tetanus and some troops had been given typhoid vaccination; but, as Treves explained, the great killer proved to be enteric fever. Contributions from Sir William MacCormac, Major W Dick of the RAMC and Dr Jameson, Director General of the Army Medical Department, caused the discussion to be continued on a second evening.

## Into the 20th century

The Society entered the 20th century as a substantial property-owner receiving rents of some £2,300 per annum from Berners Street and Hanover Square. There was the promise of a generous bequest from Mr FJ Gant, Sir Edward Sieveking presented the badge to be worn by the President while in office and MacAlister gave the President a silver master key to 20 Hanover Square (Plates 22 and 23). Special discussions and demonstrations had been instituted to vary the routine of meetings and attracted a large number of Fellows; the annual House Dinner was also popular. The Library opening hours were extended, MacAlister was breathing life into the Library committee and as Secretary and consulting Librarian from 1901 his influence pervaded the Society for the next 24 years.

1 Typescript by Edward Palmer with other papers in 'Robert Liston and the introduction of anaesthesia' compiled by Dr FW Cock FSA, Ms 518. Ellis, RH, 'Early ether anaesthesia – the enigma of Robert Liston' in Barr, A Marshall, Boulton, Thomas B and Wilkinson, David J (eds), *Essays in the history of anaesthesia* (1996) pp. 23–30.
2 Williams, Charles JB, *Memoirs of life and work* (1884) pp. 225–26.
3 Cock, FW, 'Robert Liston and the introduction of anaesthesia', Ms 518.
4 GM 11 May 1847, B7.
5 Transacs vol xxxi (1848) p. 313.
6 Duncum, Barbara M, *The development of inhalation anaesthesia* (1994) p. 258.
7 GM 10 October 1871, B9.
8 Hewitt's paper presented nitrous oxide as an advance on ether or chloroform and warned of the dangers of the latter, see Howat, DDC, 'Sir Frederic William Hewitt' part 1 in JMB February 1999 vol 7 pp. 5–10.
9 *Lancet* (i) 2 March 1889 p. 438.
10 3 July 1894 PRSM vol vi (1893–4).
11 Transacs vol lxxix (1896) pp. 1–39. Howat, DDC, 'Sir Frederic William Hewitt' part 2 in JMB May 1999 vol 7 pp. 63–68. Letters Hewitt to Silk and related papers (1895) Western Ms 5978, Wellcome.
12 L.9.c.16, 17, 18, Box 59.
13 8 February 1858 PRSM vol iii (1858–61).
14 BMJ (i) 19 June 1880 pp. 931–32.
15 Transacs vol xlvi (1863) pp. 33–55. *Lancet* (ii) 23 November 1850 pp. 583–87.

16 Transacs, *ibid.*

17 *Lancet* (ii) 20 December 1862 pp. 683–84. Gwillim, CM, 'A meeting of the Royal Medical and Chirurgical Society in the session 1861–62' in PRSM vol 55 (1962) pp. 87–91.

18 M & P p. 123.

19 22 November 1859, PRSM vol iii (1858–61).

20 Godlee, Rickman J, *Lord Lister* (1919) p. 428.

21 M & P p. 151.

22 Letter MacAlister to Osler 20 May 1914, Cushing, Harvey, *The life of Sir William Osler* vol ii (1925) pp. 408–10.

23 Fisher, Richard B, *Joseph Lister 1827–1912* (1977) pp. 193–94.

24 BMJ (ii) 9 August 1879 pp. 210–17, 232–33.

25 Bland-Sutton, Sir John, *The story of a surgeon* (1930) p. 68.

26 GM 10 February 1880, B10. McKay, W.J. Stewart, *Lawson Tait. His life and work* (1922) p. 326.

27 24 February 1857 PRSM vol i (1856–57). Presidential address 1 March 1871 PRSM vol vi (1867–71).

28 26 June 1860 PRSM vol iii (1858–61). 22 December 1892 PRSM vol v (1892–93).

29 Power, Sir D'Arcy, 'CH Moore FRCS and operations for cancer' in *British Journal of Surgery* vol xxiii October 1935 no 90 pp. 241–44. Transacs vol l (1867) pp. 245–80.

30 GM 11 November 1879, B10. Power, Sir D'Arcy, 'The first successful operation for gall stones in England' in *British Journal of Surgery* vol xxii April 1935 no 88 pp. 639–41.

31 1 October 1885 PRSM vol i (1882–85).

32 Power, Sir D'Arcy, 'Treves' first appendix operation' in *British Journal of Surgery* vol xxiii July 1935 no 89 pp. 1–3. Transacs vol lxxx (1888) pp. 165–72.

33 Trombley, Stephen, *Sir Frederick Treves* (1989) pp. 54, 72.

34 1 March 1865 PRSM vol v (1964–67). *A memoir by Sir Samuel Wilks* (1911) p. 48. Kirkes was subsequently elected a Fellow (1859). *Lancet* (i) 27 May 1905 pp. 1439–40.

35 Transacs vol lvi (1873) pp. 203–12.

36 Power, Sir D'Arcy, 'The first localized cerebral tumour' in *The British Journal of Surgery* vol xix April 1932 no 76 pp. 523–26. *The Times*, 16, 27 December 1884.

37 Macewen clearly had a claim to be called the father of brain surgery, see Bowman, AK, *The life and teaching of Sir William Macewen* (1942) pp. 259–62.

38 Bland-Sutton, Sir John *op cit* p. 148.

39 Paget, Stephen, *Sir Victor Horsley* (1919) p. 126.

40 Jackson, J Hughlings, *Neurological fragments* (1925) pp. 23, 31–32.

41 Transacs vol lvii (1874) pp. 31–75.

42 *Medical Classics* vol v (1940) p. 110.

43 Dunsmuir, WD and Kirby, RS, 'Sir Henry Thompson: the first British urologist (1820–1904)' in JMB November 1995 pp. 187–91.

44 Transacs vol lxi (1878) pp. 157–78.

45 30 March 1886 PRSM vol ii (1885–88).

46 Power, Sir D'Arcy, 'Bryant's ilio-femoral triangle' in the *British Journal of Surgery* vol xiii October 1925 no 50 pp. 201–05. Golding-Bird, CH, 'In memoriam: Thomas Bryant' in *Guy's Hospital Reports* vol lxviii (1914) pp. 1–36.

47 Presidential addresses 1 March 1862 PRSM vol iv (1861–64), 1 March 1866, 1 March 1867 PRSM vol v (1864–67), 2 March 1868 PRSM vol vi (1867–71), 1 March 1871 PRSM vol vi (1867–71).

48 M & P p. 167.

49 GM 14 November 1876, B9. Power, Sir D'Arcy, 'Sir James Paget' in the *British Journal of Surgery* vol x October 1922 no 38 pp. 161–64.

50 Presidential address 1 March 1877, PRSM vol viii (1875–80).

51 Paget, Stephen, *Memoirs and letters of Sir James Paget* (1901) pp. 286–87.

52 GM 9 February 1875, B9.

53 Stevenson, R Scott, *Morell Mackenzie* (1946) p. 37.

54 Semon, Henry C, and McIntyre, Thomas A (eds), *Sir Felix Semon MD. An autobiography* (1919) pp. 102–03.

55 *Ibid* p. 221.

56 *Ibid* p. 224. Symonds, CJ, Address at the Centenary meeting, Transacs vol lxxxviii (1905) p. cxlvi.

57 Presidential address Transacs vol lxxxviii (1905) pp. cxxxix-cxl.

58 Letter Wilks to MacAlister 12 February 1906, G1–5, Box 21.

59 *Practitioner* vol lxiii (1899) pp. 491–98.

60 Williams, Charles JB, *Memoirs of life and work* (1884) pp. 416–17.

61 8 May 1888 PRSM vol ii (1885–88).

62 *Ibid* 3 May 1888.

63 28 April, 7 May 1891 PRSM vol iii (1890–91).

64 'A student's life in 1857' in *London Hospital Gazette* no 160 vol xviii March 1912 pp. 176–78.

65 Allchin, WH, 'Life of Sir Andrew Clark' n.d., typescript Ms 15, pp. 22–23, RCP.

66 GM 14 November 1893, B10.

67 Cushing, Harvey *op cit* p. 32. Letter MacAlister to Clark, 10 November 1892, F11, Box 11.

68 1 March 1876 PRSM vol viii (1875–80).

69 Bearn, Alexander G, *Archibald Garrod and the individuality of man* (1993) p. 52.

PLATE 1: A group portrait of leading members of the Medical Society of London known as 'The Founders' Picture', by Samuel Medley, 1800. Dr John Lettsom stands to present the deeds of 3 Bolt Court to the Society. The President, Dr James Sims, is seated, wearing the presidential hat. Seven of those portrayed were soon to join the Medical and Chirurgical Society: Dr Edward Jenner in grey, behind the President, Dr J Hart Myers (*seated far left*), Dr William Saunders (*in armchair front right*), Dr John Haighton (*full face, middle row right*), Dr John Aikin (*middle row, extreme right*), Mr James Ware (*standing, second from left, back row*) and Dr William Babington (*standing, far right back row*).

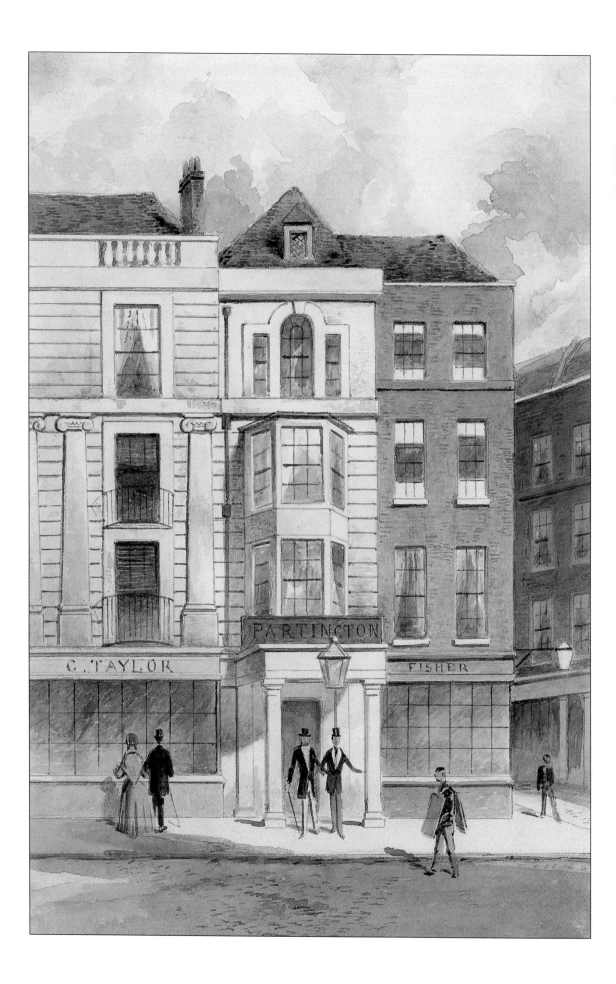

PLATE 3: Dr William Saunders, the first President of the Medical and Chirurgical Society (1805–08); oil painting by Henry Ashby, 1809.

PLATE 4: Dr John Yelloly, the chief founder of the Society in 1805 and its first Honorary Secretary; oil painting by John Jackson.

PLATE 5: Dr Alexander Marcet, the Society's first Foreign Secretary, painted by Sir Henry Raeburn.

PLATE 2: *Opposite page* The Crown and Anchor Tavern on the corner of the Strand and Arundel Street, Westminster, where the Council of the Medical and Chirurgical Society met for the first time on 2 July 1805.

PLATE 6: Portrait of Dr Edward Jenner by WA Hobday (1821), presented to the RSM by Dr WSA Griffith in 1922.

PLATE 7: Oil painting of a vaccination scene by Louis-Leopold Boilly (1807). The Wellcome Library.

PLATE 8: Sir Astley Cooper, President of the Society 1819–21, painted by Sir Thomas Lawrence.

PLATE 9: An illustration from the *Transactions* showing the characteristic appearance of a form of Bright's kidney from Dr George Johnson's paper on Bright's disease (1859). Johnson pointed out that the appearances of the kidney in different cases of the disease were very diverse. In this case the patient's kidneys were found to be much reduced in size, with yellow fat granulations. Plate 69 in this book is a reproduction of a plate from Bright's original work.

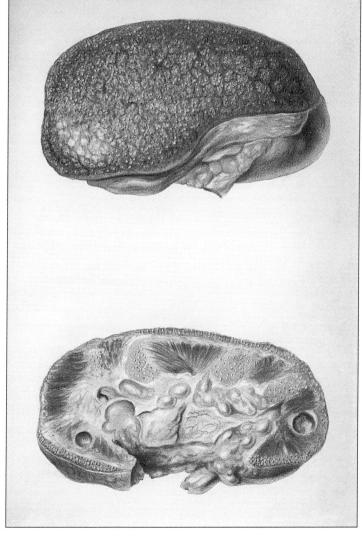

PLATE 10: Dr Thomas Addison, President 1849–51, presented a copy of his book *On the constitutional and local effects of disease of the supra-renal capsules* (1855) to the Library. This illustration shows the head of Henry Patten, a carpenter aged 26, described as being thin and pale with a face and forehead of a general yellowish hue with several patches of darkened skin and similar black patches on the lips. Despite a change in diet and medicines, Patten died shortly after consulting his physician.

PLATE 11: Another illustration from Addison's book shows Patten's liver with the diseased supra-renal capsules *in situ*, and sections thereof.

PLATE 12: *Opposite page* The three earliest books in the RSM Library were printed in 1474. This illustration is from Hieronymus (Geronimo) Manfredi's *Liber de homine* printed in Bologna. Of the same date are Petrus de Abano's *De physiognomia* and *Synonyma medicinae seu clavis sanationis*, the first printed medical dictionary, by Simon Januensis (Genuensis), also known as Simon de Cordo.

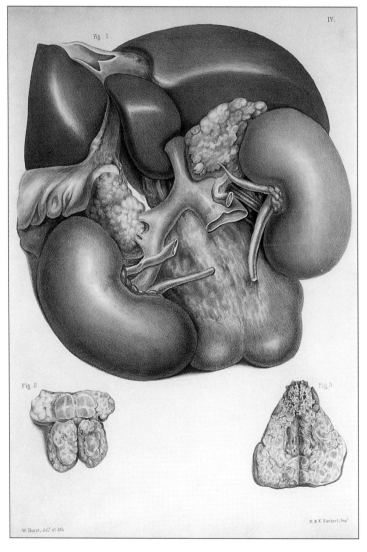

Fig. 1

Fig. 2

Fig. 3

IV.

W. Hurst, del.t et lith.

M. & N. Hanhart, Imp.t

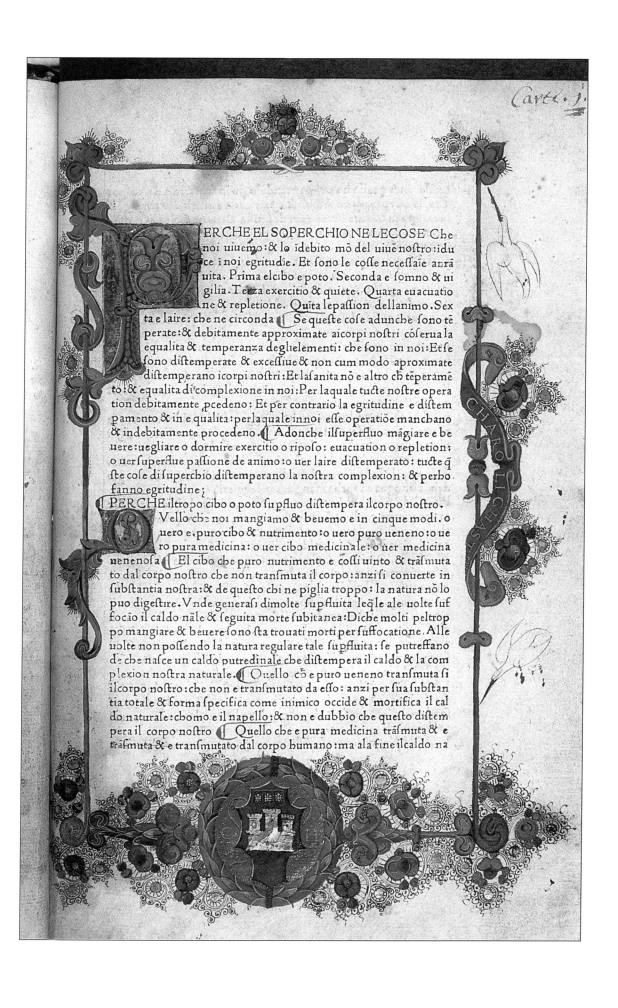

PERCHE EL SOPERCHIO NE LE COSE Che
noi uiuemo:& lo idebito mõ del uiuē noſtro:idu
ce i noi egritudie. Et ſono le coſſe neceſſaie anrã
uita. Prima elcibo e poto. Seconda e ſomno & ui
gilia. Terza exercitio & quiete. Quarta euacuatio
ne & repletione. Quita lepaſſion dellanimo. Sex
ta e laire: che ne circonda ¶ Se queſte coſe adunche ſono tē
perate:& debitamente approximate aicorpi noſtri cõſerua la
equalita & temperanza deglielementi: che ſono in noi:Etſe
ſono diſtemperate & exceſſiue & non cum modo aproximate
diſtemperano icorpi noſtri:Et laſ ſanita nõ e altro cħ tēperamē
to :& equalita di complexione in noi:Per laquale tucte noſtre opera
tion debitamente pcedeno: Et per contrario la egritudine e diſtem
pamento & in e qualita:perlaquale innoi eſſe operatiõe manchano
& indebitamente procedeno.¶ Adonche ilſuperfluo mãgiare e be
uere:uegliare o dormire exercitio o ripoſo: euacuation o repletion:
o uer ſuperflue paſſione de animo:o uer laire diſtemperato: tucte q̃
ſte coſe diſuperchio diſtemperano la noſtra complexion: & perho
fanno egritudine:
¶ PERCHE iltropo cibo o poto ſuṗfluo diſtempera ilcorpo noſtro.
Vello che noi mangiamo & beuemo e in cinque modi. o
uero e puro cibo & nutrimento:o uero puro ueneno:o ue
ro pura medicina: o uer cibo medicinale: o uer medicina
uenenoſa ¶ El cibo che puro nutrimento e coſſi uinto & trãſmuta
to dal corpo noſtro che non tranſmuta il corpo:anzi ſi conuerte in
ſubſtantia noſtra:& de queſto chi ne piglia troppo: la natura nõ lo
puo digeſtire. Vnde generaſi dimolte ſuṗfluita leq̃le ale uolte ſuf
focão il caldo nãle & ſeguita morte ſubitanea:Diche molti peltrop
po mangiare & beuere ſono ſta trouati morti per ſuffocatione. Alle
uolte non poſſendo la natura regulare tale ſuṗfluita: ſe putreffano
dõ che naſce un caldo putredinale che diſtempera il caldo & la com
plexion noſtra naturale.¶ Quello cħ e puro ueneno tranſmuta ſi
ilcorpo noſtro:che non e tranſmutato da eſſo: anzi per ſua ſubſtan
tia totale & forma ſpecifica come inimico occide & mortifica il cal
do naturale:chomo e il napello:& non e dubbio che queſto diſtem
pera il corpo noſtro ¶ Quello che e pura medicina trãſmuta & e
trãſmuta & e tranſmutato dal corpo humano:ma ala fine ilcaldo na

PLATE 13: The building on the left is 57 Lincoln's Inn Fields, the home of the Medical and Chirurgical Society from 1820 to 1834; a watercolour by TH Shepherd c.1835.

PLATE 14: King William IV, Patron of the Society, was the first monarch to sign the Obligation Book, 1834.

PLATE 15: By the charter of 10 September 1834 granted by King William IV, the Medical and Chirurgical Society became the Royal Medical and Chirurgical Society.

PLATE 16: 'The Flight of Aeneas from Troy' by John Bacon was awarded the Royal Academy's first Gold Medal for sculpture in 1769. It is now at the entrance to the Domus Medica.

PLATE 17: The chimneypiece, which is attributed to Sir William Chambers *c.*1760, was originally at 53 Berners Street and now stands in the Marcus Beck Library.

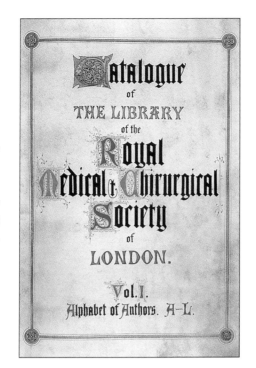

PLATE 18: Title page of the manuscript Library catalogue compiled by Benjamin Wheatley in 1879. The entries show the Society was striving to keep up to date with subjects such as Darwinism, cattle plague, skin grafting and military medicine after the experience of the Crimean War.

PLATE 19: Plate illustrating a paper of 1813 by Mr Benjamin Travers showing the different textures of cataract. 'If the operation proper to the case be selected, each will maintain its credit as neither of them is applicable in all cases'.

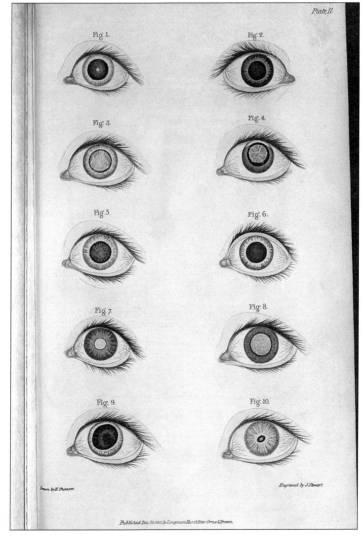

PLATE 20: Dr Thomas Bateman, the Society's first Librarian, wrote and illustrated *Delineations of cutaneous diseases* (1817), which he presented to the Library. This plate shows an example of molluscum contagiosum (Bateman's disease).

PLATE 21: During the International Medical Congress of 1881 Baroness Burdett-Coutts held a garden party for delegates at her Highgate house. The oil painting by AJ Tilt features many Fellows of the RMCS. The Wellcome Library.

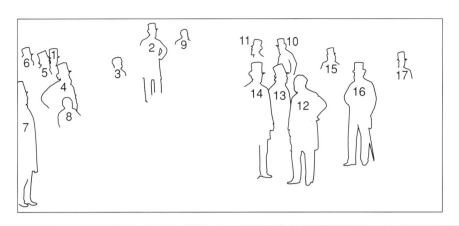

PLATE 22: The first President's badge was presented to the Society by Sir Edward Sieveking in 1890. It was made by HT Lambe and Co.

PLATE 23: The silver master key to 20 Hanover Square was presented to the President, Sir Edward Sieveking, by MacAlister in 1890.

PLATE 24: Sir John MacAlister, Resident Librarian from 1887 and Secretary to the Society from 1901 until 1925. The portrait by Eric Henry Kennington was presented by MacAlister's son, Donald MacAlister, in 1959.

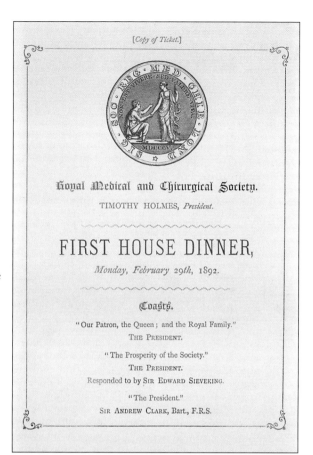

PLATE 25: The Society held its first House Dinner on 29 February 1892.

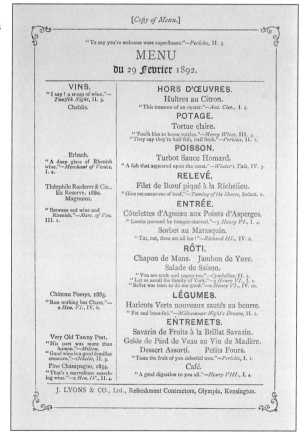

PLATE 26: The menu for the House Dinner was embellished with quotations chosen by MacAlister.

PLATE 27: 20 Hanover Square in the year 2000.

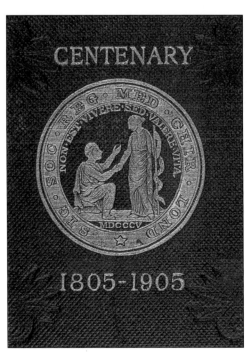

PLATE 28: The centenary seal, 1805–1905.

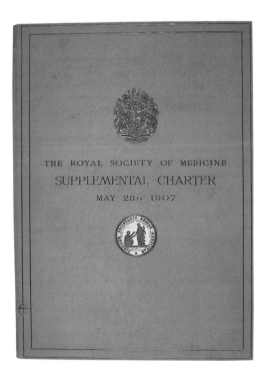

PLATE 29: The Supplemental Charter of 28 May 1907 created the Royal Society of Medicine.

# Chapter 5

# The Society at Hanover Square

THE REMOVAL OF the Royal Medical and Chirurgical Society from 53 Berners Street to 20 Hanover Square in 1889 was mainly due to the growth of the Society's Library. The prospect of the expiry of the lease of Berners Street in 1904 and Fellows' preference for a location further west were other good reasons for the move. The question was first raised in 1886 by Timothy Holmes who drew the Council's attention to a suitable site on the Embankment. In the following year JYW MacAlister (Plate 24) was appointed Resident Librarian, and the need for larger premises came to the fore when he pointed out the unsatisfactory aspects of the accommodation at Berners Street and the advantages of moving to a large freehold property which might be partly let.

## The appointment of MacAlister

John Young Walker MacAlister had applied for the post of Librarian to the RMCS in 1884; he was short-listed but was obliged to withdraw because of illness. From the astonishing number of 93 applicants, JB Bailey, sub-Librarian to the Radcliffe Library at Oxford, was selected.[1] Three years later the post again fell vacant when Bailey left to take up the librarianship of the Royal College of Surgeons. MacAlister, who had been in charge of the Leeds Library since 1880 and was briefly Librarian to the newly founded Gladstone Library of the National Liberal Club, abandoned that post in favour of the RMCS because the latter was better paid. Recommendations from the surgeon CG Wheelhouse, who was prominent on the GMC and President of the BMA 1881–84, combined with 'the strong support of my greatly loved and revered old friend, Sir Clifford Allbutt, then of Leeds' ensured that MacAlister secured the appointment of Resident Librarian to the RMCS in August 1887.[2]

As a youth MacAlister had chosen medicine for his future career. Unfortunately circumstances defeated his ambition, although he hoped that as Librarian to the RMCS in Berners Street he would have time to pursue medicine at the Middlesex Hospital nearby and eventually take the medical examinations. This was not to be, for his work for the Society left him with no leisure: 'I set myself to work according to my own ideas, to make things move', as he put it. He was not intimidated by the Council of the RMCS, nor did he respect the book of 'Acts and Precedents' containing letters and records intended to guide the Society's officers; he later confessed 'that book somehow disappeared'.[3] He insisted that the front door of 53 Berners Street was kept open and not locked, so that Fellows could walk in without being kept waiting and without ceremony. Moreover, he took stock of the Society's financial situation and assessed its future prospects. He found that the lease of 53 Berners Street, at the minimal ground rent of £14 per annum, had only 16 years to run, and MacAlister predicted that the Society might thereafter have to face a rent of some £500 per annum as well as the cost of rebuilding or extensive repairs to the building.

With a Fellowship of about 800, subscriptions just sufficed to make ends meet; if they were raised to cover an increase in rent and rebuilding expenses, it was likely that many Fellows would resign. MacAlister therefore decided 'to follow the plan of the unprovided widow, who takes a larger house and lives on the lodgers. I found the larger house (which had been derelict for fifteen years) in Hanover Square and prepared a scheme for financing the purchase and alterations and bethought me to get financial and spiritual support from Sir Andrew Clark'.[4]

MacAlister sketched out his draft scheme for the purchase of 20 Hanover Square in 1888, pointing out the benefits of a large freehold house in a situation that was more convenient to Fellows than Berners Street and which would provide adequate space for the Library. He urged speed in securing the purchase and suggested that with £3,000 to hand, £22,000 should be raised from Fellows by issuing 220 debentures at 4% interest.[5]

Clark's business acumen tidied up MacAlister's 'somewhat dreamy scheme' and Clark personally presented a cheque for £10,000 to head the debenture loan. A committee inspected 20 Hanover Square and endorsed MacAlister's opinion that the building was suitable, and the Council agreed that a purchase price of no more than £23,000 was just. A survey was commissioned from Mr Frank Elgood, an architect responsible for rebuilding much of the Howard de Walden estate on the north side of Oxford Street in the 1890s. He stressed the wisdom of acquiring a freehold property in the West End of London and reported that 20 Hanover Square had been empty for several years, having been purchased by Lord Abercrombie in 1877 and recently sold by him to EJ Vaughan and JH Gretton (barristers and property developers), who intended to demolish the early 18th-century building and construct a concert hall on the site of the garden.[6] Acting on Elgood's advice and with no further delay, Sir Andrew Clark's contribution was given as a down-payment and the purchase of 20 Hanover Square was completed in May 1889.

## 20 Hanover Square

Thus the RMCS, through the initiative of its Resident Librarian and with the blessing of Sir Andrew Clark and the Council, purchased the magnificent mansion built by the Huguenot architect/engineer Nicholas Dubois on land leased from the Whig magnate the Earl of Scarborough. Dubois had served as a military engineer in Marlborough's army in Flanders (1709–11) before turning to more peaceful pursuits, namely translating Leoni's book on Palladian architecture. He then obtained an appointment in the Office of Works and, between 1717 and 1720, embarked upon the speculative development of five sites in what was to be Hanover Square. Dubois provided residences designed to appeal to Whig landowners and those who had fought in the recent wars, as the architectural historian Sir John Summerson deduced: 'early Hanover Square was decidedly Whig and most decidedly military'.[7] The Earl of Scarborough was himself a retired general and he named the square in honour of the Hanoverian monarch. The houses were designed accordingly 'in a style evidently intended to be German'[8] – Dubois' contribution to architecture generally has been assessed as competent, not possessing any great originality or distinction and not convincingly Palladian.[9]

The first Duke of Montrose purchased number 20 Hanover Square from Dubois in 1720 (a lead cistern bearing the date 1721 was found in the house and transported to 1 Wimpole Street in 1948).[10] The Duke's seat was at Glasgow but as Privy Councillor to King George I his duties in London necessitated a town house. He was the first in a succession of distinguished owners and occupants of 20 Hanover Square: the house passed to Richard Viscount Cobham in 1736, it was demised to Richard Pennant in 1782 and in the last year of the 18th century the Rt Hon Henry Lord Stawell Baron of Somerton sold it for £6,000 to George Johnstone, from whom it descended to his daughter, the Duchess of Cannizzaro. Number 20 Hanover Square was home to the third Earl of Lucan when he left for the Crimea (his misinterpretation of commands was largely responsible for the disastrous charge of the Light Brigade at Balaclava). Lucan sold the house to Earl Poulett in 1860 and through the Earl and Countess Poulett the property passed to Viscount Bridport and William Speke. Bridport sold it to Lord Abercrombie in 1877 but as he never lived in the

Hanover Square in the late 18th century, drawn by E Dayes. Number 20, acquired by the Society in 1889, is in the right foreground with a cart outside.

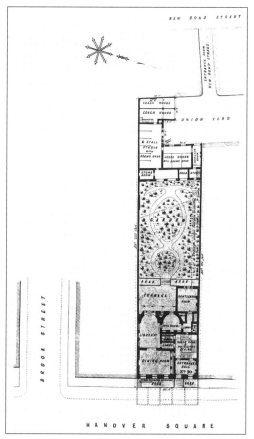

Ground plan of 20 Hanover Square in 1877. The diagonal line across the garden indicates the boundary of the freehold purchased by the Society (the house and most of the garden) and the property leased from the Corporation of London (part of the garden, stables and coach-houses).

house he disposed of it to the two barristers for development, whence it came into the hands of the RMCS in 1889.[11] The agreement between Viscount Bridport and William Speke and Lord Abercrombie includes a plan of 1877 showing the lay-out of the ground floor and garden, together with the course of an intriguing underground passage connecting the house with the servants' accommodation and stables (see page 159).[12]

When the RMCS purchased 20 Hanover Square in 1889 it was described as a 'commodious family mansion' with a frontage of 50 feet, and the property had a depth of 230 feet stretching towards Bond Street. On the top floor were bedrooms and housemaids' rooms; the principal bedrooms were on the second floor; a 'noble suite of reception rooms, most handsomely fitted and decorated' and 'a charming boudoir' occupied the first floor. The entrance hall led into the main hall with its handsome stone staircase attributed to Samuel Wyatt *circa* 1785,[13] and 'below stairs' could be found the servants' hall, a large kitchen and the usual ancillary rooms. The stabling was extensive, with standing for six carriages, and with a slice of the garden was held on a lease from the City Corporation (the RSM purchased the freehold from the Corporation in 2000).[14]

## Building work

The RMCS allocated £4,500 for alterations to the building (eventually this escalated to £8,339) undertaken under the supervision of the architect William Flockhart, who was an old friend of MacAlister,[15] acting on instructions from the Building committee chaired by

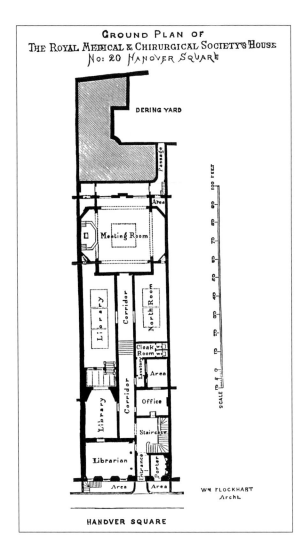

The ground floor of 20 Hanover Square as altered by the architect William Flockhart, 1889–90.

Mr Timothy Holmes, Chairman of the Building committee that supervised work at Hanover Square, and President of the RMCS 1890–92.

Timothy Holmes. Flockhart was responsible for the portico, which added importance to the entrance, a new meeting room at the foot of the garden, the extension of the Library over part of the garden, and a north room specially built to suit the exhibition of patients and specimens by the Pathological and Clinical Societies, while the reconstruction of the third floor to make it higher and the conversion of the attic provided two floors at the top of the house for the Resident Librarian. A member of the Building committee, Dr Isambard Owen of St George's Hospital, objected to Flockhart's initial plan and produced an alternative for him and the builders, Messrs Nightingale, to follow.[16]

The Chairman of the committee, Timothy Holmes, was a trenchant critic whenever necessary; he was renowned for his sharp intellect and cold manner, an attribute that was perhaps exaggerated by his false eye. MacAlister, although not a member of the Building committee, was later praised for his tact, zeal and ability, which lightened the labours of committee and Council over the period 1889–90. He set out to attract 'lodgers', as he called them, and all those who had been the Society's tenants at Berners Street came to Hanover Square, with others besides. 'Indirectly it all made for the amalgamation scheme', MacAlister recalled, 'for we were able to offer to other Medical Societies a commodious home ready for their use, and in the meantime we did our best to make No 20 widely known, and got people accustomed to regard it as a home of Societies'.[17]

## *The Society is installed*

The completion of building work was delayed until 1891 because of a dock strike, which prevented the delivery of iron work. Nevertheless the first general meeting of the Society was held in the Library at Hanover Square on 22 October 1889 when the President, Sir Edward Sieveking, opened the proceedings. 'Fellows of the Royal Medical and Chirurgical Society, Welcome to our New Home!' he began, and the meeting continued in a jubilant mood. A house-warming, or as the President Timothy Holmes put it 'this experiment in conviviality which I had the honour to initiate', was held on 29 February 1892; Fellows then enjoyed a banquet in the new meeting room. Owing to the absence of adequate kitchen facilities MacAlister set up an improvised kitchen in the north room,

The rooms at 20 Hanover Square, drawn by Elizabeth Drake in 1905. From the top: the Secretary's room; the meeting room; the approach to the reading room.

where seven large gas stoves were fuelled by gas from a main in Bond Street. The eight-course dinner, pronounced 'excellent and well-served', was attended by almost 100 Fellows including Sir Joseph Lister, Felix Semon, Jonathan Hutchinson, Robert Lawson Tait, Thomas Barlow and William Marcet (Plates 25 and 26).[18]

The Council's Report for 1890 revealed there were 23 rooms at Hanover Square, that 120 Fellows had contributed to the debenture fund and that the City had granted a new lease of its portion of the site for £30 per annum. Equally satisfactory were the rents from letting the stables in Dering Yard to Messrs Webb Miles; the music publisher Edwin Ashdown had taken the basement, and various rooms in number 20 were let to medical societies, to the British Nurses Association and to Belcher and Pite, architects (Belcher first acted as the Society's architect in 1897 and with JJ Joass he was responsible for designing 1 Wimpole Street, see pages 181–85). By 1890 tenants of Hanover Square and Berners Street were providing the RMCS with an annual income of £2,235.[19]

As Sir Edward Sieveking suggested in his address of March 1890, the presence under one roof of six scientific societies, all closely associated with the medical profession, presented opportunities for co-operation. 'There are many questions of medical science and medical government which would be more completely solved and more actively prose-cuted by joint committees of the six scientific societies working with the Royal Medical and Chirurgical Society than could be achieved by any one of them carrying on their labours alone.'[20] As MacAlister appreciated, the physical proximity of the medical soci-eties favoured co-operation and ultimately amalgamation. By 1891 there were 16 societies, associations and individuals housed in number 20 including the Pathological, Clinical, British Gynaecological and Obstetrical Societies. Over the next few years the Society of Medical Officers of Health, the Optical Society and the Society of Anaesthetists also used the rooms for their meetings. The younger societies were grateful to be associated with the Royal Medical and Chirurgical at Hanover Square; as the President of the Laryngological Society pointed out in 1905, 'had it not been for the encouragement given to us by the privilege of meeting in your rooms, we should never have been able to develop... never have been able to flourish... if you had not allowed us to meet within your fine buildings'.[21]

MacAlister was awarded a gratuity of 100 guineas for supervising 'our great removal crisis' and continued to take the leading role in choosing the furnishings and fittings. A maroon Burmese carpet was laid in the meeting room and the 18th-century chimneypiece and medallion were rescued from Berners Street.[22] When the disruption of the removal and building ceased, the Society's premises in Berners Street and Hanover Square were valued at £51,150, and Sotherans estimated that the Library of 43,901 volumes was worth £7,693.[23]

## MacAlister as Resident Librarian

It was already clear that MacAlister's skills exceeded those of the average librarian. Within two years of his appointment he had found a larger house for the Society, drafted a scheme to finance its purchase and persuaded the Council to carry it through. He master-minded the move to Hanover Square, introduced an architect, arranged for the furniture and fittings, organized the house-warming and managed the tenants, and by 1893 he had devised a plan for the amalgamation of the London medical societies.

Initially, MacAlister's influence was paramount in the Library. He instigated new purchases, increased the list of periodicals, alerted Council to book auctions, installed extra bookcases and tables, lined the corridors with books and found storage for another 10,000 volumes behind the meeting room. He regularly extended the opening hours and introduced the daily routine of typing the titles with subject cross-references of all new accessions, and these were conveniently placed for readers to consult. He found it was more economical to borrow new books from Lewis' Lending Library than to purchase additional copies, he produced a plan of the Library showing every bookcase, and he asked readers for their notes, which were typed in exchange for a copy.[24]

As the expansion of the Library was the chief reason for the move from Berners Street, its housing at 20 Hanover Square was a major consideration. The Library committee visited the proposed new premises, found them acceptable and reported to the Council

MacAlister in his office at 20 Hanover Square.

The MacAlisters' drawing room, 20 Hanover Square.

that shelving was needed for 50,000 books and that the Library must be entirely apart from the meeting-room.[25] MacAlister was supported during the 1890s by a strong Library committee whose members included JW Hulke, Dr Champneys, Dr Norman Moore, Rickman Godlee and Dr Semon. He was also assisted by the appointment of Archibald Clarke as sub-Librarian in 1895; Clarke was later promoted to Librarian and joined in 1907 by Charles Hewitt, by which time MacAlister's position was that of Secretary and consulting Librarian. His promotion had come in 1901 when the post of Resident Librarian was discontinued and the MacAlisters moved out of their residence at Hanover Square, whereupon the rooms were let.[26]

While there was no doubt about MacAlister's overall authority in the Library, there was some friction over the relative positions of Clarke and Hewitt. Clarke was described by a contemporary as well-educated, nervous and eccentric; he could translate from several languages and at one point threatened to resign if anyone was 'put over him'.[27] Hewitt, according to Professor William Osler, possessed 'a most obliging, kindly disposition';[28] he was no linguist but had been trained by JB Bailey as assistant Librarian to the Royal College of Surgeons. MacAlister consulted Rickman Godlee on the delicate matter of the rivalry between the two Librarians and as a result their duties were defined so as not to overlap: Clarke was to concentrate on cataloguing while Hewitt was in charge of shelving, book issues, accounts and binding. Notwithstanding, some ill-feeling persisted on all sides: MacAlister complained that Clarke did his private work in Library hours, Hewitt complained that he was not appreciated and Clarke complained that his services were worth more than Hewitt received for 'bossing about'.[29] The squabbles among the staff eased, however, as Clarke was appointed assistant editor and cataloguer, leaving Hewitt to reign as Librarian while MacAlister was engrossed by the creation of the Royal Society of Medicine and the move to Wimpole Street.

While still Resident Librarian MacAlister took it upon himself to prune the list of Fellows, eliminating the dead and 'unfindable'. He explained to JB Bailey at the Royal College of Surgeons that his reason for doing this 'was the discovery two or three years ago that one of these unfindable people was doing five years penal in a colonial jail. I thought this scarcely up to the standard of the Royal Medical and Chirurgical Society'.[30]

Another of MacAlister's self-imposed projects, on which he worked with Hewitt, was an Index to British medical literature. When in 1899 Dr John Billings' work on the Index Catalogue of the Library of the Surgeon General's Office in Washington was temporarily suspended, MacAlister conceived the notion of using the resources of the RMCS and the Royal College of Surgeons to compile a British *Index Medicus*. He personally bore the cost

Charles Hewitt, the Society's Librarian from 1907 to
1919. The Wellcome Library.

of the venture but could not raise the funds to publish the work, which became redundant when the original *Index Medicus* found sponsorship from the Carnegie Institution of Washington and resumed publication in 1903.

Of more permanent value to the RMCS was the card catalogue, which was initiated by MacAlister in 1903 and is still in use. A pupil assistant called Cuthbert Clayton was employed to renumber and label the books, marking the accession number on the appropriate catalogue card – this was to be his daily occupation for two years, for which he received £1 a week.[31] This labour-intensive project was financed by a legacy of £300 from Mr EU Berry, who had been a Fellow of the Society since 1845. The Library was also to benefit from the bequest of Mr and Mrs Frederick J Gant; Gant, author of *Gant's surgery*, had served on the Library committee of the RMCS and as a Vice President. In 1899 he offered £600 to fund a gold medal and lectures, but he was persuaded that his bequest should be invested to provide a regular income for the purchase of books, and when it was received in 1906 it was devoted to this purpose.[32]

In addition to his work for the RMCS, MacAlister was Honorary Secretary of the Library Association from 1887 to 1898 and founder and editor of the *Library* (1888–99). He was instrumental in promoting the Public Libraries Act of 1892 and in securing a royal charter for the Library Association. He was an active member of gentlemen's clubs, with a particular penchant for the bohemian atmosphere of the Savage Club, and he and Mrs MacAlister entertained in style at their residence on the top floors of 20 Hanover Square. MacAlister was the friend and correspondent of the American author Mark Twain (who encouraged him to invest in the manufacture of Plasmon food, a skimmed milk for invalids). He also invested unwisely in Canadian railway shares, with the result that at one time he faced bankruptcy, and he regularly complained to the Council of the RMCS that he was underpaid. Ill-health troubled MacAlister throughout his career and he blamed his illness in 1895 on prolonged overwork; in 1898 he was in need of an operation and took leave for some months, and again in 1904 his health broke down. He returned to Hanover Square in time to prepare for the centenary celebrations of 1905 and to plot the amalgamation of 1907.

20 Hanover Square *c.*1907–10. The building as it is today is shown in Plate 27.

The frontispiece to the centenary history of the Society was designed by Bernard Partridge, 1905.

## The centenary

In 1901 the RMCS came under the patronage of the new monarch, Edward VII; in the same year MacAlister was appointed Secretary of the Society while retaining control of the Library as consultant Librarian. As Secretary he was to transact the general business of the Society and its correspondence, to receive all papers and submit them to the referees, to see the Society's publications through the press, and to supervise the servants at 20 Hanover Square, where he was responsible for tenancy agreements, looking after the premises and all property belonging to the Society. He was obliged to attend all the general meetings, Council meetings, and those of the House committee; he was to be available at Hanover Square daily and to assist the Honorary Secretaries.[33] Thus empowered, MacAlister was in a position to direct the future of the RMCS, transforming it into the Royal Society of Medicine. The centenary of the Society's foundation in 1905 provided the platform to launch the campaign that resulted in the creation of the RSM two years later.

The Centenary committee was convened in 1904 to organize events. It soon spawned an Exhibition committee and a Dinner committee to cope with the organization of a banquet for 455 Fellows and guests. A conversazione was organized, a centenary exhibition, the publication of a centenary volume, and a special address by the Marshall Hall Prizeman Dr Henry Head were included in the programme of events.[34]

The centenary volume entitled *The Royal Medical and Chirurgical Society of London* was written by Dr Norman Moore and Stephen Paget, Moore being an Honorary Librarian and Paget an Honorary Secretary at the time. Dr Charles West, founder of Great Ormond Street Hospital for Sick Children, had offered to write the Society's history in 1890 when he thought the project might take two years and produce a publication worth five shillings. The Council encouraged this but West's health failed after 1891 and he applied his remaining strength to a book on *The profession of medicine*. When Moore and Paget took up the project in 1904 their aim was to write 'a plain continuous Chronicle or Annals' highlighting important papers presented by members of the Society since 1805.[35]

The centenary exhibition at 20 Hanover Square was also of historical interest. MacAlister's idea to illustrate the condition of medicine at the time of the Society's foundation extended to an exhibition of books, journals, manuscripts, instruments, medals and pictures. Most of the books were from the Society's own collection, while other items were on loan from individuals, museums and the Royal Colleges.[36] The exhibition opened on the morning of 22 May (the same day as the meeting to found the Medical and Chirurgical Society in 1805), followed by the centenary meeting, when Sir Richard Douglas Powell raised the possibility of the amalgamation of the RMCS with other medical societies, and an intake of British and foreign Honorary Fellows was welcomed – Pavloff, Ramón y Cajal, Lister and Wilks were among the illustrious names – and Professor Christian Bohr, Sir William Ramsay, Dr Robert Barnes and Dr WH Gaskell attended the meeting to receive Honorary Diplomas and sign the Obligation Book.

Sir Samuel Wilks declared he had no wish to accept 'the so-called honour'. He had become disillusioned with the RMCS on account of the Council's repeated rejection of Addison's paper describing the disease that was to be named after him, its refusal to publish Hilton's original work on *Trichina spiralis* and the scornful reception given to MacCormac's ideas on the value of fresh air in the treatment of consumption. 'My own tendencies are scientific and towards progress and advancement in our profession', he wrote to MacAlister in 1906, 'the Medical and Chirurgical has until late years been the antidote to this'. He had read of the Council's 'narrowness' in Dr Hodgkin's notes and 'Bearing all this in mind I simply declined the "honour" the Society offered me last year'. By chance his letter declining the Honorary Fellowship miscarried and having made his feelings about the Society clear, Wilks allowed his Fellowship to stand so as to avoid embarrassment.[37]

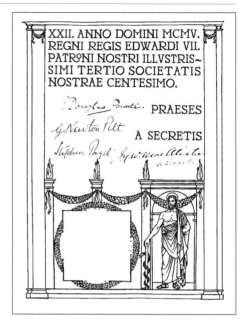

Sir Samuel Wilks accepted Honorary Fellowship of the Society, with reluctance, in 1905.
The Diploma was designed by CR Ashbee.

Others were happier to accept Honorary Fellowships, to accept the Diploma designed by the architect and decorative artist CR Ashbee and to be entertained by the Society at the centenary banquet held at the Hotel Cecil on 22 May 1905 in the presence of the Prince of Wales. He too was made an Honorary Fellow, on account of his support of the King Edward VII's Hospital Fund and the Imperial Cancer Research Fund. Two days later 2,500 guests were entertained to a conversazione at the Natural History Museum where the Royal Artillery band played in the great hall, the Meister Glee Singers provided a 'charming programme' in the reptile gallery and Messrs Lyons' refreshments gave entire satisfaction.[38] The organization of the celebrations had been MacAlister's responsibility, assisted by his clerk, Miss Mildred Williamson, whom he nicknamed Bilson and who served him assiduously for 23 years.

The centenary meeting was the appropriate occasion for 'a few congratulatory remarks on the attainment of the hundredth birthday of this great Society'. Sir Richard Douglas Powell went on to give a retrospect of the Society's achievement in promoting medical science. He referred to cases of intrinsic importance such as Cooper's ligature of the common carotid artery, Dundas' description of acute rheumatic peri- and endocarditis, and Abernethy's account of mitral stenosis – all presented in the first year of the Society's formation. He drew attention to the number of lives saved by Sir Gilbert Blane's introduction of lime juice to prevent scurvy, to Sir Benjamin Brodie's earliest use of clinical thermometry and to Dr Bostock's paper of 1838 on the clinical examination of urine. Douglas Powell claimed that Dr Webster's paper of 1843 on the brutal treatment of the insane was the forerunner of gentler, more humane methods, and that the paper read by Hamilton Roe and Thompson in 1835 on paracentesis for empyema was the beginning of a great advance in thoracic therapeutics. 'Then we have Hutchinson on the Spirometer, John Marshall on the Galvano-Cautery, Golding-Bird and Hilton on an operation for Internal Strangulation in 1846–47, Kirkes on the Detachment of Fibrinous Clots from the Interior of the Heart and their Mixture with the Circulating Fluid: and Spencer Wells's first five cases of ovariotomy a year or two later. These are amongst the more suggestive of the papers of the first half of the century, every one of which may be said to herald great future achievements in Medicine'. Douglas Powell also mentioned Marshall Hall's exposition of the reflex function of the nervous system, the discovery of safe anaesthesia, the acceptance of the antiseptic system of surgery and the recognition of the action of bacteria in specific diseases. 'The Society has had something to do with them all, and they have permeated and dominated most of its later and most brilliant records', he concluded.[39]

The speeches at the centenary banquet later on the same day gave some light relief: Dr Pye-Smith toasted Literature and Science, while Sir Arthur Conan Doyle spoke of the diseases favoured by novelists (phthisis with its wasting and ethereal beauty, fits were always exceedingly effective and what would novelists do without brain fever?). The Lord Chief Justice proposed the toast to the President, and the Duke of Northumberland replied on behalf of the guests with a jocular ditty.

## Planning the Royal Society of Medicine

Both the centenary meeting and the banquet provided opportunities for promoting the amalgamation of the London medical societies. For the first time since 1893 MacAlister found support for his scheme in the person of Sir Richard Douglas Powell, a former President of the Medical Society of London, President of the RMCS 1904–06 and President of the Royal College of Physicians 1905–10. MacAlister was also encouraged by William Osler, who arrived from Johns Hopkins University in 1905 to become Regius Professor of Medicine at Oxford University. Osler was a regular visitor to the Secretary's office at Hanover Square and was keenly interested in the consolidation of the London medical societies. He urged 'Amalgar', as he called MacAlister, not to be diverted: 'it has got to come and you are the man to do it, but you will have to get at the young men. Drop the old fossils and try to inspire the young men who have to look at the future'. MacAlister later told the Library Association that at a time when he despaired of success in his plans for the RSM, Osler's cheery optimism put fresh heart into him; he was in no doubt that 'without him that piece of work would have ended in failure'.[40]

Thus encouraged, MacAlister sketched a scheme which he forwarded to Douglas Powell; 'he was so interested that he suggested I should take a fortnight's leave to enable me to work out details, financial and otherwise'. Accordingly, MacAlister spent two weeks

Sir Richard Douglas Powell who as President for 1904–06 launched the amalgamation negotiations that culminated in the formation of the RSM in 1907.

at a hotel at St Leonard's-on-Sea in February 1905, at the conclusion of which he submitted detailed amalgamation proposals to the President. Douglas Powell ordered them to be printed and circulated, 'and from that we marched right on, till success was reached within two years, after, of course, numerous meetings of all the various societies concerned'. MacAlister's aim was 'the promotion of Medical Science by the banding together in one harmonious whole all the available talent to be found in the various societies now existing'. This laudable ideal was backed by a scheme that resembled 'a well drafted Parliamentary Bill, it passed the storm and stress of committees and became law almost in its original shape'.[41]

### The Royal Society of Medicine is born

Douglas Powell's presidential address of March 1905 gave official sanction to the proposed amalgamation: 'Why should there not be a central Royal Society of Medicine open to all, with sections representing the great divisions of medicine, each section in the enjoyment of its own autonomy, yet co-ordinated with the central body?'. At this Annual General Meeting of the RMCS the motion to invite the leading London medical societies to meet in order to consider their amalgamation was carried unanimously. Sir William Selby Church then took the lead as Chairman of the organizing committee, summoning interested parties to a meeting at the Royal College in April 1905. The leaders of the profession – Douglas Powell, Sir William Selby Church, Sir Frederick Treves, Sir Thomas Smith, Sir William Broadbent, Dr Archibald Garrod and Sir Henry Morris, representing between them the two Royal Colleges, physicians, surgeons and specialists – were all enthusiastic about the amalgamation, and the two wealthiest and oldest societies, the Medical Society of London and the Royal Medical and Chirurgical, recommended the union.[42] The latter had initiated the scheme and its officers worked indefatigably to negotiate its success, while Mr John Langton, a surgeon who was President of the Medical Society of London and was also an active Fellow of the RMCS, a member of the Clinical Society and on the committee organizing the amalgamation, did his best to persuade the Council of the MSL to pronounce in favour of the scheme: 'It was highly desirable that an effort should be

Sir William Selby Church, Chairman of the organizing committee for the amalgamation of medical societies and the first President of the RSM (1907–10).

made to unite the principal societies into a new body to be known as the Royal Society of Medicine', he stated.[43]

As MacAlister had anticipated, the societies based at 20 Hanover Square formed the basis for the amalgamation, and he hoped that they would combine with those meeting at the house of the Medical Society of London, 11 Chandos Street. Suburban and provincial medical societies were excluded from the plans, and it was decided that the Harveian and Hunterian Societies fulfilled different functions so should remain independent. During the winter of 1905–06 MacAlister corresponded with 26 London medical societies to ascertain their willingness, or not, to amalgamate. Secondly, the accounts and membership rolls of 22 societies were investigated, revealing that 7,229 memberships were held by 4,997 persons and that 1,272 members belonged to more than one society.

The proposed amalgamation had the seal of approval from the *BMJ* and the *Lancet*. Both journals reported on the negotiations at length. 'Men are tired of subscribing to so many societies, tired of listless, ill-attended meetings, tired of the old customs, formalities and conventions', commented the *BMJ* in March 1905, nodding in the direction of Sir Richard Douglas Powell, who wanted to see meetings invigorated by conversation and informality. The *Lancet* stressed the advantage of the accumulation of several fine medical libraries under one roof, and the editor took the opportunity to review the tenor of meetings at the RMCS over the last 100 years, finding that while some bordered on acrimony, most had been cordial. He drew an analogy between the Society and the House of Commons in that 'the possessors of every kind of knowledge were to be found within the ranks of the customary audience'.[44]

While some of the younger societies were honoured to be invited to join a prestigious royal medical society, others hesitated. An undated memorandum by MacAlister identified the main difficulties raised: women, financial soundness and the Library, in that order. The case of 'our lady colleagues' presented 'one of the most awkward problems in the scheme': the Obstetrical and Gynaecological Societies, the Anaesthetists and the British Laryngological, Rhinological and Otological Association were adamant that their lady members must come with them into the new society. An agreement was reached whereby women could join immediately as members of Sections, leaving the thorny question of Fellowship open (an alteration to a by-law in 1910 allowed the admittance of the first female Fellows of the RSM).

At the 'somewhat critical stage' of negotiations in 1906, the Medical Society of London agreed to join the proposed union on condition that the finances of all the societies were thoroughly investigated and found to be satisfactory, and that the privileges of its Fellows were safeguarded.[45] The privileges of Fellows raised the question of general practitioners – one of the founding principles of the MSL was to cater for and be governed by general practitioners (apothecaries as they were originally), a category largely ignored in the membership of the RMCS. Furthermore, as a letter from Lt Col Myers in the *BMJ* of December 1906 pointed out, if the MSL insisted on retaining its privileges, women would be excluded from the new society.

As for the financial soundness of the amalgamating societies, the MSL, RMCS, the Odontological and Obstetrical Societies possessed valuable libraries and substantial funds, whereas some societies could bring only their members to the union. For some reason the accountants' investigation of the societies' memberships and assets failed to satisfy the Council of the Medical Society of London, which instructed estate agents to conduct an independent valuation of 20 Hanover Square. 'I understand that your Society's decision will depend largely on the valuation of the Royal Medical and Chirurgical Society's premises', Dr Latham wrote.[46] When James Boyton of Elliot, Son and Boyton valued 20 Hanover Square at £53,275 the MSL and the RMCS expressed surprise at the high figure and rumours began to circulate that this was an overvaluation and that the finances of the RMCS were perilous. Dr Latham wrote in December 1906 that 'Rumours are being spread that the Royal Medical and Chirurgical Society had overvalued its assets and in consequence of this the Medical Society of London came to the conclusion that the financial basis of the proposed new society was unsatisfactory and so refused to join it'.[47]

James Boyton was suspected to be the source of the rumour about the rocky finances of the RMCS. When challenged he denied that he had 'stated the finances of the Royal Medical and Chirurgical Society were in such a serious condition that they have had for some time, and are likely to continue with, an annual deficit of some £600 to £700'.[48] The architect John Belcher also denied that he had made derogatory remarks about the state of 20 Hanover Square that might have influenced the Council of the MSL.[49] Whoever was responsible for the rumour, it took hold, combining with difficulties over members' privileges and the admission of women to deter the Medical Society of London from joining the Royal Society of Medicine.

The MSL was not alone. The Life Assurance Medical Officers Association, the Ophthalmological Society, the Society of Anaesthetists and the Society for the Study of Disease in Children all declined to join the amalgamation in 1907 (although two of them soon did so), while the Anatomical Society, the Physiological Society, the Medico-Psychological Association and the Medico-Legal Society found 'peculiar difficulties' in the scheme. The British Balneological and Climatogical Society, the Laryngological Society of London, the Otological Society and the Therapeutical Society expressed willingness to join under certain conditions.[50]

Midway through the negotiations, in July 1906, it was envisaged that there would be 17 original Sections of the RSM, enjoying facilities at 20 Hanover Square and 11 Chandos Street. In the event, there were 13 original Sections, all housed at Hanover Square. Tactful negotiation and compromise worked with some societies but the decision of the MSL to remain independent was a blow to the entire scheme; some thought it was ample reason to abandon the project. MacAlister had anticipated that the MSL would bring to the union a valuable library and, crucially, the house in Chandos Street to provide joint accommodation with 20 Hanover Square for the large society. Without the Chandos Street house, accommodation at Hanover Square for the meetings of the Sections and their Councils was to be a major problem.

MacAlister was to solve the accommodation problem in due course, and meanwhile the amalgamation forged ahead without the MSL and some of the younger societies. MacAlister was incredulous when a new specialist society was inaugurated just as his amalgamation scheme was reaching fruition. This was the Society of Tropical Medicine and Hygiene, originating in January 1907 and constituted in the following May. MacAlister wrote to one of its founders, James Cantlie, that he thought it was hardly worthwhile 'now that the amalgamation scheme has been settled, to go to the trouble and expense of constituting a new society, only immediately thereafter to dissolve it in order to be absorbed'[51] [into the RSM]. This was not to be, for in spite of repeated overtures from MacAlister, the Royal Society of Tropical Medicine and Hygiene remained staunchly independent.

In February 1907 the name of the new society was decided upon, 'Royal Society of Medicine' being preferred to 'Royal Academy of Medicine' because that latter implied exclusivity and risked confusion with the Royal Academy of Music. At the same meeting a petition was drawn up for a supplementary charter and some 5,000 members and Fellows of the amalgamating societies were circulated.

The new charter was granted on 28 May and on 8 June the Honorary Secretaries reported that the following societies had decided to join the RSM: the Pathological Society, the Epidemiological Society, the Odontological Society of Great Britain, the Obstetrical Society of London, the Clinical Society of London, the Dermatological Society of London, the British Gynaecological Society, the Neurological Society of the United Kingdom, the British Laryngological, Rhinological and Otological Association, the Laryngological Society of London, the Dermatological Society of Great Britain and Ireland, the British Electro-Therapeutic Society, the Therapeutical Society and of course the Royal Medical and Chirurgical Society. Before the end of the month the Otological Society of Great Britain and Ireland overcame reservations and decided to join the group.

The Supplemental Charter granted by King Edward VII to the Royal Society of Medicine was laid on the table at the last general meeting of the RMCS held on 14 June 1907 (Plate 29); the President, J Warrington Haward, admitted there was 'something a little melancholy in contemplating the dissolution of a society which had an honourable record'. The Royal Medical and Chirurgical Society had reason to be proud of its achievement, not least 90 volumes of *Transactions* which constituted 'the best possible memorial of our Society's life'.[52] The Society had even passed into folk-lore as a nursery rhyme:

'Hush little baby, Mother is nigh,
 Father has gone to the Medico-Chi'.[53]

Half an hour after the last meeting and dissolution of the RMCS, the first general meeting of the RSM was convened. The motion that 15 medical societies had agreed to unite under the name of the Royal Society of Medicine was carried unanimously; the by-laws were adopted and Sir William Selby Church was elected President of the new Society supported by the first Council and officers. At the conclusion of the formal business the meeting broke up amid much jubilation. 'We baptized the Royal Medical Society [*sic*] the other afternoon and had a most satisfactory initial meeting', Osler wrote.[54]

The practical advantages of the amalgamation lay in financial savings for those who had previously subscribed to more than one society; economies of time, management and staff were equally apparent. The publication of *Medico-Chirurgical Transactions* and the *Transactions* of other individual societies ceased and a new series of *Proceedings* commenced, reporting the meetings of the Sections of the RSM. The assets and investments of the societies varied greatly and were pooled: MacAlister calculated that the Odontological Society was worth £4,395 and the Obstetrical £3,615 but the Therapeutical, Neurological and Epidemiological Societies possessed no such funds.[55] The libraries of the specialist societies – some dating from the mid-19th century and of considerable value – were transferred to Hanover Square; the Odontological Society also brought its museum, which was soon moved to the Royal College of Surgeons, as was the collection of instruments belonging to the Obstetrical Society. The practicality of the union was indisputable, and as the *Lancet* saw it, the amalgamation of the medical societies should be welcomed: 'it is above all things in the combination of interests of those branches of medicine that tend each year to become so specialized as to lose touch with medicine as a whole that we confidently predict will be found the chief justification for the institution of the latest of all the Royal Societies and the chief warrant for its success. Floreat'.[56]

Tributes to the engineers of the amalgamation soon flowed: Sir William Selby Church acknowledged MacAlister's role and conveyed 'the warmest thanks of the organizers for all the work you have done for us. The Union is in fact your child'. MacAlister in turn praised Church for his chairmanship of the organizing committee and as 'the necessary Amalgamating President'. According to MacAlister, Dr Arthur Latham, Secretary to the organizing committee, had also played an important part: 'the Society would not be here but for you – you were the propelling force and the inspiration for the movement, and although, as Sir William Selby Church said, I was able to help by working underground, it could not have been done without your work above ground'.[57] MacAlister also recognized that the initial stimulus had come from Professor William Osler: 'I do not know if you

The common seal of the RSM. The serpent of Moses denotes healing; the supporters are the Saints Cosmas and Damian; the crest is composed of sprigs of the herb all-heal.

have ever realized how much the Amalgamation owed to you', he wrote to Osler some years later. 'At a time when I had practically given up hope, you came into my room at Hanover Square, and I told you of my dreams and you urged me to go right ahead, that the time was ripe, and I was not to worry about the old fogies! Your encouragement gave me just the stimulant that I needed'.[58]

### Expansion

Professor Osler was elected to the Council of the RSM in its inaugural year and subsequently took an active role in the work of the Society, serving on the Library committee until his death in 1919, attending meetings and suggesting topics for discussion. He also founded the History of Medicine Section and served as President of the Clinical Section in 1912, and in 1914 MacAlister tried to persuade him to stand as President of the Society. On this occasion Osler was nominated by the unanimous vote of the Council but he declined the office. Again in 1918 MacAlister attempted to cajole Osler into accepting nomination: 'Once before you were offered and refused the Presidency of the Royal Society of Medicine – an unprecedented snub to the premier medical body of the kingdom – and now I ask you unofficially and confidentially once more whether you will accept nomination, and I say to you quite seriously and solemnly that in the present crisis it is your duty to accept it, for from now on there are great things expected of, and to be done by the Society provided a man of light and leading [*sic*] is at its head, and you are the man to do it. It is the more important in view of the position you have taken up with the Post-graduate scheme'. Osler had no inclination for the role of President of the RSM, nor that of the Medical Society of London, although he was prevailed upon to accept the presidency of the Postgraduate Fellowship of Medicine in January 1919.[59] In July of that year Osler was at the RSM to celebrate his 70th birthday, on which occasion he was presented with two volumes of essays. This seems to have been his last visit. He died in December.

Meanwhile, the inaugural dinner of the RSM was held on 3 December 1907 and MacAlister urged Osler to attend and to use his influence. 'I began this work in 1892 and you will see it has taken just fifteen years to overcome the vis inertia and it will take just as long, or perhaps longer, for the logical sequence to be carried out, unless *you* can put a little strychnine into the body corporate, you simply must be there'.[60]

There were practical advantages to the amalgamation, also practical difficulties: MacAlister was besieged by letters from members and Fellows confused about subscriptions (three guineas per annum for Fellows, one guinea for members of Sections). He had to organize the meetings, the allocation of papers to the appropriate Section and the publication of the *Proceedings*, the *Calendar* and the *Official Bulletin*. He was also seeking to recruit other societies to his great union and three more soon joined: the Society of Anaesthetists, the Society for the Study of Disease in Children and the British Balneological and Climatological Society (see Chapter 8).

The expansion of the Society brought heavy pressure on the accommodation at 20 Hanover Square, and Sections' Councils were sometimes forced to hold meetings in private houses or hired rooms. Minor alterations at Hanover Square were put in hand while the House and Finance committee considered the need for larger premises and the various options. For the time being MacAlister instructed the architect John Belcher to install a replacement lift and facilities for lady members; 'one of the Sections has already lady members', he wrote, 'and the chances are that it is only a question of time before the ladies capture the Fellowship also – and it would be fatal if they also captured our lavatory'.[61]

The Council's Report of 1908 was redolent of success: the total number of Fellows had reached 2,025, there were over 600 members of Sections and most gratifying of all was the addition of 290 Fellows who had not previously belonged to any medical society. The publication of the new series of the *Proceedings* was under way, special discussions were well attended and the number of readers using the Library had doubled in the last year. The success and expansion of the RSM made the issue of accommodation urgent. The possibility of rebuilding 20 Hanover Square at an estimated cost of £51,000 was discussed, as was the purchase of Stratford House or the old Vestry Hall in Mount Street. But new proposals were put forward, and as a result the RSM was established at 1 Wimpole Street (see Chapter 6).

1 CM 12 February 1884, A7.

2 Rolleston, Sir Humphry Davy, *The Rt Hon Sir Clifford Allbutt* (1929) pp. 92–93.

3 MacAlister's speech 7 July 1920, supplement to *Bulletin* (1920) and supplement to M & P.

4 *Ibid.*

5 Draft proposals, 20 Hanover Square, F11, Box 11.

6 Building committee minutes 1889, H9. MacAlister's speech *op cit*. Elgood's report, CM 27 February 1889, A7.

7 Summerson, John, *Georgian London* (1945) p. 9.

8 *Ibid.*

9 Colvin, HM, *Biographical dictionary of British architects 1600–1840* (1978).

10 Payments Montrose to Dubois, GD220/6/2 p. 22, National Archives of Scotland. The 18th-century lead cistern stood on the second floor landing at 1 Wimpole Street; it was disposed of in 1951.

11 Hanover Square deeds, F4, 5, 7. There has been some confusion between number 20 and the house adjoining it on the corner with Brook Street, sometimes called Downshire House.

12 Hanover Square deeds, F5 (8).

13 Robinson, JM, *The Wyatts. An architectural dynasty* (1979) p. 258. I am grateful to

Dr Simon Bradley for information on the architectural history of 20 Hanover Square, and to Steven Brindle of English Heritage for a copy of his report (1990).

14 Sale particulars, Messrs Chadwick, F11, Box 11.

15 Letter MacAlister to Henry 4 June 1897, F12, Box 11.

16 Report of President and Council to Society 1 March 1890, L2, Box 49. Report of Building committee 5 February 1891, GM 18 February 1891, B10.

17 Building committee minutes 1889–93, H9. Building committee report 1891, H12, Box 38. CM 11 February, 8 April 1890, A7. MacAlister's speech, *op cit.*

18 Souvenir of First House Dinner (1892).

19 CM 9 December 1890, A7.

20 Presidential address 1 March 1890, Transacs vol lxxxiii (1890).

21 Charters Symonds' speech, Transacs vol lxxxviii (1905).

22 CM 24 June 1890, A7. Building committee minutes 29 August, 19 September, 1889, H9. Further details of fittings and furnishings are in the Building committee minutes 1889–93, H9 and in report of 5 February 1891, see GM 18 February 1891, B10.

23 Valuation by Giddy and Giddy, CM 29 May 1896. Valuation by Henry Sotheran and Co 31 July 1896, F10, Box 11. Valuation of furniture and fittings by Phillips and Son August 1896, F10, Box 11.

24 Honorary Librarian's report and report of Council, Transacs vol lxxviii (1895). Wade, P, 'The history and development of the Library of the Royal Society of Medicine' in PRSM vol 55 1962 pp. 627-36. For biographical material on MacAlister see Godbolt, L Shane, 'Sir John Young Walker MacAlister (1850–1925)', Thesis for Library Association Fellowship 1975; Godbolt, L Shane and Munford, WA, *The incomparable Mac* (1983) and *Sir John Young Walker MacAlister. A memorial for his family and friends* (1926).

25 Library committee minutes 26 March 1889, H56.

26 Report of House committee, H12, Box 38.

27 Godbolt, L. Shane *op cit* p. 465.

28 Hewitt/MacAlister folder 1901–10.

29 Letter MacAlister to Godlee 16 July 1907, G4, Box 21. Library committee minutes 24 July 1907, AC/03/J. Letter MacAlister to Clarke 18 December 1907, G4, Box 21. Letter Clarke to MacAlister 11 April 1913, folder1/G11, Box 26. Letter Hewitt to MacAlister 1 November 1912, folder 2/G9, Box 24. For Hewitt's later career see Chapter six.

30 Letter MacAlister to Bailey 8 January 1895, Autograph Letter Series, RCS.

31 Library committee minutes 1 May 1903, 23 October 1905, H56.

32 CM 29 November 1899, A8. 14 February, 14 March 1906, A9.

33 GM 1 March 1902, B11.

34 Centenary committee minutes 1904–05, H13,14. Centenary programme and correspondence 1904–07, H15,16, Box 38.

35 CM 15 June 1904, A9. Each Fellow received a copy and the authors were given 50 guineas each.

36 25 October 1904, A9. The report of Council in Transacs vol lxxxviii (1905) contains details of the centenary celebrations. *Centenary of the Royal Medical and Chirurgical Society 1805–1905. Exhibition of Books, Instruments and other objects brought together mainly for the purpose of illustrating the Condition of Medicine at the time the Society was established* (1905), Tract 1516 (2), RCS.

37 Letter Wilks to MacAlister 12 February 1906; letter Wilks to Pite 31 January 1905, G1-5, Box 21. Letter Wilks to Rolleston in Wilks, Samuel, 'On disease of the suprarenal capsules or morbus Addisonii', offprint of *Guy's Hospital Reports* (1862).

38 Centenary correspondence, tickets, programme, H15,16, Box 38.

39 Presidential address 22 May 1905, *The Royal Society of Medicine. Record of the events and work which led to the formation of that Society by the amalgamation of the leading medical societies of London with the Royal Medical and Chirurgical Society* (1914) pp. 34–40.

40 Cushing, Harvey, *The life of Sir William Osler* vol ii (1925) pp. 32–33, 587.

41 *Ibid* pp. 32–33. *The Royal Society of Medicine. Record of the events... op cit* pp. 1–7. Amalgamation correspondence, J, Box 45. Clarke, Archibald, 'A short account of the union of medical societies' n.d. G17, Box 30.

42 Presidential address 1 March 1905, *The Royal Society of Medicine. Record of the events... op cit* pp. 27–32.

43 Council Minutes MSL, 1 May, 25 September 1905, WMS/MF/4, Wellcome. *The Royal Society of Medicine. Record of the events... op cit* pp. 90, 99.

44 BMJ (i) 4 March 1905, pp. 490–91; 1 April 1905, pp. 745, 785; 15 April pp. 848–49 *et seq. Lancet* (i) 15 April 1905 pp. 848–49, 27 May 1905, pp. 1439–40 *et seq.*

45 CM 13 June 1906, A9. *Lancet* (i) 12 May 1906, p. 1335; (ii) 28 July 1906, pp. 240–41. Council Minutes, MSL, 22 November 1905 *op cit*. The MSL Council also wanted the individuality of the Society preserved.

46 Council Minutes MSL, 22 October 1906 *op cit*.

47 CM 12 December 1906, A9.

48 Letter MacAlister to Boyton 18 January 1907 and Boyton to MacAlister 18 March 1907, folder 1/G17, Box 30, also E23, Box 8.

49 *Lancet* (i) 17 March 1906 p. 789.

50 BMJ (i) 5 January 1907 pp. 54, 114.

51 Letter MacAlister to Cantlie 18 April 1907, Archives of Royal Society of Tropical Medicine, WTI/RST/DI Box 7, Wellcome.

52 *The Royal Society of Medicine. Record of the events... op cit* pp. 177-80.

53 Cushing, Harvey *op cit* p. 31.

54 *Ibid* p. 94. Clarke, Archibald *op cit. The Royal Society of Medicine. Record of the events... op cit* pp. 188–202.

55 Balance sheet of combined societies, 1 July 1907, G17, Box 30.

56 *Lancet* (i) 22 June 1907, p. 1719.

57 Letter Church to MacAlister 14 June 1907, MacAlister papers Box 1. Letter MacAlister to Latham 7 October 1913 folder 2/G13, Box 28.

58 Cushing, Harvey *op cit* p. 409.

59 *Ibid* pp. 409-10, 603-04. CM 19 May 1914.

60 Dinner committee minutes 15 October 1907. Letter MacAlister to Osler 11 November 1907, folder 3/G6, Box 22.

61 Letter MacAlister to Belcher 16 January 1908, folder 1/G6, Box 22.

# Chapter 6

# The Royal Society of Medicine, 1 Wimpole Street

THE FIRST GENERAL meeting of the RSM on 14 June 1907 was attended by the officers of the Society and 272 Fellows. Sir William Selby Church was elected President of the Society and Professor Osler seized the opportunity to map the way forward. 'I think, Sir, that what is needed now for this Royal Society of Medicine is money for a new building and for the development of the library, and I think the profession in this great metropolis can get it'.[1] The following October Osler pursued the subject with MacAlister: 'the Hanover Square building represents a large amount of good solid effort but it is quite evident that it is not adapted to so large and important a society, and it will be wholly inadequate as the library grows'. Again and again Osler stressed the importance he attached to a medical library: 'in no way can a society better help in the education of its members than in maintaining for them a good library'.[2]

With the creation of the greatest British medical library under the auspices of the RSM in mind, Osler sketched a plan to recruit financial backing from each Section, from families of notable old members and from the public; he also felt sure that Mr Andrew Carnegie, the Scottish-American steel magnate and philanthropist, would put down a lump sum.[3]

As Secretary to the Society, MacAlister made every effort to implement Osler's plans by canvassing financial backers and by searching for an appropriate home for the RSM. He hoped that Lord Colebrooke would sell Stratford House, which straddled Stratford Place north of Oxford Street, at a discounted figure of £70,000 and he wrote to Dr JS Billings, Librarian of the Surgeon General's Office in Washington and an organizer of the Carnegie Institution, beseeching him to use his influence with Carnegie and JP Morgan, the American financier, to persuade them 'to raise £100,000. The library could be named after either or both of them – and a special room for bibliography called the Billings library. Osler is very keen and enthusiastic about it'.[4] MacAlister was invited to Carnegie's Scottish castle to discuss a benefaction of £50,000 but Carnegie's health was failing and the grant was unforthcoming.[5] The enterprising Secretary also courted the London Institution, suggesting it might combine with the RSM to create in the West End 'a great temple of science and letters to house the principal scientific societies and their libraries'.[6]

Funds from Carnegie and Morgan remained elusive, the London Institution maintained its independence and Stratford House was sold to the Earl of Derby, yet MacAlister was not discouraged. He secured a site on the Howard de Walden estate, he sought out wealthy patrons and City institutions, and he wooed the public to support the building fund. He continued to cherish the hope that the Society's new house might accommodate a splendid medical library – his dream of a library, housed in a monumental building in the vicinity of Regent's Park is vividly described in *The Osler Medical Library* (1919). MacAlister's ambitions never dimmed: when a banquet was held in his honour in 1920, he spoke of his wish to see the two Royal Colleges under the same roof as the RSM, served by one staff and with a combined library that would be the finest in the world.

While Osler and MacAlister dreamed of a great medical library, the House and Finance committee of the RSM laboured over the problem of accommodation – whether to rebuild or extend 20 Hanover Square, lease the adjoining house or purchase a larger property. A

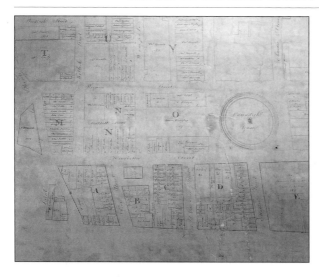

Detail from a plan by John White, c.1797–99, giving the names of the original lessees of 2–5 Henrietta Street (later Henrietta Place). The architect James Gibbs lived in the house on the corner with Wimpole Street.

more satisfactory option presented itself early in 1909 when a site at the corner of Wimpole Street and Henrietta Street (renamed Henrietta Place in 1938) became available for redevelopment.

## Henrietta Place

Henrietta Cavendish Holles, the daughter and heiress of John Holles, Duke of Newcastle, gave her name to the street that meets the south end of Wimpole Street. She married Edward Harley, second Earl of Oxford, in 1713 and the development of the Marylebone estate she had brought to the marriage commenced five years later. John Prince and Francis Seale plotted the layout of the streets around Cavendish Square and advertised the area as being more convenient for St James' and Westminster than any other of London's great squares. The first building leases were granted in 1721 when the Earl of Oxford turned to his father's favourite architect, James Gibbs, to design public buildings on the estate including St Peter's, Vere Street, built between 1721 and 1724 almost opposite the site where 1 Wimpole Street was constructed almost 200 years later. Originally known as the Oxford Chapel, St Peter's is now a chapel of ease attached to All Souls, Langham Place and serves as a base for the Institute for Contemporary Christianity. When the RSM celebrated the 50th anniversary of the National Health Service in July 1998, Fellows and guests attended a service there.

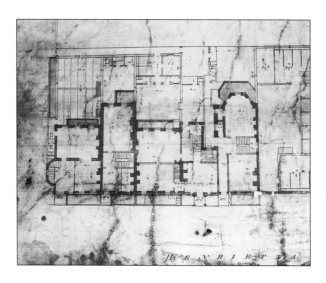

Detail from an estate plan of c.1807 giving the names of the residents of numbers 2–5 Henrietta Street. The Countess of Mornington, mother of the Duke of Wellington, lived at number 3 for 25 years until her death in 1831. The plan is attributed to John White.

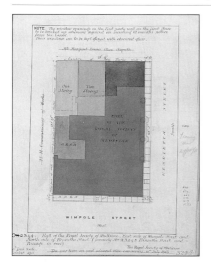

Numbers 2–5 Henrietta Street, soon to be occupied by the RSM (1911).

Gibbs was making his mark on London with the churches of St Mary-le-Strand (1714–23) and St Martin-in-the-Fields (1720–26) and with St Bartholomew's Hospital; in the 1720s he worked at Wimpole Hall in Cambridgeshire, the Harley estate that is remembered in the name of Wimpole Street. On his own account he undertook a development on the north side of Henrietta Street, taking building leases on numbers 9 to 11 and number 5 (and one other site in Cavendish Square). Gibbs designed and developed these properties as investments, with the exception of 5 Henrietta Street on the south-east corner of Wimpole Street which he built for his own occupation. Here Gibbs, who has been described as the Tory architect *par excellence* of early Georgian England,[7] lived from 1731 (or early 1732) until his death in 1754. The site of Gibbs' house is now covered by the West Hall of 1 Wimpole Street and the neighbouring 18th-century houses have also been replaced, but an inkling of their past glory can be gleaned from the first floor interior of 11 Henrietta Street, preserved in the Victoria and Albert Museum.[8]

Gibbs had access to a talented group of craftsmen – carpenters, plasterers and ceiling-painters – and he published his own book of designs in 1728, *A book of architecture*. While the exteriors of the houses in Henrietta Street were governed by the terms of the leases and current building regulations, the interior of number 11 was a masterpiece of early-18th-century decoration and Gibbs' own house, number 5, would undoubtedly have been exceedingly fine, with carvings and decorations according to the taste of one the most successful architects of the day.

In the early 19th century the Countess of Mornington, mother of the Duke of Wellington, lived at 3 Henrietta Street, Mr WJ Burt at number 4 and Major General Doveton at number 5. This last house, where Gibbs had lived and died, was demolished in 1843 when JG Elgood obtained a new lease obliging him to rebuild 'a good substantial messuage' on the site. When Elgood's lease expired in 1905, the future development of the row of houses at 2–5 Henrietta Street came up for consideration and the Howard de Walden estate decided to demolish and rebuild according to plans by one of the estate's favourite architects, Frank Elgood. This site, now ripe for redevelopment, was at this juncture brought to the notice of the Secretary of the Royal Society of Medicine.

## A new building for the RSM

The colonization of Harley Street by the medical profession began at the south end of the street as an overflow from Mayfair and Cavendish Square. Royal appointees made the area fashionable and attracted lesser mortals, so that in 1880 there were 58 doctors in Harley Street and 48 in Wimpole Street.[9] The numbers increased steadily so that by the early 20th century the area had replaced Mayfair as the base for the medical coterie of London: it was therefore an ideal location for the Royal Society of Medicine.

In May 1909 James Boyton of Elliot, Son and Boyton, surveyors and estate agents, alerted MacAlister to the property in Henrietta Street.[10] Sir William Selby Church, Dr Arthur Latham, Mr Herbert Pendlebury and MacAlister urged the Society's Council to consider the merits of the site, which had been inspected by the architect John Belcher who was confident he could design a handsome building there, the only objection being that because the Post Office adjoined it could be noisy.[11]

The calculations of the House and Finance committee and the deliberations of the Council moved slowly. The delay was compounded by an offer from an assurance office to advance £30,000 free of interest for ten years; tempting as this was, Fellows did not like the implications. Instead it was decided to launch a building fund and arrangements were made for a loan from the Union Bank at 4% interest. While these provisions were being put in place, the Council prevaricated over the suitability of the Henrietta Street site. The pace quickened in December 1909 when a decision had to be made. MacAlister, backed by Dr Latham, seized the initiative and personally secured the option of taking the building lease offered by the Howard de Walden estate.[12]

The Council was soon persuaded to ratify the decision in the knowledge that 'a highly desirable tenant' had been found for 20 Hanover Square. This was Mr Howard Frank of Messrs Knight Frank, auctioneers, surveyors and valuers of 9 Conduit Street, who agreed to take a lease on 20 Hanover Square for 80 years from March 1910 at £2,500 per annum.[13] MacAlister had at first demanded £70,000 'clear' from Mr Frank for the sale of 20 Hanover Square; Frank had offered £63,000 but on the advice of Boyton the property was leased rather than sold. Once agreement was reached early in 1910 MacAlister and Frank began to wrestle over fixtures and fittings. Frank was an authoritative figure with a formidable reputation for business, yet he was taken aback by MacAlister's barrage of letters. MacAlister was determined that the Society would take with it the Chambers chimneypiece and medallion, a double-faced clock and 30 chairs. Frank refused to allow the removal of any other chimneypieces from 20 Hanover Square and he accused MacAlister of stripping the building. Finally he admitted that he was out-witted: 'If ever I am in a tight corner I shall certainly solicit your offices to get me out,' he wrote to MacAlister, 'Your letter really is most ingenious'.[14] 20 Hanover Square was not entirely stripped when the RSM moved out, however, and was soon to undergo major alterations under the supervision of the architect E Vincent Harris.

At a special general meeting of Fellows of the RSM held on 2 February 1910 it was announced that the lease of 20 Hanover Square had been granted, that the Society had acquired the site on the corner of Wimpole Street with Henrietta Street and that some £30,000 (soon increased to £35,000) was needed to erect a suitable building there. Fellows expressed little enthusiasm, indeed the criticism from some quarters was carping and pessimistic. But a leader in the *Lancet* did its best to encourage readers to support the appeal for funds in order 'to build a house worthy of the body that has in its keeping the scientific progress and solidarity of British medicine ... Medicine has little endowment in this country and in the Royal Society of Medicine there is an opportunity for administering financial encouragement to the progress of the most humanitarian of sciences'.[15]

The old houses at 2–5 Henrietta Street were demolished by Messrs Holloway in May 1910 and G Godson and Sons were contracted to erect 'a hall and other buildings' on the site at a cost of £27,186 according to the specification provided by JJ Joass and FM Elgood under the superintendence of the consulting architect John Belcher.[16] This arrangement of joint architects working under a consulting architect was a compromise to prevent friction.

Initially Belcher had declined to accept the commission if Elgood was also employed.[17] He had his way, for Elgood soon retreated – he was compensated by other commissions on the Howard de Walden estate and a knighthood.

As a long standing tenant of the Society, John Belcher was the obvious choice as architect, having submitted plans for the extension of 20 Hanover Square soon after the formation of the RSM in 1907. He had been President of the Royal Institute of British Architects in 1904 and was awarded its Gold Medal in 1907. He had written books on architecture and designed country houses and public buildings such as the Institute of Chartered Accountants, Moorgate (1888–93), which established him as a leading Edwardian baroque architect. From 1908 he and his junior partner, John James Joass, worked on designs for Whiteley's department store in Bayswater and Joass took MacAlister to see what was being done there in October 1911. Belcher was paid more than Joass for drawings and plans of the proposed building for the RSM in 1910; as Belcher's illness took hold, however, most of the work fell to Joass. One of Belcher's assistants confirmed that Joass was the stronger character and greater man of the partnership, with his 'quick Scottish draughtsmanship and clever use of colour. It was he who detailed all the buildings of those days, and gave them that curious elongated classical form with pendant blocks and wreaths, of which Messrs Mappin and Webb's premises in Oxford Street or the Royal Insurance building in Piccadilly are conspicuous examples'.[18] With characteristic thoroughness MacAlister questioned the architects about their most recent buildings; he particularly liked their work for the Zoological Society in Regent's Park, completed in 1911. The style of the Zoological Society's building, in particular the principal entrance, long windows and iron work were to be echoed in the main façade of 1 Wimpole Street.

Belcher and Joass both attended the first meetings of the Building committee and Belcher advised Fellows to visit the Library of the Institute of Civil Engineers being built to designs by James Miller of Glasgow, as he was planning a room of similar character for the RSM. MacAlister did not hesitate to express his own views on the architecture of the proposed building (he had some experience of building work at Leeds in the 1880s). He did not like the floor-to-ceiling windows suggested for the library and he asked for a 'cheery fireplace' in the front hall. He wanted Belcher to design a book carrier similar to one he had seen in the Library of Congress in Washington: he told the architects that the building should be in the Tudor style and he made it plain that the success or failure of the building would be judged by the acoustic properties of the meeting-rooms rather than upon artistic merit. Belcher and Joass obliged in the detail but were firm in rejecting the Tudor style as 'a most unsuitable manner of dealing with the façade and would produce a thoroughly unsatisfactory building'.[19] Instead, the architecture of 1 Wimpole Street was described by its architects as 'more or less in the style of the Greek revival in England ... intended to be massive and imposing in character and representative of the Society to which it belongs'.[20]

## The building fund

The scale of the building, particularly the number of floors, depended on funding. The lease of the site had been secured for £8,000, which was raised by the sale of the Society's investments, and a further £9,000 was subscribed by Fellows and members within a few months. There remained a big gap between this sum and an estimated total cost of £30,000, so a public appeal was launched stressing 'the Society's work, its beneficial influence on the public health and its activity in effecting improvements in the prevention and treatment of disease'. It was hoped that individuals and public-spirited bodies would contribute, and MacAlister identified the City as a possible source of largesse.

Therefore in October 1910 a deputation from the RSM obtained an interview with the Lord Mayor, Sir John Knill; Professor Osler made a convincing case and the cause gained the support of Knill and Alderman Sir Thomas Boor Crosby, who was the first physician to be Lord Mayor (1911–12).[21] The response of the City institutions was variable: there was some prejudice against the appeal owing to a rumour that there was going to be a club-house element in the new building [22] – an aspect promoted by MacAlister. The Goldsmiths' Company gave the largest sum, £500; the Grocers, Clothworkers, Salters and Skinners donated lesser amounts. Heading the list of individual contributors was Lord Howard de Walden and Seaford, a generous landlord who not only contributed to the fund but also granted a favourable new lease of 999 years from 1913 at £400 per annum, for a premium of £2,000.[23] Dr C Theodore Williams, Sir Thomas Barlow, Sir Alfred Pearce Gould and Professor Osler all gave £500 to the building fund – more than Osler could afford, he claimed. By December 1911 £12,963 had been subscribed and by 1914 the fund stood at £21,512.[24]

## The naming and allocation of rooms

Some subscribers to the building fund were wooed by the immortalization of a relative in the name of a room. Mrs Barnes' gift of £4,000 guaranteed that the largest meeting hall commemorated her late husband, Dr Robert Barnes, who had taken an active part in founding the Obstetrical and the British Gynaecological Societies. Barnes had been a Fellow of the RMCS since 1861 and latterly an Honorary Fellow, yet 'certain people' objected to the naming of a room after their old rival and antagonist. Nonetheless, MacAlister's personal influence secured the deal.

Roger Beck donated £500 in memory of his brother, Professor Marcus Beck, and this went to the Marcus Beck Laboratory where Ronald Ross supervised research from 1913 to 1917 (see pages 192–93). Room 28 adjoining the laboratory was named after Sir Edwin Durning-Lawrence in 1916, until a misunderstanding with his family forced the return of funds.[25] Sir William Allchin's widow contributed £100 for the William Allchin Room – her husband had been physician extraordinary to King George V and was for many years on the staff of Westminster Hospital. Henry L Florence FRIBA, 'a grateful patient', had a room named after him, and the Toynbee family combined with Dr Dundas Grant and members of the Sections of Otology and Laryngology to ensure that Joseph Toynbee's name was given to a committee room.[26]

In his search for sources of finance, MacAlister found a new application for the Marshall Hall fund, which had been in abeyance. This was a discretionary fund and the Council agreed to channel the capital of some £700 into 1 Wimpole Street on condition that a room and a bookplate commemorated Marshall Hall, a Fellow who had received little recognition from the Society during his lifetime (see pages 93–94).[27] The most important rooms in the building were the RSM Council Room, the Sections' Council Room, two meeting halls and the Library. Besides offices, other facilities included a tea room with a smoking room adjoining on the second floor for the use of Fellows. Lady Fellows were given a room on the third floor where the décor (the ladies chose tapestry covers for the chairs) was supervised by Mrs Mary Scharlieb, the first woman to gain a London University MD and a pillar of the Section of Obstetrics and Gynaecology. It was intended to hang medical women's portraits in the Lady Fellows' room and Mrs Stanley Boyd's portrait was the first to appear. MacAlister took trouble to ensure that Lady Fellows were comfortable, while at the same time he worried that the windows of the new building might be smashed by the suffragettes.[28]

Patients' rooms (male and female) were conveniently placed for the meeting halls and MacAlister instructed the architects that a sink was required in the morbid growths room.[29] The Library arrangements were of course his forte and he took advice from the Bodleian, Cambridge University Library, Guildhall Library and other leading institutions. His personal triumph was to contrive lamps for the tables with their electrical wires concealed in the table legs – a trick that intrigued the King when he opened the building.

Fellows, Lady Fellows and members were content with the accommodation but the clerks grumbled. 'Miss Williamson – as usual – has been making herself a perfect nuisance, complaining that the Clerks' room is wholly inadequate ... She maintains that if this is the whole accommodation provided for the Clerks, the paragraphs in English history referring to the Black Hole of Calcutta will, in future generations, be replaced by descriptions of a Clerks' Room in the building of the Royal Society of Medicine',[30] MacAlister wrote to the architects.

## The building completed

Belcher and Joass reported that building work was complete in June 1912 at a cost of £30,500 exclusive of architects' fees. When that sum was added to the cost of fittings a total of £36,500 was incurred, and by 1914 the expense of the building with its furnishings amounted to £54,736.[31]

The *Architectural Review* found 1 Wimpole Street appropriate to its purpose. 'It is simple in its parts, but there is a straightforward vigour about it which holds the attention, and it possesses a dignity eminently in keeping with the institution housed within its walls'.[32] Subsequent evaluations have referred to it as 'a massive and vigorous work'; possessing 'a small but monumental front with recessed giant Roman Doric columns, and a fanciful entrance with blocked fasces below lions' heads, the detail going hard and angular as in all Belcher's later buildings'.[33]

Once the building was in use MacAlister found much to criticize, chiefly the noise from the street and fumes from the chimneys – 'the conspiracy of architects and builders to poison our staff', he complained. The Building committee wanted higher railings modelled on those outside the Banqueting House in Whitehall, preferably with sharp spikes to deter messengers who frequented the Post Office,[34] and Dr Maxwell Trotter disliked the slippery surface of the main staircase which, he said, had been responsible for him falling from the first floor landing, and suffering much pain and inconvenience.[35]

The elevations of the building as approved by the Howard de Walden estate on 31 October 1910 featured a fourth floor and a large sculpture over the main entrance. The

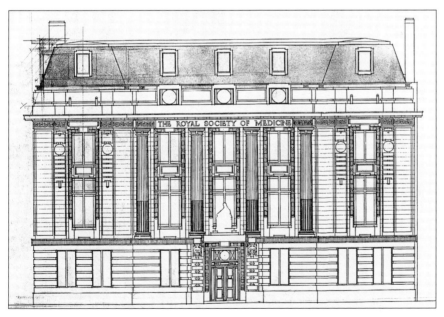

The main elevation of 1 Wimpole Street as originally planned; a large sculpture was intended to surmount the entrance. The design by John Belcher and JJ Joass was approved by the Howard de Walden estate in October 1910.

Photographs of 1 Wimpole Street taken at the time of its opening in 1912: Opposite: the main
façade, and below: the entrance hall with the chimneypiece from Berners Street and the Empire clock
and candleholders presented by the President, Sir Henry Morris. This page: the Library, where lamps
and tables designed by MacAlister were a special feature. Electrical wires for the lamps were
dispensed with by contact through the legs of the tables to which strong springs were fitted. The
springs fitted into a socket in the floor and there was a plug in the table. When not in use a table
could be placed elsewhere as its weight was sufficient to force the spring back into the table leg.

fourth floor was not commissioned for the present, nor did the mighty figure of a seated
woman over the front entrance ever appear, nor were the tablets on the façade ever carved
with the names of distinguished medical men as had been intended. Dr Latham, for one,
did not approve of 'the stone woman' presiding over the front door and conspired with
MacAlister to prevent her appearance. Joass' designs for lamps set on granite piers in the
porch met with approval once the Aesculapian snakes 'modelled on an old Roman
example' were fattened to the required thickness.[36]

MacAlister's correspondence relating to 1 Wimpole Street reveals a dedication
bordering on the obsessive. As Secretary he had responsibility for the comfort and convenience of Fellows; his supervision of the architects was scrupulous and he was supported
by the President, Sir Henry Morris, who was experienced in overseeing such things.
Sir William Selby Church was not alone in acknowledging that it was through MacAlister
'that the formation of the Society and the acquisition of our present house has been
possible'.[37] That said, MacAlister's obsession with minutiae and his lengthy negotiations
over the purchase of a vacuum cleaner (a three-horse-power turbine sweeper was finally
chosen) and laundry arrangements appear excessive. He was still berating the architects
about the defects of the building when John Belcher died in November 1913.

*The royal opening*
With the monumental building nearing completion MacAlister planned a royal opening
ceremony and negotiated for a new address. The front elevation and main entrance of the
RSM's building was in Henrietta Street, sometimes confused with Henrietta Street in
Covent Garden. Moreover an address in Wimpole Street was altogether more appropriate
and more desirable than one in Henrietta Street. MacAlister used all his persuasive skills to

obtain the change of address to 1 Wimpole Street, explaining to officials of the London County Council that although architecturally speaking the main entrance was in Henrietta Street, for most purposes the entrance used would be the one in Wimpole Street. He argued that the patients who attended the clinical meetings sometimes had to come long distances and if directed to Wimpole Street 'it is certain they will be saved many weary and painful steps'. Once he had obtained the consent of neighbours and the Howard de Walden estate, MacAlister's case was strengthened and the LCC agreed that the corner building should have the address of number 1 Wimpole Street.[38]

It had been expected that the Prince of Wales, an Honorary Fellow of the RSM, would lay the foundation stone, an engagement he was unable to fulfil. On 21 May 1912, however, as King George V he was accompanied by Queen Mary to the royal opening of 1 Wimpole Street (Plate 30) even though the court was in mourning following the death of the King of Denmark. A flurry of activity preceded the ceremony in order to ensure that the lifts worked and furnishings were in place. MacAlister organized a guard of honour, the allocation of tickets, tea and a bouquet for the Queen. This was made up from specimens of plants gathered at the Chelsea Physic Garden – an unusual assortment comprising senna, spurge, tarragon, fern, cabbage rose, tansy, artemisia, lavender, hellebore, anchusa, woad, oak and salad burnet. 'It was my own cranky idea', MacAlister admitted, and the Queen liked it; the pressed flowers and herbs were later preserved in an album.[39] The ceremony centred around speeches, after which Fellows were presented to the royal couple. The King was given a copy of the Society's centenary history and was issued with the first book to be borrowed from the new Library – a treatise written by William Clowes in 1602 on 'the king's evil' (scrofula), duly returned.

Invitations to the royal opening were limited in number, so on 22 May the President, Sir Henry Morris, gave a conversazione at his own expense for 'the whole of the Fellows and members with their best girls' – some 2,000 in all (Plate 31). Medical films were hired, a band provided light relief and a variety entertainment was provided by MacAlister's friend, Charles Collette.[40] In November hospitality was extended to the medical profession at large in the form of a series of At Homes on four separate evenings, which were attended by about 4,000 medical practitioners. They were given light refreshments, entertained by music and a demonstration of Leduc's osmotic growths; curious specimens from the Royal College of Surgeons were shown on the epidiascope and Dr Norman Moore laid out a display of rare books in the library. The Council was pleased to note that the expense of the At Homes did not exceed £30 an evening. This was due in part to 'a handsome gift' from Messrs Walter Bird and Co, who supplied up to 8,000 cigarettes of the new Rhodesian-grown Turkish and Virginian tobaccos.[41]

The library and offices at 1 Wimpole Street were open to Fellows and members on 29 May and a special general meeting was held the next day, followed by the first meetings of Sections that evening as the RSM settled down to its customary business in its new house.

## The interval at Cavendish Square

While 1 Wimpole Street was being built and with 20 Hanover Square let, the Society found a temporary home in Cavendish Square. MacAlister located somewhere suitable early in 1910: 'Jonathan Hutchinson's old house (now Boyton's committee rooms) in Cavendish Square' and he persuaded Sir William Selby Church to inspect the property with him.[42] The house, number 15 on the north side of the Square, had belonged to Sir Jonathan Hutchinson for some 30 years until he moved to Gower Street in 1907. Although the place was in a 'shocking condition',[43] the RSM rented it at £800 for one year with a monthly option thereafter. It provided a convenient base for overseeing building work at Wimpole Street but was not large enough to accommodate some meetings or the entire contents of

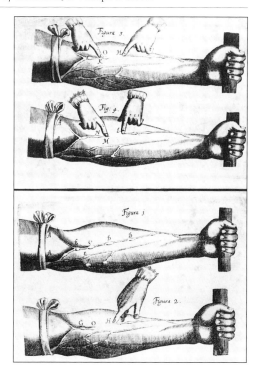

William Harvey's *Exercitatio anatomica de motu cordis et sanguinis in animalibus* (1628) was presented to the Library by Sir William Osler in 1917 and signed by him to this effect. He purchased it at auction and described it on a postcard to the Society's Librarian as 'really a beauty. The title page had to be repaired, and the leaf of Errata has been put in in duplicate. Like all copies it has been badly cut. When is the next meeting of the Library Committee at which I will present it?'. Only 55 copies of the first edition are known to have survived. The engravings, showing the action of the valves in the veins, were based on earlier illustrations by Fabricius.

the Library, so arrangements were made for the use of the large hall of the Medical Society at 11 Chandos Street, while 100 cases of books from the Library were stored in the basement of the Royal College of Surgeons.[44]

The first meeting of the Society at its temporary home was in April 1910 and the last almost exactly two years later. The dislocation of the Library (some 10 to 15,000 books were still available to Fellows) and the construction of 1 Wimpole Street did not distract MacAlister from his ambitions for the RSM Library. In the *Lancet* of June 1910 he announced a new development: 'To all our Fellows living abroad we now offer to prepare for them gratis short abstracts of papers, and even books, upon any medical subject, and to search for, or check, references to medical literature ... Men living in the Chitral valley, in the Sudan, the Cape, and equatorial Africa, who for years have had their work hindered by lack of library conveniences, say that what we now do for them is even better than they could have done for themselves had they been in London'.[45]

This was all part of MacAlister's ambition to create the greatest British medical library 'so as to place at the disposal of medical men, however poor, the whole resources of the world's medical learning'. He was supported in this by Sir William Osler (who was given a baronetcy in 1911), but despite their energetic canvassing they failed to procure the necessary funding.[46] Nevertheless the RSM Library expanded continuously, receiving large donations in the early years of the 20th century (see pages 206–07).

While the Society was at Cavendish Square Osler was the driving force on the Library committee. He urged colleagues to purchase a 1513 edition of Rösslin's *Manual of midwifery* (illustrated on page 246), he persuaded MacAlister to find room on the shelves for the records of the Medico-Botanical Society (long since defunct), and alerted him to book auctions: 'I see in the Hodgkin sale early in May another 1478 Celsus. Could we not bleed some fellows to the tune of about £30 and send a bid? It is one of the great books of the profession, which the library should possess. I will go a fiver. Who are the men likely to help in it? I will attack them'. For all his enthusiasm, Osler failed to secure the 1478 Celsus for the Library, but he met with success in 1917 when a copy of William Harvey's *Exercitatio anatomica de motu cordis et sanguinis in animalibus* came on the market. This time Osler took the matter into his own hands. 'Not to have the 1628 Harvey in the RSM is a reproach which I should like to see removed. I believe it is an exceptional copy'. He therefore purchased it (he thought it would fetch £30, it was valued at £50) and presented it to the Library.[47]

## Subjects for investigation

Between 1910 and 1912, a period of dislocation and disruption for the Society, two special topics for research were identified: tropical medicine and venereal disease. At the annual dinner of 1910 the President Sir Henry Morris stressed that the RSM wished to take a leading part in the investigation of tropical diseases, and two years later MacAlister was requested by the Council to ascertain whether Fellows and members would support a Section of Tropical Medicine. This was followed up by negotiations with the Society of Tropical Medicine and Hygiene, which declined to co-operate (see pages 342–43).

The other subject arousing fresh interest was the treatment of syphilis, discussed at meetings of the Society in June 1912 in the wake of Ehrlich's new treatment, '606' or salvarsan. Venereal disease was also being addressed by the Eugenics Education Society under the presidency of Major Leonard Darwin, Charles Darwin's fourth son, who sought assistance from the RSM. As he explained in his letter, the Eugenics Society was concerned 'with all questions affecting the racial quality of the nation' and in 1911 it sought the co-operation of the RSM to mitigate the 'national evil' of venereal disease and so avert the deterioration of the race.[48]

## Eugenics

The Eugenics Education Society had been founded in 1907 in the expectation that eugenics would bring about a utopian society. A journal, public meetings and lectures generated a good deal of publicity and committees were organized by the Society to lobby the government on issues such as the poor law and the treatment of alcoholics and the feeble-minded, as well as venereal disease. As Dr Amand Routh affirmed in an address to the Section of Obstetrics and Gynaecology in 1913, 'Eugenics, or the well-being of the race, is now one of the prevailing instincts of our generation'.[49]

The object of the joint committee formed by Fellows of the RSM and representatives of the Eugenics Education Society in 1912 was to gather statistics on venereal disease from home and abroad, to campaign for improved hospital facilities for its treatment and the better instruction of medical students, and to promote legislative reform. The report of the Conjoint committee published in 1914 concluded that all were agreed upon the urgent necessity for the better treatment of venereal diseases. The statistics gathered by the committee with help from the Foreign Office covered 40 countries and capitals and the resulting report was presented to the Royal Commission on Venereal Diseases, to which Fellows of the RSM gave evidence.

In the same year the RSM added its weight to the National Council for Combating Venereal Diseases, on which the President Sir Francis Champneys sat and which met at 1 Wimpole Street.[50]

The National Council gave invaluable help in educating the public about venereal diseases and its report was welcomed by the Council of the RSM with the resolution that the Royal Society of Medicine was strongly in favour of legislation to make it a penal offence for anyone other than a medical practitioner to advise, treat or dispense drugs or remedies for venereal disease (the Report of the Royal Commission had revealed that most people with venereal disease resorted to quacks for treatment). The Council's resolution was forwarded to the Local Government Board, London MPs and the press in 1917. The Royal College of Physicians passed similar resolutions and the recommendations were carried into effect by the Venereal Diseases Act of 1917, which prohibited the sale and advertisement of remedies to 'cure' those diseases. The following year the Venereal Diseases Service began its work throughout the country using the original Wassermann diagnostic test defined by the RSM as standard.

## International moves

The report of the Conjoint committee of the RSM and the Eugenics Education Society containing information gathered from overseas was indicative of the growing internationalism in medicine and public health. An important step in this direction had been taken in 1907 when 13 states agreed to establish a permanent public health office in Paris to collect and disseminate recent knowledge on diseases such as cholera, plague and yellow fever. The organization was slow to start and its activity was limited until after the First World War, which may explain plans to establish another international office in Jerusalem (1913–14). On being consulted about the project, the RSM advised the Privy Council that a British biologist should represent the country at the proposed International Health Bureau at Jerusalem. But 1914 was not an auspicious time for the foundation of a new international medical bureau and the plans lapsed.[51]

## Osler's tuberculosis resolution

Investigative reports, recommendations to the government and information for a Royal Commission were regarded as being within the Society's scope. Controversial or political issues, on the other hand, remained taboo. In the autumn of 1912 Sir William Osler, Vice President of the RSM and President of the Section of Clinical Medicine, warned the Secretary that he intended to raise his 'tuberculosis resolution' at the impending Council meeting. Osler had written to *The Times* the previous August proposing that tuberculosis dispensaries be established alongside existing hospitals and medical schools with the aim of the better training of students and doctors in the treatment of the disease. He evidently hoped to recruit the support of the RSM to promote this commendable plan and he proposed to start with a discussion at the Society on the relation of hospitals and medical schools to the Insurance Act, especially with reference to tuberculosis.

In view of the importance of the subject the Council called for a special meeting to define the main points of the proposed discussion and it gave its unqualified approval to a general, free discussion as proposed by Osler, which it hoped would determine the action of the authorities. A letter from Dr Arthur Latham raised objections, however, and forced the withdrawal of Osler's motion. While Latham agreed that the authorities required guidance, he argued that 'the Royal Society of Medicine has nothing to do with controversial subjects, questions of administration or education'. Apparently fears had been expressed at the time of the amalgamation that the RSM intended to be a rival to the BMA and assurances had been given to the contrary. Latham argued that if the RSM became embroiled in the question of tuberculosis dispensaries the Society's reputation for the impartial consideration of scientific problems would be dented. He won the day.[52]

## Special discussions and social evenings

Since the creation of the RSM with its increasing number of Sections, the corporate organization of the Society had altered and to begin with the only meetings were those arranged by the individual Sections. In order to bring together Fellows of the Society from the various Sections to debate subjects of general interest, special discussions were instituted. Initially suitable subjects were suggested by the President, and from 1912 a Special Discussions committee took this in hand. The discussions were opened by the President, followed by eminent speakers at several meetings on successive weeks. The contents were reported verbatim at the beginning of the first part of the annual volumes of the *Proceedings* and constituted authoritative reports to which well-known names were attached. The series commenced in November 1908 with aplomb: 'The influence of heredity on disease with special reference to tuberculosis, cancer and diseases of the nervous system'. Sir William Gowers spoke on diseases of the nervous system, Professor William Bateson explored Mendelism and Dr F Mott told of his study of heredity and insanity (he had collected statistics on patients who were related to each other in all the London asylums). Professor Karl Pearson the statistician was one of three Fellows of the Royal Society contributing to this debate, which continued for four evenings under the chairmanship of Sir William Selby Church.[53]

Sir Almroth Wright was prevailed upon to open the discussion on vaccine therapy in 1910 (see pages 226–27). Wright, the model for Sir Colenso Ridgeon in GB Shaw's play *The doctor's dilemma*, had introduced typhoid inoculation and perfected a technique for the treatment of tuberculosis by inoculation. With a wealth of experience behind him he still found that addressing the subject of vaccine therapy was exceptionally difficult and complex.[54]

The first debate held at 1 Wimpole Street was on syphilis, and in its course Mr D'Arcy Power spoke about the highly effective new treatment employed in his wards – salvarsan. After four evenings the President closed the proceedings by referring to the investigations being carried forward by the Conjoint committee of the Eugenics Education Society and the RSM.

In 1913 the subject was 'Alimentary toxaemia', occupying six meetings between March and May that were notable for the fervour of the 56 speakers, none of whom was able to define precisely what he meant by alimentary toxaemia. The drama of the debate lay in the dogmatism of Sir William Arbuthnot Lane's paper on the 'Consequences and treatment of alimentary toxaemia' from a surgical point of view, in which he argued for operative treatment, and in the opposing arguments from Sir William Hale-White and Sir James Goodhart. Lane was an innovative surgeon, provoking controversy by using internal fixations for fractures that could be treated by conservative methods and by his flap method of operating on cleft palate. Most controversial were his views on chronic intestinal stasis and his advocacy of the removal of the colon. During the debate at the RSM Hale-White maintained that surgical interference was a reproach to the patient's doctors and Goodhart took Lane's hypothesis apart. An observer reported that 'When Lane followed Hale-White he was pale, tense and tremulous with emotion' and that he left the meeting crushed. The result of the debate was inconclusive but it gave an impetus to the study of the functions and sources of disease in the alimentary canal and publicized the advances Arbuthnot Lane had made in methods of resecting the bowel, although not everyone agreed with them. Lane may have been temporarily crushed by his critics at the RSM but, undaunted, he went on to found the New Health Society in 1925.[55]

The session for 1913–14 saw the introduction of occasional lectures or social evenings, as they came to be called, when a guest speaker was invited to hold forth on his special subject. These lectures were sometimes attended by as many as 300 Fellows, their friends and families who heard a short address and partook of light refreshments afterwards. Among those invited to give the first lectures was the Japanese bacteriologist Hideyo Noguchi of the Rockefeller Institute for Medical Research in New York, who talked on microbiology. His great endeavour was to identify the causative agent of yellow fever and to develop a vaccine against the disease (of which he was to die in Accra). Dr Bayon (from Robben Island) spoke on the leprosy problem in the British Empire and Dr Comandon of

Paris on the application of 'cinematograph' to biological science. These lectures were organized by MacAlister, whose patience was tried by Noguchi's ill-health and by Surgeon G Murray Levick's modesty. Levick, 'poor Scott's medical companion' as MacAlister described him, agreed to talk about his experiences with Captain Scott's expedition of 1912 from a medical point of view. On reflection he decided his lecture was unsuitable for women and he requested that they should not be present. Dr Janet Clayton supposed he meant the stuff of 'smoking room stories' and stayed away, and to avoid blatant discrimination MacAlister quietly obtained assurances from practically all the ladies that they would not attend Levick's lecture.[56]

## The Council Club

A dinner club known as the Medical and Chirurgical Society Club had flourished briefly in the early 19th century, lapsing by 1842 (see pages 16–17). There were occasional anniversary dinners for members, and the first annual dinner for Fellows was held in 1892 once the Society was established at 20 Hanover Square. That occasion was organized by MacAlister, who was keen to encourage social contact between Fellows. He was himself a member of several London clubs and he had hoped that the Society's new building in Wimpole Street would include facilities for a Fellows' club. It was a bitter disappointment to him when on returning from convalescence he found that the fourth storey of 1 Wimpole Street, which might have accommodated club rooms and a medical museum, was not to be built owing to lack of faith in the Society's future finances and to a strong feeling against club facilities among senior Fellows.[57]

Thus apart from afternoon tea in the Fellows' room or tea and dry biscuits in the Library (under no circumstances bread and butter),[58] there was no provision for a dining or luncheon club at the Society's house. The gap was partly filled by the Council Club, which was functioning by the winter of 1910, possibly before. One of its members, Sir Humphry Rolleston, agreed with MacAlister that dinners and conversaziones were an important facet of the Society's life. 'At the Royal Society of Medicine this side was much developed by MacAlister by the creation of the Council Club', Rolleston remembered. It was composed of any Fellow or Lady Fellow of the Society who was or had been a member of the RSM Council or of a Council of any constituent Section.[59]

Before the outbreak of the First World War Council Club dinners – sometimes as many as six a session – were held at Oddenino's Imperial Restaurant at 60 and 62 Regent Street, where in 1912 members paid six shillings each for dinner. Initial enthusiasm for the Club soon waned and MacAlister urged Sir Henry Morris as President 'to infuse a more informal spirit into the gatherings by inviting men to get up and say things – and perhaps at the end of dinner to move about and change places'.

An important initial object of the Club was for men of Council rank to meet informally and discuss questions affecting the interests of the Society, and this aspect had been neglected. So had a second object: to offer hospitality to colonial, American or foreign medical men visiting London. The dinners obviously needed invigorating; a President of one of the larger Sections wrote to say that he found them 'intensely dull and [they] will ultimately prove a failure. How many men are worth paying 7/6 for the ?pleasure of sitting alongside of and talking to for a couple of hours?'.[60]

Sir Henry Morris took MacAlister's advice by inviting overseas guests to Council Club dinners, and an Entertainment committee was appointed.[61] By 1913 the Café Royal was the favourite resort of the Club, as an ample meal could be had there for five shillings a head excluding wine. The dinners were held less frequently during the First World War but were still going strong in 1924, when there was a Foundation Dinner on 22 May to commemorate the meeting of physicians and surgeons to found the Medical and Chirurgical Society in 1805.[62] Thereafter the record falls silent.

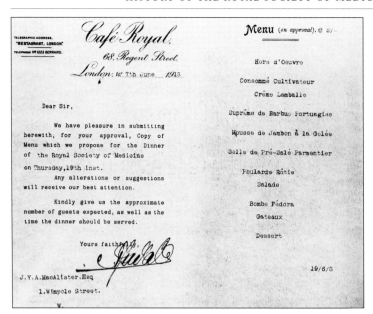

A Council Club dinner at the Café Royal, 19 June 1913.

The retirement and death of MacAlister in 1925 may have brought about the demise of the Council Club and it was not until 1948 that the Royal Society of Medicine Club was established. This was organized 'on somewhat similar lines to the club of the Royal College of Surgeons' and bore no similarity to the exclusive Council Club. To begin with the RSM Club centred on a bar which was open to all Fellows, members, Associates and executive officers. The provision of light meals soon followed, leading to a restaurant employing two chefs and making a good profit.[63]

## The Marcus Beck Laboratory

Roger Beck donated £500 towards the building of 1 Wimpole Street where a research laboratory was named after his brother Marcus Beck, a Fellow of the RMCS and Professor of Clinical Surgery at University College Hospital. Sir George Buckston Browne, who profited from Marcus Beck's supervision, described him as 'a handsome bachelor, a nephew of Joseph Lister, superior, supercilious and nearly always sarcastic'.[64] Beck died in 1893 after suffering for twenty years from diabetes.

Professor Marcus Beck, commemorated in the Marcus Beck Laboratory, now the Marcus Beck Library, which houses the Society's rare book collection.

The original idea of the endowment was to provide a laboratory for the use of Fellows. MacAlister claimed the laboratory was his hobby, 'which I succeeded in getting established against opposition in high places and I was delighted that Ross came to work here'. Sir Ronald Ross applied for the use of the Marcus Beck Laboratory in the summer of 1913 and was appointed its Honorary Director in November (he lived at 18 Cavendish Square so the laboratory was convenient).

Ross's first plan was to carry out investigations on the cultivation of malaria and possibly experiments on ovariotomy. The work required a licence from the Home Office to authorize animal experiments, and MacAlister explained to the authorities that Ross was about to begin important researches involving the inoculation of guinea pigs and other small animals.[65] The licence was duly issued and new equipment and hutches for the animals were ordered – the Library committee was alarmed to find two cages for animals among the bookstacks in the basement on their annual inspection of 1916 and suggested the roof was a more appropriate place.[66] Ross meanwhile found two assistants, Dr David Thomson, the recipient of a Grocers' Company research scholarship, and Dr John G Thomson who was a Beit research scholar.

Work in the Marcus Beck Laboratory was soon diverted from malaria to the cultivation of tissue *in vitro*: Dr David Thomson had by July 1914 successfully grown human cancer *in vitro* for the first time on record. He also showed that somatic growth could be obtained *in vitro* with certain portions of an embryonic chick and on one occasion a complete chick embryo implanted in the culture medium increased in size. Dr JG Thomson worked on the problem of spirochaetes in the alimentary track of humans, and the achievements of the team were fully recorded in the *Proceedings* for 1913–14.[67]

This research was disrupted by the First World War, during which the laboratory staff were required elsewhere. Dr AJ Venn, a Fellow of the RSM, was given the use of the room for private research until Ross hit on measles as a worthwhile project, as this was presently prevalent among troops and was also the regular cause of a very large mortality among children. Ross embarked on research with the help of a haematologist and a bacteriologist, necessitating the extension of laboratory work into an adjoining room called the Durning-Lawrence Room.[68] In the spring of 1916 Ross was ordered abroad and when he returned in November research in the laboratory concentrated on dysentery, there being an epidemic in the Mediterranean. The work was funded by the Medical Research Committee, enabling Ross to employ five staff and an attendant in the Marcus Beck Laboratory, yet in 1917 the work concluded. It was decided not to continue the appointment of a Director and the room reverted to its original use as a laboratory where members could adjourn after Section meetings to examine specimens.[69] For a brief period in 1918 the laboratory at 1 Wimpole Street was one of several rooms allocated to the Medical Assessors of the National Service, when a stream of potential recruits tramped through the building daily. At the end of the war the laboratory was again used by Sections until 1923, when it was converted into the Marcus Beck Library and fitted with bookcases for the rare book collection.[70]

## The First World War

Anxiety about the repercussions of the war surfaced at 1 Wimpole Street when MacAlister reported to the Council that the supply of German and Austrian medical periodicals had been curtailed. He managed to obtain permission from the Board of Trade to allow their import through a contact in Amsterdam, providing that no money passed to the enemy.[71]

For the duration of the war the use of 1 Wimpole Street was offered to Medical Officers of the naval and military medical services (imperial and allied). They were invited to attend the meetings, demonstrations and discussions, to take tea and to avail themselves of the Library services. The Library functioned throughout the war even though its staff was

**THE ROYAL SOCIETY OF MEDICINE**

This Society cordially invites the Commissioned Medical Officers of all the Naval and Military Medical Services (Imperial and Allied) to make free use of the Library (for reading and reference), and of the Fellows' Rooms, including Writing, Conversation, Smoking, Tea, and Dressing Rooms.

They are also welcome to attend the meetings which are held, for the reading of papers, clinical demonstrations, and for discussions. These are announced in the weekly medical journals. The Society's house is open every day, except Sunday, from 11 a.m. to 6.30 p.m.

In addition to the above, Officers when at the Fronts are invited to ask for such help as can be provided from the Society's Library and abstracts, translations, references, and notes on any Medical or Surgical subject will be sent to them as promptly as is possible.

1, WIMPOLE STREET,
CAVENDISH SQUARE, W.1.
(Principal Entrance in Henrietta Street,
2 minutes' walk from top of Bond Street.)

J. Y. W. MACALISTER,
Secretary
(To whom all communications
should be addressed).

For the duration of the First World War Medical Officers with the Forces were invited to make use of 1 Wimpole Street. The Library offered abstracts, translations, references and research notes.

depleted when Hewitt joined the City of London Volunteers and John Shields went on active service abroad. Those who remained were busy with the supply of books, papers, references, abstracts, translations, notes on any medical or surgical subject and even instruments to officers at the fronts.[72]

The number of meetings of Sections was reduced during the war but there were still between 70 and 80 a session, with an average attendance of 32 for 1915–16. The meetings, lectures and discussions of these years reflected the current situation: Osler urged MacAlister to organize 'more specific war meetings', suggesting that paratyphoid fever, war nephritis, trench fever, Dardanelles diarrhoea and soldier's heart needed discussing.[73] His proposition led to several successful meetings at the RSM, beginning with one under the auspices of the Section of Epidemiology and State Medicine in February 1915 on cerebrospinal meningitis. This had always been a soldier's disease and with the concentration of troops in camps and unusually bad weather, outbreaks had occurred in numerous places. Osler addressed the meeting and spoke about the sources of infection and serum therapy, and the ensuing discussion lasted for two meetings.[74] On later occasions Sir Bertrand Dawson spoke on paratyphoid fever, Sir Almroth Wright gave Fellows the benefit of his research on wound infections – he was working on the subject in a laboratory at Boulogne, assisted by Alexander Fleming among others, and he highlighted defects in the way the sick and wounded were treated in this war. Dr Weinberg spoke on gas gangrene, the basis of a special study published by the Medical Research Committee (1915–16), and Dr W Langdon-Brown was the principal speaker on trench nephritis, a previously unrecognized disorder (1916).

The Sections of the RSM assisted the Committee of Reference of the Royal Colleges in working out a scheme for drafting medical men for military service for the duration of the war. One Section, known as 'climates and baths' (Balneology and Climatology) found it had more work than usual in advising the War Office on suitable spas for wounded soldiers. Another Section, Ophthalmology, raised concerns about 'enemy aliens' among the Fellowship – Dr Hubert Roberts wanted the names of all Germans removed from the membership roll forthwith.[75] The Council was not to be goaded into xenophobia, for as Rickman Godlee pointed out, there were only 11 German Fellows and two German Honorary Fellows on the Society's roll and there was no knowing their political views.[76]

At a practical level Sir Almroth Wright and Colonel Burghard, with the approval of Sir Alfred Keogh, Director of Army Medical Services, organized an exhibition of fracture apparatus at 1 Wimpole Street in 1915, where officers of the RAMC demonstrated the latest and most successful methods of dealing with fractures. Similar exhibitions of appliances used in the treatment of gunshot wounds to the face and jaw were held in 1916, supported by the Odontological Section and the British Dental Association.

## *The Emergency Surgical Aid Corps*

The Society's single most important contribution to the war effort was the formation of the Emergency Surgical Aid Corps. This originated with Dr Moreland McCrea, who suggested that the RSM might organize a scheme for surgical assistance in the case of a raid on the coast or the bombardment of London. Once the President, Sir Rickman Godlee, had sanctioned the proposal, 'its inauguration, development and success were due to the initiative, energy and foresight of MacAlister'.[77]

The Corps was inaugurated in November 1914. A hundred members of the RSM volunteered to answer the summons to an emergency, day or night, and the organizing committee prepared a map identifying the centres for receiving and treating the injured in London. The Chief Commissioner of Police was at first reluctant to accept the services of

Royal Society of Medicine

Emergency Surgical Aid Corps.

——

D I N N E R

TO

Mr. J. Y. W. MAC ALISTER,
Honorary Secretary of the Corps.

——

Chairman :
Sir RICKMAN J. GODLEE, Bt., K.C.V.O., M.S.
*Chairman of the Executive Committee.*

——

CAFÉ ROYAL,
68, Regent Street, W.

——

FRIDAY, 9th MAY, 1919.

A dinner of the Emergency Surgical Aid Corps was given in honour of MacAlister, May 1919. He received a knighthood for organizing the Corps during the First World War.

the Corps, until the German bombardment of Scarborough and other north-eastern coastal towns changed his mind. The Royal Automobile Club was immediately co-operative, offering to supply members of the Corps with motor-cars at short notice; the railway companies promised to provide trains if necessary and Messrs Allen and Hanbury filled medical chests, which were stored at the headquarters of the Corps, 1 Wimpole Street.

During the first Zeppelin raids on London in the summer of 1915 members of the Corps were on alert at Wimpole Street. The first call to the scene of an emergency came in October, when a severe raid required the assistance of three parties at Charing Cross Hospital. The winter of 1915–16 was quiet in London but when it appeared that a great sea war was threatened a naval division of the Corps was formed, and by 1917 there were three divisions of the Corps – naval, military and metropolitan. In 1917 members gave valuable help following an explosion at Silvertown and during moonlight raids on the capital. At the AGM of the Society that year Dr McCrea recounted the 'stirring adventures' of the Corps – he thought one party deserved the Victoria Cross.

The last meeting of the Emergency Surgical Aid Corps before it was disbanded took place in 1919 when MacAlister was presented with a silver helmet and Miss Williamson with a gold watch. The Corps had been called out on 69 occasions altogether, earning praise and thanks from the War Office, the Admiralty and Scotland Yard, and MacAlister received a knighthood in recognition of his leadership.[78]

## Post-war reconstruction

Three years before the outbreak of the First World War Lloyd George had succeeded in pushing through the National Health Insurance Act as a preliminary to establishing a state medical system. The Prime Minister's overwhelming victory in the general election of November 1918 on the back of the promise 'To make Britain a fit country for heroes to live in' brought about the continuation of his policy by the creation of a Ministry of Health. At a time of general concern for wounded heroes, shortages and an influenza pandemic, the proposed Ministry of Health had wide appeal.

The experience of the Great War held lessons for the medical profession and for politicians: over two million British and Dominion troops were wounded and thousands died of disease. British and Allied troops had been inoculated against typhoid, and from 1915 onwards the wounded were protected against tetanus. On the other hand, malaria ravaged the army in Salonika and Mesopotamia, shellshock and soldier's heart were new maladies and venereal disease remained a major scourge. Gunshot wounds and crippling injuries were inflicted on a large scale over a long period, poison gas was used for the first time and the diseases of the trenches posed further problems.

As the result of Osler's initiative medical topics relevant to the war were discussed at meetings of the RSM and its Sections during the war years. The value of these 'war meetings' and the practical medical and surgical experience gained by those on active service prompted the foundation of the War Section, bringing the number of Sections to 21 in 1919.

### Postgraduate medical education

In January 1919 the RSM became the headquarters of the recently formed Emergency Postgraduate Scheme of the Inter-Allied Fellowship of Medicine. The deficiency of postgraduate medical education in this country had appalled Osler when he arrived to take up his post at Oxford in 1905 and he took several initiatives to remedy this. In 1918 his efforts were temporarily sidetracked by the launch of the Inter-Allied Conferences with MacAlister and Sir St Clair Thomson as the first Secretaries. The next year, the Fellowship made its headquarters at 1 Wimpole Street, where 88 lectures were held for the benefit of medical officers on leave or being demobilized.[79] MacAlister secured the co-operation of the medical schools and within the first year nearly 1,000 men enrolled for the lectures. MacAlister's hand was also discernible in the launch of the Postgraduate Medical Association at the RSM in April 1919, when Osler gave the address. Osler and MacAlister between them succeeded in securing the cohesion of many divergent elements in the Association, which with Osler as its first President was given accommodation at the RSM. The importance of postgraduate medical education was soon recognized by the Ministry of Health in the appointment of two committees to advance the cause in the 1920s. The British Postgraduate Hospital and Medical School was eventually opened at Hammersmith Hospital in 1935.

## Ministry of Health committee

As the country looked forward to a period of peace and recovery after the conclusion of the war, the Society began to examine the government's proposals for a Ministry of Health. Sir Rickman Godlee, President of the RSM from 1916 to 1918, reflected that one effect of the war had been to draw the RSM out of its scientific shell and the formation of the Ministry of Health committee was a manifestation of this broadening of the Society's interests.

Concern for the nation's health and the welfare of the medical profession found expression at three special meetings on 'The future of the medical profession under a Ministry of National Health' held at 1 Wimpole Street in the spring of 1918. Sir William Osler, Sir Bertrand Dawson and Major JF Gordon Dill were among the speakers. No one present was left in any doubt that medicine could not be the same after the war and that some form of state aid was needed. The meetings were well attended and fully reported in the *Lancet*; they evoked considerable interest, since it was a new departure for the RSM to discuss a question outside medical science.[80]

Concern about the development of a state health service prompted the appointment of the Society's Ministry of Health committee to watch the progress of the movement and the likely effects of a Ministry. Although suspicious at first, the Society reached the conclusion that the creation of a Ministry of Health was desirable and that it must be independent but have the benefit of an advisory medical council.[81]

The Society's Ministry of Health committee held 19 meetings and conferences with the BMA and the Royal Colleges before submitting a paper to Dr Christopher Addison recommending that a consultative medical council should advise the Ministry, on the understanding that the RSM would be invited to make nominations for that council.[82] Addison, a former Professor of Anatomy and Dean of St Bartholomew's Hospital, was promoting the Bill to establish a Ministry of Health; he was to be its first Minister and was later created Viscount Addison.

When the Ministry of Health was established in June 1919 it duly set up a Consultative Council, intended to be the voice of the medical profession in affairs of national health, with direct access to the Minister and the right to initiate advice. Sir Bertrand Dawson, a future President of the RSM, chaired the Council and it worked energetically in the expectation that it would continue to exert a strong influence on government health policy. Its report, *The future provision of medical and allied services*, known as the Dawson Report (1920), set down the essential structure of what was to be the National Health Service.

## Medical Parliamentary committee

The government of the day was in no position to implement the Dawson Report. Priority was given to housing, the country faced a depression and the Treasury restricted expenditure. In this climate the Consultative Council was disbanded, but there remained a Medical Parliamentary Committee on which the RSM was represented by Dr William Pasteur and Dr JF Gordon Dill. 'The Society has thus somewhat diverged from its traditional course', the President commented, 'but it is to be hoped that with care we shall avoid the rocks'.[83]

MacAlister was keen to ensure that the medical profession had strong representation in Parliament but there were those who objected to the Society's involvement in politics, notably Dr CO Hawthorne. He accused the Council of acting autocratically in appointing representatives to the Medical Parliamentary Committee (reconstituted as the Federation of Medical and Allied Societies), he maintained that the RSM had no business with medico-politics and he referred to the Society's charter. He was silenced on the understanding that the Society was not committed to any specific action or policy and when it became apparent that no major reform of the health service or the profession was imminent, the row subsided.[84]

## The RSM, the Ministry and public health

When the Society resumed the tradition of annual dinners in 1922 it became customary to invite influential guests, including the current Minister of Health. The post-prandial speeches given on these occasions were not taken lightly and invariably touched on the role of the RSM and its relationship with the Ministry of Health.

In December 1923 the Prince of Wales, an Honorary Fellow, was the principal guest and he referred to the good advice given by Sir Benjamin Brodie in the previous century that the Society should abstain from medical politics and keep clear of exciting, irritating discussions. At the same dinner, Sir William Joynson Hicks, Minister of Health, alluded to the advantages of the Society's independent status and freedom from political questions. By reason of its neutral position he hoped he could rely on the Society for help and advice 'in those great difficulties which are undoubtedly before the Ministry of Health'.[85]

At the time of the annual dinner of 1925 Neville Chamberlain was Minister of Health and he too spoke of the possibilities for co-operation between the RSM and the Ministry: 'We must work together because although our functions are different yet they are interdependent... we know that you in your Sections do not let anything that is worth noticing escape without full discussion... and we at the Ministry of Health can feel that once a weapon devised for the war against disease has passed your tests and received the seal of your approval we can safely adopt it'. He especially asked for the Society's help in establishing a postgraduate medical school in London, an object that had been fostered by MacAlister and which was to be taken forward by Lord Dawson, shortly to be the Society's President.[86]

## Physical education

The recommendations of the Dawson Report for a state health service were shelved; nevertheless, Lord Dawson's influence in matters of national health was pervasive during the inter-war period. His enthusiasm for 'fit citizens' was shared by Commander Digby Bell, whose paper promoting a national scheme for physical education was warmly received at a meeting of the RSM in January 1920.

Sir Charles Gordon Watson and Sir Anthony Bowlby supported Bell's proposals for a National Council of Physical Education/British Physical Education Association and a gymnastic institute. The President called for a conference and a committee to consider the subject of national physique, and by July the RSM's committee was rallying the Ling Association and similar societies in order to promote a National Council of Physical Education.[87] But it was 1935 before the Central Council of Recreative Physical Training was established, and 1937 before government policy promoted national physical education as a matter of urgency. The British Council of Physical Education was eventually formed in 1973.

## Representations to government

The RSM showed a measure of concern for public health and the interests of the profession by appointing a Standing Advisory committee on public health and the welfare of the medical profession in 1920. The committee directed attention to the Dangerous Drugs Act but did not become involved in wider issues.[88]

A deputation from the Society registered strong objections to the Dogs' Protection Bill in 1919, claiming that if it was passed the country's ablest workers would seek research opportunities abroad. Sir William Osler rallied the whole profession against the Bill, and it was effectively scuppered by Sir William Watson Cheyne's amendment to it.

The Society also made formal representations, jointly with members of the National Veterinary Medical Association, to urge the Ministry of Agriculture and Fisheries to introduce a Tuberculosis Order in response to the outbreak of tuberculosis in cattle in 1921.[89]

## Anaesthetics committee

The Medical Research Committee had supported Ross's work in the Marcus Beck Laboratory at 1 Wimpole Street during the war, and there was clearly room for closer liaison between this government research body and the RSM. The Medical Research Committee matured into the Medical Research Council in 1920, and three years later it called upon the Section of Anaesthetics of the RSM to form a joint committee to research the value, effects and dangers of different anaesthetic methods. The committee researched the purity of the supplies of nitrous oxide and ether on the market and in 1927 produced a report, 'Deaths during anaesthesia', intended for presentation to the Ministry of Health (see page 305)[90] and eventually published in the Annual Report of the Medical Research Council in 1934.

The committee went on to advise the Pharmacopoeia Commission on standards of purity for anaesthetics and to investigate the dangers of explosions in operating theatres. The joint Medical Research Council/RSM committee was not formally discharged until 1956.[91]

## The Radiology committee

The discovery of radium by Pierre and Marie Curie in 1898 generated enormous enthusiasm, and led to the foundation of institutes, journals and societies devoted to

Sir Humphry Davy Rolleston took a leading part in founding British radiology and was President of the British Institute of Radiology at its incorporation with the Röntgen Society in 1927. Rolleston was President of the RSM for 1918–20 and of the History of Medicine Section 1930–31.

radium and radiology. In London the Röntgen Society was founded in 1897, the British Electro-Therapeutic Society in 1902 and the British Association of Radiology and Physiotherapy (BARP) in 1917. The increase in the medical use of X-rays during the First World War and the excessive radiation exposure of practitioners led to many cases of fatal radiation-induced blood disorders such as leukaemia and aplastic anaemia. Marie Curie was herself to die in 1934 of aplastic anaemia resulting from her long hours of exposure to radium.

Meanwhile, reliable data on the effects of exposure to radium was lacking: the Röntgen Society produced recommendations for the protection of radiation workers in 1915 but it took the death of a radiologist at Charing Cross Hospital to stimulate a debate on the hazards of X-rays. The British X-ray and Radium Protection Committee was then formed and held its first meeting at the RSM in 1921.

At the same time the concept of a Radiological Institute was revived and the Medical Research Council appointed a Radiology committee, of which Sir Humphry Rolleston was a member. He had been President of the RSM from 1918 to 1920 and may have been responsible for the inclusion of representatives of the Electro-therapeutical Section of the RSM in a joint committee with members of the Röntgen Society and BARP in 1923. That committee, acting with admirable promptitude, resolved to found the British Institute of Radiology and to appeal for funds (see page 285).[92] The RSM/Röntgen Society/BARP committee worked singlemindedly towards the foundation of the British Institute of Radiology, which opened its doors in 1924. The incorporation of the Röntgen Society was achieved in 1927 with Rolleston as President, since when the Institute has made steady progress.[93]

## The Cancer committee

In March 1923 Mr Joseph E Adams identified the RSM as the headquarters of scientific intelligence in the medical profession and therefore the appropriate society to take the initiative in the control of cancer. He cited the American Society for the Control of Cancer (founded in 1913) and urged the formation of a British counterpart.

Having listened to Adams's address to a meeting of the RSM, Dr Charles Childe, President-elect of the BMA, referred to a book he had written on the control of cancer and Sir Arthur Stanley, Chairman of the British Red Cross, agreed to collaborate with the RSM in educating the public about the disease. The Red Cross had published manuals on subjects such as First Aid and Nursing and these had proved popular, so a leaflet on cancer seemed a logical sequel. As a result of the meeting, the RSM formed a Prevention of Cancer committee which met with the Red Cross and the Ministry of Health with the intention of producing a leaflet entitled 'What ought to be known about cancer'. This presented bleak facts and warnings such as 'neglect spells death', and was intended for public distribution.[94]

Dr Sydney Monckton Copeman, among others, thought that the Ministry of Health and not the RSM was the appropriate organization to educate the public in such matters, not least because the Ministry had recently formed a Departmental Cancer Committee under Sir George Newman (Copeman sat on the committee). At the same time the British Empire Cancer Campaign was launched amid disputes between the Imperial Cancer Research Fund, the Royal Society and the Medical Research Council. Discord among the cancer charities and research bodies had a negative effect, and the leaflet drawn up by the RSM and the Red Cross never materialized. The Ministry of Health's Cancer committee made a half-hearted attempt to educate the public by issuing memoranda to local authorities (1923, 1924) but the Ministry was afraid of arousing public alarm and preferred the emphasis to be placed on research rather than propaganda.[95]

## Financial difficulties

A report of 1893 on the financial position of the Royal Medical and Chirurgical Society declared that 'it is a doubtful advantage for a learned society to become inordinately wealthy'.[96] At that time the Society was reaping good rents from the numerous tenants of 20 Hanover Square so could afford to be complacent. By 1909 the situation had changed and for the next decade the Society was beset by financial difficulties.

In that year the Honorary Treasurer, Mr Alfred Pearce Gould, was the first to hint that the Society's house was expensively managed and that staff salaries were too high – and this was before the expense of the move to 1 Wimpole Street.[97] Criticism of the financial administration resurfaced in a letter from 'an old Fellow' in December 1912 suggesting that the Library staff were paid too much and that a serious lack of economy in the administration had prevented many Fellows from contributing to the building fund for 1 Wimpole Street. The situation was investigated by an Economy committee, which reported in the spring of 1913 that the financial position of the Society was indeed unsatisfactory. There was insufficient control over expenditure, the system of checking subscriptions and postage was inadequate and a bill for £153 had gone unnoticed. Despite the fact that subscriptions yielded an income of over £1,200 for 1912–13, the Society faced a probable deficit of £800.[98] The accountants Newson-Smith, Lord and Mundy confirmed that the book-keeping was slack and Paterson, the cashier, was promptly dismissed, complaining of mistreatment and misunderstandings.[99] Paterson was the scapegoat, but more serious allegations were raised by Dr Arthur Latham in relation to the printing of the *Proceedings* and in September 1913 Latham resigned from the General Purposes and Finance committee in a gesture of no confidence in the Society's financial management.[100]

In responding to Latham's criticism John Nachbar, editor of the *Proceedings* and the Society's Deputy Secretary, crossed swords with MacAlister. Nachbar reported that MacAlister was 'apt to underrate the importance of the regular routine work of the Society when carrying out his new schemes'. MacAlister, who was unwell, replied in angry tones to the insinuation that he had 'cooked the accounts deliberately'. He estimated that the financial services he had rendered the Society amounted to a total capital gain for the RSM of £44,750.[101] He did confess that he had not been able to keep the strict watch over petty expenditure 'as it was my pride to do in earlier days', and embarrassed by what he called a temporary extravagance, he offered to sacrifice half his salary 'viz. £500 a year until such time as the finances of the Society justify a return to £1,000'.[102] MacAlister resented Dr Latham's 'mysterious campaign' against him and denied that he tried to shift the blame for the bill for the *Proceedings* on to Nachbar. Latham, whose outspoken manner antagonized many colleagues, did not hesitate to tell the President about the Society's financial maladministration and in resigning from the General Purposes and Finance committee he warned that more care should be taken.[103] Nachbar likewise resigned his position in 1914, leaving MacAlister to edit the *Proceedings* for the next 10 years.

A second storm blew up when the subscriptions of Fellows living within one mile of 1 Wimpole Street were increased from three to five guineas in 1919. The increase had been tabled in 1914, postponed until after the war and when it came into effect in 1919 there was confusion. Some Fellows paid twice, many bankers' orders were not altered and MacAlister, who had recently suffered a stroke, decided to treat subscriptions that should have been returned as ordinary income. According to Sir Henry Tidy, who was to be President from 1942 to 1944, MacAlister 'managed to pull the wool over the Honorary Treasurers' eyes (it was only when Edwards became Secretary on MacAlister's retirement that the extent of the deception – some £2,000 – was revealed). To avoid embarrassing MacAlister who was (just) alive, the publicity was kept to a minimum and the subscriptions quietly returned'.[104]

The increased subscription was the reason for 30 Fellows' resignations, 11 of them members of the Odontological Section. MacAlister's flippant suggestion that the aggrieved Fellows might be placated by being made Honorary Fellows did not amuse Sir Frank Colyer.[105]

The raising of subscriptions to five guineas did not suffice to cover expenditure, therefore in 1921 country members' subscriptions were raised to four guineas. Country and foreign members were well served by the Library, which supplied parcels of books, transcripts, précis and basic research at no extra cost and there were few objections to paying five guineas a year for these facilities. At the Annual General Meeting of 1922 Sir James Dundas-Grant interpreted the comparatively small number of resignations consequent upon the increased subscription as an indication of the strong corporate feeling of Fellows. He concluded that the 'Slump in Harley Street' had not affected the pockets of Fellows to the degree that the daily press supposed.[106]

An effort was made to attract younger members of the profession to join the Society in 1922 by creating a new category of Associates. This was designed to appeal to medical men and women within five years of their first qualification who were invited to join the RSM at an annual subscription of three guineas without an admission fee.[107] Only eight took advantage of the offer in the first year.

## The Gold Medal

The Society received a multitude of gifts and benefactions in the years between the two world wars: bequests to endow lectures, trust funds for prizes and research, a scholarship, gifts of books for the Library, portraits, clocks, a Presidential badge and many curious items. The Jenner Medal came to the RSM with the Epidemiological Society (see page 231) and continued to be awarded from time to time. The Society's own medal had first been mooted at a Council meeting in 1822. Almost a century later the Gold Medal of the Royal Society of Medicine was instituted on the initiative of a Fellow, Dr Robert Murray Leslie of 143 Harley Street. He cited the 'splendid work carried out by the Royal Society of Medicine since its foundation', especially the services of its Fellows in the Great War. He proposed to found a Gold Medal with the object of encouraging original medical and scientific research by transferring to the RSM £200 in Exchequer Bonds and £30 for the first medal, to be awarded in 1920 and triennially thereafter.

The Gold Medal of the RSM, established in 1920 through the generosity of Dr Robert Murray Leslie. It shows Hygeia the daughter of Aesculapius bestowing a wreath upon research, and (right) Chiron the centaur teaching Aesculapius the art of healing.

Research for the design of the medal cast doubt upon the authenticity of the Society's seal, supposedly based on a coin of Caracalla. Experts at the British Museum were consulted and they searched in vain among the Roman coins for the one that was believed to have been the model for the RSM seal. Moreover the Secretary was advised that Salus is never represented with the staff of Aesculapius, nor does she ever raise a kneeling figure.[108] The designer of the medal, E Carter Preston, therefore chose to feature Hygeia, goddess of health and the daughter of Aesculapius, bestowing a wreath upon Research on the obverse, and the reverse shows Aesculapius being taught the art of healing by Chiron the wise centaur.

The first recipient of the 15 carat Gold Medal was Sir Almroth Wright, the donor having intimated that he would like the presentation to take place on the anniversary of Armistice Day, 11 November 1920. The donor also approved of the choice of recipient, for Wright's bacteriological researches had proved invaluable in rendering the British forces fighting in the Great War immune to typhoid.[109] The second award of the Gold Medal went to Professor Frederick Gowland Hopkins, the Cambridge University biochemist who discovered vitamins. Recent recipients include Sir Derrick Dunlop (1980), Sir James Black (1989) and Sir David Weatherall (1992).

## The President's badge, chain and gown

In 1925 Sir St Clair Thomson, the current President, gave the Society a 17th-century chain of office for the President's use. This required an appropriate badge, the badge suggested a crest and the crest entailed a coat of arms. As St Clair Thomson explained in his after-dinner speech, it was a case of 'one damn thing after another'.[110] The end result was that the RSM obtained a grant of arms from the College of Heralds in 1927 and the President's badge featured the authentic coat of arms, complete with crest and supporters (Plates 32, 33 and 34). St Clair Thomson was a generous benefactor: in addition to the Presidential badge and chain, the Society received two legacies after his death.

The Presidential dignity was further enhanced by the gift of a claret-coloured silk ceremonial robe and cap based on the outfit worn by the Rector of Padua and presented by Lord and Lady Dawson of Penn in 1932, Lord Dawson having been President from 1928 to 1930. A modern chain of office has since been presented by Sir David Innes Williams who was President from 1990 to 1992; the Presidential robe was replaced in 1959 by a more conventional black and gold gown (Plate 35).

## Viscount Dawson of Penn

As President of the RSM Lord Dawson put the Society's finances on a firmer footing by actively encouraging donations to the Society's funds and by persuading the Council to appoint its first Honorary financial adviser. The 'kind offices of Lord Dawson' also secured a grant of £2,800 from Lord Beaverbrook's Fund in 1928, enabling the RSM to purchase equipment such as screens and projectors,[111] and the RSM Trust Fund was thereby established. Having tackled the Society's finances Dawson turned to the facilities at 1 Wimpole Street, insisting on more staff and better lighting and equipment, including the RSM's first 'photostat'.

In the wider scheme of things, Dawson pulled the RSM into more active participation in medical and professional issues. He made remonstrations to the LCC on behalf of the RSM and the profession at large about the regulation of establishments for massage or special treatments, obtaining an assurance that LCC officials would carry out their duties in a spirit of friendliness to the profession. He asked representatives of the RSM to liaise with the advisory committee on the new British Pharmacopoeia being planned by the GMC, and he launched a National Fund for the Acquisition of Radium. This appeal to the public was in the nature of a thank-offering for the King's recovery – George V had nearly died in 1928 and the public attributed his survival to Dawson.

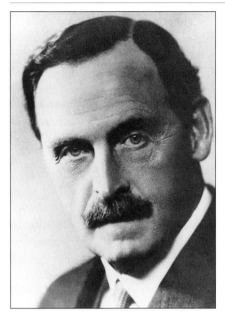

Viscount Dawson of Penn,
President 1928–30. The Dawson Report of
1920 outlined the structure of the National
Health Service.

Horizons were widened by the appointment of delegates to represent the Society at medical congresses at home and abroad and on BMA committees. The profile of the RSM was further enhanced by Dawson's influential contacts and friends who were invited to the Society's dinners – the Rt Hon Winston Churchill (Chancellor of the Exchequer), the Prime Minister Ramsay MacDonald, the Archbishop of Canterbury and Rudyard Kipling were among those who repaid the hospitality with some notable speeches. Dawson himself took the opportunity provided by the captive audience at the annual dinner to speak on matters of national and professional concern such as the Local Government Act and how to bring medicine into a closer understanding with government. He pleaded for the conjunction of skilled knowledge with informed administration in semi-autonomous bodies that might really improve the health of the nation, and for the alliance of statesmanship with science: 'medicine should have contact with statesmanship but perhaps is right in its instinct to view politics from afar'.[112]

The Minister of Health Arthur Greenwood attended the annual dinner in 1929; he urged the medical profession to co-operate fully with the Ministry in promoting the nation's health. By the 1930s bodies such as the India Office, the Board of Trade and the Central Midwives Board were looking to the Royal Society of Medicine for scientific advice;[113] This was largely due to Dawson's work as President and past President. He went on to be President of the Royal College of Physicians, of the BMA (twice), and was created a Viscount in 1936. Occupying a supreme position in the profession he promoted the RSM, the Medical Research Council, the British Postgraduate Medical School and towards the end of his life he revived the idea of an Academy of Medicine.[114]

## Lectureships and legacies

Occasional lectures had been part of the Society's programme since the session of 1913–14 and they had proved popular. Other lectures were provided for the Society through endowments of individual benefactors or by memorial trusts. Unfortunately the first and most substantial bequest of the period seems to have escaped the Society at the last minute. In 1916 Professor Charles Cumston of the Faculty of Medicine at Geneva conveyed to the Secretary his intention of leaving £16,000–17,000 for a lectureship on the History of Medicine, together with the purchase of manuscripts and books. Cumston was an active member of the History of Medicine Section and his endowment was to have been augmented by Mrs Cumston, bringing their joint legacy to over £40,000 and the promise of the Charles Cumston lectures on the History of Medicine. The President reported that the Society expected to receive the legacy in 1919, an expectation that was not fulfilled – possibly because Cumston insisted that the lecturers must not be American, German or Austro-Hungarian nor a native of any ally of Germany, Austria or Hungary in the Great War.[115]

Dr David Lloyd Roberts' legacy, on the other hand, materialized, and has proved to be of lasting benefit. His will of 1920 left £5,000 to the RSM and another £500 for an annual lecture on any subject of medical or scientific interest, arranged in turn by the RSM, the Medical Society of London and the Royal College of Physicians. The first Lloyd Roberts lecture was given by Edmund Gosse in 1923 on 'Personal relations between medicine and literature'.[116]

The Hughlings Jackson lecture had been founded by the Neurological Society in 1897, and in 1932 a sum of over £1,000 was collected to pay for a Hughlings Jackson Gold Medal and an honorarium for the lecturer (see page 264).[117] Also in 1932 the RSM accepted a trust fund in memory of Henry Hill Hickman, who had established the principle of inhalation anaesthesia in 1824. As the centenary of Hickman's death in 1830 approached, the President of the Section of Anaesthetics suggested that he deserved commemoration and the RSM gave £10 towards the restoration of Hickman's grave and a memorial in the church of St Mary, Bromfield, Worcestershire. A memorial fund was also established and £200 was collected to finance the Henry Hickman Medal for original work of outstanding merit in anaesthesia. The medal, showing Hickman's portrait and a representation of the triumph of anaesthesia over pain (see page 306), was awarded on the recommendation of the Section and the first recipient was Dr Wesley Bourne of McGill University, Canada (1935).[118]

The first Samuel Hyde memorial lecture in rheumatology and rehabilitation[119] was given to the Section of Balneology and Climatology in 1932 and the following year the Dixon Memorial Committee raised £700 in memory of Professor Walter Dixon of King's College London, a former President of the Section of Therapeutics and Pharmacology. The first Dixon lecture was held in 1934, when Sir Henry Dale received 100 guineas for delivering an address on 'Pharmacology and nerve endings'.[120] Also in 1933 the first Wallis lecture for the Sections of the History of Medicine and Odontology was given by Miss Lilian Lindsay under the intriguing title of 'The sun, the toothdrawer and the saint'.[121]

The bequests of the 1920s were especially favourable to otologists. In 1922 Lady Dalby gave £500 in memory of her husband Sir William Dalby, a founder of the Otological Society, which was applied to a quinquennial Dalby Memorial Prize in Otology from 1928.[122] In 1927 the Section of Otology asked the Council of the RSM to accept as a trust £1,000 presented by Norman Gamble to fund a research prize of £50 every four years on the recommendation of that Section.[123] Prizes in other specialties included the Colyer Prize, founded to mark Sir Frank Colyer's 25-year curatorship of the Odontological Museum.[124] In a similar arrangement the Section of Obstetrics and Gynaecology advised on the award of the Nichols Prize, the result of a legacy of £2,200 from Dr Robert T Nichols in 1921. This yielded £250 every three years for the most valuable contribution towards the discovery of the causes and prevention of death in childbirth from septicaemia.[125]

The conditions of the Society's only scholarship for medical women were specified by Miss Maud Gibson of Australia, who in 1919 set up a fund of £6,000 in memory of her father, William. Miss Gibson stated that the administration of the scholarship must be in the hands of an equal number of men and women and that the recipient should be given an income of £250 per annum in regular payments over two years.[126]

Many other bequests, lecturerships, prizes and scholarships have accrued to the Society and its Sections and these have been listed by Dr John Moll in his book on the Society's Presidents.[127]

## Donations to the Library

The Library received many gifts each year and the names of the donors were meticulously recorded in the *Official Bulletin*. Mrs Eliza Macloghlin, the widow of a Wigan general practitioner who died in 1904, Sir Henry Morris and Sir Thomas Lauder Brunton's family gave large donations. Dr T Colcott Fox gave 600 books and pamphlets on dermatology in 1913, and Mrs WHH Jessop gave her late husband's library to the RSM in 1917. The Ophthalmological Society's Bowman Library of 5,000 volumes was housed at 1 Wimpole Street from 1913 and formally presented in 1927. Sir Felix Semon gave 500 works from his library and Mr AH Tubby, a consultant surgeon with the British forces in the Mediterranean and Egypt from 1915 to 1919, gave 350 books in 1921.

Undoubtedly the most valuable collection came from Mrs Chalmers in 1922. Dr AJ Chalmers of Khartoum had left a number of his rare books in the safekeeping of the RSM Library, including a first printed edition of Celsus (1478), and after his death the collection was officially presented by his widow. Moreover she gave £5,000 to establish the Chalmers Library on the third floor at 1 Wimpole Street, which opened in 1922.[128] Dr Chalmers had specialized in tropical diseases and sanitation, and his 1,450 books and periodicals reflected these interests. Another 350 volumes demonstrated his enthusiasm for the history of medicine – there were five 15th-century works, rare 16th-century herbals and 109 books dating from the 17th century. Mrs Chalmers added her own gifts of Dioscorides' *De simplici medicina* (1512) and Lemnius' *The touchstone of complexions* (1633).

Some Fellows left funds for the purchase of books in their specialties, such as Dr Wallace who died in 1908 aged 54: the Wallace Memorial committee was to purchase books of

Dr William Turner's *Herbal* (1568), part of the valuable collection of books
formerly belonging to Dr AJ Chalmers which was presented to the Society in 1922. Turner's
herbal was the first to present botany in a scientific manner and is also noteworthy for the
numerous fine woodcuts.

bacteriological interest.[129] Similarly, Mrs Ellen Law gave £500 for otological, rhinological and laryngological works in 1930, as her late husband was a former President of that Section.[130] Miss Gladys M Medwin of Bournemouth left the bulk of her property to the RSM as capital for the purchase of neurological works, with a second donation in memory of her mother, Margaret Medwin: 'martyred by Parkinson's disease, she wished that part of her estate should by expended in the furtherance of studies to alleviate the sufferings caused by nervous maladies'.[131] Other benefactions came from Lady Singer in 1928, in memory of Sir David Ferrier who had been an Honorary Fellow of the Society, and Lord Illingworth's gift of £500 formed the basis of the Library endowment fund in 1930.

When Sir Rickman Godlee died in 1925 he left a bequest to the RSM of £5,000 subject to the life interest of his wife. Godlee had a long record of service to the Society, as Honorary Librarian from 1895 to 1916, President of the Section of Surgery from 1909 to 1911 and President of the RSM from 1916 to 1918. His biography of his uncle, Lord Lister, was another lasting memorial.[132]

Numerous miscellaneous, unsolicited gifts were thrust upon the Society each year: portraits, engravings, cartoons, watercolours, photographs, autograph letters and diplomas. Among the unusual gifts was the house flag presented by Dr T Watts Eden who was President from 1930 to 1932; Lord Howard de Walden gave a marble chimneypiece for the Council Room and Sir Richard Douglas Powell gave the head of a moose shot by his son in Canada.

## Sir John MacAlister retires

MacAlister's knighthood in 1919 was celebrated at a dinner in his honour held at the Connaught Rooms in March 1920. Over 300 Fellows and members assembled as an expression of their personal regard for him and to convey their appreciation of the services he had rendered the Society during the last 33 years. Sir William Selby Church, Sir William Arbuthnot Lane, Sir Rickman Godlee, Sir Humphry Rolleston and Sir Francis Champneys led the eulogies to MacAlister, who was credited with the creation of the RSM and its establishment in Wimpole Street. MacAlister replied with a resumé of his achievements and his hopes for the future, which centred on the amalgamation of the Royal College of Physicians, the Royal College of Surgeons and the RSM 'under one dome with three radiations'. He hoped that he would live to see the joint library of those three institutions established as the greatest medical library in the world, served by double the staff, an expert team of researchers and open until midnight.[133]

Meanwhile the Library of the RSM suffered a loss when Charles Hewitt left in 1919 to take a post with the League of Red Cross Societies in Geneva.[134] His successor, HE Powell, had been with the RSM since 1907 and now faced a considerable increase in the work of the Library as the result of demobilization and a large intake of new Fellows. The number of readers reached a record high of 17,859 with 9,313 books borrowed in the year 1919–20. The Honorary Librarians added to Powell's workload by inviting Fellows to apply for duplicate copies of books and some 2,000 were thus disposed of.[135]

As MacAlister approached 70 his health deteriorated, compelling him to take a long leave of absence in 1924, which was followed by his resignation in June 1925. The Council put it on record that 'in accepting his resignation the members fully realize that the society as at present constituted owes its creation to his organizing powers; that its growth and success are chiefly due to his zealous devotion to his duties; and that its welfare and reputation have been his life's work'.[136]

Sir John was elected an Honorary Fellow with no more ado and at the annual dinner in 1925 the President, Sir St Clair Thomson, reviewed the growth of the Society since 1887 when MacAlister took the post of Resident Librarian. In that year the Society was composed of 745 Fellows; in 1925 there were 4,000 Fellows and members of the RSM.

The annual income in 1887 was £1,676 and now stood at £19,000. The volume of the *Transactions* for 1887 had cost £406 compared with the present volume of the *Proceedings*, which at some 1,232 pages cost £4,000 per annum and was 'big and heavy enough to be used for pressing trousers'. During the session of 1924–25 the Society and its 24 Sections had held 171 meetings.

These figures testified to a thriving organization, an amalgamated society that was the largest of its kind in the kingdom and which boasted the most complete medical Library in the British Empire. The President was equally proud of the fact that the RSM retained the character of 'the old Medico-Chirurgical Society... Our Society is a guild for the diffusion of knowledge in the science and art of medicine. The gold of this guild is dug up in our practice, our wards, our laboratories and museums, and is also garnered from the progress of many neighbouring sciences. We test it, we mint it, and we put it into circulation'.[137]

MacAlister's successor as Secretary, Geoffrey Edwards, was selected from 462 candidates. His first achievement was to improve facilities for members: the Library was to remain open during the summer and two evenings a week until 10pm and he encouraged Fellows to make better use of the services; references and bibliographies on any medical subject could now be provided. He also persuaded the Council to allow light luncheons to be served in the Fellows' room, and to install a bathroom for Fellows.

MacAlister died in December 1925, six months after his resignation. The RSM opened a fund for a commemorative portrait which soon totalled £833, with which a copy of Kennington's portrait was commissioned and an epidiascope and a microscope were purchased. The original paintings of Sir John and Lady MacAlister, by EH and TB Kennington respectively, were presented to the Society by Donald MacAlister in 1959 (Plate 24).[138]

Sir William Arbuthnot Lane, who had first made MacAlister's acquaintance when the Society was based at Berners Street, was among many who recognized MacAlister's achievements as Secretary, 'at Hanover Square and finally at 1 Wimpole Street where he created for himself and for the medical profession an organization of vast use to the public generally'. Lane had operated on MacAlister, prolonging his life and his services to the RSM by several years, and he was one of the few to pay tribute to MacAlister's humanity: 'he was a man full of interest and love of his fellow creatures; so sympathetic, so kind and so patient with the frailties of human nature'.[139]

1 *The Royal Society of Medicine. Record of the events and work which led to the formation of that Society by the Amalgamation of the leading medical societies of London* (1914) p. 195.

2 Osler, Sir William, *Aequanimitas* (1946) pp. 329–45.

3 Cushing, Harvey, *The life of Sir William Osler* vol ii (1925) pp. 106–7. By 1918 Carnegie had funded 2,025 library buildings, also numerous pension funds and charitable trusts.

4 Letter MacAlister to Billings 23 June 1908, folder 1/G7, Box 22.

5 Typescript 6 May 1920, MacAlister correspondence, folder 2/G18, Box 31.

6 Letter MacAlister to Frazer 19 July 1907, folder 2/G17, Box 30.

7 Colvin, HM, *A biographical dictionary of British architects 1600–1840* (1978) p. 338.

8 Summerson, John, 'Henrietta Place, Marylebone and its associations with James Gibbs' in the *London Topographical Record* vol xxi (1958) pp. 26–36. De Falbe, Sophy, 'Building, decoration and Society in Henrietta Street 1720–1730' V & A/ RCA dissertation (1983), Buildings File, and file on 11 Henrietta Street WS-1960, Department of Furniture and Woodwork, Victoria and Albert Museum. The first floor room of 11 Henrietta Street will re-open in the British Galleries of the V & A in 2001. Lease to Gibbs for 94 years from 1731, Terms of Contracts 5a, no. 572, Howard de Walden archives.

9 Cope, Sir Zachary, *Some famous general practitioners* (1961).

10 Letter MacAlister to Boyton 16, 25 June 1909. Plan (tracing) by FM Elgood of 2–5 Henrietta Street, 16 June 1909, folder 2/G17, Box 30.

11 Report on question of increased accommodation, June 1909, E25.

12 Letters MacAlister to Church 11 December 1909, folder 4/G20, Box 33. Letter MacAlister to Pearce Gould 31 December 1909, folder 9/G20, Box 33. MacAlister correspondence, folder 5/G20, Box 33.

13 Draft agreement and reference 2 February 1910, folder 2/G17, Box 30. Agreements and correspondnece, Hanover Square, 1910, F16, Box 12.

14 MacAlister/Frank correspondence 1909–10, F16, Box 12.

15 *Lancet* (i) pt 1, 12, 19 February, 8 March 1910, pp. 470, 532, 657–58.

16 Articles of Agreement 1 December 1910, folder 2/F26, Box 13. The initial sum was for just two storeys, the question of the third or fourth floor being as yet undecided. Detailed progress of the building work can be followed in Building committee minutes 1910–13, H11.

17 MacAlister correspondence January–June 1910, folder 4/F26, Box 13.

18 Service, Alastair, *Edwardian architecture* (1977) p. 180. Reilly, Charles H, *Scaffolding in the sky* (1938) pp. 49,55. The partnership of Belcher and Joass is discussed by Alastair Service, see 'Belcher and Joass' in *Architectural Review* vol cxlviii (1970) pp. 283–90.

19 MacAlister correspondence 1910–11 folders 3,4,6/F26, Box 13.

20 New Building for the Royal Society of Medicine, Belcher and Joass, June 1912, folder 1/G8, Box 23. CM 7 June 1912, Box 101.

21 Memorial to the Lord Mayor 3 October 1910, printed in full in Davidson, Maurice, *The Royal Society of Medicine. The realization of an ideal 1805–1955* (1955) pp. 59–64. MacAlister correspondence 1910, folder 5/G20, Box 33, folder 1/G20, Box 32.

22 *Bulletin* 11 (1911).

23 MacAlister correspondence 1913, folder 2/G12, Box 26. Title deeds received and recorded, CM 17 February 1914.

24 Cushing, *op cit* pp. 302–03. Memorandum on appeal signed by H Rolleston n.d., E24. List of subscribers, E26. CM 16 June 1914.

25 £560 was returned to the family, see Durning-Lawrence bequest 1913–17, M5, Box 50.

26 MacAlister correspondence 1912, folder 6/G20, Box 33 and G17, Box 30. Memorandum on MacAlister's Financial Services 1903–12, G21, Box 33.

27 MacAlister correspondence 1911, folder 6/G20 Box 33.

28 Building committee minutes 15 February 1912, H11. MacAlister correspondence 1913, folder 2/G13, Box 28. The portrait of Mrs Boyd MD was presented by the Association of Registered Medical Women.

29 MacAlister correspondence 1911, folder 4/F27, Box 14.

30 *Ibid* folder 3/F27, Box 14.

31 CM 19 May 1914.

32 Service, Alastair, 'Belcher and Joass' in *Architectural Review* vol cxlvii (1970) pp. 283–90.

33 *The Royal Society of Medicine. Opening of the new building by His Majesty the King accompanied by Her Majesty the Queen, Tuesday May 21 1912* (1914). Cherry, Bridget and Pevsner, Nikolaus, *London 3: North West* (1991) p. 611. Draft Report of Council, CM 7 June 1912, Box 101.

34 Cost of building October 1912, MacAlister correspondence folder 1/G9, Box 24. *Ibid,* 1911–12 folder 7/F26, Box 13 and 1913, folders 1,2/G11, G12, Box 26. CM 7 June 1912.

35 MacAlister correspondence 1910–13, folder 4/G12, Box 26.

36 *Ibid* 1910, folder 6/G20, Box 33. Building committee minutes 29 July 1912, H11. The lamps were executed by Messrs Singer of Frome and are now at the Wimpole Street entrance. MacAlister correspondence 1911, 1912 folders 8,9/F26, Box 14.

37 Letter Church to MacAlister 19 July 1913, MacAlister papers, Box 1.

38 MacAlister correspondence 1911, folder 1/F27, Box 14.

39 *The Royal Society of Medicine. Opening of the new building … op cit.* MacAlister correspondence 1912, folder 4/G8, Box 23.

40 MacAlister correspondence 1912, folder 1/G8, Box 23.

41 CM 17 December 1912.

42 MacAlister correspondence 1910, folder 5/G20, Box 33.

43 Letter MacAlister to Boyton 24 June 1912, folder1/G8, Box 23.

44 Letters from MacAlister, Hewitt and Church to the Royal College of Surgeons (1910), correspondence, RCS.

45 *Lancet* (i) pt 2, 25 June 1910, p. 1783.

46 Wade, P, 'The history and development of the Library of the Royal Society of Medicine' in PRSM vol 55 August 1962, pp. 627–36. Typescript 6 May 1920, folder 2/G18, Box 31.

47 Cushing *op cit,* pp. 405, 570. The copy of William Harvey's work presented by Osler was valued recently at £150,000.

48 CM 12 January 1911.

49 CM 8 March 1912. PRSM vol 6 pt 2 (1912–13).

50 CM 19 April 1912, 10 November 1913, 16 June, 21 July 1914, 15 June 1915.

51 *Bulletin* 18 (1914).

52 Letters MacAlister to Osler 16 October, Latham to Champneys 21 October 1912, MacAlister correspondence folders 2 and 3/G9, Box 24.

53 PRSM vol 2 pt 1 (1908–09).

54 *Ibid* vol 3 pt 1 (1909–10).

55 Tanner, WE, *Arbuthnot Lane. His life and work* (1946) pp.118–119. Layton,TB, *Sir William Arbuthnot Lane* (1956) p. 53. PRSM vol 6 pt 1 (1912–13).

56 MacAlister correspondence 1913, folder 2/G13, Box 28, folder 2/G14, Box 29.

57 Letter MacAlister to Colyer 27 November 1919, folder 7/G18, Box 31 (Colyer wanted MacAlister to institute a luncheon club). MacAlister correspondence 1912, folder 3/G20, Box 32.

58 Letter MacAlister to Hewitt 17 June 1912, folder 2/G8, Box 23.

59 Rolleston, Sir Humphry, 'Medical friendships, clubs and societies', a lecture founded as a memorial to JYW MacAlister in *Annals of Medical History* n.s. vol ii May 1930 no 3 pp. 249–66. Rolleston dated the Council Club dinners 1912–24 (based on an attendance book). It is clear from correspondence between MacAlister and the President that several dinners had taken place before January 1911.

60 Letter MacAlister to Morris 18 January 1911, folder 2/G19, Box 32. MacAlister correspondence 1912, folder 3/G8, Box 23 and folder 3/G9, Box 24.

61 MacAlister correspondence 1911, folder 8/G20, Box 33 and 1913, folder 3/G8, Box 23.

62 Council Club Attendance Book 1912–24, N1. Council Club indexed address book n.d., N2. Letter MacAlister to May 1924, RCS.

63 Council Club committee minutes 1948–57 AC/02/d, 1957–67 AC/05//2.

64 Dobson, Jessie, and Wakeley, Sir Cecil, *Sir George Buckston Browne* (1957) p. 46.

65 CM 18 November 1913. MacAlister correspondence 1913, G12, G13, Box 27, and folder 2/G17, Box 30.

66 MacAlister correspondence 1913, folder 2/G14, Box 29. Letter MacAlister to Thomson 16 October 1913, and correspondence 1913, folder 2, G13, Box 28.

67 Marcus Beck Laboratory Reports June 1914, *Bulletin* 18 (1914). CM 19 June 1914. PRSM vol 7 pt 1 (1913–14).

68 Marcus Beck Laboratory Report June 1915, CM 28 June 1915. Lady Durning-Lawrence and her niece donated money for Ross' purchase of equipment and room, see Durning-Lawrence correspondence M5, Box 50.

69 CM 17 May 1917. CM Section of Pathology 29 March 1917.

70 CM 15 April, 20 May 1924.

71 CM 20 October 1914.

72 Annual Report of Council 1916–17, *Bulletin* 24 (1917). Sheet distributed to Allied forces 1914–18 gives details of hospitality offered to Medical Officers.

73 Cushing *op cit* p. 497.

74 PRSM vol 8 pt 2 (1914–15). Cushing *op cit* pp. 497–98.

75 CM 16 February, 15 June 1915.

76 Presidential address, *Bulletin* 26 (1918).

77 Clarke, Archibald, 'A short account of the work of the Emergency Surgical Aid Corps', n.d., MacAlister correspondence folder 4/G18, Box 31.

78 Clarke, *op cit. Bulletin* 20 (1914), 26 (1918), 29 (1919).

79 AGM 1919, *Bulletin* 29 (1919).

80 *Lancet* (i) 20 April, 8 June 1918 pp. 570–73, 804–06. Presidential address, *Bulletin* 26 (1918).

81 BMJ (ii) 13, 20 July 1918 pp. 23–26, 56–60. CM 18 June 1918. *Bulletin* 26 (1918). Ministry of Health committee 10 June, 18 July 1918, 8 August 1919.

82 Presidential address, *Bulletin* 29 (1919).

83 *Ibid*.

84 AGM 1920, *Bulletin* 30 (1920); AGM 1921 *Bulletin* 33 (1921).

85 Speeches at the Society's annual dinner 1923, *Bulletin* 39 (1924).

86 Speech at the Society's annual dinner 1925, *Bulletin* 43 (1926).

87 PRSM vol 13 pts 1–2 (1919–20). Physical Education conference and committee 9 March, 17 May 1920, H3. Bailey, Steve, and Vamplew, Wray, *100 years of physical education 1899–1999* (1999).

88 Annual General Meeting 1922, *Bulletin* 35 (1922). CM 15 June 1920.

89 CM 15 April 1919, 19 April 1921. In 1925 the Sections of of Epidemiology and State Medicine, Comparative Medicine and the Study of Disease in Children urged the Council to press the government to re-enact the Tuberculosis Order, CM 17 March 1925.

90 *Bulletin* 47 (1928). CM 15 February, 12 April 1927, 18 December 1928.

91 Thomson, A Landsbrough, *Half a century of medical research* vol ii (1975) pp. 36–37. Austoker, Joan, and Bryder, Linda (eds), *Historical perspectives on the role of the MRC* (1989) p. 190.

92 Rolleston, Sir Humphry, 'Presidential address at the amalgamation of the Röntgen Society and the British Institute of Radiology, 17 November 1927' in *British Journal of Radiology* n.s. vol i (1928) pp. 1–16. CM 21 November 1922. Peh, Wilfred CG, *101 years of a new kind of rays* (1996).

93 The BIR is now at 36 Portland Place, W1. I am grateful for information from Dr Adrian Thomas and assistance from Mrs K Sanders of the Institute.

94 CM 20 March, 19 June 1923. Prevention of Cancer committee 30 April, 29 May, 12 June 1923, H3.

95 *Lancet* (i) 17, 24 March 1923 pp. 491, 509–10, 7 April p. 612. Austoker, Joan, *A history of the Imperial Cancer Research Fund 1902–86* (1988).

96 Report of the committee to enquire into the financial position of the Society, Ms 713/123, RCP.

97 MacAlister correspondence 1909, folder 9/G20, Box 33.

98 Letter from 'An Old Fellow', December 1912, MacAlister correspondence G15, Box 29. Economy committee report 18 April 1913, MacAlister correspondence folder 2/G17, Box 30.

99 MacAlister correspondence 1913, folder 3/G11, Box 26; G12, Box 26.

100 *Ibid* folder 2/G13, Box 28.

101 Memorandum on MacAlister's Financial Services 1903–12, G21, Box 33.

102 Latham/MacAlister correspondence 1913, G15, Box 29.

103 *Ibid.*

104 Tidy, H, 'Returnable subscriptions' (1958).

105 MacAlister correspondence with Colyer 1920, folder 7/G18, Box 31.

106 AGM 1922, *Bulletin* 35 (1922).

107 AGM 1923, *Bulletin* 37 (1923).

108 Gold Medal correspondence 1920–26, M15, Box 53.

109 Gold Medal of the Royal Society of Medicine, *Bulletin* 32 (1920). Gold Medal committee minutes 1920–47, M14.

110 Presentation speech at the Society's annual dinner 1927, *Bulletin* 47 (1928). CM 18 October 1927.

111 MacAlister correspondence, Beaverbrook Fund 1929, folder 3/G19, Box 32. *Bulletin* 55 (1932).

112 Speeches at the Society's annual dinner 1929, *Bulletin* 51 (1930).

113 *Bulletin* 57 (1933).

114 Watson, Francis, *Lord Dawson of Penn* (1950) pp. 5, 217–18.

115 Report of Council 1917–18, Bulletin 26 (1918). Presidential address 1919, *Bulletin* 29 (1919). MacAlister correspondence 27 January 1917, folder 2/G18, Box 31.

116 MacAlister correspondence 1920, folder 8/G18, Box 31. CM 17 June 1924. Lloyd Roberts Legacy and Lecture Fund 1920–61, M25, Box 56.

117 CM 21 June 1932. The Hughlings Jackson lecture, *Bulletin* 55 (1932). Hughlings Jackson Medal 1931–33, M18, Box 53.

118 CM 19 June, 17 July 1928, 21 June 1932. Hickman Memorial Fund 1928–33, M17, Box 53. For details of the trust deed 17 November 1931 and list of medallists see Young, TM, *A short history of the Section of Anaesthetics of the Royal Society of Medicine and the Society of Anaesthetists* (1998).

119 CM 15 February 1927.

120 WE Dixon Memorial Prize 1933–38, M4, Box 50.

121 CM 21 June 1932, 20 June 1933. The lecture in memory of CE Wallis was to be held every fifth year, CM 21 June 1927.

122 CM 20 March 1928.

123 CM 12 April 1927. Gamble Fund and Research Prize *c.*1930, M6, Box 50.

124 MacAlister correspondence 1926, G19, Box 32. Colyer Prize 1932, M3, Box 50.

125 CM 19 June 1928. Nichols Prize 1920–63, M21, 22, Box 54. MacAlister correspondence 1921, folder 6/G18, Box 31.

126 Trust deed 2 April 1919, MacAlister correspondence folder 2/G18, Box 31. Gibson Research Scholarship committee 1919, H3 and minutes M7–13, Boxes 50, 51, 52.

127 Moll, JMH, *Presidents of the Royal Society of Medicine* (1996) pp. 15–17.

128 *Royal Society of Medicine. Opening of the Chalmers Library* (1922).

129 Wallace Memorial committee 23 March 1916, H3.

130 CM 21 October 1930, 16 June 1931.

131 CM 17 June 1930. Margaret Medwin Collection, MacAlister correspondence June 1929, folder 2/G19, Box 32. Bookplate.

132 CM 21 April 1925. Rickman Godlee bequest, CM 22 June 1926.

133 Complimentary dinner and testimonial to MacAlister, *Supplement to Bulletin* (1920).

134 I am grateful to AR Hewitt for biographical notes about his father. The appointment has been erroneously reported elsewhere as being with the Red Cross or the League of Nations.

135 Honorary Librarians' report, *Bulletin* 30 (1920).

136 CM 21 April 1925.

137 Presidential speech at the Society's annual dinner 1925, *Bulletin* 43 (1926).

138 CM 22 June 1926, 19 June 1928. RSM, *Annual Report of Council 1958–59*.

139 Tanner, WE, *Arbuthnot Lane. His life and work* (1946) p. 123.

# Chapter 7

# The first Sections of the Society

THE ROYAL SOCIETY OF MEDICINE was created by the amalgamation of 15 medical societies in 1907 (see Chapter 5):

- the Royal Medical and Chirurgical Society founded in 1805
- the Pathological Society of London founded in 1846
- the Epidemiological Society of London founded in 1850
- the Odontological Society of Great Britain founded in 1863
- the Obstetrical Society of London founded in 1858
- the Clinical Society of London founded in 1867
- the Dermatological Society of London founded in 1882
- the British Gynaecological Society founded in 1884
- the Neurological Society of the United Kingdom founded in 1886
- the British Laryngological, Rhinological and Otological Association founded in 1888
- the Laryngological Society of London founded in 1893
- the Dermatological Society of Great Britain and Ireland founded in 1894
- the Otological Society of the United Kingdom founded in 1899
- the British Electro-Therapeutic Society founded in 1902
- the Therapeutical Society founded in 1902.

The Supplementary Charter dated 28 May 1907 authorized the change of name from the Royal Medical and Chirurgical Society to the Royal Society of Medicine (Plate 29). The 15 medical societies dissolved and agreed to transfer their assets and property to the RSM within which they were reconstituted as 13 Sections: Medical, Surgical, Pathological, Epidemiological, Odontological, Obstetrical and Gynaecological, Clinical, Dermatological, Neurological, Laryngological, Otological, Electro-therapeutical, Therapeutical and Pharmacological. Members of the dissolving societies transferred their memberships to the new Society without paying an admission fee and thereafter were given the option of subscribing three guineas per annum for Fellowship of the RSM or one guinea for membership of a Section. The amalgamation united several branches of the profession in 'a compact and influential body' with a famous medical Library and a handsome 18th-century house in Hanover Square.[1]

The successful amalgamation, which took two years to negotiate, was due to the hard work of MacAlister backed by Sir Richard Douglas Powell (President of the Society 1904–06 and of the Royal College of Physicians 1905–10), Sir William Selby Church (President of the Royal College of Physicians 1899–1904 and President of the RSM 1907–10) and Sir William Osler, Regius Professor of Medicine at Oxford University. Sir Geoffrey Keynes paid tribute to Osler's 'quite extraordinary capacity for overcoming discordant feelings among his friends and acquaintances, while inducing them to unite in forwarding some common cause... The outstanding example of this faculty was the successful amalgamation of a large number of medical societies in London, into a single institution under one roof, this being the enlarged Royal Society of Medicine. Many other people, Sir John MacAlister among them, played prominent parts in bringing this about. In fact, Osler's name was not mentioned in the medical journals at the time, though in reality it was he who had been the anonymous catalytic agent. He had stood at MacAlister's shoulder with suggestions and encouragement and had dropped hints in many other quarters where they were needed. He was never eager to take credit, being perfectly content to enjoy the result of his influence and witness the satisfaction of others'.[2]

In the new structure the Medical and Surgical Sections corresponded to the major interests of the RMCS, medicine and surgery. The two dermatological societies combined in one Section; with persuasion members of the Obstetrical Society of London joined those who had belonged to the British Gynaecological Society to form the Section of Obstetrics and Gynaecology; laryngologists, rhinologists and otologists fell into two Sections, Laryngology and Otology. Other Sections were the direct successors of the now defunct medical societies.

The arrangement was pragmatic: obvious advantages arose from the saving of time and money for members and participation in a wider sphere of professional interest. The house and Library at Hanover Square were major attractions, and those societies whose attendances had been declining anticipated a revival as Sections of a new and prestigious Royal Society.

The amalgamation was significant in that it signalled the acceptance of specialization by the establishment after a long period of resistance. It had become clear that the scientific and technical advance of medicine led inexorably to specialization, and that the specialist hospitals were successful. At a time when specialization seemed to threaten the disintegration of the profession, the unity offered by the Royal Society of Medicine was an enticing prospect.

At a meeting of over 200 Fellows and members of the medical societies of London assembled at the Royal College of Physicians in April 1905 to hear the amalgamation proposals, Sir William Selby Church declared his strong support for such a view: he was in no doubt 'that there would be very great advantages to medicine in London and to the profession, if some such society could be established which should embrace the whole of the medical art and the sciences which are affiliated to medical practice. At the present time, owing to the enormous advance in knowledge, and also to the necessity for now making use of special instruments to a very much greater extent than was ever the case before, medicine is necessarily split up into a large number of branches'. It was in the interests of the profession to maintain a close connection between general medicine and the specialties, and the RSM promised this.[3]

Two years later with the union in sight, the last President of the RMCS, J Warrington Haward, reinforced this support. He spoke of the increasing danger of a narrow and restricted view of medicine 'as an antidote to which it is much to be desired that in whatever department of practice, we should be in touch with the work of our colleagues in other directions', and this would be a function of the RSM.[4] The majority agreed: both the *BMJ* and the *Lancet* had promoted the amalgamation from the moment the scheme was floated in 1905. The *Lancet* was particularly enthusiastic, recommending the scheme on the grounds that it would remedy the fragmentation of medicine caused by specialization.[5] Thus the Royal Society of Medicine was created in the expectation that it would unify the profession in the face of the specialization that besieged it. The desire for unity was also evident in the founding of the Association of Physicians of Great Britain and Ireland in the same year as the RSM. This too had Sir William Selby Church for its first President.

The Sections and the RSM flourished immediately: the number of Fellows increased from 1,322 in June 1907 to 2,025 by March 1908 (including 291 Fellows who had not belonged to any of the dissolved medical societies) and there were over 600 members of Sections. The largest Sections were the Surgical, Clinical, Medical, Obstetrical and

Gynaecological and Pathological in that order, to be followed by the Section for the Study of Disease in Children when it joined the RSM in 1908. The RSM began with a balance of assets over liabilities of more than £37,000; the two wealthiest societies joining were the Obstetrical and the Odontological, in recognition of which those two Sections were represented on the Finances and General Purposes committee. Subscriptions exceeded expectations, an inaugural dinner at the Hotel Cecil on 3 December 1907 symbolized fellowship and in August 1908 King Edward VII agreed to be Patron of the Society.

The presentation of papers and cases, which had been the *raison d'être* of the Medical and Chirurgical Society since it was founded in 1805, now became the responsibility of the Sections. Each Section's papers were published in the *Proceedings* almost verbatim, and in the seven years before the outbreak of the First World War the potential of the individual Sections as sources of scientific expertise began to be recognized.

During that war many Sections reduced the number of meetings and attendance was sparse; those meetings that did take place often dealt with current problems such as war injuries and shellshock. Some Sections were called upon to advise the authorities: for instance the Section of Balneology and Climatology supplied the War Office with information on the appropriate resorts and cures for the rehabilitation of the wounded.

Some Sections became involved with national issues relating to public health and medical education: the Section of Obstetrics and Gynaecology with the Section of Epidemiology and State Medicine pressed for the registration of stillbirths (1913), and the former pressed for the better training of medical students in obstetrics and gynaecology (1919). The Section for the Study of Disease in Children made its views known on the medical inspection of schoolchildren (1909) and the supply of pure milk (1925). The Council of the RSM was taken aback by the early initiatives and in 1914 reined in the Sections by a standing order restraining their direct communication with government departments or other outside bodies – in order to avoid 'diverse views' the President and Council had to approve (or not) dealings between the Sections and government authorities. Thenceforward the Society's name was attached to the investigations and reports

The inaugural dinner of the Royal Society of Medicine was held at the Hotel Cecil on 3 December 1907.

handled by the Sections, and by 1933 the *Official Bulletin* of the RSM reported with pride that scientific advice had been sought by bodies such as the India Office and the Board of Trade and that scientific reports and enquiries had been handled by the Council jointly with the Sections.[6] This referred to the report of the Section of Otology on 'Hearing tests' and the Section of Radiology's report on the 'Scientific aspects of radium and X-ray therapy' (1932). The Board of Trade's request involved testing a new method of resuscitating the apparently drowned, and the India Office, having launched an Indian drugs enquiry (1930–31), obtained advice from the Section of Therapeutics and Pharmacology.

Some Sections provided the impetus for the foundation of faculties and even Royal Colleges. For instance the Section of Anaesthetics was the precursor of the Association of Anaesthetists, founded in 1932, which in turn instigated the Faculty of Anaesthetics at the Royal College of Surgeons in 1948. The Section of the History of Medicine gave birth to the Society of Apothecaries' Faculty of the History of Medicine and Pharmacology in 1959, and the formation of the Section of General Practice in 1950 has been described as a dress rehearsal for the foundation of the College two years later.[7]

*The nature of meetings*
The vitality of a Section and the interest of its meetings depended to a great extent on the initiative of its President. Each Section enjoyed a degree of autonomy and a different character, enabling it to pursue its special subject as well as contributing expertise to joint meetings and the life of the RSM as a whole. This remains the case.

Within a few years of amalgamation officers of the Society were summoned to a conference at which they were urged to avoid lengthy papers and duplication by closer co-ordination; the cost of publishing the papers of 20 Sections in the *Proceedings* had escalated and there was need for economy (the wartime paper shortage soon had this effect).[8] Sir Francis Champneys was particularly concerned that there was a lack of 'intercommunion' between the Sections which might render the amalgamation a mere matter of form.[9]

The problem of duplication was difficult to avoid when some subjects held wide interest, for instance syphilis and duodenal ulcers were subjects common to several Sections. A solution was found by encouraging joint meetings, following the example set by the Surgical Section, which in October 1907 joined with the Clinical, Laryngological, Medical, Obstetrical and Gynaecological Sections to hear an address by Professor E Goldmann on cancer. Combined discussions were particularly fruitful during the First World War when several Sections contributed to debates on 'Trench nephritis', 'Shellshock' (1916) and 'Toxic jaundice among munition workers' (1917). The Sections of Anaesthetics and Laryngology organized a discussion on 'Anaesthesia in throat operations' in 1920 and for the session of 1923–24 joint meetings were officially promoted: the Medical and Surgical Sections then collaborated in a meeting on the 'Surgical treatment of pulmonary tuberculosis' – Sir James Kingston Fowler was strongly in favour, and his example served to encourage the development of thoracic surgery generally. The Section for the Study of Disease in Children was first drawn into a joint meeting in March 1924, combining with Neurology, Obstetrics and Gynaecology, and Orthopaedics on the subject of 'Birth injuries'.[10] Joint meetings continue to be popular: in 1998 a combination of the Sections of Clinical Neurosciences and History of Medicine and the Open Section on 'Music, the brain and the mind' included a recital from the Ravel String Quartet.

Section meetings were not always at the Society's house. From 1912 the Section of Psychiatry specified that discussions there should alternate with practical work in laboratories connected with hospitals for mental disease; similarly, members of the Section of Pathology attached great importance to their laboratory meetings. The laryngologists were quick to organize an annual dinner and provincial meetings, while the Balneological and Climatological Section regularly met at the spa towns.

Meetings were also arranged with outside organizations, local societies and associations: an obvious combination was the Section of Anaesthetics with the Association of Anaesthetists. In 1927 the Neurological Section, keen to keep apace of advances in the USA, invited members of the American Neurological Association to Wimpole Street and this Section has held many successful meetings with overseas colleagues. Contacts were cemented by the Inter-Allied Conferences held at the RSM between 1942 and 1945, and in 1949 the Section of Psychiatry took advantage of an international meeting in Paris to invite American colleagues to an Anglo-American Symposium at the RSM.

## The Section of Medicine (Plate 36)
### incorporating Experimental Medicine and Therapeutics from 1973

The direct ancestor of the RSM and the oldest of the societies combining in the new incorporation was the Royal Medical and Chirurgical Society, founded as the Medical and Chirurgical Society in 1805. The Medical and Surgical Sections of the RSM carried on the tradition of the RMCS with little change and were the first Sections to appoint officers.

The first Council meeting of the Medical Section was held in July 1907 and the Section was ready to receive papers by August. Sir Thomas Lauder Brunton and Dr Humphry Rolleston recommended that the first general meeting of the Section should be of wide medical interest; the chosen topic was 'Pneumonia', and the discussion was opened by Dr Hector Mackenzie. In his introduction, Dr Samuel Gee, the first President of the Section, called into question the meaning of the word medicine. He foresaw the difficulties facing the Section, *primus inter pares*, yet challenged by Sections and sub-Sections that 'had committed such ravages upon Medicine's garment that they had hardly left their ancient parent raiment enough to clothe herself withal'. He admitted that attendances at meetings of the old Society had become very small of late, no doubt owing to the counter-attractions of other societies.

### Decline

Unfortunately the same fate was to befall the Medical Section. In terms of membership numbers this was one of the largest Sections, yet its meetings did not attract many. Fellows found the proceedings of the specialized Sections more instructive than the general topics discussed at the Medical Section. Just five years after its inception Sir Richard Douglas Powell acknowledged that the Section was starved of interesting papers and poorly attended.[11] Another problem was that this Section was often presented with papers that were more suitable to another Section, and some were not suitable at all: one on 'Causes of death' was dismissed as 'inopportune' in 1915.

Sir William Osler did his best to revive the ailing Section, writing to Rolleston in December 1912: 'Med Section RSM. Why should it not be rejuvenated? Let us make a personal appeal to all the Assistant Physicians at the Lond. Gen. Hospitals for the special ones to make it their first duty; & help put it in the position of the Société des Hôpitaux'.[12] Members were sent circulars with promises that the next session would feature rare medical affections fully illustrated by cases and specimens and they were encouraged to bring forward interesting cases. Osler personally supported the Section by participating in discussions on 'Paratyphoid fever' (1915) and 'Trench nephritis', held jointly with the Section of Therapeutics and Pharmacology in 1916.

In 1919 a proposal that the Medical Section might be regenerated by the inclusion of 'experimentalists' did not meet with approval; a new Section of Experimental Medicine was the preferred alternative, although it was not until 1943 that the Section of Experimental Medicine and Therapeutics was constituted. The fusion of the Medical and

Clinical Sections was also proposed as a possible solution to the low attendance at the Medical Section's meetings. This too was rejected, but the Council did agree that papers on comparative medicine would be welcome (Professor Hobday soon persuaded the RSM that comparative medicine warranted a separate Section).[13]

### Presidents and speakers

The Minute Books record batches of resignations in the 1930s, although the Section was sustained by well-known Presidents such as Sir Edward Farquhar Buzzard: this was his third presidency of a Section (preceded by Psychiatry and Neurology) and he was concurrently Regius Professor of Medicine at Oxford where he engineered the Nuffield medical benefaction. Another famous name was that of Sir Geoffrey Marshall, the chest physician who treated Sir Winston Churchill and King George VI; Marshall was President of the Section in 1941 and elected President of the RSM in 1958.

The names of some of the speakers are also familiar: Professor Alexander Fleming was present at the discussion on the use of sulphonamides and penicillin in the treatment of syphilis in 1944 and two years later he spoke to the Section on his special subject. Professor Alexander Haddow spoke in 1947 on the need to encourage the study of the chemotherapy of cancer and Sir William Allen Daley gave an assessment of poliomyelitis during the outbreak of 1947; other contributions from Sir Henry Tidy, EW Riches and Dr Bernard Hart reflected the wide range of interests covered by this Section.

### Subjects for discussion

As might be expected there was no enthusiasm for specialization among the members of the Section of Medicine who took part in the discussion on 'Specialization – its value and abuse' in March 1949. Sir Robert Arthur Young opened the meeting with his favourite definition of the specialist as 'one who devotes more and more time to less and less'. Chief concerns expressed by the speakers turned on the declining status of the general practitioner *vis-à-vis* the specialist, the narrowing of outlook consequent upon specialization and the baneful effects of overspecialization in teaching.[14] In this mood the Section refused to sanction a proposal for a Section of Haematology.

### Saturation

The medical aspects of smoking, the use of antibiotics and the actions and abuse of drugs were topical subjects at meetings of the 1960s but they failed to draw large audiences, and for the sessions of 1971–72 and 1972–73 neither the Medical Section nor the Section of Experimental Medicine and Therapeutics offered a programme. The problem was identified by the RSM's Working Party as one of saturation. Many of the Sections duplicated activities performed by national societies, colleges and postgraduate institutions throughout the country. The older Royal Colleges were taking an increased interest in postgraduate education and the newer colleges of general practitioners, psychiatrists and pathologists were also pursuing this end. Since the war, postgraduate medical education had exploded, and by 1973 there were over 300 centres in England providing clinical demonstrations, discussions, libraries, seminars, symposia and courses that were attractive to both students and lecturers.

In particular, the Section of Experimental Medicine competed for members with the Section of Endocrinology; it was also adversely affected by the Forum for Clinical Pharmacology and Therapeutics, which attracted the rising young clinical pharmacologists. It became increasingly difficult for a more generalized Section such as Medicine to find stimulating subjects and speakers without treading on the toes of another Section. In order to discuss such problems the President of the RSM called a 'Meeting on Meetings' for representatives of all Sections in March 1972 and a Working Party subsequently made sweeping recommendations aimed at the revitalization of the Society. For the Section of Medicine this meant amalgamation with the Section of Experimental Medicine and Therapeutics.

### Medicine, Experimental Medicine and Therapeutics

The merger of the Section of Medicine with the Section of Experimental Medicine and Therapeutics (formerly the Section of Therapeutics and Pharmacology, see pages 289–94) created the Section of Medicine, Experimental Medicine and Therapeutics in 1973. The combination boosted the Section's membership figures but did not solve the problem. Like its predecessors, the new Section was generalist in a specialist world. The Council of the Section of Experimental Medicine and Therapeutics had recognized that there was no role for that Section in the London medical scene of 1971 and perceived correctly that amalgamation with the Section of Medicine and possibly with Measurement in Medicine was irrational because the same problems beset those Sections. Nevertheless Medicine and Experimental Medicine did combine in 1973, only to face a struggle for survival.

A special effort was made during the session of 1979–80 to obtain sponsorship and provide entertainment, star speakers and publicity, which brought temporary popularity by attracting members from other Sections to meetings. As the 1980s advanced, however, attendances fell to an average of 12% of the Section's membership attending just two or three meetings a session; the only meeting for 1985–86, called to hear the presidential address, was attended by just 29 members and guests.

The Executive Director of the RSM made it clear that it was wasteful of the Society's resources to continue support for this Section, particularly when new Sections and Fora were being established, and the newly formed Forum of Clinical Pharmacology and Therapeutics catered for one of the major interests of the dying Section of Medicine, Experimental Medicine and Therapeutics. The last President of the latter could not disagree – he blamed the decline in attendances on competition from other Sections, institutions and associations.

Thus the decision to disband the Section of Medicine, Experimental Medicine and Therapeutics was taken without dissent in the summer of 1987. Members' attention was directed to the other 35 thriving Sections and ten Fora of the RSM.[15]

## Section of Surgery (Plate 37)

The first meeting of the Council of this Section was held on 3 July 1907 to draw up regulations and organize forthcoming meetings; there were to be eight a session, between October and June.[16] With J Warrington Haward as its first President and John Bland-Sutton, Rickman J Godlee, Charles Ballance, James Berry, Andrew Clark and Sir Victor Horsley on the Council, the future of this Section looked promising. The first papers confirmed expectations: Professor E Goldmann wrote on the value of X-rays, James Berry reported on 274 operations for removal of goitre (he capped this in 1921 with another 500 to report) and Berkeley Moynihan presented a case in which he had removed the whole stomach.

### Lord Moynihan

Berkeley Moynihan had been the first British surgeon to perform a complete gastrectomy and his paper to the Section dwelt on his second success. The President thanked him for an 'extraordinarily interesting' paper and advised the audience that the patient was on view in the next room along with specimens and preparations of his stomach.[17] Moynihan had contributed papers to the *Transactions* of the RMCS in the early years of the 20th century and following his gastrectomy paper of 1907 he presented his work on 'The diagnosis and treatment of duodenal ulcer' to the Section in December 1909.[18] He opened with the confident statement that 'there are few diseases whose symptoms appear in such a definite and well-ordered sequence as is observed in duodenal ulcer', and went on to recommend surgical treatment for recurrent attacks. Harold Collinson then gave an analysis of 197 cases of duodenal ulcer operated upon by Moynihan between 1900 and 1908. In the discussion that followed Sir Thomas Lauder Brunton agreed that an operation was required for obstinate ulcers, but not all shared this view and the debate continued with the publication of Moynihan's book on *The duodenal ulcer* in 1910.

Lord Moynihan's name was to be associated permanently with the duodenal ulcer and his monograph on *Abdominal operations* gained him an international reputation at the age of 40. He is also remembered for the use of green (as opposed to white) in the operating theatre, as a protagonist of gentle surgery and his emphasis on the importance of 'the pathology of the living'.[19]

## Orthopaedic surgery

Robert Jones, the pioneer of organized orthopaedic surgery in this country, gave his famous address on the 'Treatment of fractures in the neighbourhood of joints' to the Surgical Section in November 1910. He acknowledged the brilliant and earnest work of Arbuthnot Lane, a fellow-member of the Section and made no great claims for himself: he was merely exposing his own methods and principles of treatment, the result of long practice in a manufacturing and mining district. Forty years later this paper was recognized as having laid down the principles of mobilization of elbow injuries. Jones was also prominent in the Section for the Study of Disease in Children and the Section of Orthopaedics (see pages 311–12, 357–58).[20]

EW Hey Groves, the founder of the *British Journal of Surgery* and a pioneer bone-

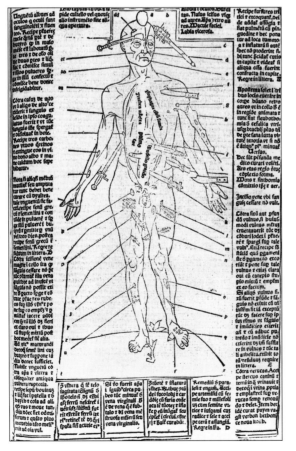

A woodcut from Johannes de Ketham's *Fasciculus medicinae* (1513) indicates the sites of wounds most dangerous to the internal organs and gives instructions on the treatment of wounds and broken bones. The first edition of 1493/4 was the first medical book to contain anatomical illustrations.

grafter, was another orthopaedic surgeon who took part in the meetings of the Surgical Section prior to the formation of a sub-Section in orthopaedics. In June 1911 he opened the discussion on 'Spinal nerve roots' in which Professor Foerster of Breslau took part.[21] Elmslie, Spencer, Rushton Parker of Liverpool and Sampson Handley also gave papers on orthopaedic surgery at this time. The last paper presented before the sub-Section of Orthopaedics was formed came from Albert Martin of Newcastle. His record of 449 operations in cases of injury of the semilunar cartilages surprised the London audience, who had no inkling of the prevalence of these injuries among the miners of Northumberland and Durham.[22]

The Surgical Section was the only Section to approve sub-Sections – in orthopaedics, proctology and urology in 1913, at a time when the specialties begged recognition and received little. All three sub-Sections matured into Sections (see pages 356, 369 and 349 respectively).[23]

The first provincial meeting of the Surgical Section was held in 1913 at the Birmingham General Hospital. The party witnessed operations, inspected a large number of surgical cases and was entertained to dinner. The outing was judged a great success and the following year Robert Jones hosted the Section's visit to Liverpool.

## The First World War

The outbreak of war halted such activities and the Section arranged meetings on subjects of current gravity: wound treatment, gunshot fractures and bone-grafting with a cinematographic demonstration of methods of grafting used in America by Professor Frederick Albee (1916). Another visitor from America, Dr William O'Neill Sherman, opened a discussion on 'The sterilization of wounds': at the outbreak of the war wound infection had been the great problem confronting surgeons.[24]

Sir Anthony Bowlby was President of the Section from the beginning to the end of the war even though he was on active service throughout, as Consulting Surgeon to the Forces. He had acquired knowledge of military surgery and organization during the Boer War, experience that proved valuable in France where he insisted that surgery must be carried out as soon as possible at the front rather than at base. 'The Baron', as he was called, succeeded Sir George Makins as President of the Section; on Makins' retirement from active service 'The Baron' assumed Makins' duties abroad as Adviser on Surgery for the entire British area.

In the aftermath of the war those who had served in the RAMC gave the Section the benefit of their experiences, which with the example of leaders like Makins, Bowlby and Jones led to the development of new techniques, procedures and practice in several branches of surgery.

## Sir John Bland-Sutton

Surgeons were beginning to apply the lessons of war to civilian practice at the time that Sir John Bland-Sutton was elected President of the Section in 1918. He was the leading gynaecological surgeon at the Middlesex and Chelsea Hospitals, where he pioneered hysterectomy for fibroids. He had been a member of the Odontological and Neurological Societies in the late 19th century and was soon to be President of the RSM. The presidential address he gave to the Section of Surgery was, strangely, omitted from the *Proceedings* but appeared in full in the *BMJ*.

Bland-Sutton set great store on pathology – he endowed the Pathological Institute of the Middlesex Hospital and was an admirer of John Hunter – and both his enthusiasms figured large in his address. He urged members of the Section to study the important collection of pathological specimens at the Royal College of Surgeons: 'If these preparations were systematically studied much that is useful could be co-ordinated and this

Sir John Bland-Sutton, President of the Section of Surgery 1918–20 and President of the Society 1920–22. A contemporary ditty portrayed him as a gentle surgeon:
'Some surgeons cut you up like mutton,
But that is not the way with Sutton,
Bland is his name, though stern of eye,
He couldn't bear to hurt a fly'.

Section should be the medium for collecting some of the "choicest spoils" obtained by surgeons in London'.[25]

### The 1920s and 1930s

Mr James Berry's presidential address of 1922 offered a fresh approach: instead of focusing on historic advances or a specific achievement, he dwelt on 'Mistakes in diagnosis and treatment'. Many in the audience admitted to 'oversights', and George Gask confessed that he had several times made the mistake of diagnosing tuberculous abdominal glands as appendicitis. In 1934 he was elected President of the Section and gave an address on 'The fight against cancer'.

Tudor Edwards, Grey Turner and E Rock Carling were others active at Section meetings during the interwar years, a time when surgical practice was changing as a result of the war experience and the growth of the major specialites – orthopaedics, neurosurgery, plastic surgery and urological surgery. New techniques and aseptic methods came into use, and at Section meetings the epidiascope and radiographs were used to illustrate the new methods. There were regular demonstrations of specimens and patients, a pathological evening every session, visits to provincial hospitals were resumed and in 1927 an American tour was organized for 25 members and some wives.

In 1929 the Section of Surgery was the forum for a discussion on 'Surgery of the spinal cord' led by Hugh Cairns and Geoffrey Jefferson. Cairns' contribution was judged to be 'remarkably authoritative from one who had returned from Cushing only two years before'. Three months later Cairns was speaking before the Section of Otology on 'Brain abscess' and he was soon taking part in meetings of the Neurological and Laryngological Sections.[26]

### Body armour in the Second World War

The Section of Surgery responded quickly to the Second World War with recommendations for the better protection of the fighting forces. This arose from a discussion led by

Sir Harold Gillies, Colonel Max Page and Surgeon Rear Admiral Gordon-Taylor, which concluded that 'the physical protection of the members of the armed forces can and should be improved by a closer collaboration between the medical profession and the appropriate technical experts at the Admiralty, the War Office and the Air Ministry'. As a matter of extreme urgency the Council of the RSM reinforced this resolution and a committee chaired by Lord Horder produced a report on body armour, which was forwarded to the Prime Minister and relevant government departments in 1940. With the aid of diagrams the report showed how steel plates could protect the soldier's vital organs against high-velocity bullets and small splinters, which were the cause of 75% of the casualties among ground personnel. It was recommended that a reinforced battledress would give better physical protection and would also be of strong psychological value.[27]

The Sections of Surgery and Pathology combined to confront the problem of blast injuries in 1941, when Professor Solly Zuckerman opened the discussion by presenting his hypothesis about lung injuries based on his experiments with monkeys. By the time he came to write his autobiography, the influence of his paper was acknowledged and 'soon nothing more was heard of the conventional explanation of blast injuries'.[28]

Sir Harold Gillies participated in meetings of this and several other Sections, along with Sir Archibald McIndoe: both were making their names as founders of reconstructive or plastic surgery in this country. Richard Battle, the first plastic surgeon to be sent abroad with the British Expeditionary Force (in December 1939), also contributed to meetings. One of the most successful meetings of the war period was held jointly with the Section of Anaesthetics to discuss anaesthesia and analgesia in abdominal operations. Even though many members were on active service 150 Fellows, members and visitors were present.

## Debate

As soon as hostilities ceased the Section resumed discussions on cancer, ulcers and hypertension and some of these meetings attracted over 300 members and guests. Sir Gordon Gordon-Taylor, President of the RSM from 1944 to 1946 and past President of the sub-Section of Proctology, was probably the most distinguished surgeon participating in these discussions, yet during the debate on breast cancer his methods and statistics were questioned. The discussion was prolonged during December and January 1947–48 and the editor of the *Proceedings* felt it necessary to abridge the most vehement contributions.

Gordon-Taylor began his speech by referring with reverence to Charles Moore's 'epoch-making paper' of 1867 (see page 138) and the work of Sir Alfred Pearce and W Sampson Handley. As for himself, 'I am not, and have never been a "cancer specialist", I have never had a cancer clinic or sat among the mighty in Cancer Campaigns. I am a simple soul, a simple surgeon profoundly ignorant of the recondite mysteries of radiation therapy'. Nonetheless, Gordon-Taylor claimed to have 645 radical operations for mammary cancer to his credit. His radical approach and his figures came under immediate attack from Dr R McWhirter, who told the Section about the treatment of breast carcinoma at the Royal Infirmary, Edinburgh. His method, namely simple mastectomy with post-operative radiotherapy, had been developed in an attempt to overcome the causes of failure of the radical operation.

One of those present on this occasion remembered that 'there was a packed house and Geoffrey Keynes later told me that he had been unable to get in'. Reginald Murley was struck by 'the uncomfortably hostile atmosphere' in which McWhirter's paper was received, the lack of any truly constructive debate and the manifest inadequacy of the statistics quoted by Sir Stanford Cade and Sir Gordon Gordon-Taylor. 'The punchline of the evening came when Duncan FitzWilliams, a St Mary's surgeon, having pointed out that certain of Sir Gordon Gordon-Taylor's figures were too good to be true, went on to say "So the best advice we can give any woman approaching middle age is to develop a stage 1 breast carcinoma; but above all to go to Sir Gordon Gordon-Taylor for radical mastectomy. Thereby her prospects will better those of her cohorts in the same age group who have never had cancer"'. To Murley the meeting was the turning point that inspired him to research the results of radical mastectomy, and in general more conservative surgery for breast cancer began to be favoured.[29]

In 1959 Sir Harold Gillies entered the debate when he tried to convince the Surgical Section of the virtues of prompt breast reconstruction. The issue was controversial and Gillies wrote that 'In trepidation, I am showing cases of breast reconstruction after mastectomy or other cases of absence of one breast. It is going to be a hard tussle to persuade the general surgeon to plan for new breast when he is excising. She deserves it'.[30]

## New and recurrent problems

In the 1960s the new subjects that made for stimulating meetings were the advances in endocrine surgery, cardiac surgery and the chemotherapy of cancer. Meetings of the 1970s were specifically devoted to new techniques, procedures and instruments in order to keep members up to date.

A consistent and longstanding preoccupation of Section meetings from the 1950s to the 1990s was with cancer, tumours and melanoma. Papers, discussions and on one occasion a trans-Atlantic link with American colleagues explored the location and management of cancer of the breast, the excision of major tumours, reconstruction, chemotherapy and malignant melanoma; the latter was the subject of an address by the Section's first female President, Miss Phyllis George, in 1984. Three years later, Sir Patrick Forrest put the case for the earlier screening, diagnosis and treatment of breast cancer – the Barnes Hall was packed to capacity and many were forced to stand.

In the face of the increasing specialization of surgery Section meetings cultivated a multidisciplinary approach to disease and surgery at meetings on 'The problem of obesity' and 'The management of testicular tumours with radiology', for instance. As various alternatives to surgery gained ground, discussions took place on 'Retreats in surgery' and 'Inappropriate surgery'. On other occasions the Section looked to the future of microsurgery (1980) and reflected on the depressing figures for colonic cancer deaths in Britain (1982), while violence in Belfast and the Middle East generated papers on high-velocity missile injuries and gunshot and bomb injuries (1982).

## Disquiet

In the late 1970s the Minutes of the Surgical Section register confusion over the Section's finance and disquiet about the *Journal of the Royal Society of Medicine*, which superseded the *Proceedings* in 1978. The Council put it on record that it 'unanimously reiterated its opinion that the Journal should revert to its former format and thus enable it to be more closely linked with Section matters and allowing younger contributors to Section meetings more opportunity of having presentations published than was possible at present'; this was followed by a vote of no confidence in the Society's editorial policy. The Section was eventually placated by the promise of a new style of *Journal* for 1986.[31]

## The new millennium

In the last decade of the 20th century the Section's Council was confronted by the problem of how to maintain and stimulate interest in general surgery in the face of increasing specialization. While the meetings centred on the Norman Tanner Prize and the Glaxo Prize for clinically based papers remained popular, the Medical Insurance Agency Prize (for laboratory-based research papers) had limited appeal and reached a point when the only people attending were the presenters of the papers and the members of Council called upon to judge them. It was therefore decided to adopt a new approach to add variety to

The Norman Tanner Medal was first
awarded in 1990.

such meetings by inviting a guest speaker and by including a video film, which resulted in greatly improved attendance. Similarly, the subjects for regular meetings were deliberately chosen to be relevant to all: medico-legal matters were of general concern and made for popular meetings while oncology proved a hardy perennial.

For the 1999–2000 session the President's address on 'The lottery of liver secondaries' was delivered to a packed house, and the Section's tour to Beaune in April also proved very popular. For the first time the President's day in June was held jointly with the Section of Coloproctology, at Basingstoke, and the concert at the end of the day was oversubscribed. Another first was the joint meeting with the Royal College of Surgeons of Edinburgh and the College of Surgeons of Hong Kong in October 2000. Thus the Section of Surgery entered the 21st century in a flourishing state with over a thousand members and a programme with general appeal.

## Section of Pathology (Plate 38)

In the mid-19th century the Pathological Society of London was an energetic rival to the RMCS and attracted many of its members. Indeed it was founded during a surge of discontent felt by some members of the older Society (see pages 102–03). The first President of the Pathological Society, Dr Charles B Williams, headed a core of founder-members from University College and Guy's Hospitals who constituted the Pathological Society for 'the exhibition and examination of specimens and drawings, microscopic preparations, casts or models of morbid parts with accompanying written or oral descriptions illustrative of pathological science'. It was resolved at the first meeting in May 1846 that application should be made to the RMCS for the use of its rooms, an application that was rejected. The Pathological Society then secured accommodation with the Horticultural Society, and with the practical arrangements in place, 108 members enrolled.[32]

Dr Williams went on to be President of the RMCS (1873–75) and by the end of the century the Pathological Society was comfortably installed with the RMCS at Hanover Square. According to Sir Victor Horsley, however, the Pathological Society had declined into 'an emporium of morbid anatomy... a night school for morbid anatomists' by 1891. Horsley's criticism and his founding of the Medical Research Club inflicted severe damage on the Pathological Society, which lent itself too easily to the mere exhibiting of specimens:

Stephen Paget wrote that members were inclined to call attention to the specimens as a means of calling attention to themselves.[33] More fundamental to the Society's decline was the rise of bacteriology, of which the older members knew little.

When the then President of the Pathological Society, Sir John Burdon Sanderson, was approached on the subject of amalgamation in 1905 he was strongly in favour, going as far as to urge the incorporation of the two Royal Colleges in the scheme. He died before the end of the year leaving Dr PH Pye-Smith to continue negotiations on behalf of the Pathological Society, whose chief objection to amalgamation was the title of Royal Society of Medicine.[34] While the negotiations proceeded, the Pathological Society of Great Britain and Ireland came into being, and managed to attract 264 members by 1908.

Members of the older Pathological Society transferred their allegiance to the new Section of the RSM in June 1907, when Dr SG Shattock recorded the demise of the Society: *Dissoluta est jam de die quarto Junii 1907, Societas Pathologica Londinensis*. He assumed the presidency of the Section for the forthcoming session, insisting that formal debate was abolished and that papers given at the Section meetings would have to withstand the fire of questions and interruptions in the manner of Socratic dialogue.[35]

## Sir Almroth Wright

In the early 20th century pathologists were encouraged by the work and spirit of Sir Almroth Wright, who is chiefly associated with vaccine therapy. His students, however, were less than reverential, nicknaming him Sir Always Wrong or 'old Almost Right... a fierce, hoary lion of a man who never spoke to a woman, who hated students of any sort and who refused to teach (except for the few statutory lectures he had to give)'.[36]

Almroth Wright may not have enjoyed teaching students but he made a strong case to his audience at the RSM in 1910 when he opened the debate on vaccine therapy, its administration, value and limitations. He affirmed that bacteriology was an essential and indispensable part of medicine and warned his audience that 'The new wine of bacterial vaccines cannot with impunity be poured into the old bottles of ancient medicine'; the discussion extended over six sessions of the Section. Wright claimed consultant status for

Sir Almroth Wright, one of the first members of the Section of Pathology and a Vice President in 1908, pioneered vaccine therapy.

the bacteriologist and by inference for the pathologist. In his history of *Pathology as a profession in Great Britain*, WD Foster comments on the importance of his manifesto: 'his contribution to the corpus of scientific truth is not large... Yet there is no doubt that without Wright's sincere and forceful advocacy of what in fact was a bogus laboratory test and a bogus form of therapy less resources would have been made available for hospital laboratories, and the opportunities to earn a living practising as a pathologist far fewer'.[37]

Sir William Osler (President of the Clinical Section in 1912) and Dr Amand Routh (President of the Section of Obstetrics and Gynaecology 1911–13) lent their weight to the pathologists' cause, encouraging the establishment of more laboratories at the hospitals, and Routh also tried to promote a sub-Section of chemical pathology within the RSM.[38]

## Members and meetings

Sir Almroth Wright was a Vice President of the Section together with Professor Hewlett under the presidency of Dr Frederick Mott from 1908 to 1910. One of the most loyal supporters of the Section was Dr Frederick Parkes Weber, who had belonged to the Pathological Society in the 1890s. Among the new members were William Girling Ball, E Rock Carling, and WG Savage. Hewlett succeeded as President in 1911 and was followed by Dr FW Andrewes, who was lecturer in pathology at St Bartholomew's Hospital for 30 years and knighted in 1920.

Sir Felix Semon and Sir Patrick Manson belonged to the older generation of distinguished members of the Section and their deaths were recorded in 1921 and 1922 respectively, with due reverence. During the presidency of JCG Ledingham (1922–24) Professor Frederick Hobday, Dr Alexander Fleming and 'the handsome, remote Sir Bernard Spilsbury, the Home Office pathologist'[39] served on the Council. Fleming, Dr SC Dyke and Dr EH Kettle were Honorary Secretaries: Dyke went on to be Secretary of the British Pathologists' Association and Fleming became President of the Section in 1932 for two years.

The meetings of the Section favoured demonstrations, short papers and communications, the occasional discussion, and regular laboratory meetings at the School of Tropical Medicine, the Lister Institute or the Imperial Cancer Research Fund. One of the few lengthy papers to be delivered in the early years was the work of Dr H Charlton Bastian: 'Remarks on further experiments concerning the origin of life'. Bastian was primarily a neurologist interested in aphasia and paralysis, and he was convinced that there was no strict line of demarcation between non-living and living matter. He believed in spontaneous generation and claimed that his experiments proved his case. Members of the Pathological Section were intrigued and requested that he repeat four crucial experiments as the basis for a report. Bastian reinforced his argument with a second paper but members' interest in his origin of life theory seems to have dwindled.[40]

The Section had evidently established a sound reputation by 1914 when it was consulted by the Royal Commission's Committee on Venereal Diseases about the value of the Wassermann method, and in 1917 this Section was one of several asked for advice on the adequate staffing of London hospitals.[41]

## Sir Alexander Fleming

Famous names appear in the Section's records for the 1920s, including many Fellows of the Royal Society. None were more honoured than that of Fleming, who was awarded the Nobel Prize in 1945 jointly with Sir Howard Florey and Sir Ernst Chain for the discovery of penicillin. Fleming's early work was as part of Sir Almroth Wright's team; he went on to discover lysozyme and in 1928 he described the essential properties of penicillin. It was lysozyme that he chose as the subject for his presidential address in October 1932 – 'because I have a fatherly interest in the name' – leading one commentator to claim that 'he

Sir Alexander Fleming, President of the Section 1932–34. He was made an Honorary Fellow of the Society in 1954.

seemed to have lost all interest in penicillin'.[42] Although he appeared to have abandoned penicillin as his main research interest he did refer to some trials using it as a local antiseptic in a paper to the Section of Therapeutics and Pharmacology in February 1941.[43] On another occasion he spoke to a joint meeting of the Surgical and Pathological Sections on the intravenous use of germicides; he did not mention penicillin as a possible systemic antiseptic but thought that mercurial compounds offered the best hope. In 1943, however, at a discussion held by the Section of Experimental Medicine and Therapeutics he stated categorically, 'Penicillin is the name which I gave in 1929 to an antibacterial substance produced by a mould of the genus *Penicillium*'. Fleming and Howard Florey shared the platform at this meeting and were fêted as 'The Two Great Men of Penicillin'.[44]

Sir Alexander Fleming was awarded the Gold Medal of the RSM in 1947 and elected an Honorary Fellow in 1954. He was an active member of this Section and others for 40 years, demonstrating a simple method of serum diagnosis of syphilis to the Clinical Section in 1909, speaking in the debate on vaccine therapy in 1910 and still demonstrating specimens at a meeting of the Pathological Section held in 1950, appropriately enough, at the Wright–Fleming Institute at St Mary's Hospital Medical School.

### A centenary

The centenary of the foundation of the Section's predecessor, the Pathological Society of London, was celebrated in July 1946. Professor HR Dean, one of the few surviving members of the old Society, addressed the Section on its history, stressing the practical nature of the meetings at which abstract points were avoided: the accumulation of facts had been the Society's first care.

At the same meeting Professor J McIntosh, an Honorary member who could remember being taken to meetings at 20 Hanover Square as a young man, recorded with pride some of the important discoveries in which members of the Section had played a part. He mentioned Barnard and his ultraviolet microscope, the preparation and purification of vaccinia virus by Copeman, and in the demonstration of elementary bodies in smallpox vaccine the names of Mervyn Gordon and Ledingham; 'one of the most outstanding discoveries ever made in the virus field', he added, 'was made by a member of this Section, Professor Twort, who discovered the bacteriophage'. McIntosh also referred to the many papers on the virus theory of cancer that had been read to this Section, especially on virus tumours in animals such as the Rous sarcoma in fowls and the Shope papilloma by Gye, Andrewes, Peacock, Selbie and himself. Professor SF Bedson had been partly responsible for establishing the virus nature of psittacosis in 1930, and he was to enlarge on this at a meeting in 1947.

After the five short addresses at this centenary meeting 80 members adjourned to the West Hall for a buffet supper.[45]

## The BPA, the Pathological Society and the College

The Section survived the formation of the British Pathologists' Association in 1927 (renamed the Association of Clinical Pathologists in 1932), the growth of the Pathological Society of Great Britain and Ireland and the foundation of the Royal College of Pathologists in 1962. Several members were prominent in the BPA while others belonged to the Pathological Society, although according to Professor RJV Pulvertaft (President of the Section 1958–60 and later an Honorary member) that Society was oligarchic and out of touch. It was during Pulvertaft's presidency that the Section first discussed DNA and biological research; a paper given by Dr W Hayes in March 1960 raised new questions, not least what might happen if the DNA of one species was transferred to the cells of another.[46]

Pathologists under the new National Health Service possessed no power to deal with their own affairs and lacked a higher qualification equivalent to the MRCP or FRCS; for these reasons they desired a faculty and/or college. Professor Geoffrey Hadfield, who had opened the discussion on blast injuries with Professor Zuckerman in 1941 (see page 223), led the committee to consider founding a faculty or college of pathologists, a goal that was achieved in 1963. The Section promoted an Honorary Fellowship for Sir Roy Cameron in recognition of his work as President of the College, and the RSM was the location chosen for the AGM of the College in 1964.

Initially the Association, Society and College do not appear to have had an adverse affect on the membership numbers of the Section of Pathology at the RSM, which reached a record level of 443 in 1963. The Council noted that the function of the Section was to bring the various disciplines of pathology together and not to compete with the more specialized role of individual learned societies, or with the professional and/or political interests of the College.

But by 1973 the Council was expressing consternation at 'the number of resignations including many distinguished practising pathologists' – 10 at the previous meeting and now another 42. Membership of the Section had fallen from 765 to 615 over the last few years and this was attributed to the increased subscription to the Society (in January 1972 the subscription for London Fellows had been raised from £15 to £25 and for country members from £10 to £20).[47]

Other Sections were experiencing similar difficulties and in March 1972 the President of the RSM called a meeting of Section Presidents to discuss the problems. In the ensuing discussions and enquiries this Section recorded its profound dissatisfaction with the *Proceedings,* high subscription rates and low attendances at meetings, which were still a matter for concern in 1977. A past President of the Section, Sir John Dacie, resigned as President of the RSM in 1978 and while the Society as a whole awaited reform, the Section of Pathology languished owing to the frequency of pathology meetings in London organized by the College and the Association of Clinical Pathologists. For the session 1979–80 the Section decided to offer something different in the form of symposia, educational meetings, and more joint meetings with other Sections and outside organizations, sometimes followed by a buffet supper.

*The work of the Section today*[48]

The rapid expansion of knowledge of the scientific basis of medicine has caused training in each of the main constituent disciplines of pathology – cellular pathology, chemical pathology, haematology and microbiology – to become independent from a very early stage. In addition, the four main disciplines have each given rise to sub-specialties, such as forensic pathology, molecular pathology, blood transfusion and virology, which require further special training, and which tend to become related professionally to cognate branches of clinical medicine, rather than to other disciplines of pathology.

To counterbalance this tendency towards narrow specialization, the Section of Pathology currently organizes scientific meetings to provide practising pathologists and trainees in one discipline with insights into other branches of pathology and relevant aspects of clinical medicine. At the same time the Section tries to include in its programme state-of-the-art presentations that will attract specialists and trainees in any one particular branch of pathology. Reconciling these objectives is the task of the Section's Council, which offers a selection of events each year. Up to three meetings can be allocated to contributions from trainee pathologists, one of these being the President's Prize meeting at which junior pathologists and scientists compete for the award of two cash prizes each accompanied by a certificate. Council members encourage their juniors to submit abstracts of original work and the standard of papers is usually high, which can make judging diffi-cult. A competitive atmosphere is generated by the supporters of each candidate in the audience, making for a stimulating evening.

There is an annual 'update' meeting, mounted by each major specialty in turn, at which selected recent research topics are reviewed. Two or three meetings a year are held jointly with other Sections or outside societies, and the presidential address usually focuses on his or her professional interest. The remaining meetings are devoted to case reports or subjects of topical interest which need airing in the context of pathology; one of the most popular of recent years was *The ABC of molecular genetics*.

## Section of Epidemiology and Public Health
originally Epidemiology

Dr George S Buchanan and Dr William Hamer began to organize the Section of Epidemiology of the RSM in June 1907 by calling a meeting at the Public Health Department of the London County Council. The following October Dr John Tatham, the last President of the Epidemiological Society of London, introduced Dr Arthur Newsholme as the first President of the Section. Newsholme had advanced from being a mere visitor at the first meeting of the Section, to membership and the Presidency with ease and speed. He was already known for his work as Medical Officer to Brighton where he had created a model health programme and he shared Tatham's concern for infant mortality, an impor-tant issue of the day. Early in 1908 Newsholme left Brighton upon his promotion as Medical Officer to the Local Government Board in Whitehall.[49]

As the direct descendant of the Epidemiological Society, founded in 1850 to promote the control of infectious disease, the Section claimed to be the third in seniority of the Sections. Its membership had included Dr Benjamin Babington, Dr Thomas Addison, Dr Richard Bright, Sir William Jenner, Sir John Simon and Dr John Snow, and the Society had strong links with the RMCS in the 19th century (see page 104). It had also founded the Jenner Medal in 1896, had produced regular *Transactions* since 1859 and had published a rare, first-hand account of the Great Plague of London entitled *Loimographia* by William Boghurst (the transcription of Boghurst's account was the work of Dr JF Payne, an epidemiologist whose promotion of medical history paved the way for the History of Medicine Section).

## *The Jenner Medal*

The Epidemiological Society had instituted the Jenner Medal in 1896 to commemorate the centenary of Edward Jenner's discovery of smallpox vaccination. Funds were raised by an appeal to the whole profession for a medal to be awarded from time to time for distinguished work in epidemiological research. The bronze medal, designed by Allan Wyon, featured Jenner's face and on the reverse a representation of the earth (the symbol of the Epidemiological Society). It was first awarded in 1898 to Sir William Henry Power who, as Medical Officer for London, had formulated the theory of the aerial conveyance of smallpox and had chaired the Royal Commission on Tuberculosis.[50]

The Jenner Medal was instituted by the Epidemiological Society in 1896 to mark the centenary of Jenner's first vaccination of a boy against smallpox. The Medal was first presented in 1898 by Sir Patrick Manson to Sir William Henry Power. It features the head of Jenner and the globe symbol of the Epidemiological Society.

When the Epidemiological Society evolved into a Section of the RSM a new die for the medal was necessary, and it was also commissioned from Wyon.[51] Recipients have included Mr AT Glenny for his contributions to diphtheria immunization (1953), Sir Richard Doll for outstanding studies on the epidemiology of cancer (1981) and in 1996, the year the Jenner bicentenary was celebrated, the Medal went to Sir Donald Henderson for his contribution to the world-wide eradication of smallpox.

### Sir Arthur Newsholme

Newsholme's first paper to the Section addressed 'Poverty and disease', with special reference to typhus fever and phthisis in England and Ireland. The Royal Commission on the Poor Laws and Relief of Distress was sitting at this time and the problems of poverty and disease were commanding attention. Newsholme was particularly interested in the inter-relation of poverty with tuberculosis and typhus fever, and he was convinced that 'Poverty and disease are allied by the closest bonds, and nothing can be simpler and more certain than the statement that the removal of poverty would effect an enormous reduction of disease'.[52]

Sir Arthur Newsholme, now established at his Whitehall desk and on the way to becoming the leading authority on public health in Britain, was invited to open the general discussion on influenza held at the RSM in the wake of the flu pandemic of 1918–19, which caused many deaths. There was considerable public criticism of the health authorities for failing to respond promptly or positively to the epidemic. Newsholme explained that he had prepared an official memorandum on the subject the previous July but its distribution had not been considered expedient: 'There are national circumstances in which the major duty is to "carry on"', he claimed, and in any case influenza was so poorly understood that prevention was virtually impossible.[53]

It has been alleged that Newsholme's mishandling of the influenza epidemic was the reason for his being passed over for the chief medical appointment with the Ministry of Health on its formation in 1919 and that he was subjected to a 'vigorous post-mortem

Sir Arthur Newsholme, the first President of the Section of Epidemiology (1907–09) and Medical Officer to the Local Government Board in Whitehall from 1908.

examination' at the Society's discussion in November 1918.[54] It was certainly a lengthy and topical debate in which Newsholme's principal critic, Dr Major Greenwood, took part. Newsholme's contribution has a defensive tone, but if there was any overt criticism of him it was carefully deleted from the report in the *Proceedings*.

## A mighty Council

Apart from Newsholme, the leading lights of the Section in its early years were Sir Shirley Murphy, Dr EW Goddall, Dr GS Buchanan, Dr CJ Martin and Dr Theodore Thomason. The Local Government Board and its successor, the Ministry of Health, were well represented in the Section by Newsholme of course, Dr Buchanan (President 1918–19 and Jenner medallist in 1934), Dr Greenwood and Sir Weldon Dalrymple-Champneys who were all Presidents in their time. The membership was founded on a bedrock of Medical Officers of Health who worked in the towns and cities of Britain for the improvement of public health. Their own Society (of Medical Officers of Health) had been eliminated from the amalgamation of 1907 because it did not fit the apolitical, London-oriented character of the RSM. Nevertheless many individual Medical Officers of Health took an active part in the Section – Newsholme had served as President of the Society of Medical Officers and edited its journal, James Niven of Manchester became the second President of the Section, Dr John McVail was another President, and Sir Shirley Murphy, Medical Officer of Health and Schools in London was succeeded in that post by a fellow-member of the Section, Dr Hamer.

The Council and officers of the Section formed a weighty body, representing the public authorities in this country and the worldwide interests of epidemiologists. The two Honorary Secretaries (Buchanan and Hamer) were augmented by Secretaries for the army, navy and Scotland, and 18 foreign and colonial Secretaries allocated to countries from Polynesia to Germany. Eleven Vice Presidents were appointed including Sir Patrick Manson, 18 Honorary members, 20 corresponding members and 17 other Council members. Usually no more than a dozen appeared at the Council meetings.

## Papers

As might be expected, papers presented to this Section dwelt on the infectious diseases of early 20th-century Britain and the Empire such as diphtheria, scarlet fever, summer diarrhoea and rubella. In Britain mortality from tuberculosis, typhus, typhoid, scarlatina, smallpox and cholera had declined since the foundation of the Epidemiological Society in 1850. On the other hand, deaths from measles had almost doubled and deaths from whooping cough, diphtheria, influenza and puerperal fever had increased over the same period.[55]

During the first session, RC Punnett's paper on 'Mendelism in relation to disease' was conspicuously different. The author introduced himself modestly (he was shortly to succeed William Bateson as Professor of Biology at Cambridge University), then began 'Since the rediscovery of Mendel's paper a few years ago [in 1900 after a dormancy of 34 years] the experimental study of heredity has made rapid progress'. Punnett's careful exposition was greeted with a good deal of disbelief and criticism from those present, including the statistician Mr George Udny Yule who was puzzled by the figures (he was one of the first to investigate whether the observed correlation between parents and offspring could be accounted for by multifactorial Mendelian inheritance). Widespread interest in current theories of heredity and disease warranted a general discussion at the RSM in November 1910, which was attended by members of several Sections and by Fellows of the Royal Society.

As the severity of infectious diseases declined there was a gradual broadening of the subjects of papers; many reflected social change and recent legislation. The introduction of old age pensions in the year the Section was founded, followed by the Reports of the Poor Law Commission on poverty and its remedies opened new areas of research for epidemiologists. For example Dr James Niven, President of the Section 1909–10 and Medical Officer of Health for Manchester, gave a paper drawing attention to the relationship between employment, poverty and disease in Manchester. His study showed that trade cycles and the system of casual labour were closely related to poverty and disease.[56]

Population statistics were an essential tool of those researching the epidemiology of disease. From its start in 1801 the census was taken every 10 years – not frequently enough for epidemiologists like Newsholme. The first formal resolution issued by this Section was in favour of an early Census Act so as to put in train a more detailed census for 1911.[57]

### Poliomyelitis

One of the first major epidemics of polio in England occurred in Devon and Cornwall in 1911, and this was reported to the Section by RJ Reece the following year. The disease faded from memory until the epidemic of 1947, when 7,776 cases were confirmed in England and Wales, prompting discussions at Section meetings in October 1948 and April 1950. The latter dwelt on poliomyelitis following inoculations and was led by Professor FM Burnet of Melbourne and attended by 225 Fellows, members and visitors. Sir Macfarlane Burnet, as he became, later admitted that he had adopted 'a wholly defeatist attitude towards the problem of poliomyelitis' after his earlier research had failed to gain recognition. He had given his first paper to the RSM aged just 26, on the relation between bacteriophage and O-agglutinins, and he had not been impressed. 'As a rule there isn't one or two of the audience interested in the subject being talked about so nobody arises and attempts to slay you (scientifically) when the paper is finished which is disappointing to a dramatically minded author'.[58] Notwithstanding his criticism, Macfarlane Burnet accepted the Honorary Fellowship of the RSM in 1952. Ten years later he shared the Nobel Prize for medicine and physiology with Sir Peter Medawar, and he received the RSM's Gold Medal in 1974.

Outbreaks of poliomyelitis in this country, America and Copenhagen were discussed regularly during the 1950s, culminating in an address from Professor Jonas Salk of the University of Pittsburgh in 1959. Salk's poliomyelitis vaccine had been announced safe in 1955 and had proved effective, and his lecture posed the question 'how much is enough?'.

The introduction of other prophylactic measures to control infectious disease was discussed promptly at the Section meetings. Diphtheria immunization was discussed in 1937 and again in 1943, within a few months of the inauguration of a national campaign of prevention. Immunization against influenza began in 1937 and the following year Dr Christopher Andrewes reported to the Section on the results.

### Epidemiology and State Medicine

The first years of the Section coincided with a vigorous government policy of social legislation, particularly under Asquith's liberal administration. The activities of the Local Government Board, which under Newsholme's direction pursued some of the boldest initiatives ever seen in public medical services, the investigations of the Poor Law Commission, the work of the Society of Tropical Medicine and of the London School of Hygiene and Tropical Medicine (after 1929) to some extent overshadowed the work of the Epidemiology Section, where meetings rarely attracted more than 20 and usually consisted of just one paper followed by its discussion. Dr GC Low, Secretary of the Society of Tropical Medicine, reported that by 1913 'the old Epidemiological Society' had sunk to an unenviable position: 'no-one ever hears of them now or thinks of attending their meetings'.[59]

In a bid to broaden the Section's appeal and to keep pace with the public health movement the name was changed to Epidemiology and State Medicine in 1913, at the suggestion of Sir Shirley Murphy and Dr Goodall. The objects of the Section were then defined as 'the investigation of epidemic or endemic diseases in respect of the circumstances and conditions which favour, prevent or are otherwise associated with the occurrence, their persistence or their variations in type or character'.[60]

### Stillbirths

The high rate of maternal and infant mortality in the early 20th century was the subject of several official reports. Spurred on by the Royal Statistical Society, the Sections of Epidemiology and State Medicine and Obstetrics and Gynaecology investigated stillbirths, drawing up a definition and pressing for the official registration of stillbirths in 1913. The Council of the RSM took the matter further, notifying the Home Office of its willingness to assist in formulating regulations for the compulsory registration of stillbirths (see page 248).[61]

### 1914 to 1949

From 1914 to 1918 the sufferings of those fighting in France inspired papers on the louse problem, trench fever, the epidemiology of TNT illness, and typhoid, and Sir William Osler spoke on cerebrospinal meningitis. Better times were signified by the founding of the Section's dining club in 1919 and an invitation to send delegates to the International Health Conference held in London that year.

In 1921 a committee was appointed to investigate the best methods of dealing with diphtheria carriers, and in 1925 after a joint meeting with the Section of Comparative Medicine on the subject, a resolution was submitted to the Council of the RSM to press the government to re-enact the Tuberculosis Order immediately, with a view to reducing the incidence of mortality in children and to ensure a pure milk supply. The Section also took positive action by endorsing the declaration signed by 1,100 Medical Officers of Health, reinforcing the argument for smallpox vaccination (1943).[62]

Connections between the Section and the Ministry of Health remained strong. Dr Sidney Monckton Copeman, Medical Officer to the Ministry from 1919, was awarded the Jenner Medal in 1925 and became President the next year. Sir Arthur McNalty was elected President of the Section in 1937 shortly after his appointment as Chief Medical Officer of the Ministry with a brief to co-ordinate wartime medical arrangements, and he was later made an Honorary Fellow of the RSM. Sir William Allen Daley, the leading figure among Medical Officers of Health when the NHS was established, became President in 1948.

In the 1920s and 1930s the emphasis of meetings shifted to the problems of industrial medicine at home. Dr Norman Howard Mummery tabled a resolution in favour of a new section of industrial medicine in 1925, to be told that the subject was the province of the Section of Epidemiology and State Medicine and was to remain so (the Section of Occupational Medicine was not formed until 1964). Meanwhile papers on industrial medicine came before the Epidemiological Section: HH Bashford (Sir Henry) who was Chief Medical Officer to the Post Office, numerically the largest single industrial concern in the country, reported on a workforce in which malingering was exceedingly rare and industrial relations good. 'Health and happiness are, fortunately, as contagious as are some diseases... supervisors who are sympathetic and are really interested in their fellowmen and who have the golden capacity for being blind at the appropriate moment, can perhaps do more to reduce absence from illness than any other single factor'.[63]

The wide arena of the Second World War generated papers on 'Hepatitis in the Middle East' and 'Medicine in jungle warfare', and accounts from those who had personal experiences to share. Sir Weldon Dalrymple-Champneys was the Section's President during the last stages of the war; he had chosen preventive medicine as a career after the First War, joining the Ministry of Health in 1927. He was prominent in the Royal Society of Health and at the RSM he served at different times as President of three Sections (Comparative Medicine, the History of Medicine and Epidemiology).

As the population resumed normal life after the war, the importance of industrial medicine was recognized by the appointment of a spokesman for the subject on the Council of the Epidemiological Section; joint meetings were arranged with the Association of Industrial Medical Officers and members visited factories.

## Epidemiology and Preventive Medicine

After the Second World War the subjects of papers and meetings were broad and less specific than previously. Instead of a paper presented by an individual followed by comments from the audience, the Council chose subjects such as food poisoning, accident prevention and health centres for general discussion. An exceptional meeting was arranged to publicize the work of the recently founded World Health Organization when its Director of Epidemiological Services, Yves Biraud, endeavoured to explain its myriad functions and aims.

At another level Dr WH Bradley tried to enthuse members about the new concept of social medicine, which he insisted was not just another name for preventive medicine but referred to socialized state medicine (a definition that was never accepted in the UK).[64] The time had come to reconsider the function and objects of the Section and its effectiveness, burdened as it was by a large and unwieldy Council and the tendency of office-bearers, especially Vice Presidents, to cling to their posts for long periods. In 1951 the Council was trimmed and the following year the name of the Section was changed to Epidemiology and Preventive Medicine to describe its interests more accurately. Eventually in 1963 the Section's objects were formally redefined: 'to study the occurrence and character of diseases, populations and the means of their prevention'.[65]

Prevention was now the key word, with meetings on the prevention of influenza, the prevention of atmospheric pollution and the prevention of accidents involving motor vehicles. Some papers ventured into the realm of occupational medicine; the President of this Section for 1953–55, Sir Austin Bradford Hill, was a major influence on the use of epidemiological methods in medicine and he was to be the first President of the Section of Occupational Medicine in 1964.

The 1970s saw the Section's summer meetings discontinued through lack of support and 36 resignations were recorded at a Council meeting in January 1973 – subscriptions had recently increased and the RSM was in need of reform. The Wolstenholme Report attempted to do so but this was greeted without enthusiasm by this Section with responses such as 'no action necessary' and 'not applicable'. When a proposal to establish a new Section of Community Medicine was tabled in January 1974, the Section of Epidemiology and Preventive Medicine maintained that it had always embraced the interests of those who carried out research or practised in every aspect of epidemiology and community medicine. The Society's Council objected to the proposal for a separate section devoted to community medicine, agreeing instead to a change in the name of this Section to Epidemiology and Community Medicine in 1975.

## Epidemiology and Community Medicine

Community medicine was defined in 1955 as 'that branch of social medicine which deals with matters relating not to individuals but to groups'. The discussion about community medicine commanded much attention and culminated in a series of reports and papers in the late 1960s. The Royal Commission on Medical Education (1965–68) promoted the subject as part of the curriculum and the Faculty of Community Medicine of the Royal Colleges of Physicians of the United Kingdom was established in 1972.

Thus by the mid-1970s the definition of epidemiology as the study of health and disease in populations was outdated: epidemiology had come to mean the science of preventive and community medicine as applied to health and health services. Once the Section had embraced community medicine in its title in 1975, the subject was thoroughly aired at meetings on 'Community medicine – what does it mean?' and 'Problems and problem solving in community medicine'. By 1982 the term was out of favour and condemned as unfortunate by Professor WH Holland in his presidential address, 'Community medicine – myth or change agent?'. He identified 'a series of blocks' that hindered the specialty's development and he concluded 'We do have the potential still to become agents for change and thus may avoid becoming a myth. One consequence of this, however, must be a change in the name of our specialty. Community medicine is an unfortunate term, leading to confusion and false expectations. It was a mistake to drop the term public health since our concern is with the health of the public and with the provision of public health services – i.e. services that serve the public community. Reinstating the term public health, would, I believe, help our cause since it describes more accurately than any other term the aims of our discipline, and thus perhaps we may persist'.[66]

## Epidemiology and Public Health

It was several years before the Section did alter its name. Dr Michael Joffe raised the question and 'in view of recent national trends' the name was altered to that of Epidemiology and Public Health in 1990.[67]

The 1990s brought the Hutchison and Brooke bequests to the Section, resulting in the first Alexander Hutchison lecture (1992) while the Brooke bequest was applied to the Berzelius Symposium. The Swedish chemist JJ Berzelius had been entertained by members of the Medical and Chirurgical Society during his visit to London in 1812, and 180 years later contacts were rekindled when the Section of Epidemiology and Public Health joined the Swedish Society of Medicine in organizing the Berzelius Symposium at the RSM. The subject of the first conference was 'Water and public health' and the symposium attracted 100 delegates from Sweden, France, Germany and the UK. Presentations were made at the symposium dinner held at London Zoo and Mrs Hutchison came from Monaco to present Sir Richard Doll with the first Hutchison Medal. Sir Richard prefaced his lecture, on

The Hutchison Medal, awarded in memory of Dr Alexander Hutchison.

'Chemicals in drinking water', with a tribute to Dr Hutchison, ' best known in England for his leadership as Medical Officer of Health for Hull where he promoted the Sabin oral poliomyelitis vaccine and persuaded the local authority to undertake the first mass campaigns for screening for phenylketonuria and cervical cancer and to provide free family planning'.[68]

The Berzelius Symposium was held in Stockholm two years later when the 'Health aspects of indoor air' were discussed – there had been much publicity on asthma and the Swedish National Asthma Campaign was soon to be launched. The Berzelius Symposium is now a regular event and the proceedings are published.

In the millennium year the Section held an anniversary meeting to mark the 150 years of advance and achievement in public health since the Epidemiological Society of London had been instituted for the investigation of epidemics among the human race and animals in 1850.

## Section of Odontology (Plate 39)

The dental profession in this country has its origins in the Odontological Society of London and the College of Dentists of England, both founded in November 1856; the Odontological Society wins the claim to be the first professional dental association in England by just one day. Rivalry between the two parties – the College of Dentists, headed by Samuel Lee Rymer, and the Odontological Society, led by John Tomes, Samuel Cartwright (Plate 42) and Edwin Saunders – centred on qualifications, or lack of them. The Odontologists were London men with recognized medical or surgical qualifications who established a scientific society to foster their specialty. The College of Dentists of England was a larger group that included unqualified dentists who advertised their services.

Rivalry between the two associations was resolved by amalgamation in the Odontological Society of Great Britain in 1863, three years after the first Licences in Dental Surgery had been granted by the Royal College of Surgeons as the essential qualification for the dental profession in England. The men who fought for the LDS (Cartwright, Tomes, Saunders and Rogers) had founded not only the Odontological Society but also the first Dental Hospital of London in 1858 and the London School of Dental Surgery in 1859. The same group campaigned for the Dentists Act of 1878 and founded the British Dental Association in 1880 with Tomes as its first President.[69]

The Odontological Society for the Advancement of Science and Dental Surgery as it was initially known, existed for 'the encouragement and diffusion of a knowledge of dental surgery and the promotion of intercourse among members of the dental profession'. These principles were upheld by the Odontological Society of Great Britain from 1863 and carried on by its successor, the Odontological Section of the RSM. The first President of the Section, Mr John Howard Mummery, stood for continuity between the Odontological Society and the new Section, about which he was optimistic. As he emphasized in his address of 1907, 'The history of the Odontological Society is the history of the emancipation of our profession, and to the efforts of its members are due our recognition by the Royal College of Surgeons of England and the founding of the Dental Hospital of London and its Dental School'.[70]

The preliminary meeting of the Odontological Society had been held at Samuel Cartwright's house in Old Burlington Street on 27 October 1856 'for the purpose of considering the expediency of establishing an association for the encouragement of knowledge in Dental Surgery'. The group met again at Edwin Saunders' house in November and for the first two years of its existence the Society found a base with the Medical Society of London, 32A George Street, Hanover Square. For nearly half a century meetings were held at the Dental Hospital and School, first in Soho Square and from 1874 in Leicester Square.

When the new Royal Dental Hospital School was built in 1900, the Odontological Society moved into three rooms on the third floor of 20 Hanover Square where its library and museum were installed. Building alterations were supervised by the resident architect, John Belcher, and completed in January 1902. The Odontological Society was thus well established at the house of the RMCS prior to the amalgamation of 1907.

In replying to the amalgamation proposals of 1905 the Council of the Odontological Society expressed many reservations. While the Society would gain in prestige from inclusion in the proposed Royal Academy of Medicine, the surrender of some £4,500 worth of investments as well as its library and museum was a good reason to hesitate, and affiliation was preferred to amalgamation. The persuasion of MacAlister, consultation with the whole membership and the influence of Howard Mummery overcame these reservations. Howard Mummery was a past President of the Odontological Society and was to occupy the positions of President, Foreign Secretary and trustee to the Section. He believed firmly in the co-operation of scientific societies within the RSM: 'a most excellent and wide-spirited movement. There has been in all departments of knowledge for many years past too great a tendency to specialization and subdivision, too much exclusiveness'. He looked forward to close co-operation with other 'departments of the healing art' which might come to appreciate 'how very intimately the health of the body generally is dependent upon the maintainance of a healthy condition of the mouth and teeth'. To Howard Mummery the amalgamation signified not the termination of the Odontological Society but its reincarnation, and the Society was to be commemorated by a special lecture to the Section every five years.[71]

The Society brought with it the Odontological Museum of some 2,900 items under the curatorship of Frank Colyer (transferred to the Royal College of Surgeons in 1909), a library of approximately 5,000 volumes on teeth, dentistry and odontology in many languages, some £5,000 of consols and 370 Fellows and members. These assets put it in a

The Odontological Society's Museum was housed on the third floor at 20 Hanover Square from 1900 until it was transferred to the Royal College of Surgeons in 1909.

strong position, but relations between the Section and the Society did not run smoothly. The Secretary of the RSM was concerned about the threatened resignation of Mr C Tomes, and rumours circulated about a rival odontological society.[72]

When Sir Dyce Duckworth, a past President of the Clinical Society, realized that Licentiates in Dental Surgery could be nominated to the Fellowship of the RSM he wrote to the Secretary of the RSM, alleging that they were not adequately trained in medicine, surgery or midwifery and 'must certainly be ineligible' for Fellowship. Another correspondent, WB Paterson, suspected that the Secretary was indiscriminate in his attitude to dentists because he was in a hurry to recruit members. MacAlister was himself quite surprised that some of the Section's candidates were not blackballed by retrogressive Fellows.[73]

Six years later 11 Fellows and many more members of the Odontological Section resigned over the increased subscription. Colyer told MacAlister that there was a feeling that 'the dental members form a Section of the RSM largely on sufferance' and there were rumours of the secession of odontologists from the Society. Striving to placate the Section, MacAlister replied that he had always thought the Odontological Society and the Section were most business-like and well managed.[74]

## Early papers and debates

Dentistry was revolutionized by the introduction of anaesthesia, first used for dental surgery in London in 1846, and the discovery of X-rays in 1895. In the 20th century the chief advances have been in the scientific understanding of dental disease, new techniques, equipment, improved materials and the acceptance of preventive dentistry.

As far as dental disease was concerned, pyorrhoea was the main subject of meetings of the Section, beginning with papers by JG Turner and Ernest Sturridge in 1908. Kenneth Goadby (who had coined the word 'plaques' in 1906) suggested that pyorrhoea was due to milk infection; others thought gout was a cause and told their patients that they suffered from 'gouty gums'. In 1908 Sturridge demonstrated that he had 'overcome one of the knotty points' in its treatment and gave practical advice on replacing and retaining the teeth using platinum pins and a stiff plate wire strengthener, which his audience thought very useful and 'a step in advance'.[75] One member, Mr Harry Forsyth of 58 Wimpole Street, boasted that he had a secret cure for pyorrhoea. This contravened the rules of the RSM and caused irritation to the Section; Forsyth was invited to explain his pretensions to a meeting, but chose not to.[76]

## Dental Caries committee

At the suggestion of Mr FJ Bennett the Section agreed to investigate dental caries and a committee led by Howard Mummery, Colyer and Dr J Sim Wallace was appointed for this purpose in 1908. It was firmly resolved to pursue the subject by every available means and the committee devised a scheme to implement this. The immensity of the task seems to have defeated the small committee; its suggestions were handed to the Odontological Section of the BMA and the Dental Caries committee dissolved. Wallace alone submitted a report focusing on bread with reference to the aetiology of caries.[77] The scientific basis of caries prevention was still being pursued in 1984 when the Section held a symposium on the subject.

## JG Turner

The discussions that followed the delivery of papers were lively because those who participated did not agree. Goadby, JW Eyre and J Lewin Payne advocated vaccine therapy while Sturridge doubted their claims, and favoured 'ionic therapy'. Turner doubted the role of malocclusion, Stanley Mummery put forward bold ideas on heredity and dental disease and the discussion introduced by Mr Badcock on modern orthodontics 'was marked by the expression of diverse opinions, as was to be expected' and had to be adjourned 'because there were yet other warriors ready to take the field'[78] (the British Society for the Study of Orthodontics had been founded in 1908, largely as the result of the initiative of George Northcroft, President of the Section 1928–29).

JG Turner presented several papers on pyorrhoea to the Section between 1908 and 1924, when he was elected President. In 1923 he set out to be provocative, throwing out challenges in a discussion about what he termed 'a dirt disease'. His views were not accepted by Sir Harry Baldwin or Sturridge, and critics caused the discussion to be prolonged. Turner wanted to see the patient taught how to clean his teeth: 'The means we have at our disposal are the toothbrush, waxed silk and worsted thread' – he particularly recommended worsted thread (the precursor to dental floss).

Turner's views were put more forcibly by Sir William Willcox, opening the discussion on 'Dental sepsis as an aetiological factor in disease of other organs'. Willcox belonged to the Clinical, Therapeutic and Pharmacological, and Medical Sections and the particular issue he wanted to stress to the odontologists was the influence for harm that infected teeth can exert on general health. 'It is certainly true that infection of the teeth and gums, by reason of the streptococcal infection arising from them, is one of the greatest sources of disease in adult life', he stated. His argument was reinforced by cases showing dental sepsis as the cause of liver complications, blood conditions and of his last 100 cases of rheumatoid arthritis, 72 had shown evidence of dental infection, 10 had infections of the nose and throat and 13 were examples of intestinal infections. This paper was capped by Willcox's 'Retrospect of dental sepsis' in 1930.[79]

Turner continued to crusade for local cleansing to prevent pyorrhoea in 1924 but chose to give his presidential address on the need for the better education of dental students. This was at a time when the dental schools were unable to supply enough qualified dentists to meet the demand. Turner even challenged the RSM to organize a course of instruction 'capable of turning out an efficient dental practitioner'.[80]

## Sir Frank Colyer

JF Colyer, Honorary Curator of the Odontological Museum from 1900 to 1954 and President of the Section from 1919 to 1920, was a mainstay of the meetings, contributing papers, demonstrating skulls from the collection and giving an exposition on elephants' teeth. He wrestled regularly with various aspects of periodontal disease and in January 1912 he posed the question 'what is a cure?' going on to proclaim: 'We are at the top of the wave of dental disease. With a profession possessing an adequate knowledge of the pathology of the teeth, and basing their treatment on that knowledge, aided by the intelligent education of the public, dental disease, will, I feel confident, rapidly disappear from our midst, until perhaps in less than half a century, from being a universal scourge, it will have shrunk to insignificant proportions'. The President, H Lloyd Williams, thanked Colyer for his comments and reflected that if the prophecy was fulfilled dentists would soon not be wanted and find themselves mere curiosities in a museum.[81]

To mark Sir Frank's 25-year curatorship of the Museum the Section raised £200 in 1926 for a prize, first awarded in 1932 to Martin A Rushton who received 30 guineas.[82] Sir Frank Colyer was made an Honorary Fellow of the RSM in 1943.

## War injuries

At the outbreak of the First World War Fellows and members were reminded of the duties of the profession in time of war by the President Dr AWW Baker. Although many Fellows and members were abroad and meetings were reduced to three a session in 1915, some 300 attended one meeting in February 1916 for the discussion on 'War injuries to the jaws and face'.

The Section took up the cause of those suffering from injuries of the face and jaw as a result of the war, advising the Ministry of Pensions on their care and treatment. The committee, chaired by Sir Henry Baldwin, made recommendations on the supply of dentures and the appropriate treatment of those receiving pensions. This report went towards the Ministry of Pensions' *Instructions on the treatment of disabled men* (1918).[83]

## Regulation

The unsatisfactory, some said deplorable, state of the dental profession was brought to the notice of the British Dental Association in 1908. The Dentists Act of 1878 had not succeeded in eliminating unregistered practice, and unqualified practitioners continued to exploit the public. A Departmental Committee investigated the situation and reported in 1919 in favour of a Dental Board, the provision of school dentists and a public dental service. The Dentists Act of 1921 eventually ensured educational and ethical control for the profession, the number of dentists increased and dental education and research was stimulated.

The spirit of the Dentists Act pervaded the Section's Council which in 1922 redefined membership regulations, limiting it to 'only those who possess a diploma or degree in medicine or dental surgery registrable in the United Kingdom or are directly interested in the progress of dentistry generally'.

Otherwise, the Section continued along the same path as before the Great War. Its pillars, Lewin Payne, Colyer, Schelling, Howard Mummery (who was made an Honorary Fellow of the RSM in 1921) and Gabell kept the discussions alive even when attendances were low.

Douglas Gabell, elected President of the Section in 1923, celebrated the progress of 'mechanical dentistry' over the last 35 years. He summarized the advances as most beneficial – 'fewer springs, fewer clasps, longer cusps behind and better looking teeth in front, greater efficiency and cleanliness'. [84]

Each year the Odontological Museum was inspected and reported upon, and from 1914 the Section held its Annual General Meeting at the Royal College of Surgeons. The Museum received a grant of £85 per annum from the RSM and the collection was guarded jealously by the Section. The loan of specimens from the museum to Edinburgh was refused in 1924, although the Council was happy to give a complete set of the *Transactions of the Odontological Society* to the Dental Federation of Japan when it was in need of dental books to replace those destroyed in an earthquake.

## The 1930s

Mr Carl Schelling, President of the Section from 1930 to 1931, had dealt with the opening negotiations for amalgamation when he was Secretary to the Odontological Society. His long association with the Society and Section was marked by his presentation of the presidential badge in 1931 (Plate 39). During his year in office Mrs May Mellanby (later Lady Mellanby) put in an appearance to present her paper on 'Periodontal disease in dogs', one of the earliest animal research papers on the topic, in which she stressed the effects of vitamins A and D.

Other notable papers of the 1930s were highlighted by AB Wade in his historical review of the Section (published in 1985):[85] HH Stones' contribution on the surgical treatment of pyorrhoea alveolus was judged to be the beginning of a complementary surgical approach in this country – complementary because Stones stressed the need for thorough cleaning. Then in 1937 Dr E Wilfred Fish summarized his research with a poetic description of the disease, which 'in an established case is characterized by a deepened periodontal sulcus, ulcerated and lined with a granulated tissue on which a degenerate epithelium grows either in sickly luxuriance, like a plant kept in a cellar, or wilts, as a scantly remnant'.[86]

Sir Wilfred Fish, later an Honorary member of the Section, was appointed Chairman of the Dental Board in 1944 and was to take the profession into the NHS.

## The Second World War

The Second World War resulted in the development of maxillo-facial techniques, better anaesthesia and better biological education, which in turn improved standards of oral surgery. Above all, the advent of antibiotics allowed the expansion of treatment. At the RSM the odontological papers for 1940–41 concentrated on the surgical and dental treatment of fractures of the jaws in war, facial injuries and facial restorations, and a discussion was held on 'trench mouth' in 1943.

The close of hostilities brought recognition to the female sex in the election of Dr Lilian Lindsay, the first woman in Britain to gain the LDS (1895), as President. Her papers reflected wide interests (she was President of the History of Medicine Section in 1950); she spoke on 'Dentistry as one of the fine arts' (1928), for example, and gave the first Wallis Memorial Lecture on 'The sun, the toothdrawer and the saint' in 1932. As a preface, Dr Lindsay paid tribute to CE Wallis, one of the first school dentists appointed under the London County Council and the author of many articles on the history of dentistry. The commemorative lecture had been founded in 1927 with the proviso that the lecturer must be fluent and interesting on the subject of dental history.[87]

## Centenary

In January 1957 the Section celebrated the centenary of the foundation of the Odontological Society and the jubilee of the RSM with a dinner. Members also heard an address from the President, JAS Wright, on 'A hundred years of dentistry'. In his conclusion, the author looked to the future: 'While great advances have been made during the hundred years of the life of the Odontological Society and of this Section, in the conservative surgical and prosthetic treatment of dental disease, comparatively little has been learned about its prevention'. Experiments with fluoridation offered some prospects but Wright wanted to see the evidence of many years and a country-wide campaign of instruction in oral hygiene, if only the profession could agree upon its essentials. Whatever the means, Wright was sure that 'the next phase of dentistry, which may be only just over the brow of the hill will be the era of preventive dentistry'. Twenty years later his successor as President, Professor AS Prophet, was still calling for a shift in emphasis in the practice of dentistry from the treatment of established disease towards prevention.[88]

In the 30 years between 1955 and 1985 papers by Professors Lucas, Framer, Alldritt, Emslie, Sloan and Powell have been singled out for commendation. The one that attracted the greatest international attention was by Professor B Cohen on 'Comparative studies in periodontal disease' (1960) in which he demonstrated the concave nature of the interdental gingival tissue to which he gave the name col, 'which will surely last forever'.[89] Cohen was to be President of the Section in 1980 when he spoke on 'The scientific basis for the prevention of caries and periodontal disease'.

Dr T Lehner's paper on 'Auto-immunity in oral disease' has been praised by Professor B Cooke as 'a great milestone in the history of the Section... a most painstaking piece of research' (210 cases). At the same meeting in November 1967 a lighter note was struck by Mr C Bowdler-Henry's communication 'The field marshal's dentures' (antiques belonging to the first Duke of Wellington).[90]

One of the few Presidents to speak out on the present and future state of the profession was Mr JH Hovell in a challenging speech on 'Dentistry at the crossroads' in 1969. He maintained that dental practice was out of touch with public needs and in danger of being separated from medicine, and he called for a Royal Commission on dental education and practice.[91]

*Readjustments*

Between 1909 and 1948 the membership of the Section fell, then remained static for the next 10 years and increased by 50 (to 288) in 1968. These figures were compiled as part of a reassessment of the function and organization of the Section in 1967 – with remarkable foresight the Council was taking steps to put its house in order several years before the RSM's Working Party addressed the problems.

The Odontological Section perceived that its Council was too large to be effective and reduced the number of Council members to 19; the nature and popularity of meetings was examined and as a result symposia were encouraged and publicity sought. In looking at the role of the Section in the light of the many specialist societies and associations to which dentists in London might belong, the Council decided that the function of this Section was to act as a unifying force between the dental specialties and to provide interchange between dentistry and medicine.

There was some reduction in the number of meetings during the 1980s, the aim being to attract more to fewer, as for instance at the Facial Pain Symposium in 1982, and for the 1988–89 session the Section concentrated on three international meetings.

Morale was lifted by the extension and refurbishment of 1 Wimpole Street, where the restaurant facilities continue to be appreciated by the neighbouring colony of dental surgeons and specialists. In recent years two issues have regularly come before the Section's Council: first, the provision of a varied programme to interest members whatever their specialty and, secondly, the possibility of updating the name of the Section to reflect modern dental science. Neither has been resolved: the Section retains the name of its founding Society and is challenged by the task of embracing in just one Section the interests of academics, practising dentists, orthodontists and other specialists. A presidential address or a guest speaker from overseas can attract more than 200 to a meeting; on the other hand a meeting devoted to a special subject holds appeal for just the dedicated few. As Mr Barry Scheer pointed out in his presidential address of 1997, meetings of other Sections have much to offer members of this Section, as has the RSM generally.

## Section of Obstetrics and Gynaecology (Plate 41)

The accoucheurs, man-midwives and obstetricians had fought hard for recognition in the 19th century. A major step in the recognition of obstetrics was the foundation of the Obstetrical Society of London, inaugurated under the chairmanship of Dr Edward Rigby in 1858 (see pages 104–05). At its first meeting Rigby praised the energy and perseverance of Dr Tyler-Smith who promptly moved the resolution 'to institute a Society for the promotion of knowledge in all that relates to obstetrics and the diseases of women and children'. Rigby was elected the first President, and the other leading officers were Sir Charles Locock (the Queen's accoucheur), Dr Robert Barnes (after whom the Barnes Hall is named) and of course Tyler-Smith.

The Obstetrical Society campaigned for the compulsory education and examination of midwives, establishing a Diploma in midwifery in 1872, and the movement culminated in the Midwives Act of 1902. The Society investigated infant mortality at the behest of the Registrar General in 1869 and was instrumental in achieving recognition for obstetrics and gynaecology by the General Medical Council in 1885. In that year the Society's 'only daughter' – the British Gynaecological Society – was incorporated, its foundations having been laid late in 1884 by Dr JH Aveling and Dr Barnes.[92]

*Baker Brown*

The Obstetrical Society lodged with the Royal Medical and Chirurgical Society between 1859 and 1868, and thus the expulsion of Isaac Baker Brown, a past President of the Obstetrical Society and of the Medical Society of London, took place in the meeting room of the RMCS at 53 Berners Street. Every seat was taken, some members had to stand and tempers ran high, for this was the climax to the uproar caused by Baker Brown's book *On the curability of certain forms of insanity in females* (1866) detailing 47 clitoridectomies he had performed.

The *BMJ* led the campaign to disgrace Baker Brown, and on the evening of 3 April 1867 Dr Charles West and Dr Robert Barnes took leading roles in his downfall. Baker Brown stood accused of mutilation and quackery but the main charge was not the propriety of clitoridectomy so much as the impropriety of performing the operation without the knowledge of the women or their husbands. Although he defended himself at length, of the 237 who cast their votes, 194 were against him. Baker Brown was found guilty, expelled and ended his days in poverty and disgrace.[93]

## At Hanover Square

The Obstetrical Society resisted proposals for amalgamation with the RMCS in the 19th century although it was a tenant at 53 Berners Street and later at 20 Hanover Square. In 1905 its Honorary Secretaries, M Handfield-Jones and Robert Boxall, conveyed their Council's approval of the amalgamation while expressing concern over the preservation of the Rigby Library and the admission of women – the Obstetrical Society had opened its doors to qualified medical women in 1902. Likewise, Dr H Macnaughton-Jones, who had been a foundation Fellow of the British Gynaecological Society, replied that his Council wanted the word 'men' deleted from the membership requirements of the RSM. Sir Francis Champneys, Professor Herbert Spencer and Macnaughton-Jones managed to smooth over the differences between the obstetricians and gynaecologists, encouraging the two societies to merge in one Section that would admit women.

The Obstetrical Society brought to the RSM a library of some 15,000 volumes, £3,000, an osteological collection, antique obstetrical instruments and 485 London Fellows; the British Gynaecological Society had under £300 in investments and a large, scattered membership. Together the two societies formed a strong Section that was to maintain the tradition of the Obstetrical Society in promoting better education in the specialty and the improvement of maternal and infant mortality figures.

The accommodation necessary for the new Section put a strain on 20 Hanover Square and with the demands of additional Sections exacerbating the problem, relocation became imperative. The large force of obstetricians and gynaecologists felt that they deserved to be adequately housed and the Society's temporary home at 15 Cavendish Square was thought to be 'scarcely stylish enough' for them, so for the interim ordinary meetings were held at the Medical Society of London.[94] By the summer of 1912 the Society and the Section were installed at 1 Wimpole Street, and in the same year Sir Francis Champneys was elected President of the RSM – the first obstetrician to hold the office.

## A strong start

As the lineal descendant of the two principal societies for obstetrics and gynaecology and with members in London and throughout Britain, the Section was broadly based and in a unique position to pursue 'the promotion of knowledge in all that relates to obstetrics and gynaecology'.[95] In 1907 there was no rival society or association in London, nor any college, institution or faculty devoted to obstetrics and gynaecology. The Section attracted the giants such as Champneys, Sir William Smyly, Professor Herbert Spencer, Dr Macnaughton-Jones, Mr Victor Bonney, Dr Comyns Berkeley, Sir William Fletcher Shaw and Dr William Blair-Bell, who was shortly to found the Gynaecological Visiting Society (1911). Most of the founders of that Society also belonged to the Section of Obstetrics and Gynaecology of the RSM and were to be active in founding the College of Obstetricians and Gynaecologists in 1929.

The first Council meeting of the Section was chaired by Dr Spencer, who was elected President forthwith, and the first general meeting of the Section was called for 10 October 1907 to formalize regulations, appoint a pathology committee and to hear papers from Dr Amand Routh and Mr J Bland-Sutton; there was an epidiascope demonstration on the 'Physiological action of the placenta' and Dr T Watts Eden showed various specimens.

For the first session 10 evening meetings were organized, each boasting several papers and demonstrations given by some eminent members: Blair-Bell, Watts Eden, Munro Kerr, Routh, Doran, Lockyer and Louisa Garrett Anderson (the suffragette daughter of Elizabeth who was soon to be joined by another woman, Mrs Mary Scharlieb).[96]

Spencer made no special comment on the proceedings of the Section in his presidential address but in 1910 his successor, Macnaughton-Jones, chose to give a retrospective view of 'The lessons of a session'. He told his audience that the aims of the Section must be to present 'some distinct gain in progress, either in the substantiation of previously advanced views or the demolition of those which do not stand the test of time... what there is not room for is the study of generally accepted ancient history'. He wanted to see his Section as 'the accepted source of reference and tribunal of appeal in this country for deciding those critical questions which arise in the every-day practice of obstetrics and gynaecology'. He went on to evaluate recent papers: he was unhappy about the optimistic views of Dr Curtis Webb on electro-therapeutic treatment, which held unknown dangers; he congratulated Dr Comyns Berkeley and Mr Bonney on 'one of the most interesting and original obstetrical communications on leukoplakic vulvitis' – the paper presented their original studies on the disease, describing its four stages, in which cancer was found to develop from either the third or fourth. Berkeley and his junior colleague Bonney were joint authors of *A textbook of gynaecological surgery* (1911, published in its ninth edition in 1986) and they took a leading part in establishing the Wertheim operation in this country; Bonney was to

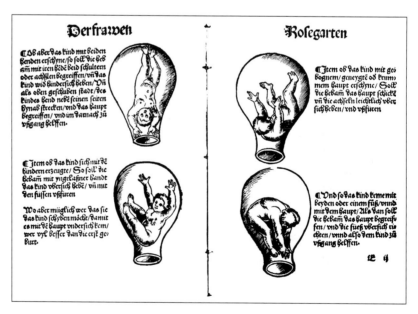

The birth figures from Eucharius Rösslin, *Der swangern frawen und hebammen roszgarten* (1513), the earliest printed textbook for midwives. This copy was purchased for 11 guineas and donated to the Library by Sir William Osler, Dr Norman Moore, Dr M Handfield-Jones, Dr Herbert Spencer, Dr Amand Routh, Dr H Williamson, Dr Walter Tate and Dr Charles Singer in 1916.

follow in Berkeley's footsteps as President of the Section (1931–32). During the session of 1909–10 Macnaughton-Jones had also enjoyed the originality of Dr E Hastings Tweedy's communication on 'Modern methods of delivery in contracted pelvis', which had given rise to an animated discussion among 'the obstetric stalwarts of London'.[97]

In his turn as President (1911–13) Dr Amand Routh had special praise for Dr Louise McIlroy's paper on ovarian secretion, for he recognized that 'the significance of the whole subject of internal secretion is enormous and its full recognition is still in its infancy'. As Dame Louise, Dr McIlroy was elected President of the Section in 1942, the first female President of any Section of the RSM.

Dr RH Paramore's views on intra-abdominal pressure in pregnancy did not meet with Routh's approval and Paramore was warned that he would have to advance more scientific proof to gain credibility. Routh was dubious about Charles Childe's promotion of Wertheim's 'panhysterectomy' for cancer: 'the value of the operation can only be determined by a large series to evaluate the risks and cure'. The operation was being done mainly by the younger surgeons, most successfully by Bonney who eventually had over 500 to his credit.[98]

## *Maternal and infant mortality*

During his presidency Dr Routh encouraged the Section to become involved with the national issues of maternal and infant mortality, and following his lead the Section took an active part in reporting to the Ministry of Health on this and several other matters of national concern. The period of activity ended with the Section's 'Report on Maternal Mortality' printed in the year the Royal College of Obstetricians and Gynaecologists was founded (1929). Thereafter the Section tended to refer such matters to the College.

Routh's Council was first concerned about the implementation of the National Health Insurance Act of 1911 which (among other provisions) granted a thirty shillings maternity benefit. It was intended that this would allow more women to pay general practitioners or midwives to attend them in childbirth. As the Council perceived, however, there were

Dr Amand Routh, obstetric physician to Charing Cross Hospital and President of the Section of Obstetrics and Gynaecology 1911–13.

loopholes in the arrangements that could have a disastrous effect on the training of medical students and midwives. It appeared that women might lose the benefit if they were attended in their homes by medical students or pupil midwives, even under qualified supervision, and this would have a negative effect on training. Dr Routh wanted women to give birth in approved institutions or hospitals rather than at home, and he sent his Section's recommendations to all members of the GMC.[99] As it happened, many general practitioners and midwives responded to the maternity allowance by raising their fees, negating the purpose of the exercise; maternal mortality continued to rise.

## Stillbirths

Statistics showed that infant mortality fell in the first decade of the century and continued to do so, but the authorities were alarmed that maternal mortality figures rose between 1910 and 1914, and with the deaths of so many young men in the Great War there was a fear of depopulation. In 1913 Dr Routh drew the attention of his Section to the situation, in particular to the high incidence of stillbirths: in 1909 there were about 19,000 stillbirths in England and Wales and in 1910 the official figures for London alone were 2,312 (2.2% of the total number of births). 'To lessen this terrible death rate is one of the main objects of the Royal Society of Medicine and more especially of its Obstetric Section', Routh proclaimed. 'Eugenics, or the wellbeing of the race, is one of the prevailing instincts of our generation. The value of the potential mother and her unborn babe to the nation is becoming increasingly recognized'.[100]

The Royal Statistical Society needed an authoritative definition of stillbirth and the RSM's Section of Epidemiology and State Medicine, with its core of Medical Officers of Health, was consulted first. During the session of 1913–14 that Section and the Section of Obstetrics and Gynaecology held several meetings and discussions on the subject, and a committee drew up a definition of a stillborn child. This was 'a child which measures more than 13 inches in length from the top of the head to the heel, and which, when completely extruded from the body of the mother (head, body and limbs but not necessarily the afterbirth), exhibits no sign of life by crying or breathing, or by pulsation in the cord at its attachment to the body of the child. NB – the final test of life is the pulsation of the heart, but this can only be ascertained by an expert'.[101] The work of the committee was approved by the Council of the RSM and forwarded to the Home Office with a recommendation for legislation to enforce the registration of stillbirths.[102]

This was implemented in England and Wales in 1927. The definition of a stillborn baby is now made on the basis of the length of the pregnancy rather than the length of the baby, as the Section had suggested.

## Maternity and child welfare

The Royal Commission on Venereal Diseases (1913–16) was served by Mrs Scharlieb, whose work was recognized by the award of the DBE, and by the Section's committee which provided evidence on syphilis in the newborn, abortions and the effect of anti-syphilitic treatment on both mother and child.

This was all part of the Section's work on maternity and child welfare for which it was earning a reputation. In 1916 Dr William Fothergill, who with Archibald Donald perfected 'the Manchester operation' for prolapse, urged the Council to provide guidance for the Local Government Board; 'what is wanted is opinions from some central recognized body such as the Section. I say the only thing worth doing is to start a decent maternity hospital in every town and that all this talk about "expectant mothers" and "antenatal clinics", new and illiterate names for old and familiar things, is a bit off the true line of progress... The municipal committees largely consist of enthusiastic spinsters and the like who know nothing. It is time for the profession to give guidance'.[103]

The Section's Council duly organized a committee to take the matter further and arranged a discussion on the need for the improved care of pregnant women, opened by Dr SG Moore in November 1916: 'this subject is of national importance', he stressed. In the discussion Professor Krivsky explained how antenatal care was organized in Russia and Miss Rosalind Paget spoke for the midwives in this country.[104]

## The teaching of obstetrics and gynaecology

The fashion in obstetric analgesis or 'twilight sleep' was investigated by a committee of the Section in 1917 but there is no evidence of a report. The Section was more worried about the education and training of medical students in obstetrics and gynaecology, upon which the welfare of mothers and infants largely depended. Dr T Watts Eden put his finger on the problem in 1918 when he proposed that a committee should investigate the teaching of those subjects to medical students and graduates in London. He recruited Dr Russell Andrews, Dr GF Blacker, Dr JS Fairbairn, Dr McCann and Mr Gordon Ley to outline a more satisfactory system. This was a formidable team and it produced a 27-page report recommending radical improvements in training and facilities.

Unfortunately the impact of the Report was lost when Dr Spencer, Dr Williamson and Lady Barrett criticized its recommendations and produced an alternative. The Council found itself in a difficult position and compromised by issuing a 'Report on the Reports on the Teaching of Obstetrics and Gynaecology', which was forwarded to the Conjoint Examining Board of the Royal Colleges in 1919.[105]

## Co-operation with the MRC and the Ministry

The Section addressed the problem of eclampsia in 1922 with the blessing and a grant of £50 for clerical expenses from the Medical Research Council. Statistics were needed from the London hospitals, from provincial hospitals and institutions and from Scotland with a view to assessing the geographical distribution of eclampsia in the United Kingdom and extending research. Circulars were posted and plans laid, but after two years the Eclampsia committee was still gathering case reports. Responsibility lay with the committee's chairman, Watts Eden, who was devoting much of his time to establishing a college of obstetrics and gynaecology. He failed to produce a final statement on the committee's work and subsequently retired from it. Few centres had responded to the circular, so the committee that had been formed with admirable and broad ambitions was disbanded in 1935.[106]

While the Eclampsia committee was still functioning, Sir George Newman of the Ministry of Health wrote to the Section about puerperal sepsis. He referred to the recent report on maternal mortality issued by Dr Janet Campbell for the Ministry, and he had one special concern: 'The Minister is anxious to reduce the incidence of puerperal sepsis which accounts for so large a proportion of the morbidity and mortality associated with childbirth'. He sought professional guidance so as to enable the prompt notification of puerperal fever, its definition and advice about nursing and treatment. Puerperal or childbed fever was the most common cause of maternal mortality: a woman could have a successful delivery yet be dead within five days, and the risk of dying from puerperal fever was as high in the 1920s and early 1930s as it had been in the 1840s.

The Section arranged a joint discussion on 'The notification of puerperal sepsis' with the Section of Epidemiology and State Medicine, and a committee consisting of Dr Russell Andrews, Sir Ewen Maclean, Mr Aleck Bourne and Dame Janet Campbell reported its recommendations to Newman: 'Any case in which there is rigor or temperature of 102 degrees or above for twenty-four hours during the first ten days of an abortion or confinement must be notified'. 'We shall find your report of great value', Sir George Newman replied, anticipating that official recommendations would be published in 1932.[107]

## Report on Maternal Mortality

In 1919 the obstetrician Victor Bonney told a meeting of the Section that in the conduct of labour very little more than an antiseptic bowl stood between contemporary practice and that of the 1860s. His paper on 'The continued high maternal mortality of childbearing, the reason and the remedy' was a depressing review of 'woefully little' improvement in the death rate associated with childbearing over the last 70 years. Bonney tried to persuade his listeners that midwifery was a department of surgery, and that maternity hospitals should be established throughout the country. 'The whole edifice of obstetrics and gynaecology needs to be set in order', he urged and other speakers agreed that increased hospital deliveries would lower maternal mortality. Bonney stressed the importance of teaching and maternity hospitals or centres, yet in order to deal effectively with maternal mortality it was also necessary to establish obstetrics and gynaecology as a recognized specialty and only a college could do this. Bonney was not personally in favour of a separate college, but once it was established he accepted it with good grace.

The Blair-Bell Medal, designed by E Carter Preston, was first presented to Dr John Munro Kerr in 1950. Sir William Blair-Bell, who died in 1936, bequeathed £500 for a gold medal in obstetrics and gynaecology.

The last report issued by the Section before the foundation of the College was offered to the Ministry of Health Committeee on Maternal Mortality appointed by Sir George Newman in 1928. The Section was asked to provide evidence, particularly about the training of medical students in obstetrics and gynaecology, the provision of a national maternity service and for comments on puerperal sepsis. The resulting report emphasized the fact that education in those subjects was wholly inadequate and that puerperal fever required further research.[108] The Section's contribution went towards an interim report of the Ministry of Health (1929), the preliminary to another report of 1932 and a thorough-going document of 1937. These reports have been appraised recently as constituting 'the most comprehensive account of maternal mortality ever produced in Britain'.[109]

## *The Royal College of Obstetricians and Gynaecologists*

Sir William Blair-Bell of Liverpool and Sir William Fletcher Shaw of Manchester outlined a plan for a college to a meeting of fellow-members of the Gynaecological Visiting Society in February 1925 (Shaw credited the late Sir William Japp for the original idea). The committee that advanced the project was formed by Blair-Bell, Comyns Berkeley, Ewen Maclean and Fletcher Shaw, all members of the Section of Obstetrics and Gynaecology.

The many official reports on maternal and infant mortality, the figures themselves and Stanley Baldwin's electioneering campaign of 1929 (which put the reduction of maternal mortality high on the political agenda) worked in favour of a college. Indirectly the Section assisted in this process, through its reports, the leadership of its members and the encouragement it gave to the specialty.

One of the Section's preoccupations since the Great War had been the better training of medical students in obstetrics and gynaecology, and adequate training and examination was a major issue facing those who were planning a college. In December 1925 Dr Henry Russell Andrews sounded out the idea of a postgraduate, registrable Diploma in obstetrics and gynaecology among members of the Section of the RSM. A committee of TG Stevens (the current President), John S Fairbairn and Russell Andrews then did the ground-work, recommending an exacting preparatory training but stumbling on the question of examination. After discussion, the report was withdrawn, suggesting dissension – among those present were Sir George Blacker and Dr Herbert Spencer, who were not in favour of a new college.[110]

Preliminary work on a scheme of training in obstetrics and gynaecology and the possibility of a Diploma had thus been done by one of the Section's committees, while several members of the Section were promoting the foundation of a college. Fairbairn, Watts Eden and Russell Andrews were nearing that goal when in February 1929 Watts Eden called for a special meeting of the Section to discuss the proposed formation of a College of Obstetrics and Gynaecology. Dr Fairbairn, the current President, was known to support the idea but only 17 Fellows and members of the Section assembled to hear about the proposed 'British College of Obstetrics and Gynaecology'. The minutes do not reveal what was said.[111]

The next meeting revolved around the future of the maternity services and in November the Section tackled the Departmental Committee's 'Report on the Teaching and Employment of Midwives'. This came in for heavy criticism, for the committee was not representative and only one of its 13 members had any knowledge of the subject; the Section's adverse comments were sent to the Ministry of Health and the two Royal Colleges.

Meanwhile, and despite opposition from the Royal Colleges of Physicians and Surgeons, the College of Obstetricians and Gynaecologists was constituted in May 1929, 'a College in name but without a home except in my Secretary's office', Sir William Fletcher Shaw remembered, without personnel except the nine signatories and with no machinery of government.[112]

Strong links were maintained between the Royal College (as it became in 1937) and the Section, and many of the Section's Presidents held the presidency of the College: Sir William Blair-Bell, Sir Walter Fletcher Shaw, Professor JM Munro Kerr, Dr John Fairbairn, Sir Eardley Holland, Sir Arthur Gemmell, Sir Ewen Maclean and Dame Hilda Lloyd. The RSM also claims a share of distinguished obstetricians and gynaecologists as its Presidents: Sir Francis Champneys, Dr Watts Eden, Sir John Bland-Sutton, Sir William Gilliatt, Sir Hector MacLennan, Sir John Stallworthy and Sir George Pinker.

The vigour of the Section during the early decades of the century and in the absence of a college began to dissipate in the 1930s. The Eclampsia committee collapsed, Dr Theobald's call for a new standard of maternal morbidity was referred to the College, which co-operated with the Section to produce a standard of puerperal morbidity in the Empire (1936). Another committee appointed by the Section worked for three years on a scheme to standardize the clinical reports of maternity hospitals before ceding this to the College.[113]

The Section then reverted to its routine meetings and the commissioning of a Blair-Bell Medal. Dame Louise McIlroy and Mr Reid complained that papers were too long in 1947 and new or risqué topics were unwelcome. A communication on female circumcision was rejected and in 1956 Dr Grantly Dick-Read's film on natural childbirth had to be approved by referees before it was shown to a meeting (from which the press was banned).

## A genial President

Professor Chassar Moir, who had published his discovery of ergometrine in 1935 and who was an expert on the repair of urinary fistulae, was elected President in 1962. Moir's presidential address did not mention his own achievements but dwelt on his mentors, including Munro Kerr, who had been President 1941–42. He commended an anecdote about Munro Kerr to younger members of the RSM: arriving late at a meeting for which he was the first speaker of the afternoon, Munro Kerr opened with a beaming smile, 'Gentlemen, there are three essentials to public speaking. You must be well dressed. You must have dined well. You must show the audience you are enjoying yourself. I now leave you to guess which of these precepts I may have followed too faithfully in honouring you this afternoon'. Moir added, 'It is with this happy thought of enjoyable meetings ahead that I open this new session of our society'.[114]

## In vitro fertilization

As President for 1967–68, Sir John Peel took the opportunity to engage the Section's attention on abortion, sterilization and contraception (this was the decade of the introduction of the contraceptive pill). During his presidency a discussion was held on 'New techniques in obstetrics and gynaecology', at which Mr PC Steptoe's comments concerning laparoscopy formed the first contribution.

The pioneers of laparoscopy were Frangenheim of Germany and Palmer of Paris. Dr Raoul Palmer wrote extensively on laparoscopy and opened a discussion at the RSM in 1959 on modern methods of salpingostomy. Palmer was continuously developing instruments and techniques so that laparoscopy became a safe and desirable procedure; he was the founder of the International Federation of Fertility Societies, and he taught Patrick Steptoe. The latter, a consultant at Oldham in Lancashire, met Dr RG Edwards of Cambridge at the RSM early in 1968. It seems to have been a meeting held jointly by the Section of Endocrinology, the Endocrine Society and the Society for the Study of Infertility in February 1968. 'I brought down some electrifying colour slides of these disordered ovaries which I had taken through the laparoscope', Steptoe wrote. Most endocrinologists and gynaecologists were unaware that the laparoscope could provided naked eye views of the internal organs and that these could also be photographed and filmed. When a member of the audience suggested that without laparotomy the only way to visualize the ovaries was by X-ray, Steptoe recorded that he leapt to his feet and shouted '"Nonsense!" There was sudden silence. I repeated myself. "Absolute nonsense", I said. "You're quite wrong. I carry out laparoscopy regularly each day, many times a day"'. Steptoe went on to prove his point by showing his slides. 'Very soon I was to encounter Robert Edwards in the foyer and so for that reason I would never forget this particular meeting at the RSM'. Edwards, working at the Physiological Laboratory in Cambridge, set up a small laboratory at Oldham where he and Steptoe researched the fertilization of a human egg outside the body. As a result of their work the first *in vitro* fertilization baby, Louise Brown, was born in July 1978.[115]

Steptoe attempted to convince the Section of Obstetrics and Gynaecology of the safety of laparoscopy in November 1968, maintaining with justification that it was 'one of the most valuable advances made in gynaecology in the last twenty years'. The laparoscope is now the essential tool of every gynaecological unit, and the derivative of laparoscopy known as keyhole surgery has proved revolutionary.

A joint paper by Edwards and Steptoe on 'The control of human ovulation, fertilization and implantation' (1974) referred to difficulties yet to be overcome, and in 1975 the Section presented the Blair-Bell Medal to Steptoe although he was three years from achieving his ambition. A final paper by Edwards and Steptoe reviewed the progress of *in vitro* fertilization to 1982.

## Recent years

Professor John Stallworthy was President of the Section 1969–70 and President of the RSM 1973–75, coming to the rescue in 1980 for a second term – the only President to serve twice. His address to the Section was entitled 'New wine in old bottles', in which the wine was modern medicine and the bottles the media. He spoke of the responsibility of the medical schools, Royal Colleges and the RSM for educating the public as well as the profession on developments in medicine.[116] This point was to be taken up by the Society and its Sections in time, but meanwhile there was widespread concern about falling attendances at Section meetings. On being consulted about the problem, this Section was in the happy position of being able to report this was not the case, even though its meetings were held on Friday evenings, a slot that was popular with no-one.

Miss Josephine Barnes, as she was then known, was elected President in 1972; she was a determined and pioneering figure who was proud of being the first FRCOG to give birth, and her presidential address was on 'The moment of birth'. She was the first woman President of the BMA, an author and examiner who served on many committees, and her achievements were acknowledged by the award of the DBE in 1974 and the Honorary Fellowship of the RSM in 1988.

Although this Section was not seriously affected by the vicissitudes of the 1970s some changes were implemented to make meetings more attractive: the clinico-pathological meetings were replaced by debates, and efforts were made to find internationally known speakers. The Council was most concerned about poor communications between it and the Society's Council over the publication of *The A-Z of pregnancy and baby care* in 1982, about which it had not been consulted.[117]

Meetings of the 1980s included an Anglo-American Symposium on Fetal Health held at the RSM over three days in 1981, a meeting in Flaine, and outings to Windsor and Cambridge. The debates at ordinary meetings were deliberately provocative and proved popular. 'The attraction of obstetrics and gynaecology as a specialty is in jeopardy' was the motion debated in 1983 (no vote was taken) and another was 'This house believes an expanding private sector is essential for the health of British medicine' (approved by a large majority).

In 1994 the historians Michael O'Dowd and Elliot E Philipp described the Section as 'vigorous and thriving. This Section meets once a month and the meetings are attended by obstetricians and gynaecologists both fully trained and in training (registrars are encouraged to present cases) so that new techniques as well as old theories can be presented and discussed'.[118] Registrars are tempted by an annual prize, providing the basis for a meeting, and a good proportion of juniors have been seen at recent meetings. While retaining some formality in that the President and speakers wear evening dress to meetings, the aim has been to entertain as well as to educate. For instance the presidency of Mr Peter Saunders saw The Balloon Debate in which six speakers were 'airborne' and had to justify their place in the balloon – a lawyer, a midwife, a trainee, an ultrasonographer, a urologist and a private practitioner each argued that they were indispensable to a consultant's survival kit. As has long been the tradition, each session opens with the President's address and ends with an out-of-town meeting; and in 2000 the latter culminated in a dinner at the Millennium Dome.[119]

## Clinical Section

Members of the Clinical Society voted unanimously in favour of amalgamation, a major consideration being the facilities of the RSM Library. An announcement in the *BMJ* made it clear that the meetings of the Clinical Section would be conducted on lines similar to those of its predecessor.[120]

The Clinical Society of London had been founded by Dr Headlam Greenhow and Dr John Burdon Sanderson in 1867 'for the cultivation and promotion of practical medicine and surgery by the collection of cases, especially such as bear upon undetermined questions in pathology and therapeutics'. 110 original members joined the Society whose first President was Sir Thomas Barlow. The Society rented rooms from the RMCS at 53 Berners Street and after an interlude at the Medical Society of London it returned to the RMCS at 20 Hanover Square. According to Dr JD Rolleston, the most interesting historical event connected with the Clinical Society was the first medical demonstration of X-rays in this country. This took place on 30 March 1896 at 20 Hanover Square when the Society invited Professor Silvanus Thompson, the celebrated physicist, to demonstrate the new discovery. The evening marked a turning point in the acceptance of the discovery of X-rays and led to the foundation of the Röntgen Society.[121]

In the normal course of events meetings consisted of the exhibition of cases accompanied by brief case histories, business that was counterbalanced by a series of reports produced in the 1880s and 1890s on subjects such as spina bifida, myxoedema and the antitoxin of diphtheria. The tradition of reports was not continued by the Section, which concentrated solely on meetings at which patients were presented by members and their cases discussed. Occasionally a short paper was read or specimens demonstrated and as time went on some meetings were held at the hospitals where a large number of cases could be seen conveniently.

### *Cases not subjects*

At the time of the amalgamation the Clinical Society/Section numbered 572 ordinary members and 16 Honorary members. At the first meeting of the Section on 11 October 1907 Sir Thomas Barlow referred to some of the outstanding papers of the past (Gull had described anorexia nervosa to the Society in 1874, and there were other important contributions by Ord, Hutchinson, Jenner and Murchison). 'We are concerned', Barlow insisted, 'with cases, not subjects'. Continuity was thus maintained and in 1908 Archibald E Garrod, who had belonged to the Clinical Society since 1887 and was currently Honorary Secretary of the Section, was pleased to report that the Section was 'as successful as could be desired... the attendance has been very good and the cases shown have been well discussed'.[122]

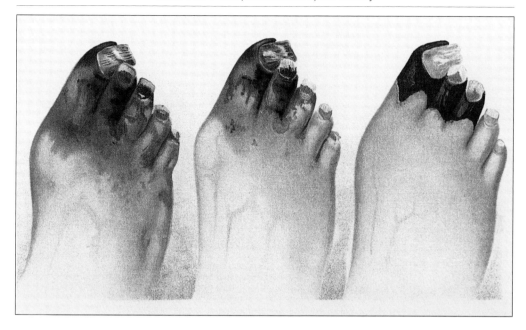

One of the first cases presented to the Clinical Section: Dr C Ballance (later Sir Charles Ballance), surgeon to St Thomas', described a case of arterio-venous anastomosis for senile gangrene. The figures show (left to right) the foot on the morning of the operation, three days later, and at the time of death in February 1908.

Sir Thomas Barlow's famous paper on cases of acute rickets, 'probably a combination of scurvy and rickets', had been delivered to the RMCS in 1883 (see page 120). As the first President of the Clinical Section he was supported by Dr William Pasteur, GH Makins, Dr W Hale-White, Anthony Bowlby, Charters Symonds and Sir Felix Semon as Vice Presidents. Their reputations and comments on cases attracted a large intake of new members in the first year. As Barlow said in his valedictory speech, this Section was a meeting ground for physicians and surgeons (the presidency alternated accordingly) who found the demonstrations instructive. Many members of the Section belonged to other Sections that fulfilled a different purpose and came to this Section not to hear erudite papers but to gain practical knowledge by the examination and discussion of classic cases such as examples of Addison's disease as well as rare and problematic cases. For example, Professor William Osler spoke on 'Splenic polycythaemia with cyanosis' (Vaquez–Osler Disease) in December 1907, a follow-up to his trail-breaking paper of 1903; Dr Alexander Fleming showed the Section a serum reaction for syphilis, and the pioneering radiotherapist Dr Neville Finzi demonstrated treatment by radium.

Sir William Osler (he accepted a baronetcy in 1911) was elected President of the Section in October 1912, finding time amid all his other interests to preside over the meetings held at 1 Wimpole Street on the second Friday of each month. Dr Frederick Parkes Weber, who was said to attend every Section and was on the Councils of seven, was the doyen of the Clinical Section (see page 256). On the occasion of his 80th birthday, which coincided with his completion of 50 years as physician to the German Hospital in London, his collected writings were listed, recording (among other works) his 313 contributions to the *Proceedings* between 1907 and 1943.[123] Parkes Weber's unrivalled support of the Society was acknowledged by an Honorary Fellowship in 1958, and he is remembered with Osler in the triple eponymous Rendu–Osler–Weber disease.[124]

Dr Frederick Parkes Weber, physician to the German Hospital in London and stalwart of several Sections of the RSM. He was made an Honorary Fellow in 1958.

## Particular concerns

It was of paramount importance to this Section that facilities at 1 Wimpole Street were adequate and its Council took care to ensure that both halls, adjoining dressing-rooms and the services of a nurse were available for the Section's meetings. Another special concern was the publication of case reports in the *Proceedings* of the RSM. Rising costs forced restrictions on the number of pages allocated to each Section in the annual volumes; these economies perturbed the Clinical Section particularly, 'because the information is not usually published in any other form and thus there is much international interest in the description of well-documented clinical problems of an unusual nature'.[125] The importance of the continued publication of its proceedings was to be a persistent cry.

## A shortage of cases

During the Second World War the supply of cases dried up and meetings were cancelled. Interest revived with the papers presented by Sir Harold Gillies, such as that on plastic surgery accompanied by 10 illustrative cases (1948). In the 1950s the debates were full of cut and thrust and sometimes the patients themselves had their say. This was followed by a period of uncertainty, with a plethora of new Sections at the RSM and an increasing emphasis on investigation.

When the *Proceedings* were superseded by the *Journal*, the Council expressed grave concern about the viability of the Section if cases presented at meetings were not published. The Sections of Dermatology and Paediatrics were also 'extremely exercised' that there would be fewer case reports in the *Journal*, and there was general criticism of the new editorial policy. In 1979 the Section membership dropped to a low point of 572 (compared with 859 ten years before) and in an effort to boost attendances tea was provided at meetings, paid for by a bookseller's stand. Basically the problem was identified as an acute shortage of cases and of new members coming into the Section. Combined with the low rate of publication in the *Journal*, the Council thought the Section might fold in 1988. It was decided to persevere and an influx of new members in the early 1990s justified this decision.

ROYAL SOCIETY OF MEDICINE

1, Wimpole Street, London, W. 1

———

. FIRST .

# ANNUAL DINNER

OF THE

## CLINICAL SECTION

*Friday, May 11th, 1934*

*President:*
BERNARD MYERS, C.M.G., M.D.

*Honorary Secretaries:*
HAROLD EDWARDS, M.S.    J. L. LIVINGSTONE, M.D.

———

" VERNON HOUSE "
PARK PLACE,
ST. JAMES'S STREET,
S.W.I.

The first annual dinner of the Clinical
Section was held in 1934.

As the Honorary Secretary of the Section emphasized in a piece that argued for the continued publication of case reports in the Society's *Journal*, 'The Royal Society of Medicine is unique in that there is a separate Section devoted to the discussion and presentation of individual cases. This Section is called the Clinical Section and it encompasses the entire range of clinical subjects. Not only are these patients fascinating but also the discussion that follows is interesting and provocative. There is the additional advantage that for junior members of the medical profession here is an ideal opportunity to develop the skill required in the research and presentation of a paper'.[126]

At the time of writing the Section has a membership of over 700, yet its meetings are poorly attended. The number of members is explained by the tendency of those joining the RSM to join the Clinical Section almost automatically. The reason for the low attendance at meetings is perhaps that they are usually of general interest and therefore appeal more to medical students and junior doctors than to those who have pursued a specialty. In order to rectify this, from time to time the Section tries to arrange meetings to appeal to a particular interest – on thyroid/melanoma for instance. Meetings at hospitals usually attract excellent on-site presentations and are often followed by 'a pleasant drug-company dinner'.[127]

The two prizes awarded by the Section commemorate Alan Edwards, the Honorary Secretary who died in 1976, and Brigadier Haywood, President of the Section 1993–94 and Professor of Military Surgery at the Royal Army Medical College, Millbank. Brigadier Haywood developed cancer in the year of his presidency yet he managed to attend every meeting of his Section, the last one being at Millbank. He died in September and the Section decided to name the prize for the best student presentation after him. 'He would have been very honoured and particularly pleased to see young people brought into the RSM in this way'.[128]

## Section of Dermatology

The Section was created by the amalgamation of the two most important dermatological societies of the kingdom. The Dermatological Society of London founded in 1882 was the first of its kind in England: its 23 original members included all the illustrious figures active at the time, and it held its 25th anniversary dinner just before amalgamation with the RSM in 1907. The Dermatological Society of Great Britain and Ireland, founded in 1894, was more broadly based: it included general practitioners who were not full-time dermatologists and it held its meetings at St John's Hospital for Diseases of the Skin.[129]

The decision to amalgamate within the RSM was taken with 'a tug at the heart strings': members of the Dermatological Society of London nursed reservations about sinking the individuality of 'our almost private club in the great society'.[130] In the end the formation of the Section under the auspices of the RSM was considered to be in the best interests of both the specialty and medicine, so the two 19th-century societies disbanded. Among those attending the inaugural meeting of the Section at 20 Hanover Square in July 1907 were Dr H Radcliffe Crocker, Dr T Colcott Fox, Mr Malcolm Morris, Dr Arthur Whitfield, Dr SE Dore and Dr E Graham Little.

The first Section meeting was held on 17 October 1907 under the presidency of Radcliffe Crocker, with Whitfield and Graham Little (later Sir Ernest Graham Little) as Secretaries. The latter, described as 'rather peculiar... a rubicund though thin, down-to-earth chap with a small dry cough very easy to caricature in the Xmas pantomime', was indeed memorable.[131] He was elected MP for the University of London in 1924 and for the next 26 years devoted much energy to giving dermatology a higher profile.

In his inaugural address Radcliffe Crocker noted that the Section was a 'not unimportant step in the recognition of the state of dermatology in medicine'. He went on to speak of the 'byeways and tracks enough... still to be explored' and an important principle was established: that patients should be examined on a raised chair and after the exhibitor had given an account of the case, the President opened the discussion. Among the six cases shown at this first meeting was one of Hutchinson's chilblain lupus (not then referred to by this eponym) and a 'chronic cheilitis' in a young woman of 'neurotic disposition'. At the second meeting the number of cases had increased to 22 but this was exceptional and soon settled to a more manageable number.[132]

### Early years

The Secretaries reported in January 1909 that there had been a flood of applications for membership immediately after the Section was formed, and in order to limit members to a practical number for the individual examination of patients, a dermatological qualification had been imposed upon all new members. The Section then stood at 113 members, with an average attendance of nearly 29 at each meeting, and for the session of 1908–09 a total of 156 exhibits had been shown. This was deemed satisfactory: 'That it is popular and that it deals with a wealth of material is, we think, proved by the number of Members, their attendances and the number of exhibits brought to the meetings'.[133]

In his valedictory address as President, Radcliffe Crocker noted that the RSM had 'more than justified its existence' and was 'growing continually in influence and power'. Of the Dermatological Section he spoke in similar terms: it had kept up the tradition of the old societies by making meetings as clinical as possible and by endeavouring to preserve friendly intercourse and the interchange of ideas, which was of the highest value.

The future of the Section was now secure, but on 22 August 1909 its 'elder statesman' Radcliffe Crocker died at the age of 64. The Council recorded the tact with which he had directed meetings 'in the unavoidably confused period of transition which followed the amalgamation of the old societies. Very much of the pronounced success which has attended the Section must be attributed to his energy and personality'.[134]

Sir Malcolm Morris (left) and
Dr H Radcliffe Crocker (hatless) were
founder-members of the Section of
Dermatology; Radcliffe Crocker was the
Section's first President and was followed by
Morris in 1911. They are pictured here with
Dr PG Unna from Hamburg.

Colcott Fox, who was elected President in 1909, donated his books, memoirs and papers to the Library of the RSM in 1913, 'in remembrance of the happy and instructive meetings I have attended at the present Section, and at the old Dermatological Society'.[135] According to Graham Little, Colcott Fox was seen at his best as President: 'his deep learning combined with modest self-effacement, his diagnostic acumen and his masterly summing up of the historical and clinical features of each case made him an ideal President'.[136] The third President was Sir Malcolm Morris, during whose term of office the RSM was based at its temporary home in Cavendish Square; the Section of Dermatology chose to hold its meetings at 11 Chandos Street in rooms where older members felt at home.

In the early years syphilis and tuberculosis provided numerous cases; bullous diseases and dermatitis herpetiformis were still poorly delineated and the subjects of much discussion; lichenoid, parakeratotic and hyperkeratotic conditions always aroused interest and the odd artefactual disease provided the usual puzzle of detection. Molluscum contagiosum was then a comparatively rare disease and evoked interest (it had first been described by Dr Bateman, the Society's Honorary Librarian in 1817, see Plate 20). The first case of keratoderma blennorrhagica in the United Kingdom was shown to the Section in 1910 by Dr JH Sequeira (see page 260), and in 1912 JER McDonagh described his naevoxantho-endothelioma.

From time to time foreign guests were invited to give talks or discuss cases: Dr Louis Wickham, Superintendent of the Radium Institute in Paris, addressed a distinguished audience that included the Lord Mayor and Lady Mayoress at a Section meeting in 1909, speaking on the treatment of diseases by radium. In 1911 Dr R Sabouraud's paper on eczematoid ringworm of the extremities and groin opened the discussion; that year also saw the first of many discussions on the role, dose-regimes and toxicity of salvarsan, the 'magic bullet' that opened up an entirely new line of work and was to transform the treatment of syphilis until the arrival of penicillin.

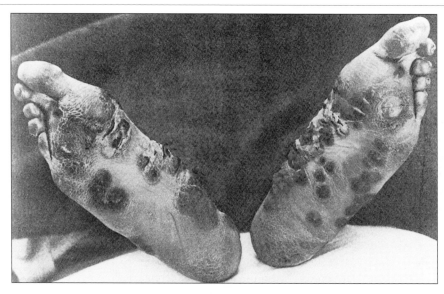

JH Sequeira's case of 'kératodermie blennorrhagique', 1910. Colcott Fox, the President of the
Section, commented that as far as he knew this was the first case shown in this country.
Dr James Sequeira was President of the Section 1925–27.

## 1914–18

During the first years of the war Dr JJ Pringle was President of the Section and by all
accounts a tower of strength, 'initiating special discussions amongst its depleted membership, editing with meticulous care the *Transactions* and generally stimulating its
activities'.[137] The impact of the Great War began to be felt in 1915 when the President
noted that 'the numbers of our Fellows engaged in war and military duties is very considerable'. One such was Archibald Gray, who was attached to the general staff yet still
managed to attend many meetings of the Section. In 1918 he became consultant dermatologist to the British Expeditionary Force and was awarded the CBE – the first of many
honours – in 1919. He was President of the Section from 1931 to 1933, President of the
British Association of Dermatologists (1938–39) and President of the RSM from 1940 to
1942, the first and only member of the Section to occupy the office.

Papers given during the war years dealt with subjects of military concern: infections,
infestations and of course syphilis, for which Germany had been using neo-salvarsan from
1912, whereas Britain had to start manufacturing its own substitute. In 1916 McDonagh
showed a case of mercurial poisoning cured by Intramine, which he was using at the Lock
Hospital.

The increase in the number of cases being shown necessitated selection, and paper
restrictions led to economies in the publication of the *Proceedings* in which the Section had
to fight hard to preserve adequate space for dermatology. The large proportion of papers
on syphilis prompted a proposal from Sir Malcolm Morris and Dr Pringle that the
Section's name should be changed to Dermatology and Syphilology in 1917. The motion
was seconded but not voted upon.[138]

In an ironical footnote to history, members of the Section had been invited by Professor
Zieler to the jubilee meeting of the German Dermatological Society in May 1914. The
Council wisely left the reply to the discretion of individual members.

## Between the wars

After the First World War the Section began to reorganize itself and re-establish contacts
with Europe. Among the first Foreign Corresponding members elected were Brocq,

Sabouraud, Darier, Pellizzari and Dohi. The post of 'past President' was established, and an editorial sub-committee was formed. One meeting in each session was now devoted to papers, and several distinguished foreign dermatologists were invited to participate; the Section also benefited from joint meetings with the Section of Tropical Medicine and Parasitology and the Section for the Study of Disease in Children. In 1922 Dr Agnes Savill became the first woman member of the Section, soon to be joined by Dr Alice Carleton, but women remained thin on the ground until after 1946.

The customary dinner after the Section's AGM had to be cancelled in 1926 due to the General Strike, but in 1932 a special dinner was held in honour of Dr James Sequeira. He had been President of the Section from 1925 to 1927 and was on a rare lecturing visit to London; his textbook on *Diseases of the skin* went into five editions in his lifetime.

The annual meetings of the British Association of Dermatology commenced in 1920 but these did not detract from attendances at the Section meetings at the RSM; during the 1930s between 40 and 60 members were to be seen at each meeting, excluding visitors. Many university hospitals in Britain were beginning to appoint physicians who practised dermatology exclusively, and for them the monthly meetings of their Section at 1 Wimpole Street became an important professional activity, for it was there that discoveries were presented and new information discussed.

## The Second World War

The Second World War made a greater impact on the Section than that of 1914–18, and the average attendance dropped as many members were temporarily lost to the Section. In October 1939 the Section cancelled its programme for three months and in the absence of Dr WS O'Donovan on active service Dr SE Dore acted as President.

It is remarkable that even in 1941, as many as 13 cases were brought to a meeting attended by 36 members. It is also pleasant to record that Walter Freudenthal from Breslau, who was given asylum in England in 1933, was elected a member of the Section. His expertise in dermato-histopathology – then somewhat neglected in this country – added a new dimension to the discussion of cases. He was the first of several talented colleagues who had been compelled to flee from persecution in their own countries; Henry Haber and Theresa Kindler were among others to join the Section.

As in the First World War, the papers – and even the cases shown – reflected military experience. Penicillin had just arrived on the scene and had transformed therapy; mepacrine and DDT followed. By 1943 a new impetus had been given to the Section by an invitation extended to all American dermatologists who had arrived in the country. Throughout these years joint meetings had been arranged with other Sections, notably a discussion on 'Chronic diseases of the vulva' which perhaps gave HJ Wallace the germ of his subsequent classic paper on lichen sclerosis.

As the Second World War drew to a close the Section began to resume its normal rhythm, but to a different tune. The 1940s saw the birth of the scientific revolution which affected every branch of medicine, with the introduction of chemotherapy and cortico-steroids. It was followed in 1948 by the birth of the National Health Service, which provided training and appointments for consultant dermatologists in most of the larger hospitals. Their increased numbers and an influx of young ex-servicemen greatly expanded attendances at meetings of the Section. In 1945 Pierre Deville became a member; in 1991 his wife bequeathed £5,000 to the Section, and Deville is now commemorated by an annual oration.

In the aftermath of the war in Europe a letter was sent to Dr Emile Petracek of Prague congratulating him on his 'safe re-emergence into European medical life' and inviting him to give a paper to the Section. For many other colleagues no such invitation was possible.

*Important presentations*

Some of the important new presentations at the Dermatology Section's meetings were on molluscum sebacum (later called kerato-acanthoma) by MacCormac and Scarff; the treatment of lupus vulgaris with calciferol by Drs GB Dowling, EW Prosser Thomas and HJ Wallace in 1945; cases of pemphigus and pemphigoid by AJ Rook and I Whimster, and the treatment of fungus infections with griseofulvin.

Dr Geoffrey Dowling remembered the first case he ever showed at the RSM vividly. This was 'an unusual case (to him) of urticaria pigmentosa [*sic*]. He was humbled by the total absence of comment from either the president or the audience. Another time he showed the first case there of trichostasis spinulosa and he immediately remembered the patient he had shown with Walter Freudenthal in 1938, as benign acanthosis nigricans (which he always felt was wrong), when the same condition was shown in 1971 as a "pigmentary anomaly of the axillae" and which is now known as Dowling–Degos disease. As one might have expected it was at a meeting of the Royal Society of Medicine that he chose to present his discovery of the calciferol treatment for tuberculosis of the skin'.[139] Dowling was President of the Section 1951–53 and later an Honorary Fellow of the Society. He is remembered in the annual Dowling Oration, first delivered in 1956 and endowed from 1970.

A longstanding and distinguished member of the Section was Dr Frederick Parkes Weber, one of the small band who kept the Section alive during the war years. His paper on 'Chronic fibroid subcutaneous syphilomata of the legs' was the first to draw attention to this condition, and he presented hundreds of cases and papers to meetings of this and other Sections (see pages 255–56).[140] He would rise to make a comment on the majority of the cases and his memory was phenomenal. In the early days the President had a button to illuminate a red light to halt the speaker if his contribution was too long. Not infrequently Parkes Weber simply placed his hand over the red light and continued.

Until 1978 the most important papers were published in the *Proceedings* of the RSM. For dermatologists these formed a major part of the quoted literature throughout the world. The replacement of the *Proceedings* by the *Journal* was seen by dermatologists as a major loss.

Dr GB Dowling, President of the Section of Dermatology 1951–53.
He was made an Honorary Fellow of the Society in 1961.

Over the past 20 years fewer Sections of the RSM presented patients at their meetings, but dermatology is largely a visual subject and the opportunity to see live patients with rare and unusual skin conditions was always the main reason for attendance and drew members from many parts of the United Kingdom. Attendance at the meetings steadily increased and in 2000 the Section had 461 members and was proud to claim two Honorary Fellows of the Society: Professor Charles Calnan and Dr Darrell Wilkinson.

The large attendance at meetings poses problems: the Barnes Hall at 1 Wimpole Street is unable to contain the numbers and standing room has been restricted by fire regulations. At present, attendance at the clinical meetings of the Section is regarded as a vital part of the training and continuing education of all dermatologists in Britain; if, however, the Society is unable to accommodate live patient presentations, the membership of the Section will diminish.

## Section of Clinical Neurosciences (Plate 40)
originally Neurology

One of the founder-members of the Neurological Society of London, Sir John Bland-Sutton, claimed that the foundation of that Society was the outcome of a meeting of the Royal Medical and Chirurgical Society in May 1885 at which Hughes Bennett and Rickman Godlee gave news of their removal of a tumour from the brain (see page 140).[141] Before the end of that year Sir William Broadbent and Dr Hughlings Jackson had taken the lead in founding the Neurological Society, which first met on 14 January 1886. Hughlings Jackson was then elected President with Broadbent, JS Bristowe, HC Bastian, D Ferrier, J Hutchinson, A de Watteville, V Horsley, J Crichton-Brown, G Savage, F Semon and S Wilks leading the 95 original members. The first Secretaries were de Watteville and Hughes Bennett.

The first ordinary meeting was held at the National Hospital, Queen Square, in March when Hughlings Jackson gave an inaugural address covering the aims and scope of neurology and the manner in which the Society might advance the science.[142] Laboratory meetings were essential to the work of the Society and some of the most successful were

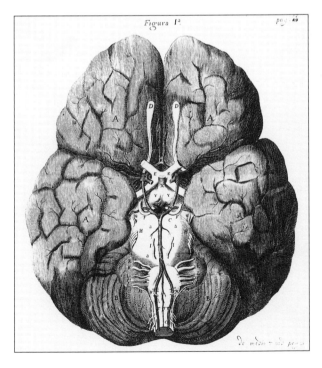

An illustration of the base of the brain drawn by the architect Sir Christopher Wren for Dr Willis' *Cerebri anatome nervorumque descriptio et usus* (1664), which contains an accurate description of the nervous system and describes the 'nerve of Willis' and the 'circle of Willis'. Willis acknowledged the contribution made by his friend: 'Dr Wren was pleased out of his singular humanity wherein he abounds, to delineate with his own most skilful hands many Figures of the Brain and Skull'.

held in the physiological laboratory of University College where Sharpey-Schäfer, Horsley and Semon gave memorable demonstrations.[143] From the beginning the Society fostered neurology and neurosurgery in tandem. Shortly after its dissolution in favour of the Section, Thomas Buzzard, who had been a founder-member, remembered that from the very first the Society was established 'on no narrow basis' and that Presidents were chosen by rotation to represent 'one year special neurology, another general medicine, another surgery, another psychology, another physiology, each with special bearings upon the subject of the nervous system'. Buzzard claimed that Sir James Crichton-Brown had a good deal to do with the inception of the Society. Another correspondent, 'L.H.', alleged that Sir William Gowers refused to join it owing to his dislike of de Watteville: 'he is reported to have said that the Society was founded by a charlatan (de Watteville) to keep out a quack (Julius Althaus)'.[144]

## Hughlings Jackson lecture

The Neurological Society undertook responsibility for the publication of *Brain* (1887–1907) and in 1897 Hughlings Jackson gave the first of the lectures that commemorate him. Dr WS Coleman had first suggested founding a lecture in honour of Hughlings Jackson in 1896 and the Council approved, noting especially Hughlings Jackson's discovery of cortical epilepsy and its relation to cerebral localization.[145] Successive lecturers included Horsley, Gowers and Head and in 1927 Dr Charles Dana of New York. He started the fund to provide an honorarium for subsequent lecturers, and this was implemented by Mr Leslie Paton as President of the Section of Neurology in 1931. Subscriptions amounted to over £1,000 and provided for an honorarium of 100 guineas and a gold medal designed by Percy Metcalfe for the lecturer.

## Amalgamation

In 1903 the Council of the Neurological Society of London decided that because nearly half of its 230 members were 'extra-metropolitan', the name should be changed to the Neurological Society of the United Kingdom. It was one of the few medical societies to pronounce immediately in favour of the proposed confederation of societies in the RSM, as put to its Council in 1905.

The Hughlings Jackson Medal, designed by Percy Metcalfe, was first awarded in 1932.

The Section's Council met at the Medical Society of London's house in July 1907 and held its first meeting at 20 Hanover Square in October, still under the presidency of Dr Charles Beevor, the last President of the Neurological Society. The Council arranged a programme of short papers and clinical meetings alternating with visits to the National Hospital or the Maida Vale Hospital, and apart from a few resignations the new Section ran smoothly. During its first session the Council firmly vetoed a suggestion that a sub-Section be formed from members of the Medical Society for the Study of Suggestive Therapeutics, and it chose Sir William Gowers as the Hughlings Jackson lecturer.[146] Professor Charles Sherrington was elected President in 1909 and in 1957 the Section founded the Sherrington Memorial lecture to mark the centenary of his birth: at the first of these Lord Adrian, who was to be President of the RSM 1960–62, spoke about 'The analysis of the nervous system'.

## Gordon Holmes

Gordon Holmes of the National Hospital, Queen Square, collaborated with FE Batten (after whom the Batten Unit at the Hospital was named) to present the first of many papers in 1908; this was on the nervous system of a dog. Holmes gave another joint paper that year with the young Robert Foster Kennedy, who wrote to his fiancée of his excitement at meeting Holmes at 20 Hanover Square, then dining with him 'and work all evening. Voila! Such a narration makes me glow with virtue'.[147] Foster Kennedy was soon to make his career at the Neurological Institute, New York, where he wrote his paper on what is called the Foster Kennedy syndrome.

Holmes' presidential address to the Section in 1929 on the 'Dislocation of the ocular movements' was reported in the *Lancet*, and in 1931 he opened the discussion on 'Mental symptoms associated with brain tumours', held jointly with the Section of Psychiatry when Dr Russell Brain, Dr Charters Symonds, Dr FL Golla and Dr Edward Mapother had their say. At the age of 79 Holmes received the Gold Medal of the RSM, and was the Hughlings Jackson lecturer for 1955.

## Dr Henry Head

Within a year of its formation the Section was attracting Gordon Holmes, E Farquhar Buzzard, Wilfred Harris, Henry Head, Victor Horsley, Foster Kennedy and Parkes Weber to its meetings. In 1909 historic papers were given to the Section by Wilfrid Harris describing the first cases of trigeminal neuralgia treated by alcohol injection, and by N Bishop Harman who reported his tests of binocular vision.[148] Dr Henry Head had represented the Neurological Society during the amalgamation negotiations of 1905–07 and he was on the Council of the new Section from the start, becoming President in 1918. His researches on sensation in humans (in the course of which he had his own left radial and external cutaneous nerves cut and sutured so that he could map the effects) were written up in *Brain* (which he edited), establishing his reputation, and in 1903 he was awarded the Marshall Hall Prize. Head came to the notice of a wider public through his treatment of Virginia Woolf, having been recommended to Leonard Woolf much to the annoyance of Sir George Savage who was Head's senior. Head was called in to help the depressive Virginia Woolf on the night of her unsuccessful suicide attempt in 1913 – ultimately neither Head nor Savage were able to help the novelist, who later wrote a coruscating indictment of Harley Street and its specialists in *Mrs Dalloway* (1925).

As President, Head addressed the meeting of the Section after the close of 'the greatest war in the history of the world'. Looking back over the quarter of a century since he had read his first paper to the Neurological Society, he judged that there had been no startling discoveries in the specialty but he anticipated challenges ahead. 'The cataclysmic events of the last four years have shaken men's belief in the old order, and medicine has not escaped the universal demand for a restatement of current values'. Interest in the functions of the nervous system was growing and Head expected that the next generation would criticize conventional explanations and search for new ones. He described the role of the neurologist in poetic terms, 'We work in the passage-way between the physical universe and the dwelling-place of the mind. We can watch the processes of evolution, visible in the actual behaviour of the central nervous system. We see the coming and the going, and we alone can record which of the many aspirants has conquered the right to enter or leave that council chamber of human activities'.[149]

Head continued to take an active part in the Section meetings, joining the discussion on war neuroses with Wilfred Trotter and Farquhar Buzzard in 1919, and in November 1920 he gave the Hughlings Jackson lecture on the subject of aphasia. As Macdonald Critchley remembered, James Collier, SA Kinnier Wilson, Stanley Barnes and Herbert Parsons then gave their views; 'This was apparently the first and the last occasion when Head's views were seriously discussed, and the reception of his argument was on the whole most sympathetic. Head's work upon this subject found complete and eventual expression in his *Aphasia and kindred disorders of speech* published in two volumes in 1926. This is certainly the finest monograph on the subject of aphasia in neurological literature'.[150]

## A neuro-radiological discussion

The American neurosurgeon Walter Dandy achieved a breakthrough in neurological methods of diagnosis in 1918 with his discovery of ventriculography. New methods were slow to reach England, and it was not until 1924 that Dandy's methods were evaluated during a neuro-radiological discussion organized by the Section. Dr James Collier was President at the time and the young Geoffrey Jefferson came forward with his views on the value of X-rays in the localization of cerebral and spinal tumours with special reference to ventriculography and lipiodal injections. Mr Percy Sargent opened the discussion by describing Professor Sicard's method of investigating spinal lesions by radiography using lipiodal (the Paris physician Sicard had introduced positive contrast myelography in 1921). In reference to Dandy's work, Jefferson voiced his objections to ventriculography, its risk and 'no guarantee that we are going to obtain anything very useful from it'. Even so, Jefferson was more optimistic than some of those present. The Professor of Medicine in Lisbon, Egaz Moniz, read a report of this meeting in *Brain*; 'Clearly the English, he later wrote, were not altogether satisfied with ventriculography. This apparently spurred him on to seek help in another way and led to his discovery of cerebral arteriography'.[151]

## Sir Hugh Cairns

Cairns, who was to be the first Nuffield Professor of Surgery at Oxford, made his debut at the RSM with a paper to the Surgical Section in 1929. Two years later he presented (with Dr Douglas McAlpine) some unusual cases to a meeting of the Neurological Section at the Maida Vale Hospital. One case in particular, the first patient in whom an acoustic neurinoma had been removed completely with the preservation of the facial nerve, was much quoted over the years. Cairns' papers to this Section were given jointly with W Russell Brain (1932) and with CS Hallpike (1938), while with Margaret Taylor he opened the discussion on the treatment of tuberculous meningitis with streptomycin in 1949, at a meeting that drew an audience of 260. He took a leading part in the discussion of Jefferson's paper on rehabilitation after injuries to the nervous system in 1941, and in 1943 he was elected President of the Section. His address on that occasion focused on gunshot wounds of the head and *en passant* he gave a cautious welcome to penicillin: 'the results are not unpromising'. Cairns' wartime presidency saw many Canadian and American officers at the RSM and he encouraged them to take part in the proceedings of his Section.

Cairns was the first to campaign for compulsory crash helmets for motor cyclists. It was alleged that his interest originated in 1935 when he and Sir Edward Farquhar Buzzard were summoned to Bovington to treat TE Lawrence (of Arabia) after his crash, which proved fatal. When Cairns spoke to the Laryngological Section in 1942 on injuries of the sinuses he dwelt mainly on motor cycle crashes; he wanted to see more research from the army and the introduction of scientifically designed protective helmets. It was only after Cairns' death that crash helmets became compulsory.[152]

In the first Hugh Cairns Memorial lecture given in 1958, Geoffrey Jefferson referred to the immense care that Cairns had given to his paper with Hallpike on Ménière's disease (1938). Another colleague, Professor Leslie Witts, was among those who recognized Cairns' magnetism which attracted people to work with him. 'After Cairns died', said Witts, 'there was no real leadership left in the School' (the school of neurosurgery at Oxford).[153]

## The 1930s
The Association of British Neurologists established its own forum to discuss clinical and research problems in 1933, and 51 invitees promptly accepted membership of the new Association. Yet in spite of rivalry from it and from the Society of British Neurological Surgeons (which had been founded in 1926), the Section of Neurology did not falter, sustained as it was by papers from FL Golla, Gordon Holmes, Edward Mapother and by the presidencies of Golla (1935–36) and Sir Geoffrey Jefferson (1939–40).

In 1935 Professor Golla addressed the Section on 'The nervous system and the organic whole', described as 'a masterly exposition of his views of the vital importance of physiological observation and reaction'. He spoke of the day he hoped to see 'when a neurologist will be a humanist in the widest sense, when the psychiatrist will no longer shun the laboratory, and the neurophysiologist will be a trusted collaborator of the psychologist'.[154] This vision was to sustain the Burden Neurological Institute, where Golla held the post of Director from 1939 to 1959.

Inspired by Harvey Cushing (an Honorary Fellow of the RSM), Geoffrey Jefferson initiated neurological surgery as a specialty in this country and founded the Society of British Neurological Surgeons in 1926. Jefferson's contributions to neurosurgical knowledge are world-famous, and his personality, talents and presidency of the Section played a large part 'in welding the structures of the specialty in this country'.[155] Jefferson's papers to the Neurological Section, including his presidential address of 1940, have been evaluated by his biographer as both very important and controversial.[156] Sir Geoffrey was awarded the Hughlings Jackson Medal and an Honorary Fellowship of the RSM in 1955.

## Trouble
The Section was driven to consult the Secretary of the RSM over its 'internal difficulties' in 1942. The exact nature of the problem went unminuted, but it called for a repetition of the regulations and the Secretary alluded to troublesome members who needed to be controlled. 'If anybody talks too much or talks nonsense, surely it is the job of the President to stop him for the sake of the efficiency of the meeting. Gadgets are provided in considerable variety for the purpose... the type of speaker who indulges in self-advertisement rather than in an attempt to further the scientific work of the meetings is being more and more firmly and systematically sat upon'.[157]

## Post-war
The end of the Second World War heralded an active period for the Section with as many as 200 attending each clinical meeting, forcing the Council to issue tickets and restrict guests. A first meeting with overseas colleagues had been held in 1927 with a delegation

from the American Neurological Association. After the war a meeting was arranged with the Société de Neurologie de Paris, when Sir Hugh Cairns opened the discussion on 'Penicillin in neurology'. Eminent French neurologists and neurosurgeons attended including Clovis Vincent, who spoke on cerebral oedema. Further successful meetings have been held with Belgian, Romanian and Italian neurologists and members of the Section ventured as far as St Petersburg in 1998 for a conference with the All Russian Association of Neurologists.

In 1946 Ludwig Guttman, a refugee from Nazi Germany, came to a meeting to open the discussion on 'Traumatic paraplegia', giving an account of his experience at the Spinal Injuries Centre at Stoke Mandeville since 1944.[158] The unit he founded at Stoke Mandeville, now world-famous, was the earliest and largest paraplegia unit and Guttman was knighted for his work there. He later established the International Olympics for the Disabled.

Geoffrey Keynes, who also supported the Section of Surgery, opened a symposium in 1946 on 'Myasthenia gravis' at the National Hospital, Queen Square, where 30 patients had been assembled for inspection by members of the Neurological Section. The main purpose of this meeting was to provide a clinical demonstration of the results of thymectomy for myasthenia gravis: Keynes had performed the operation 63 times on patients whose ages ranged from two to 56; he recorded seven deaths among the first 21 patients, and only two among the next 42 – which said something about the benefit of experience.[159]

Dr W Russell Brain was elected President of the Section in 1950, during his first year as President of the Royal College of Physicians; his many attributes brought honours and a baronetcy in 1954. Dr Macdonald Critchley was President of the Section 1952–53 while a fellow neurologist, Sir Francis Walshe, was President of the RSM. Macdonald Critchley had been an active member of the Section since the 1930s and he chose to give his presidential address on the 'Neurological aspects of Braille reading'.

Professor F Nattrass was elected President of the Section in 1954. His report on recurring polyneuritis published in the 1920s was acknowledged as being of fundamental importance and has a place in French medical literature as *la maladie de Nattrass*. He later became more interested in muscle disease, and this was the subject of his presidential address; he was to become the first Chairman of the Muscular Dystrophy Group of Great Britain.

As a founder of the Association of British Neurologists, a past President of the RSM and author of *Diseases of the nervous system*, Sir Francis Walshe broke a silence of 30 years to speak about the future of neurology in 1955. He expressed his anxiety about the future of neurological medicine because it was advancing fast without any clearly thought-out direction: 'our activities remain individual and uncoordinated without general principles or common aim'. He was critical of the ineffectual and uninspired educational scheme devised by the Royal College of Physicians committee and of the irrelevance of much neurological research to the problems of disease. He did, however, have some faith in the RSM as a forum, 'the only one available to us, for an open discussion of the purely humane and scientific problems involved in the creation of an active and fruitful future for neurological medicine'.[160]

Papers given in the year of Walshe's speech illustrated the variety of subjects covered by the Neurology Section, from the future of neurology to a meeting commemorating the bicentenary of the birth of James Parkinson, author of *An essay on the shaking palsy* (1817). Another meeting brought neurologists and RAF personnel together to discuss the nervous system in relation to high-performance flying.[161]

The Section's Council made valiant efforts to liaise with the Association of British Neurologists and the Society of British Neurological Surgeons to plan mutually convenient programmes, but there was no doubt that the Section lost some of its authority to the many associations and societies catering not just for neurologists and neurosurgeons but also for an increasing number of sub-specialties. The rapid growth of both neurology and neurosurgery made it impossible for the Section to devote sufficient time to the discusssion of surgical subjects, prompting some neurosurgeons to propose a separate section for neurosurgery in 1967. The Section's Council opposed this, claiming that it was already planning to devote more time to neurosurgical subjects.[162] The neurosurgeons' proposal did prompt some changes: the time of meetings was altered and their number reduced to six in the light of dwindling audiences, and a change of name to the Section of Neurological Sciences was considered.

In March 1973, 22 resignations were recorded following an increase in the RSM's subscription, and the remaining years of the 1970s were fraught with problems. The new *Journal* was criticized, the Council expressed 'its grave disquiet' over the resignation in 1978 of the President of the RSM, Sir John Dacie, about the apparent move away from the Society's academic role to a more commercial one and about the proposed freezing of funds for the Library; it also objected to the sale of Chandos House (see Chapter 10).[163]

## Section of Clinical Neurosciences

Once the Society had settled into the expanded and modernized premises in 1986, the Neurology Section took positive steps to recruit new members and improve international links. During his presidential year of 1990–91 Dr F Clifford Rose increased the number of sessions from the usual five to fifteen, most of them in association with other Sections. This programme was included in a mail-shot to neurologists on an international basis, resulting in a doubling of the membership, making the Section the most numerous in the RSM at that time.[164]

As neurology expands in terms of sub-specialties, new drugs and technology, research and treatment, the Section currently encompasses an expanding field and its chief strength lies in its function as a meeting place and training ground for all those within the discipline: neurosurgeons, neurologists, neuroscientists, neuropsychologists, neurogeneticists, neuropathologists, neuroepidemiologists, neuroradiologists, neuropaediatricians and so on. The change of name to the Section of Clinical Neurosciences in 1997 reflected the widening sphere of the specialty and the Section, which in 2000 was the second largest Section of the Society (the Section of History of Medicine taking first place).

## Section of Laryngology and Rhinology (Plate 44)
originally Laryngology

The contributions made to laryngology by Professor Czermak and Señor Garcia had been recognized by the Royal Medical and Chirurgical Society in 1862 and 1905 respectively, and of course a President of the Medical and Chirurgical Society, Dr Benjamin Babington, had made a significant contribution to the development of laryngology when he invented the 'glottiscope' in 1829 (see page 79).

The specialty had been further advanced by Morell Mackenzie, who as founder of the first dispensary for Diseases of the Throat (1863), of the *Journal of Laryngology and Rhinology* (1887) and of the first British society devoted to laryngology, the British Rhino-Laryngological Association (1888, embracing Otology from 1895), was 'truly the father of British laryngology'.[165]

Sir Morell Mackenzie's protégé, Felix Semon, founded the Laryngological Society of London in 1893 and this Society held its meetings at 20 Hanover Square for over a decade. The laryngologists refused to countenance amalgamation with the Section of Otology at International Congresses, yet the Society did agree to fuse with the British Laryngological,

Rhinological and Otological Association within the RSM. As the last President of the Association, Mr Chichele Nourse negotiated the terms of the amalgamation, key conditions being separate Sections for Laryngology and Otology and 'that ladies shall be admitted with the same privileges as men'. As the probability of joining the RSM increased, the Association nominated Council members to both the proposed Sections of Laryngology and Otology, while ordinary members could choose to join one or both Sections.[166]

The Laryngological Society had already installed its library at 20 Hanover Square in 1902 and its President, the pioneering Mr Charters Symonds, spoke in 1905 of the debt of gratitude his Society owed to the RMCS for the privilege of meeting at Hanover Square and the encouragement this gave to the Society, 'without which we should never have been able to develop'.[167] Relations between the Laryngological Society and the RMCS were evidently cordial, although Sir Felix Semon harboured some regrets about the dissolution of the Society he had founded. Its Council made clear its preference for the title Royal Academy of Medicine for the new corporation and expressed concern about the admission of people who might not be experienced in the use of the laryngoscope to meetings – this would of course be detrimental to patients and to the reputation of the Section.

The Laryngological Society brought 150 members into the RSM and under the presidency of Dr JB Ball the meetings of the Section of Laryngology arranged for the first session of 1907–08 set the pattern for the presentation of cases, specimens and discussions which made for a varied and lively programme. For the first half of the first session an average of 46 members attended each meeting, well in excess of the combined figure for the two societies that had preceded the Section. The Morbid Growths committee continued its work, Mr L Hemington Pegler was appointed Curator to oversee the Section's collection of specimens and the compilation of a catalogue, and the Section's first annual dinner was held jointly with the Otological Section at the Café Royal.

During the First World War members of the Section volunteered to apply their expertise to the more effective treatment of throat and ear disease prevalent in the forces, but the RSM Council disapproved of the memorandum and the Section had to be content with advising the Committee of Reference on the staffing of London hospitals during the emergency.

*Resignations of Sir Felix Semon and the President*
Semon overcame his reservations about the Section and agreed to be a Council member in 1907; he took part in discussions and presented two cases to the meeting in June 1908 (he also supported the Sections of Pathology and Neurology). At a meeting of the Laryngological Section in March 1911 he was interested to hear about Professor Hobday's operation to relieve 'whistling' or 'roaring' in horses, the question being whether the operation might be applied to man. 'What becomes of the voice?' Semon asked. Hobday replied that if the operation was successful the horse became dumb. 'Ah', Semon replied, 'that finishes it for man and indeed for women too, for men and women do not mind whether they can run a mile but they do mind whether or not they can talk'.[168] Semon's comment was given more gravitas in the official version, for he was esteemed as the 'honoured doyen' of laryngology.[169] The Semon Medallion was 'suspended in the house' as soon as the Section was established at 1 Wimpole Street and a dinner was given in his honour, yet in January 1919 Semon resigned from the Laryngological Section after a row about the Semon lectureship at London University.

The issue hinged on Semon's German roots at a sensitive time in Anglo-German relations. Early in 1919, a petition was presented by 12 members of the Section asking for the suspension of the Semon lectureship – the award had lapsed during the war but in the normal course of events would have been revived, and the President and a past President of the Section exerted a strong influence over the award. When the matter was raised at a Council meeting, Semon appeared and put up a strong defence. He declared that the German Athenaeum had nothing to do with the lectureship fund (which had been subscribed by friends and colleagues on his retirement in 1909) and he went to great length to explain that he had lived in this country for 40 years, was a naturalized British citizen, had been expelled from the laryngological societies of Berlin and Vienna and that he had publicly denounced German methods of warfare after the sinking of the *Lusitania*. Nevertheless, the Section protested against holding a Semon lecture and made representations to the supervising Board accordingly. A week later Semon resigned from the membership of the Section and had no more to do with it.[170] The Semon lectureship resumed in 1921, the year of Semon's death, and it continues to be given annually at the RSM.

Another to resign from the Section at this time was its President, Major EB Waggett, one of the first in Britain to practise direct oesophagoscopy and bronchoscopy. Waggett had been on active service throughout the Great War, which had instilled in him a hatred of the enemy. As he explained to the Vice President, Thomas Mark Hovell, he objected to the tolerant attitude the Council of the RSM and his Section had adopted towards 'representatives of German Medicine. I resent very deeply the retention of their names upon the list of the Society and am therefore unwilling to appear to welcome their Fellowship'. He therefore tendered his resignation of the Section and the Fellowship of the RSM in 1920.[171]

## Lengthy proceedings

The number of cases, specimens and the discussions at this Section's meetings were reported to be 'uniformly heavy' by Mr Dickinson, the shorthand writer employed to record them. The proceedings at a single meeting sometimes ran to 60 sheets, for which Dickinson demanded a fee of £2 10s, compared with the two guineas that was his charge for reporting the meetings of less voluble Sections.[172] The Section's business continued to fill a large proportion of the *Proceedings*: volume 12 for 1918–19 contained 258 pages devoted to laryngology, including the papers presented at the Section's first Summer Congress which was held at the RSM in May 1919. The excessive length and hence heavy cost of printing the papers of the Sections (the Laryngological being the worst offender) forced the Council to restrict the total annual expenditure on the *Proceedings* to £4,000 in 1920.

## Summer Congress 1919

Before such economies were enforced, the *Proceedings* of this Section recorded the successful Laryngological Summer Congress of 1919 held during the presidency of Herbert Tilley. Tilley was simultaneously President of the Otological Section; he was also the first ear, nose and throat surgeon to University College Hospital and one of the pioneers of surgery of the nasal sinuses.

For the benefit of those attending the Congress, instruments, apparatus and specimens were arranged in a 'museum' and the scientific relics of Sir Morell Mackenzie could be seen in the Barnes Hall at 1 Wimpole Street. Manuscripts and documents formerly belonging to Mackenzie were presented to the Society by Mr E Mayer and the exhibition of memorabilia went some way towards restoring Mackenzie's reputation. Her Royal Highness Princess Marie Louise visited the exhibition and was received by leading members of the Section; she was greatly interested in the plastic facial war injuries from Queen's Hospital, Sidcup, and the Morell Mackenzie documents and instruments.[173]

Dr James Irwin Moore, the energetic Honorary Secretary of the Section at the time of the Summer Congress, was a leading figure in British endoscopy and in the 1920s there was hardly a meeting of the Laryngological Section at which he did not show cases or instruments – he invented a large-diameter oesophagoscope and cutting shears. He had formerly been Morell Mackenzie's assistant and was determined to redress the balance of opinion in his mentor's favour. As the tenant of Mackenzie's house at Wargrave, Moore arranged a summer outing there for members of the Section, incorporating a memorial service for Mackenzie. He also wanted to present the RSM with a portrait of Morell Mackenzie and when this was refused, Moore remonstrated by declining to attend any more meetings of the Laryngological Section. When the portrait (illustrated on page 147) was eventually accepted in 1951, Moore, then in his eighties, reappeared.[174]

The exhibition and demonstration of specimens and instruments continued to be a strong feature of Section meetings. In 1920 the 'aurorascope' was demonstrated and it was generally acknowledged that the instrument would be a boon to general practitioners, enabling them to examine the throats and ears of patients in their homes. The enthusiastic manufacturer then printed an 'objectionable circular' implying that Fellows endorsed the product, much to the annoyance of the RSM's Secretary.[175]

### Sir William Milligan

Sir William Milligan, one of the first to use radium in cancer of the larynx and author of *Diseases of the ear* (1911), was President of the Section for the session of 1921–22 when the Sections of Laryngology and Otology began to press for a Diploma. Milligan was a vigorous President (see below) and at the end of his time in office he presented a presidential badge for his successors to wear (Plate 44). Sir James Dundas-Grant thanked his old friend for 'a beautiful badge of office with a very charmingly selected motto in elegant and simple Latin, emphasizing the necessity for friendship among those who are working together'.[176] Not to be outdone, Dr W Jobson Horne presented the Section with a silver hammer as a memento of his year in office (1920–21). Horne also enlightened members about the history of their patron saint, St Blaise, a bishop who was martyred in 316 AD.[177]

### Examinations in otolaryngology

'Does laryngology occupy the position in the medical curriculum which its importance and its utility demand? I say without hesitation that it does not and until it is made a subject of compulsory study it never will.' Thus Sir William Milligan campaigned, with the backing of the Section for a qualifying examination 'in the diagnosis and treatment of the more common diseases of the throat, nose and ear and in the use of the more ordinary instruments'. A joint petition from the Sections of Laryngology and Otology was submitted to the Royal Colleges in 1921 with a tardy but satisfactory result.

In his Semon lecture given at the RSM in November 1923, Dr A Logan Turner (President of the Section 1924–25) elaborated on the teaching of the specialty, laryngology and otology having recently become a compulsory part of the medical curriculum as a result of the Section's petition. After the lecture Sir St Clair Thomson held a reception at the RSM for the Presidents of the Royal Colleges, the Vice Chancellor of London University and many members of the Sections of Laryngology and Otology. The evening was an acknowledged success and as the *BMJ* reported, 'the cultivation of the social side of the work of these two Sections also helps to explain their activity, and the existence of a most admirable camaraderie'.[178]

Not only had pressure from the two Sections secured from the GMC new regulations making the instruction of laryngology and otology compulsory for medical students; it had also persuaded the Conjoint Board to grant a Diploma in Laryngology and Otology, for which the first examinations were held in December 1923. The *Lancet* welcomed improved education in the specialty and anticipated that the Diploma would become 'a hall-mark for medical officers working under the Ministry of Health and the educational authority, whose duties are largely concerned with disease of the throat and ear'.[179]

## Tonsils and Adenoids Report

During Sir William Milligan's term as President the Section took up the issue of qualifications for otolaryngologists, discussed a medal or lectureship to honour Morell Mackenzie, appointed a committee to follow up interesting cases shown at meetings and conducted an investigation into operations on tonsils and adenoids. A leading article in the *Lancet* for 17 December 1921 questioned the necessity for the removal of tonsils and adenoids, and the following April the Laryngological Section entered the debate with recommendations on the best means of ensuring that these operations, undertaken on a great number of children of poor parents, were performed under favourable conditions (this was at a time when hospital accommodation for children was restricted).

The Tonsils and Adenoids Report produced by the Section in 1922 insisted that patients should be treated by specialists and by qualified anaesthetists, that children should stay in hospital for 48 hours after the operation and be issued with after-care instructions. That the committee found it necessary to specify elementary standards of hygiene and care – proper waiting room facilities, a clean recovery room and a visit from a nurse – indicates the hardships commonly suffered by children undergoing the operation in the early years of the 20th century. The Report also suggested that in cities where it was impossible to provide hospital accommodation children could be treated in open-air buildings nearby. Copies of the Section's recommendations were sent to practically all the hospitals in England, Scotland and Wales, where they were well received. The reaction of the Ministry of Health went unrecorded.[180]

## Sir St Clair Thomson

St Clair Thomson (Plate 43) had belonged to the Laryngological Society of London in the 1890s, becoming President of the Laryngological Section in 1911, President of the RSM in 1924 and President of the History of Medicine Section in 1933. He wrote the 'Laryngologists' Bible', *Diseases of the nose and throat*, and was especially renowned for his work on cancer of the larynx and improvements to the operation of laryngofissure. Among his many contributions to medical journals and societies, his obituary in the *BMJ* singles out a paper given to the Section of Laryngology in November 1927 on 'Laryngofissure for intrinsic carcinoma'. On this occasion St Clair Thomson exhibited four of his patients – all medical men – upon whom he had performed the operation. They provided living proof that if correct techniques were adopted the operation should be free from danger and give a lasting cure.[181]

Tuberculosis of the larynx also interested St Clair Thomson and one of his many cases of the 1920s was described to the Section. This patient had been healed by a combination of sanatorium treatment, 23 months of silence and the use of the galvano-cautery. As a result he was well, living in an open-air hut and had resumed his profession as a showman of sea-lions.[182]

St Clair Thomson outlined the 'Evolution of otolaryngology' in a paper to the History of Medicine Section in 1931. He acknowledged Morell Mackenzie as 'a bright Briton, a genius in his way' and cited two events that had 'marked the history of the last 73 years of this specialty. One was the discovery of cocaine – more used in rhino-laryngology than in any other department – and the other was the perfection of per-oral endoscopy'.[183]

St Clair Thomson's elevation to the Presidency of the RSM (1924–26) was the occasion for a special dinner for the Section, and in 1932 members subscribed to his portrait 'as a mark of his long and valuable services to this Section and to laryngology'.[184] For his part, St Clair Thomson gave the RSM its presidential badge and chain, and he went to considerable trouble to secure an authentic coat of arms for the Society (see Plates 32, 33 and 34 and page 203).

## A large Section

The large membership of the Section caused problems in relation to the examination of patients at clinical meetings. Many patients disliked repeated examinations by an unlimited number of enthusiastic laryngologists and declined to attend. Faced with a shortage of cases, St Clair Thomson suggested that when patients had suffered enough they should be dismissed; alternatively perhaps there was an apparatus that would permit several observers to examine the patient at once?

The large numbers being proposed for membership of the Section called for repeated revisions in the regulations to make the Section more exclusive, and by the 1950s the problem of reluctant patients was solved by holding clinical meetings in hospitals where cases were readily available for inspection.

## Committees: tonsils, war and education

Dr Dan McKenzie, editor of the *Journal of Laryngology and Otology*, President of the Laryngological Section for 1929–30 and author of romantic novels, was one of the first to use diathermy in malignant disease of the throat and in 1924 he showed the Section an example of his success with the diathermy knife. He was an ardent member of the Sections of Laryngology and Otology: the index of the *Proceedings* for one session alone lists 47 entries under his name (1912–13). While President he called for an investigation of the cause of hypertrophy of tonsils with a view to its prevention, and a committee was set to work on the examination of children from birth to five years.

During the Second World War the Sections of Laryngology and Otology co-operated in committees on all matters affecting otolaryngology, on the better organization of work in the Emergency Medical Service hospitals and on undergraduate and postgraduate education in the specialty (see page 278). In 1961 the President, JH Otty, was still campaigning for better training in otolaryngology: 'we have been looked upon as practising a minor specialty and I fear that in many places we are still not accepted as equals by our surgical brethren'. He wanted to see wider recognition by the universities, more encouragement of research and greater investment to raise the status of otolaryngology.[185]

## New techniques and developments

From the time it commenced meetings in 1907 the Section had encouraged the exhibition of new instruments and welcomed news of improved surgical techniques. With the pace of technological advance quickening after the Second World War, papers and discussions were held on subjects that were not dreamed of by the Section's founders: the meeting on 'Lasers in laryngology', for example, which concluded that they were a useful if expensive tool. Speakers participating in the discussion on 'The voice laboratory' outlined the exciting developments taking place in the objective analysis of voice and laryngeal disorders; one meeting dwelt on 'Modern investigational techniques', and a paper of 1986 explained the uses and advantages of 'Fibre-optic nasolaryngology and videostroboscopy'.

Some things did not change: the subject of tonsils was a recurrent one, likewise cancer of the head, neck and mouth, and Dame Cicely Saunders spoke to the Section on 'Terminal care in laryngology'. Unlike some Sections, Laryngology did not suffer from poorly attended meetings and low morale; when changes were recommended by the RSM's Working Party in 1978, this Section resolved not to alter the format of its meetings because they were successful as they stood.

## Laryngology and Rhinology

The Sections of Laryngology and Otology were close but separate. Presidents and members overlapped, joint meetings were organized and the Sections shared a summer meeting in the provinces, Scotland, Guernsey or the Isle of Man. In many hospitals laryngologists and otologists were almost indistinguishable and, as Mr RJ Cann observed while President, 'it is perhaps surprising that our Sections of Laryngology and Otology still retain their identity and tradition'.[186]

In spite of the Section's roots in the British Laryngological, Rhinological and Otological Society, formal recognition for rhinology was slow in coming. The American Rhinology Society was founded in 1955 and two years later a growing appreciation of the importance of non-infective disorders of the nose and sinuses was noted by the Laryngological Section's Council, which also observed the increased interest in rhinology in 1970. By 1986 the President, Mr John Schofield, had good reason to speak about 'The renaissance of rhinology', by which he meant the more scientific approach to surgery of the nose and sinuses that had developed over the last decade.

The Council of the RSM approved the change in the Section's name to give due recognition to the importance of rhinology in 1992 and the new title came into effect for the session of 1993–94. In the latter year a past President of the Section, Sir Donald Harrison who had occupied the chair of Laryngology and Otology at London University for 27 years, took office as President of the RSM.

The two Sections – Laryngology and Rhinology, and Otology – remain today among the most successful of the Society, with large attendances at each meeting. The numbers far exceed the capacity of the Barnes Hall, requiring the use of the second lecture hall. There are no competitive academic bodies to equal the two Sections, whose regular meetings occupy a whole day.

## Section of Otology (Plate 45)

The Otological Society of the United Kingdom was founded on the wave of enthusiasm that accompanied the sixth International Otological Congress, held in London in August 1899. The list of the initiating committee for a new society devoted to otology included Sir William Dalby (usually cited as its chief founder), Dr William Milligan, Mr Victor Horsley, Professor W Macewen and Mr Charles Ballance, and Mr Arthur Cheatle had a large share in organizing the Society. Its objects were the exhibition and demonstration of patients, models, drawings and specimens illustrating the anatomy, physiology, pathology and therapeutics of the ear, the reading of papers, the discussion of questions of otology and the investigation by committees of matters of public importance relating to otology and new methods of investigation or treatment of diseases of the ear.

The Otological Society held its meetings at the Medical Society of London and organized an annual dinner, at the second of which Sir James Crichton-Brown congratulated otology on having secured a divorce, 'or rather a judicial separation from laryngology but he playfully hinted that this fissiparous division must not go too far, or else we should have a cochlear, a labyrinthine, and a semi-circular society'. Sir James Dundas-Grant remembered that the rules of admission to the Society were strict and that the discussions tended to be severe, focusing on obscure questions. The Society's Presidents (Dalby, Pritchard, Barr and Cumberbatch) ruled for two years each, Mr Alphonso Cumberbatch yielding to amalgamation with the RSM in 1907.[187]

At a special general meeting of the Otological Society held in January 1907 practically all the members spoke against the proposed amalgamation. The Council of the Society registered its objections to the scheme and specified certain conditions of amalgamation: first, that there must be separate sections for otology and laryngology (either would take rhinology); secondly, that the new body should be called the Royal Academy of Medicine. The first item was conceded and the second over-ruled, and in this spirit of compromise the Otological Society agreed to join the RSM.[188]

At the first Section meeting in December 1907 Dr Peter McBride acknowledged the work of the two 19th-century predecessors of the Otological Section. He sketched some salient developments of otology in the past and his outlook was somewhat pessimistic: he could not 'foresee room for advances of anything like such a striking character in the future. It almost looks as if we shall be thrown back upon developing knowledge of details anatomical and physiological, but above all pathological and clinical'.

In 1913 Dr James Dundas-Grant, then President of the Section, voiced his opinion that on the whole the amalgamation 'has been for the better, though some of the older members of the joining societies felt that there was some loss of autonomy, however slight, and some detriment to the intimacy of the fraternity which had previously existed'.[189] The Section might have lost the club-like ethos of its predecessors, but under the auspices of the RSM it was soon established as a source of research and expert advice on hearing aids and tests, otosclerosis and deafness.

## Committees

The Section produced a report on the value of instrumental hearing aids in 1911, available for perusal in the Library but not for wider circulation. The research committee appointed in 1916 was more ambitious in its aims, setting out to tackle the standardization of hearing tests, to promote post-mortem investigations of deaf cases and to encourage the exchange of cases for research purposes. The scheme the committee produced for hearing tests in 1917 involved a whistle, a whisper, a tuning fork and a watch; a more sophisticated report was forthcoming in 1932 (see below).

The committee that commenced work in 1919 stressed the serious incapacity and danger to the community of neglected ear disease. It produced statistics to support this and pursued the subject with the Ministry of Health and the Royal College of Surgeons, pointing out that the proper treatment of ear disease required otologists with special training, and to achieve this a Diploma was necessary. The resolution to petition the two Royal Colleges to this effect originated with Arthur Cheatle and Dundas-Grant and was backed by the Section of Laryngology in 1920. The influence of Sir William Milligan, Sir Charles Ballance and the work of a large committee achieved success when the Diploma of the Royal College of Surgeons gave recognition to otolaryngology as a specialty in 1923.[190]

## Reports on otosclerosis, hearing tests, deafness

In 1927 the Section proposed a national investigation on otosclerosis and appointed a committee chaired by Sir William Milligan, past President of this and the Laryngological Section, to implement it.[191] The idea expanded after the International Congress of Otology and Laryngology that met in Copenhagen in 1928, when it was decided that the British contribution to the investigation should be the clinical aspect of otosclerosis.

The Section's responsibility consisted in the preparation of a questionnaire which was sent to British otologists in 1930; it contained 159 queries and the replies formed the basis for the Section's 'Report on the Clinical Aspect of Otosclerosis' (1931).[192]

There were differences of opinion about the diagnosis of the condition and little progress had been made in this respect since the mid-19th century, when Toynbee had pronounced that the chief symptom was gradually progressive deafness. The dangers of operating were of paramount concern and in the 1920s it was still considered by many to be an unjustifiable procedure. As the Section's committee began its investigation, Professor Maurice Sourdille of Nantes attended a meeting in May 1930 in order to describe his multi-stage operation. As Simson Hall recalled nearly 30 years later, 'Since the common attitude to otosclerosis was entirely defeatist, the work described by Professor Sourdille could not fail to arouse interest and curiosity'.[193] Sourdille returned to the Section in 1937 to tell members about his improved technique for the surgical treatment of severe and progressive otosclerosis – he could now claim 150 successes.[194] Later in the same year he went to New York to present his work to the Academy of Medicine.

The Section resumed work on hearing tests in 1929, appointing a committee of 12 that included Sir James Dundas-Grant, Somerville Hastings, William Mollison, FC Ormerod, Norman Patterson and AR Tweedie. Their long and complicated Report of 1932 acknowledged the assistance of Messrs Ragg of Sheffield (tuning fork manufacturers) and the National Physical Laboratory.[195]

While the committee on hearing tests was at work, the National Institute for the Deaf asked for the Section's assistance on the classification of deafness. Tweedie and Dr Kerr Love submitted a table to help assess deaf children in special schools in 1929.

## Mollison, Cairns and Hallpike

In the 1920s and 1930s individual members of the Section made important contributions to otology and to the work of the Section. William Mollison sat on nearly all the committees of the Section and on his election as President in 1929 he gave an address on the history of the mastoid operation, referring of course to James Hinton in the previous century. Mollison's own reputation rested largely on his skill in performing the operation, and disciples from overseas crowded to his clinics to witness the master at work. He was also to serve as President of the Laryngological Section in 1934–35, and again during the Second World War.

The charisma of Hugh Cairns infiltrated several Sections of the RSM during the interwar years: he gave papers to the Sections of Surgery, Laryngology and Otology as well as Neurology. His first paper to the Otological Section (1930) was on 'Brain abscess' from the point of view of the neurosurgeon (he thought the treatment of brain abscess in this country was 'simply disgusting').[196] More important was a joint paper of 1938 with Dr CS Hallpike on 'The pathology of Ménière's syndrome', which presented their findings on the temporal bones of two patients who had died. This was the first description in English of the idiopathic hydrops of the pars inferior characteristic of Ménière's disease; Cairns and Hallpike also drew attention to the fibrosis surrounding the endolymphatic sac. Since then their findings have been confirmed again and again.

Hallpike had been awarded the Norman Gamble Prize for research in 1934, and he became a major channel of information on current otological research and developments for the Section. He dominated the summer meeting in Oxford in 1960 and as President of the Section (1964–65) he revealed the work he was doing for the Medical Research Council on oto-neurology.

## Tuberculosis of the ear

During the Presidency of Mr AR Tweedie (1930–31) the Section held a discussion on tuberculosis of the ear, to which Professor FC Ormerod and Sir St Clair Thomson had much to contribute. The latter had examined the ears of all the patients admitted to the Edward VII Sanatorium in Midhurst over a period of 19 years, enabling him to draw some generalizations on tuberculosis of the middle ear.

Tweedie was himself chiefly interested in problems of the labyrinth and the welfare of the deaf, but he had searched the pages of the Society's *Proceedings* for information on tuberculosis of the ear and had found little, illustrating the rarity of the condition. Sir James Dundas-Grant, Sydney Scott and JF O'Malley, all of them past or future Presidents of the Section, shed light on the subject and were able to show cases.[197]

## An advisory body

Shortly before the outbreak of the Second World War members of the Section joined a committee of the British Standards Institute to advise on audiometers, and in the 1940s the

Councils of the Otological and Laryngological Sections advised the Ministry of Health on undergraduate and postgraduate education in otolaryngology. VE Negus (later knighted), who had been a member of the Otology Section since 1926 and was President of the British Association of Otolaryngologists while President of the Section of Laryngology, pressed for a five-year training after qualification for a full consultant in otolaryngology.[198] Partly as a result of the committee's work on medical education, a specialty Fellowship of the Royal College of Surgeons was established in 1947. The British Association of Otolaryngologists and the Institute of Laryngology and Otology had recently been founded and Professor Ormerod took the first chair in the subject in 1949.

By 1950, therefore, the specialty was formally recognized, although the training of medical students in otolaryngology left much to be desired. A discussion at the Section's summer meeting in 1964, led by Mr EH Miles Foxen, was severely critical of undergraduate and postgraduate teaching of otolaryngology. Mr Philip Reading questioned why colleagues had failed to interest undergraduates in this branch of surgery – Reading was himself an inspiring teacher who brought his department at Guy's Hospital into the modern era, ensuring that students were introduced to the new instruments and advances. He was President of the Section from 1968 to 1969 and gave his address on James Hinton.

*Recurrent subjects*

Tinnitus, facial palsy, vertigo and glue ear were subjects that regularly came before the Section. Terence Cawthorne, its President in 1958, President of the RSM four years later and President of the History of Medicine Section 1968–70, chose 'Vertigo' as the subject of his address. His experience of the condition was based on patients referred to him by colleagues at the National Hospital for Nervous Diseases, King's College Hospital and elsewhere, and he also paid tribute to papers by Dix and Hallpike, Jefferson and Spillane published in the *Proceedings* of the RSM.

Cawthorne's session as President dealt with 'The problems of the deaf child', and 'Facial paralysis' was the topic for the joint summer meeting with the Section of Laryngology. This was opened by a Danish specialist, Dr Karsten Kettel, with contributions from Miss Josephine Collier, a future President, and Dr Deryck Taverner: 'Although there is an

Sir Terence Cawthorne when President of the Society in 1962; he was President of the Section of Otology 1958–59 and later President of Section of the History of Medicine.

enormous literature about spontaneous facial palsy, we are still quite ignorant of its causation, and there is no treatment of proved value and there is little agreement about the prognosis'. Taverner's paper concentrated on the management of the condition and the results of his study of 341 patients suffering from Bell's palsy which remained 'an unsolved problem'. By 1973 Taverner was able to report that the frequency and severity of denervation could be reduced by oral steroids.[199] Taverner's work was influential; his reports and other investigations presented to the Section, such as the one carried out by Dr TJ Watson on a six-year study on 3,300 schoolchildren with glue ear (1969), were valuable contributions to the problems otologists continue to wrestle with.

In 1952 Air Vice Marshal Dickson described the effects of ultrasound on the ear, and noise deafness was a particular concern at this time, leading to the appointment of a committee to enquire into impaired hearing in workers exposed to excessive noise (the problem of noise-induced hearing loss persists, and was the subject of a meeting in 2000).

Reverting to 1953, the President, Mr RR Simpson, spoke on 'The heritage of British otology' – Simpson was an examiner, a JP and the author of *Shakespeare and medicine* (1959). He traced the heritage to Sir William Macewen, through Dr Albert Gary and JS Fraser, mentioning Donald Watson's paper of 1948, which questioned the necessity for certain current operations; he commended Dan McKenzie's work on cholesteatoma (1931), and T Ritchie Rodger's paper on noise deafness (1915). The latter's presidential address reported on 500 cases of syphilis of the ear, nose and throat and here there had been a substantial improvement – whereas between 1925 and 1934 he had seen an average of 50 cases a year, by 1938 the annual average had fallen to less than half that number. Yet, Simpson pointed out in 1953, despite penicillin and the sulphonamides, chronic otitis media was still seen every day by the otologist of the 1950s.[200]

### Recent meetings

Following the formation of the British Society of Audiology in 1967 some joint meetings were arranged with the Section, and medical audiologists were nominated for membership. The first meeting with the Dutch Otolaryngology Society was held in Amsterdam in 1980, Section members attend the British Academic Conference on Otology regularly and the combined summer meeting with the Section of Laryngology has become traditional. Joint meetings, ordinary meetings with papers and a short papers meeting are augmented by eponymous lectures (named for Semon, Toynbee, Yearsley and Edith Whetnall) and the Section has in its gift several prizes named after benefactors. Apart from a period when attendance at the eponymous lectures was disappointing, the Section of Otology continued to prosper when others did not; its Council reported an excellent attendance record in 1979 and saw no reason for change.

The prosperity of the Section continues. Its meetings are conveniently arranged on the same day as those of the Section of Laryngology, making the first Friday in the month sacrosanct for ENT consultants, who cancel their appointments in order to attend a day of Continuing Medical Education at the RSM. The very success of the meetings, when the Barnes and the West Halls at 1 Wimpole Street are full to capacity, creates problems: joint meetings with other Sections and the introduction of trainees, both of which are desirable, have become impractical.

## Section of Radiology (Plate 46)
originally Electro-therapeutics

The news of Röntgen's discovery of X-rays broke in London in January 1896 and two months later Silvanus Thompson, Professor of Applied Physics at the City and Guilds College in Finsbury, demonstrated the process to members and guests of the Clinical

Society at the Royal Medical and Chirurgical Society's house in Hanover Square. The discovery of radioactivity by Henri Becquerel in the same year, followed by the isolation of radium by Pierre and Marie Curie in1898, generated great interest among the medical profession.

The Röntgen Society held its first meeting at the Medical Society of London in June 1897, attracting medical men, scientists, physicists, engineers, amateurs and aristocrats. This disparate membership was doubtless a factor in the decision of 15 doctors to found another society to cater for their special interests, i.e. the medical applications of radiographs and the use of X-rays as a diagnostic tool. At a preliminary meeting the object of the new society was declared to be 'the study of Electricity in its relation to Medical Science' and arrangements were made for the inaugural meeting of the British Electro-Therapeutic Society on 10 January 1902 when the names of 58 founders were listed. The first President was Dr WS Hedley, who was supported by Lewis Jones, Hall-Edwards, Reginald Morton and Cecil Lyster, with Chisholm Williams as the London Secretary.[201]

The new Society was an immediate success and within a few years its membership reached 106. As the historian of British radiology points out, it was the first national association in Britain for clinical radiologists 'and its meetings (and those of its successor, the

Professor WC Röntgen (above) published an account of his discovery of X-rays in 1895. Right, an early advertisement for X-ray apparatus.

Electro-therapeutical Section of the Royal Society of Medicine) became the testing arena of British radiologists. Young men, and old, soon felt obliged to bring any new observation, radiographic technique or theory before the Society where it could be subjected to the informed scrutiny of the leaders of the profession'.[202]

The British Electro-Therapeutic Society published a journal, held exhibitions and an annual conversazione, and was evidently flourishing when it joined the RSM. Dr Lewis Jones and Dr Reginald Morton put the resolution to join the proposed union and in October 1905 wrote that their Society was in favour provided there was a special Section or sub-Section of Electro-Therapeutics or Physio-Therapeutics to provide 'a meeting place for members interested in a well-defined sphere of medical work'.[203] Within 10 years of the discovery of the X-ray, electro-therapeutists had established their specialty, first as a Society and in 1907 as a Section of the RSM. The BMA, having rebuffed electro-therapeutists in 1903, was to authorize a Section of Electrotherapy and Radiology at its 1907 meeting, a few months after the Section of the RSM had been inaugurated.

The first President of the Section, W Deane Butcher, gave the address at its first meeting, choosing as his subject 'The future of electricity in medicine... a survey of the entire field of clinical electro-therapeutics including the first 10 years of the Röntgen rays and speculation about their future uses'. Deane Butcher was a brilliant pioneer of the introduction of radium and of measures to protect X-ray workers.[204] His paper was followed by others from leaders in the exciting new field – Dr G Harrison Orton, who was radiologist to St Mary's Hospital for 27 years and one of the martyrs of radiology; Dr W Ironside Bruce, who wrote *A system of radiology* (1907) and Dr Reginald Morton, electro-therapeutist to the London Hospital and one of those who introduced deep X-ray therapy into Britain after the First World War.

In addition to the presentation of papers at meetings, the Section maintained a tradition of the defunct Society by holding an annual conversazione. The first was at the Queen's Hall in December 1907 where the most up-to-date electro-medical and X-ray apparatus was exhibited.[205]

### *Papers in the* Proceedings

The publication of the Section's papers covering the whole field of diagnostic and therapeutic radiology in the *Proceedings of the Royal Society of Medicine* gave the *Proceedings* a reputation as the leading radiological journal in Britain at the beginning of the 20th century. By the time the first volume of the *Proceedings* was published in 1908, radiological practice and technique had advanced to the point at which medicine was beginning to benefit and X-rays were altering ideas about the human body. Members of the Section were especially interested in the application of electro-therapeutics to diseases of the heart, lungs and alimentary tract, and Dr Samuel Sloan's address of 1909 focused for the first time on the use of electro-therapy in gynaecology.[206]

For its first 20 years the Section of Electro-therapeutics was the meeting place for London radiologists: 'No important event or scientific advance escaped discussion at the monthly meetings', and the discussions were reported in the *Proceedings*. After the First World War the *Proceedings* 'never regained its pre-war position as the leading radiological journal', losing ground to *Archives of Radiology and Electrotherapy* and hampered by economies imposed by the RSM.[207]

Several notable papers on chest diseases were given to the Section, including one by Dr Stanley Green who pleaded for the use of X-rays in detecting early tuberculosis, a subject taken up by Sir Richard Douglas Powell in a discussion of 1913. Speaking as a conservative physician, Douglas Powell questioned X-ray findings: 'I have always regarded them as shadows which have to be rightly interpreted'.[208]

The value of X-rays in diagnosing diseases of the digestive system was the subject of a paper by Dr AE Barclay in 1909. Barclay, 'perhaps the greatest of the pioneer British radiologists',[209] was to be President of the Section (1919–20), of the Röntgen Society (1924–25) and adviser on radiology to the Ministry of Health during the Second World War. His paper was the first of many on the use of X-rays in the examination of the intestines, oesophagus and gastric ulcers, a line of enquiry that led to an important report on the relative advantages of the bismuth and barium meal.

### Bismuth breakfast or barium meal?

Dr George A Pirie of Dundee spoke to the Section on the value of bismuth in 1909: the bismuth breakfast had recently been introduced to Britain and Pirie had used it in 30 cases. As Dr Archibald Reid reported in his survey of the previous year's work in electrotherapeutics great progress had been made in the examination of the alimentary canal by means of bismuth, and the technique and standardization of bismuth meals was the topic for the discussion opened by Dr Morton in November 1913. He referred to a resolution passed at a meeting of the BMA's Section of Electrotherapy in July, and a subsequent communication from the BMA requesting that the appropriate Section of the RSM might recommend a standard meal as the preliminary of radiographic examination of the abdomen. Morton had conducted his own enquiries which led him to conclude that 'the talk about the disagreement of doctors is an ancient gibe, but the truth of it was never more in evidence than when I came to tabulate the details of these bismuth meals' and this was borne out by a variety of recipes proffered by the audience.

The Council of the Section then appointed a committee to investigate the matter scientifically. The resulting 'Report of the Committee on the Standardization of the Opaque Meal' recommended half a pint of either bread and milk or porridge taken on an empty stomach into which two ounces of either barium sulphate or bismuth oxychloride should be mixed. The majority agreed with Dr Hertz that barium sulphate was preferable for hospital use; for one thing it was cheaper (Guy's Hospital had saved £50 per annum thereby).[210] The recommendations made in this report brought the wider use of the barium meal, which superseded the bismuth breakfast in the diagnosis of bowel disease.

### Apparatus

The exhibition of new apparatus was essential at a time when this was developing and improving and it was encouraged at meetings. George Batten expounded on the virtues of his photographic plate rocker in 1909, and in 1915 Sir James MacKenzie Davidson showed a new commutator attachment for rectifying the current-supply to the X-ray tube. Sir James invented several devices of a similar nature and had recently been knighted for his services to medicine. Six months before he died in 1919 he gave a paper to the Section on 'Stereoscopic radiography' in which he described a table he had designed for localization work.[211] The MacKenzie Davidson family were generous benefactors of the specialty, and the RSM became involved with the MacKenzie Davidson lecture, first given in 1920 by Sir Ernest Rutherford.

William Coolidge had achieved a breakthrough with the invention of the hot-cathode tube in America in 1913, but its manufacture in Britain was delayed by the outbreak of war, which caused existing stocks of gas X-ray tubes to be commandeered for military use. Faced with a shortage and with the usual lines of supply blocked, the situation became critical. The Section's Council made an earnest plea that immediate steps must be taken 'to encourage the production of X-ray tubes in this country as a measure conducive to the efficacy of this branch of medical science, the advancement of science generally and the benefit of the public at large'.[212] Whether this resolution had any influence is hard to judge but it is true to say that British glassmakers were persuaded to produce soda-glass and by the end of the war gas X-ray tubes were being manufactured in this country.

## Radiation injuries

The BMJ carried the first report of X-ray damage to the skin in April 1896 and by the turn of the century the first deaths due to injuries associated with the use of X-rays had occurred.[213]

X-ray workers began to shield themselves, but a British code of practice was not formalized until 1915. Meanwhile X-ray and radium martyrs continued to suffer; when the Martyrs Memorial was erected in Hamburg (1936) it was inscribed with the names of some early members of the Electro-therapeutics Section: Dr JF Hall-Edwards, Dr C Lyster, Dr W Ironside Bruce, Stanley Melville and GA Pirie.

Dr Hall-Edwards drew the attention of the Section to the hazards in a paper 'On X-ray dermatitis and its prevention' in 1908, one of the first authoritative descriptions of the problem by a radiologist. Hall-Edwards' own right hand had recently been amputated and in all he lost a hand, forearm and several fingers of the left hand through radiation injury. He recalled noticing changes in his right hand at least four years prior to the radiograph (below) and had 'long suspected some mischief in the bones and had many times described the pain as being similar to that which would be experienced were rats gnawing at the bones'. He hoped that his experience, personal and public, would influence those outside the Society and the President was keen to take the matter further by formulating rules for the protection of both patient and operator.[214] The Röntgen Society assumed this task and issued *Recommendations for the protection of X-ray workers* in 1915.

Dr Lyster, the first Director of the Electrical Department at the Middlesex Hospital and President of the Section 1918–19, died in 1920 from cumulative radiation injury and the

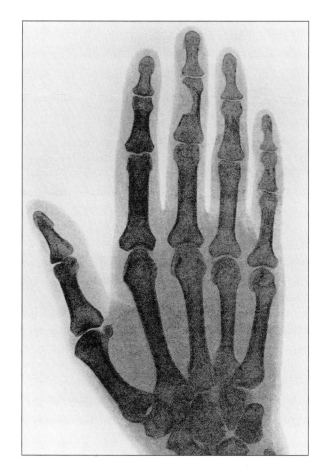

Radiograph of Dr John Hall-Edwards' right hand taken a few days before amputation, showing degeneration of bone in the ring and little fingers, absorption of terminal phalanges and a clean-cut hole in the second phalanges of the middle finger. He presented his case and others to a meeting of the Section of Electro-therapeutics in November 1908.

death the following year of Dr Ironside Bruce (President 1914–16) aged just 44, emphasized the urgent need for the thorough investigation of radiation injury and protection from it. The British X-ray and Radium Protection Committee was appointed in 1921 under the chairmanship of Sir Humphry Rolleston, a past President of the RSM and soon to be President of the Royal College of Physicians. The committee included two members of the Section of Electro-therapeutics and having held its first meeting at the RSM, it continued to use that address. It produced safety guidelines on the manufacture of radium and on X-ray equipment for the first International Congress of Radiology held in London in 1925. Further reports were printed, and when the committee was finally disbanded in 1952 its work was continued by the Medical Research Council and the Ministry of Health. The first thorough epidemiological study of British radiologists was published by PG Smith and Richard Doll (a founder-member of the Section of Oncology) in 1981.

## War injuries

Sir Archibald Reid, President of the Section 1911–12, was instrumental in organizing radiology installations for those wounded in the First World War including the forwarding of 14 mobile X-ray units to the army in France. At the RSM the Presidents of the Section (Ironside Bruce and Harrison Orton) retained the presidency for two years each during the war. One meeting was devoted to the treatment of war injuries, another to a discussion on the localization of foreign bodies such as bullets by means of X-rays, and Sir James Mackenzie Davidson opened a third on the electrical treatment of wounds, sinuses and frost-bite in relation to the present war. [215]

The Section was eager to assist the War Office and Admiralty with advice on suitable apparatus, X-ray installations and lists of competent operators during the emergency. The resolution stated confidently that 'This Section represents almost all the qualified men who are engaged in X-ray work in the country'. Its enthusiasm to assist government departments was tempered by the Council of the RSM, which established itself as a filter between sectional initiative and the authorities. The Section's energy was then channelled into the investigation of the 'Simpson light', a lamp that was not as revolutionary as its inventor suggested.[216]

## Reputability

Members of the Section were unhappy about the London County Council Act of 1920, which required annual inspections of the premises of those working in the field of electro-therapeutics. An appeal to the RSM Council and the negotiating powers of Lord Dawson secured a concession from the LCC, whose inspectors were willing to exempt from inspection those on the lists of the Institute of Radiology and the RSM on account of their guaranteed reputability.[217]

## Sir Henry Gauvain

Sir Henry Gauvain was proud of his achievement at Lord Mayor Treloar's Cripples' Hospital at Alton in Hampshire. He was its first Medical Superintendent (1908–45), throwing himself wholeheartedly into the treatment of tuberculosis in children by fresh air and sunlight. He condemned operative treatment for non-pulmonary tuberculosis and showed better results could be obtained by conservative methods, namely sea-bathing and light. His experience at Lord Mayor Treloar's Hospital made him an expert in hospital administration and planning and he was both inventive and innovative, as his paper of 1925 'On the organization and work of a light department in a surgical tuberculosis hospital' showed. Gauvain had studied the Danish methods of treatment by artificial light, and after the war he realized 'a cherished ambition to have a properly equipped light department at Alton'. Gauvain confessed that his conviction of the value of sun treatment for surgical tuberculosis was based on practical experience rather than scientific principles. It was experience that had led him to establish a department where sunlight could be supplemented or replaced by artificial light. Moreover he was working on a portable sun lamp for patients too ill to move.[218]

Gauvain became President of this Section in 1927 and President of the Section for the Study of Disease in Children four years later, when he arranged for members to visit Alton. His achievement at Alton also interested the Section of Orthopaedics which met there in 1947.

## British Institute of Radiology

The Section's first President, Deane Butcher, was one of the first to promote the idea of a radiological institute in London, an idea that was taken up by the Röntgen Society and by the British Association for the Advancement of Radiology and Physiotherapy (BARP). In the spring of 1922 a joint committee of representatives from the Section of Electro-therapeutics, BARP and the Röntgen Society met with the aim of founding an Institute of Radiology in central London (see page 200).

Sir Archibald Reid, co-founder of BARP, chaired the joint committee to promote the Institute. He was responsible for locating a house near his own in Welbeck Street where the British Institute of Radiology (BIR) opened its doors in 1924. The Röntgen Society and the BIR were incorporated three years later, so that the Institute at 32 Welbeck Street became the centre of British radiology. In these circumstances support for meetings of the Section of Electro-therapeutics at the RSM began to decline, leading the President to reflect that 'the subject of radiology has grown so much that in our Section it threatens to act like a benevolent cuckoo and push electrology out of its nest'.[219]

Some gratification could be gleaned from the fact that radiology was now established as an accepted specialty in the United Kingdom. The Sections of the RSM and the BMA had played an important part in the process, with support from BARP, followed by the Society of Radiographers, the British Institute of Radiology, and the British Association of Radiologists which united with the Society of Radiotherapists of Great Britain and Ireland to form the Faculty of Radiologists in 1939. The Cambridge Diploma in Radiology and Electrology was first awarded in 1920, and by the 1930s full-time medical radiotherapists were being appointed to the London hospitals.

## The Section of Radiology

There was a move tabled by Drs Batten and Cumberbatch to expand the Section of Electro-therapeutics by including physiotherapists in 1925, a proposal that received short shrift from the Secretary of the RSM: 'I do not know who these people are, but if I did and they are not already connected with the Society, it would be impossible for me to carry out your suggestion'.[220] Nevertheless a growing interest in physiotherapy and physical medicine prompted a discussion between this Section and that of Balneology and Climatology (1928–29). Then in November 1930 Professor JM Woodburn Morison alerted the Section to 'certain activities' taking place outside the RSM for the formation of a Society of Physical Medicine. This sparked a proposal to found a new Section for that specialty within the RSM, whereupon various suggestions arose: for embracing physical medicine within the Section of Electro-therapeutics or for fusion with the Section of Balneology and Climatology, while 70 radiologist members of the Electro-therapeutical Section wanted the separation of radiology from Electro-therapeutics. The matter was deputed to a committee to confer with the Section of Balneology and Climatology about amalgamation and to discuss with those interested in physiotherapy the possibility of a new Section of Physical Medicine.[221]

Negotiations produced a solution whereby members of the Section of Balneology and Climatology agreed to join members of the Section of Electro-therapeutics in a new Section of Physical Medicine (see page 319) and radiologists would constitute a separate Section. Two Sections were thus dissolved and two new Sections, Radiology and Physical Medicine, emerged in 1931. The event was cause for a joint dinner at Claridges in April 1932 when the Society's President, Dr T Watts Eden, spoke of the challenges facing both Sections. He directed the Radiology Section towards radio-therapeutics: 'I submit that the position of radium and X-ray as therapeutic agents has yet to be determined' and this was a matter 'of great pith and moment which must engross our Section of Radiology'. [222]

Dr Neville Finzi, who had been a member of the Electro-therapeutical Section since 1908, took a leading part in the movement to form a separate Section of Radiology. His book on *Radium-therapeutics* had been published in 1913 and he established a world-wide reputation for the X-ray department at St Bartholomew's Hospital. His obituary tells of his love of the Alps, dinner-parties and music, describing him as 'the pioneer of radiation therapy in this country, a man of culture and many interests'.[223] He perceived that few radiologists would join the old Section while its name indicated that it was confined to electro-therapeutics; he wanted the new Section to include radiodiagnostics and radiotherapeutics, and he was supported by 159 founder members of the Section of Radiology.[224] Finzi was to be President of the Section 1943–44, and also its benefactor (see page 288).

## Dr Russell J Reynolds

The last President of the Section of Electro-therapeutics, Woodburn Morison, who occupied the first chair of radiology in this country, presided over the first year of the Section of Radiology. He was succeeded by Dr Russell J Reynolds in 1932, the first to explore the possibility of obtaining human cine films in which X-ray shadows on a fluorescent screen could be photographed. By 1934 he had established a cineradiological unit and his fame was spreading, so he was invited to demonstrate his X-ray cinematography to the RSM in May 1934. He was confident that his new method of X-ray diagnosis would open a large and varied field of research.[225]

Dr Russell Reynolds gave a lecture to the Society in May 1934 describing 'a practical method of X-ray cinematography by which permanent records may be rapidly and inexpensively obtained'. He gave a demonstration of the apparatus.

Dr RS Paterson was President at the time, and his organizing ability served radiology well. He was a prime mover in forming the British Association of Radiographers in 1934, the forerunner of the Faculty of Radiologists (1939) which developed into the Royal College of Radiologists in 1975.

## Committee work

The Section was concerned to contribute 'something materially useful towards solving the many problems which arise from the recent increased facilities for giving X-ray and radium treatment' and set about collecting evidence for the National Radium Trust and Commission in 1932. The Section's 'Report on the Scientific Aspects of Radium and X-ray Therapy' was published in 1934, soon followed by another on 'The Place of Radiology in the Medical Curriculum', which was forwarded to the GMC in 1936.[226]

The Second World War prompted papers by AE Barclay and Major DB McGrigor on 'Radiology in wartime' (1939). As advisor in radiology to the Ministry of Health during the war Barclay organized the entire civilian X-ray service, while McGrigor was consultant in radiology to the War Office. There was little Section activity between 1939 and 1943, but then members began to look to the future, discussing the organization of a fluorographic service for the civilian community. Dr Finzi was elected President in 1943 when his address on 'Impending new developments in radiology' tackled the combined X-ray and stilboestrol treatment of carcinoma of the prostate. Dr George Binnie explained that he was experimenting by treating tumours by the combined method and with stilboestrol alone, but it was early days.[227] Another meeting, on the treatment of cases of cancer of the breast with stilboestrol, prompted the appointment of an Oestrogen committee with co-operation from the Sections of Experimental Medicine and Therapeutics, Urology, Pathology, Surgery and Obstetrics and Gynaecology. By 1945 the committee was organizing research into the use of oestrogens in cancer at 80 clinics with the support of the British Empire Cancer Campaign.[228]

When the conclusion of hostilities allowed it, the Section became involved with the terminology of radiology, radiologist and radiographer for the British Standards Institution (1948).

The Section of Radiology's annual dinner at Claridges in May 1937.

## Professor J Ralston Paterson

The inter-war years had seen major changes in radiotherapy practice, and many of these developments emanated from the Holt Radium Institute in Manchester, where Ralston Paterson had been the Director since 1931. He established Manchester as a leading radiotherapy centre, with a colleague he formulated the Parker-Paterson Radium Dosage System and he stimulated many fundamental developments in clinical radiotherapy. Having served as President of the British Association of Radiotherapists and been influential in founding the Faculty of Radiologists, he was elected President of the Section in 1951. He seized the opportunity to promote research; 'research workers remain by tradition the financial Cinderellas of medicine. Yet research talent is rare and ought to be encouraged as something precious and should command special rewards'.[229]

## Advances

A successor as President, Dr Constance Wood, reviewed the past and future prospects of radiology in 1953. She spoke about the development of the two-million-volt generators designed to give a better dose distribution to the patient than had ever been possible before. Dr Wood's trials for the Medical Research Council showed there was no significant difference in biological effect between radium gamma-rays and high-voltage X-rays, and she realized that 'the improved technique will not materially increase the cure-rate for cancer'.[230]

In the same session GW Blomfield's paper encapsulated three years' experience with two-million-volt therapy, which he had found particularly successful in carcinoma of the cervix at the Sheffield Centre for Radiotherapy. At the time of his death in 1964 he was President-elect of the Section.

## Finzi bequest

The Section was favoured by a legacy of £26,000 from the late Misses Winifred and Isobel Finzi, the sisters of Dr Finzi who died in 1968. The administration of the legacy took some while to settle, as a result of friction between the Councils of the Society and the Section. While the Section planned to use the fund to pay for a visiting lecturer from overseas, the Society thought that part of it could be used to provide new audiovisual equipment for general use at 1 Wimpole Street.

The Section's Council resented the implication that it was expected to 'whitewash' decisions taken by the Society's Council and Honorary Treasurer. These wrangles caused the arrangements for the distribution of the bequest, which amounted to £79,000 by 1984, to go into a fourth draft before it was agreed that the fund would replace and upgrade audiovisual facilities in the two halls at 1 Wimpole Street and endow an annual lecture.[231] Since 1997 Finzi prizes have been awarded annually to junior radiologists and radiotherapists who give presentations at a Section meeting, competing for first, second and third prizes. A separate legacy of £100 from Dr Finzi paid for the Section's presidential badge (Plate 46).

## The leaders

The leaders in electro-therapeutics and radiology gave their support to the several societies, associations, sections and the Institute: Mackenzie Davidson was the benefactor of the BIR, the Section at the RSM and a founder of BARP; Sir Humphry Rolleston was at different times President of the Röntgen Society, BARP and BIR; Ralston Paterson was active in the British Association of Radiotherapists, President of the Section and a founder of the Faculty of Radiologists. Shared interests led to combined meetings, beginning with one between the Section, the Röntgen Society and the Institution of Electrical Engineers in 1920. Joint meetings of the Section, the Faculty (and later the Royal College of

Radiologists) and BIR soon became a regular feature of the calendar. Meetings between the Sections of Radiology, Dermatology, and Obstetrics and Gynaecology, and from 1970 with the Section of Oncology, were also arranged.

The Section's Council deliberately set out to enrol all radiological Fellows and members of other radiological bodies in 1950 and it took care to liaise with the Institute and Faculty or College in organizing meetings. Excellent relations with other institutions placed the Section of Radiology in an enviable position at the RSM; in 1975 it was noted with satisfaction that attendances were good and this was attributed largely to the interest of combined meetings. Forced to define its role in 1978 the Section responded that its aim was 'to encourage professional practice of the highest standard. The scientific meetings should provide a forum for the introduction of new work and developing techniques. The presentation of original work at these meetings should continue to be encouraged'.

### Röntgen centenary

The Section was one of several societies, associations and colleges brought together for the Röntgen Centenary Congress held in Birmingham in June 1995 to celebrate Röntgen's discovery and the contribution radiology had made to medicine in the 20th century. Opened by HRH Princess Margaret, the Congress lasted a week and attracted international support. Among those giving papers was Professor RJ Berry, a past President of the Section, who reviewed the risks and benefits of radiation. The Finzi lecture and the Röntgen Centenary lecture formed part of the programme and the latter, given by Professor I Isherwood, looked to the future: 'Developments will come from improvements in visual systems, instrumentation, robotics, microengineering and, above all, from the remarkable advances already being made in computing'.[232]

Technological advances certainly came to notice at the RSM: the Section's programme for the year 2000 opened with meetings on 'Imaging in head and neck surgery', 'Clinical reporting by radiographers' and an all-day meeting on PET scanning was sustained by 14 speakers from London hospitals, Cambridge, the USA and Germany.


## Section of Experimental Medicine and Therapeutics
### originally Therapeutics and Pharmacology

This Section derived from the Therapeutical Society, which was just five years old when members voted to amalgamate with older societies in the RSM. The Society had been inaugurated at Apothecaries' Hall, Blackfriars, where it usually met, and its first President, Sir William Thiselton-Dyer, was Director of the Royal Botanic Gardens at Kew (1885–1905). The Honorary Treasurer of the Society, Dr George Crichton, objected to union with the RSM on the grounds that one-fifth of the members of the Therapeutical Society resided abroad and one-third lived in the provinces, so fewer than half stood to gain from the advantages offered by the London-based Society. Furthermore many members of the Therapeutical Society were botanists and analytical chemists without medical qualifications, and he thought individuality would be lost in the amalgamation: 'The committee seem to have some old wine skins in Hanover Square, and in trying to put all of the societies therein, perhaps some of the wine will be spilt'.[233]

Members of the Therapeutical Society faced an increased subscription on joining the RSM, yet despite the disadvantages of joining only 14 voted against the motion and the decision to amalgamate was taken in April 1907. The new Section of Therapeutics and Pharmacology was then formed under Dr TE Burton Brown, 'to promote the extension of therapeutical and pharmacological knowledge in the subjects which are of the greatest importance in the treatment of disease'. The Section preferred to hold its meetings at Apothecaries' Hall rather than at Hanover Square, sometimes combining them with a

THE ROYAL SOCIETY OF MEDICINE
20, HANOVER SQUARE, W.

## Therapeutical and Pharmacological Section.

**The Ordinary General Meetings of the Section will be held at the Apothecaries Hall, Blackfriars, E.C., at 4.30 p.m.**

| | | |
|---|---|---|
| 1907. October | 22nd. | Dr. T. E. BURTON BROWN, C.I.E.:<br>Inaugural Address.<br>Dr. ROBERT HUTCHISON, F.R.C.P.:<br>Will open a discussion on Functional<br>Dyspepsia. |
| November | 26th. | JAMES CANTLIE, Esq., M.B., F.R.C.S.:<br>Tropical Diseases and their Therapeutics.<br>Dr. WILLIAM MURRAY, F.R.C.P.:<br>Therapeutics of Indigestion. |
| December | 17th. | Dr. JAMES MACKENZIE:<br><br>Dr. WILLIAM SOPER:<br>Reminiscences of an Apprentice fifty<br>years ago. |
| 1908. January | 28th. | Prof. W. E. DIXON:<br>Arterio-sclerosis and its Causation.<br>Prof. CUSHNY:<br>Nutmeg Poisoning. |
| February | 25th. | CONVERSAZIONE. |
| March | 24th. | Dr. JOHN MILNE BRAMWELL:<br>Hypnotism. |
| April | 28th. | |

H. CHARLES CAMERON, M.B., C.M., ⎫
J. GRAY DUNCANSON, M.B., C.M., ⎬ Hon.
Wingfield House, Shooter's Hill, ⎱ Secs.
London, S.E.
(*to whom all communications should be addressed*).

**This Card to be kept for reference.**

The programme of meetings of the Therapeutical and Pharmacological Section at Apothecaries' Hall, 1907–08.

conversazione or exhibition. Papers were usually brief and dealt with a wide range of subjects – the speakers and visitors were drawn from many different fields. Among the first to present papers were Dr Robert Hutchison on 'The treatment of dyspepsia', F Gowland Hopkins on 'Diseases due to deficiencies in the diet', James Cantlie on 'Tropical diseases' and Dr James MacKenzie on 'The action of digitalis on the human heart'.

Dr William Withering's *Account of the foxglove* (1785) was the classic work on the medical uses of digitalis (Plate 47), and among Withering's letters (bequeathed to the RSM on Osler's death in 1919) are expressions of appreciation from readers who benefited from 'foxglove tea'. Since the publication of Withering's manual, however, digitalis had been displaced by other treatments and MacKenzie's paper reversed this trend, reviving 'the rational and practical use of digitalis and raised it from the cloud of disrepute under which it had fallen'. Mackenzie gave papers to several Sections and his painstaking work, often with Professor Cushny, continued for many years resulting in publications on *Diseases of the heart* (1908) and *Principles of diagnosis and treatment of heart affections* (1916).[234]

This Section also staged early discussions on aspects of endocrinology, a specialty that did not achieve the status of a Section until 1946. Professor GR Murray, who had first used sheep's thyroids to treat myxoedema in 1891, and Professor EH Starling, who discovered secretin in 1902, made 'masterly contributions' to the meeting on 'The therapeutic value of hormones' in 1914.[235]

Professor William Osler, Sir Thomas Lauder Brunton, Sir Thomas Clifford Allbutt, Professor Alexander Fleming and Sir Donald MacAlister all joined the Section in its early years. The contributions of such eminent men provided stimulation, although attendances rarely rose above a dozen. As well as the presentation of papers, the Section usually organized one provincial meeting a session; the summer outing of 1907 was to Oxford, where members enjoyed a tour guided by Thiselton-Dyer and a garden party at Professor Osler's house.[236] On other occasions the Section visited the Pharmacological Laboratory in

Cambridge or the National Institute for Medical Research in Hampstead. Two exceptionally popular meetings with an audience of between 40 and 50 were on 'The teaching of therapeutics in the hospital wards' by Clifford Allbutt in 1909 and on 'The value of alcohol as a therapeutic agent', opened by Sir Henry Dale in 1920.

## Professor WE Dixon

In 1912 Professor Dixon gave his presidential address on 'The action of drugs on nerve endings', a paper that was soon followed by one from the Vice President of the Section, Dr AR Cushny, on 'The action of drugs in respiration', and a discussion on 'The use of salvarsan and neo-salvarsan in diseases other than syphilis'. As Dixon stressed in another debate on 'The propriety of patent and secret remedies' (1910), this was 'the very dawn of pharmacology'. He deplored the fact that 'quack-medicine traffic has been growing by leaps and bounds in this country during the last fifty years', and he lamented the failure of medical schools and universities in this country to promote proper departments of pharmacology.[237]

Over the next 30 years Dixon and Cushny were to be instrumental in changing the perception of pharmacology and therapeutics, and for founding chairs and lectureships in the universities. Dixon worked in pharmacology at Cambridge University where he revolutionized the teaching of the subject, making it 'a living, attractive science based on pharmacological experiments but freeing it from half obsolete materia medica and empirical therapeutics'.[238] In 1929 he told an audience in Cape Town that pharmacology was the most neglected branch of medicine in Great Britain, and that Britain was behind other countries in the production of new remedies. His own research, teaching and the ardent support he gave to his Section at the RSM did much to alter the situation. Sir Henry Dale, who gave the WE Dixon Memorial lecture in 1934 – the first lectureship in pharmacology in England – described Dixon as a vigorous, inspiring personality who 'more than any other, was responsible for the awakening of interest, here in England, in pharmacology as a progressive science'.[239]

Professor WE Dixon, Professor of Pharmacology, King's College, London and President of the Section of Therapeutics and Pharmacology 1912–13. After his death in 1931 a memorial lecture was established, first given by Sir Henry Dale in 1934.

By 1941 the scope of pharmacology had widened, as Professor JA Gunn noted, 'The subject has become one of the greatest attraction and importance numbering among its great chemotherapeutic discoveries the arsphenamine group of compounds, new anaesthetics and a large number of valuable additions to the pharmacological armamentarium'. Another development, begun in Dixon's lifetime and acquiring increasing momentum, had been 'the establishment of commercial pharmacological laboratories'. Gunn was uncertain about the effect these would have on academic studies but he was in no doubt about the importance of research devoted to the discovery of new remedies and the investigation of new synthetic compounds.[240]

### Sir William Willcox versus Sir Maurice Craig

As scientific analyst to the Home Office before the First World War, Willcox was known for his involvement with trials for murder and manslaughter; he encouraged Dr Bernard Spilsbury to follow in his footsteps. Willcox was also active in framing regulations for the sale of drugs and poisons, for he was one of the first to recognize the dangers of hypnotic drugs and drug addiction. He was also instrumental in introducing the combined TAB vaccine, which replaced Sir Almroth Wright's typhoid vaccine. Willcox gave papers to several Sections, sat on the Society's Council for three years and was in his element at the meetings of the Therapeutical and Pharmacological Section.

Willcox had been warning the medical profession about the use and abuse of hypnotic drugs since 1913, so that by the time he came to address this Section in May 1927 his researches and convictions were strong. 'I believe that this research is of far-reaching importance and that it opens up a new line of investigation into the effects on the central nervous system caused by toxic substances whether of an artificial chemical nature or of biological origin'. He reinforced his argument by reference to Sir Frederick Mott's work, which had shown the pathological changes in the nervous systems of animals after taking hypnotic drugs of the barbituric acid and sulphonal groups (Mott, founder of the Section of Psychiatry in 1912, had recently died). Dr Helen Young and Dr FH Pickworth's papers added to Willcox's case, and nobody at the meeting disagreed.

It was left to Sir Maurice Craig to take issue with Willcox. Craig was a past President of the Section of Psychiatry and a believer in the prevention of mental disorders by the use of barbiturates, then available on the open market under names such as veronal, luminal and dial. Craig decided to oppose Willcox through the pages of the *BMJ*, opening a spirited debate. Willcox replied by quoting the Registrar General's statistics for 1906 to 1925, which gave no less than 257 deaths by poisoning from these drugs. The correspondence columns of the *BMJ* for May and June 1927 resounded with the shots fired by Willcox and Craig, reinforced by Dixon, who encouraged Willcox to demolish Craig.

The two opponents eventually came face to face at a joint meeting of the Sections of Therapeutics and Pharmacology and Psychiatry in December 1933 on 'The uses and dangers of hypnotic drugs other than alkaloids'. Willcox opened in confident fashion, pointing out there were 21 barbiturates on the market and the dangers they presented in terms of allergy, addiction and death. Once Dr Golla, Dr Mayer and Dr Curran had had their say, Sir Maurice Craig scored a point: 'For years he could not understand how two practising physicians such as Sir William Willcox and himself had come to such widely opposite views on the barbiturate acid group. The riddle had been solved this evening when Sir William told the meeting he had never prescribed any of these drugs'. From this admission Craig deduced that Willcox had no clinical experience in their use, therefore his observations were of little or no importance. [241]

The argument was prolonged in the pages of the *Lancet*, in the *British Journal of Inebriety*, *The Times* and the *Daily Mail*, giving publicity to the death of Mrs Hamilton-Russell, who accidentally overdosed on dial, and the suicide by gas of Dr WH Houghton (he was a morphine addict treated with luminal, and he left a note advising that all drugs in the barbituric acid groups should be studiously avoided). Sir Maurice Craig died shortly afterwards in January 1935 and Willcox triumphed, in that he was influential in adding barbiturates to the schedule of the Pharmacy and Poisons Act, whereby their purchase was limited to prescription.

Having been on the Council of the Section for 20 years, Willcox was President-elect at the age of 69, when his health began to fail and 'his self-confidence showed signs of wavering for the first time in his life'. Nevertheless, he accepted the honour and gave his address on Pharmacy and Pharmacology in October 1936, with due emphasis on the historical roles of the Society of Apothecaries and the Pharmaceutical Society. 'Swillie' as he was known, 'a big, sleepy-looking man, ponderous and slow', died in July 1941.[242]

## The Drugs committee

'The Battle of the Barbiturates' as the contest of Willcox *versus* Craig has been called, was just one aspect of the challenges facing the medical and pharmaceutical professions and the government as new drugs became easily available. While Willcox, the Privy Council and the Home Office worked towards legislation in this country, the India Office consulted the Section of Therapeutics and Pharmacology about the control of drugs in that continent (1930–31). The Section's report stressed the great need for legislative action, for the better training of pharmacists in India and for a cautious approach. The proposal to compile an Indian Pharmacopoeia was strongly deprecated – 'the world needs fewer not more pharmacopoeias' –and having been approved by the Council of the RSM, the Report was forwarded to the India Office in March 1933.[243]

## Banting and Fleming

Professor FG Banting of Toronto took part in a discussion on 'The new mercurial diuretics' in 1930, and eight years later as Sir Frederick he returned to give the second Dixon Memorial lecture on 'Resistance to experimental cancer'. Banting is best known for his discovery of insulin in 1921 and it is not widely recognized that he devoted more time and thought to cancer research; his Dixon lecture was based on the vast amount of experimental work he had covered over the last ten years.[244]

Professor Alexander Fleming was active in the Section from 1939, when he talked about vaccination against whooping cough. In 1943 he opened a debate on penicillin, and Professor Howard Florey produced a film to show the use of penicillin in the treatment of war casualties.

The treatment of burns in war also came under discussion: in his opening remarks Surgeon Rear Admiral Cecil Wakeley pointed out that at the outbreak of hostilities treatment by tannic acid had been considered completely satisfactory. Experience had disproved this and, as Sir Harold Gillies remarked, 'they had to get together to make these hopelessly deformed hands and faces better'.[245] The Section returned to the subject of penicillin in two consecutive years, 1946 and 1947, and this was just the beginning. In response to the worldwide demand for antibiotics the pharmaceutical industry expanded dramatically, producing new drugs whose properties and uses were of intense interest to this Section. Whole meetings were allocated to discussion on streptomycin, the antihistamine drugs, vitamin $B_{12}$ and the new antibiotics.

## Experimental Medicine and Therapeutics

An informal conference on a proposed Section of Experimental Medicine was held in 1919, but on being circulated on the subject Fellows of the RSM were reticent.[246] It was not until 1943 that experimental medicine was officially recognized by the metamorphosis of the Section of Therapeutics and Pharmacology into the Section of Experimental

Medicine and Therapeutics. The renamed Section reported on the need to safeguard DDT supplies in 1946, and assisted the British Pharmacopoeia Commission with its new edition, advising 'a very critical attitude to new remedies. The mere multiplication of drugs of nearly equivalent action favours confusion and probably hazard'.[247]

The postwar years brought exciting subjects for Section meetings: on the applications of the newer antibiotics and on chloromycetin, for example. In 1950 Dr Philip Hench, who was to receive the Nobel prize in 1956 for his work on cortisone, was invited to the RSM by Sir Henry Dale. Hench's paper on 'The present state of cortisone and ACTH in general medicine' was presented to members of several Sections who crowded into both the Barnes Hall and the West Hall.[248]

Complaints about uninvited visitors at 1 Wimpole Street brought a definition of the Section of Experimental Medicine and Therapeutics in 1954 as one that 'differs from others in the Society in the great diversity of interests which it represents and which are expressed in the subjects of its meetings. The audience varies from meeting to meeting and the success of meetings depends to a great extent on discussion and the attendance of a high proportion of informed visitors who are not members'. For these reasons this Section was the only one to oppose the resolution to restrict the access of visitors to the building. When this was enforced, however, there was a very satisfactory increase in the number of new members of the Section.[249]

For the session of 1967–68 the programme was reorganized: besides three ordinary meetings, one meeting was allocated to the Dixon lecture and another to the President's address; two joint meetings were arranged and an all-day symposium around a topic such as shock, hypertension or arrhythmia. The formula was designed to stimulate, but it failed and attendances were low. The Council attributed the problem to the generalist role of this Section and the fact that its only specialist function (clinical pharmacology) was better covered by the British Pharmacological Society.

While Professor Miles Weatherall was President in 1971 an invitation to amalgamate was issued by the Section of Medicine and the possibility of a tripartite combination to include the Section for the Measurement in Medicine was considered. Meanwhile the programmes of both the Medical Section and the Section of Experimental Medicine and Therapeutics ceased. In March 1972 the situation was put to the Meeting on Meetings called by the President of the RSM, and it was soon agreed that the Sections of Medicine and Experimental Medicine and Therapeutics should form one Section, which survived for another 30 years (see page 219).

The *Proceedings of the Royal Society of Medicine* provide the major source for papers presented at Section meetings 1907–77. Page numbers for papers in the *Proceedings* have not been given because, confusingly, they sometimes occur in two sets and the system changed periodically; the volumes are well indexed. From 1978 some papers are published in the RSM *Journal*.

1 *Lancet* (i) 22 June 1907 p. 1719.
2 Keynes, Geoffrey, *The gates of memory* (1981) pp. 406–7.
3 *Royal Society of Medicine. Record of the events and work which led to the formation of that Society by the amalgamation of the leading medical societies of London with the Royal Medical and Chirurgical Society* (1914) p. 85.
4 Presidential address 1907 in *Record of the events... op cit*, pp. 73–76.
5 *Lancet* (i) 22 June 1907 p. 1719.
6 *Bulletin* 57 (1933).
7 *Forty years on. The story of the first forty years of the Royal College of General Practitioners* (1992) p. 24.
8 Officers' Conference 27 October 1913, H3.
9 Letter Champneys to Presidents of Sections 9 October 1913, MacAlister correspondence, folder 2/G18, Box 30. *Bulletin* 18 (1914).
10 *Bulletin* 39 (1924).
11 Letter Douglas Powell to Osler 3 August 1912, MacAlister correspondence, folder 3/G9, Box 24.
12 Cushing, Harvey, *The life of Sir William Osler* vol ii (1925) pp. 624–25.
13 CM Section of Medicine 1907–29, K65.
14 PRSM vol 42 (1949).
15 Medicine, Experimental Medicine and Therapeutics Disbandonment 1986–87, MS/42 f2, Box 112.
16 CM Section of Surgery 1907, K177.
17 PRSM vol 1 pt 3 (1907–08).
18 *Ibid* vol 3 pt 3 (1909–10).
19 Bateman, Donald, *Berkeley Moynihan* (1940). Moynihan's letter of 9 September 1915 to the *Lancet* recommended green towels, sheets, floors and walls for the operating theatre. The phrase 'pathology of the living' was originally Clifford Allbutt's, see Transacs vol lxxxvi (1903) p. 324.
20 Griffiths, DLl, 'Some classics of British orthopaedic literature' in *Journal of Bone and Joint Surgery* vol 32B November 1950 p. 677. PRSM vol 4 pt 3 (1910–11).
21 PRSM vol 4 pt 3 (1910–11).
22 *Ibid* vol 6 pt 3 (1912–13).
23 CM 15 April, 16 December 1913.
24 PRSM vol 10 pt 3 (1916–17).
25 BMJ (ii) 23 October 1918 pp. 593–97.
26 Fraenkel, GJ, *Hugh Cairns* (1991) p. 71.
27 GM Section of Surgery, 26 June 1940, K180. Final Report of the committee to consider

the best means of physical protection of members of the armed forces 1940, MS/84/f1, Box 71.
28 Zuckerman, Solly, *From apes to warlords* (1978) p. 118.
29 Murley, Reginald, *Surgical roots and branches* (1990) pp. 170–73. PRSM vol 41 (1948).
30 Pound, Reginald, *Gillies. Surgeon extraordinary* (1964) pp. 234–35.
31 CM Section of Surgery 1970–91, MS/82, A1.
32 Minute Book, Pathological Society of London 1846–57, I125.
33 Paget, Stephen, *Biography of Sir Victor Horsley* (1919) p. 144. Bland-Sutton, Sir John, *The story of a surgeon* (1930) pp. 148–49.
34 Minute Book, Pathological Society of London 1899–1907, I130.
35 BMJ (ii) 19 October 1907 pp. 1092–93. Presidential address, PRSM vol 39 (1945–46).
36 Buckley, Elizabeth I, and Potter, Dorothy U (eds), *Ida and the eye* (1996) p. 70.
37 PRSM vol 3 pt 1 (1909–10). Foster, WD, *Pathology as a profession in Great Britain and the early history of the Royal College of Pathologists* (1983) p. 14.
38 Presidential address, PRSM vol 6 pt 2 (1912–13).
39 Buckley and Potter, *op cit* pp. 70–71.
40 GM Section of Pathology, 19 November 1912, 4 May 1915, K152. PRSM vol 6 pt 3 (1912–13).
41 CM Section of Pathology, 3 March 1914, 24 April 1917, K151.
42 PRSM vol 26 pt 1 (1932–33). Macfarlane, Gwyn, *Howard Florey* (1978) pp. 218–19.
43 PRSM vol 34 (1940–41).
44 *Ibid* vol 24 pt 1 (1930–31), vol 37 (1943–44). Macfarlane, Gwyn, *Alexander Fleming. The man and the myth* (1984) p. 204.
45 PRSM vol 39 (1945–46). GM 2 July 1946, K153.
46 PRSM vol 53 (1960).
47 CM Section of Pathology, 13 February 1973, MS/68/A1.
48 I am grateful to Dr JD Acland for information and memories.
49 Eyler, John M, *Sir Arthur Newsholme and state medicine 1885–1935* (1997).

50 *Transactions of the Epidemiological Society of London* vol xv1 (1896–97) pp. 287–88, vol vxii (1897–98) p. 120.

51 The new die cost 10 guineas, MacAlister correspondence 1907, G7.

52 PRSM vol 1 pt 1 (1907–08). Newsholme, Sir Arthur, *The last thirty years in public health* (1936) pp. 66–72.

53 PRSM vol 12 pt 1 (1918–19).

54 Eyler *op cit* p. 389.

55 Table 2, Causes of Mortality 1850, 1907, 1963 in presidential address, PRSM vol 58 (1965). This address is the source for much of the Section's history.

56 PRSM vol 3 pt 2 (1909–10).

57 Section of Epidemiology 1910, MS/22/f1, Box 63.

58 Sexton, Christopher, *The seeds of time. The life of Sir Macfarlane Burnet* (1991) pp. 59, 90. PRSM vol 43 (1950). Burnet's paper of 1927 was not published.

59 Letter Low to Leishman 20 January 1913, Archives of the Royal Society of Tropical Medicine and Hygiene, Box 7 WTI/RST/DI, Wellcome.

60 GM Section of Epidemiology 28 February 1919, K41.

61 CM Section of Epidemiology and State Medicine 24 January 1913, CM 19 May 1914.

62 GM Section of Epidemiology and State Medicine 2 March 1925, K41. GM 22 January 1943, MS/22/B1.

63 PRSM vol 31 pt 1 (1937–38).

64 PRSM vol 44 (1951).

65 CM Section of Epidemiology and Preventive Medicine 18 January 1963.

66 PRSM vol 75 (1982).

67 CM Section of Epidemiology and Preventive Medicine 9 November 1989.

68 Golding, AMB, Noah, N, and Stanwell-Smith, R (eds), *Water and public health* (1994) p. 279.

69 I am grateful to Mr Barry Scheer for a copy of his presidential address to the Section (1997) and access to his historical notes.

70 Presidential address, PRSM vol 1 pt 3 (1907–08). Ms 229 contains autograph letters of the original members of the Odontological Society and other communications (1856–63).

71 PRSM vol 1 pt 3 (1907–08).

72 Correspondence MacAlister/Payne 1907–08, K111, Box 47.

73 MacAlister correspondence 1913, folder 7/G18, Box 29. CM Section of Odontology 26 January 1914.

74 MacAlister/Colyer correspondence 1920, folder 7/G18, Box 31.

75 PRSM vol 1 pt 3 (1907–08).

76 CM Section of Odontology 23 June 1913, K97.

77 Dental Caries Sub-committee 1908–10, K107.

78 Valedictory address, PRSM vol 6 pt 3 (1912–13).

79 PRSM vol 16 pt 3 (1922–23), vol 23 pt 2 (1930).Willcox, Philip HA, *The detective-physician. The life and work of Sir William Willcox* (1970) pp. 227–29.

80 PRSM vol 17 pt 3 (1923–24).

81 *Ibid* vol 5 pt 3 (1911–12).

82 Minutes of special committees 1932, H5. CM 22 June 1926.

83 Report of committee for Ministry of Pensions 1918, CM Section of Odontology, K98.

84 PRSM vol 17 pt 3 (1923–24).

85 Presidential address 1985, MS/52/f1, Box 63 (this provides much information about the Section).

86 PRSM vol 30 pt 2 (1937).

87 *Ibid* vol 26 pt 2 (1933). Wallis lecture correspondence 1932–33, Box 82.

88 PRSM vol 59 (1957). GM Section of Odontology 23 October 1978, MS/52/B3.

89 Presidential address 1985, Box 63.

90 GM Section of Odontology 27 November 1967, MS/52/B2.

91 *Ibid* 27 October 1969.

92 Presidential address, PRSM vol 62 (1969). British Gynaecological Society, list of officers and members 1907, I54, Box 43.

93 Obstetrical Society of London, Removal of Baker Brown 1864–67, MS/48. BMJ (i) 9 March, 6 April 1867 pp. 271, 395–410. Black, John, 'Female genital mutilation: a contemporary issue, and a Victorian obsession' in JRSM vol 90 July 1997 pp. 402–5 and correspondence October 1997 p. 586–87. I am grateful to Mr Alasdair Fraser for pointing out these references.

94 Letter MacAlister to Pearce Gould 26 May 1910, folder 9/G20, Box 33.

95 'Laws', CM Section of Obstetrics and Gynaecology 1911, K80.

96 PRSM vol 1 pt 2 (1907–08).

97 *Ibid* vol 4 pt 2 (1910–11).

98 Valedictory address PRSM vol 6 pt 2 (1912–13) and vol 52 (1959).

99 CM Section of Obstetrics and Gynaecology 6 June 1912, K80.

100 Presidential address, PRSM vol 6 pt 2 (1912–13).

101 Valedictory address, PRSM vol 6 pt 2 (1912–13).

102 CM 19 May 1914.

103 Fothergill letter 7 June 1916, CM Section of Obstetrics and Gynaecology, K80.

104 PRSM vol 10 pt 2 (1916–17).
105 CM Section of Obstetrics and Gynaecology 5 December 1918, 6 March 1919, 20 October 1920, K81. Report and criticism 1919, K91, Box 47.
106 Eclampsia committee 1922–35, K85,86.
107 CM Section of Obstetrics and Gynaecology 1924–26, K81.
108 Report of the committee to advise the Maternal Mortality Committee 1929, K90, Box 47.
109 Loudon, Irvine, *Death in childbirth* (1992) p. 210.
110 CM Section of Obstetrics and Gynaecology 3 December 1925, 4 March 1926, K81.
111 GM Section of Obstetrics and Gynaecology 11 March 1929, K84.
112 Shaw, Sir William Fletcher, 'The birth of a College' in *Journal of Obstetrics and Gynaecology of the British Empire* vol 57 (1950) pp. 875–89.
113 PRSM vol 21 (1928).
114 Moir, J Chassar, *Men I have known* (1962).
115 Edwards, Robert and Steptoe, Patrick, *A matter of life. The story of a medical breakthrough* (1980) pp. 76–77. Steptoe's memory of a joint meeting of the Section of Endocrinology and the Section of Obstetrics was inaccurate. There is no mention of Steptoe's outburst in the *Proceedings*.
116 PRSM vol 63 (1970).
117 CM Section of Obstetrics and Gynaecology 1970–91, Ms/48/b2.
118 O'Dowd, Michael and Philipp, Elliott E, *The history of obstetrics and gynaecology* (1994) p. 599.
119 I am grateful to Mr Peter Saunders for information.
120 BMJ (ii) 14 September 1907 p. 688.
121 Presidential address, PRSM vol 37 (1943–44).
122 Letter Garrod to MacAlister 1 March 1908, MS/08/f2. CM Clinical Section 1907–12, K11.
123 *F Parkes Weber's collected writings* (1943).
124 Gibbs, DD, 'Rendu–Osler–Weber disease: a triple eponymous title lives on' in JRSM vol 79 1986 pp. 742–43.
125 CM Clinical Section 9 February 1973.
126 JRSM vol 89 (1996) p. 95.
127 I am grateful for information from Mr David Melville.
128 Information from Dr Jennifer Haywood.
129 The greater part of the history of this Section was written by Dr DS Wilkinson and Professor CD Calnan. I am grateful to them and to Dr Andrew Griffiths.
130 Whitfield, Arthur, 'British dermatology in the early eighties' in *British Journal of Dermatology* vol 45 (1933) pp. 449–57.
131 Buckley and Potter *op cit* p. 53.
132 CM Section of Dermatology 1907–08, K23 and GM 1907–08.
133 CM Section of Dermatology 21 January 1909, K23. PRSM vol 1 pt 1 (1907–08).
134 *Ibid* 31 May 1910.
135 Copy letter Colcott Fox to Morris 10 October 1912, K23.
136 Little, Sir Ernest Graham, 'Celebrated British dermatologists of the past 50 years' in *British Journal of Dermatology* vol 50 (1938) pp. 503–17.
137 *Ibid*.
138 CM Section of Dermatology 2 May 1917, K24.
139 Calnan, Charles, *The life and times of Geoffrey Barrow Dowling* (1993) p. 185.
140 *F Parkes Weber's collected writings* (1943).
141 Bland-Sutton, Sir John, *The story of a surgeon* (1930) p. 148.
142 Minutes of the Neurological Society of London 1886–1901, I63.
143 Bland-Sutton, *op cit*.
144 Letter and notes, CM Neurological Society 1907, I62.
145 CM Neurological Society 1898–1907, I62.
146 CM Section of Neurology 1907–09, K73.
147 Butterfield, Isabel Kennedy, *The making of a neurologist* (1981) p. 34.
148 Schurr, Peter H, 'Outline of the history of the Section of Neurology of the Royal Society of Medicine' in JRSM vol 78 February 1985 pp. 146–48.
149 PRSM vol 12 (1918–19).
150 Critchley, Macdonald, *The black hole and other essays* (1964) p. 103.
151 Bull, JWD, 'The history of neuroradiology' in PRSM vol 63 (1970).
152 Fraenkel, GJ, *Hugh Cairns* (1991).
153 *Ibid* pp. 223–24. Jefferson, Sir Geoffrey, 'Memories of Hugh Cairns' in *Journal of Neurology, Neurosurgery and Psychiatry* vol 22 (1959) pp. 155–66 – this concludes with a bibliography citing all Cairns' papers published in PRSM.
154 PRSM vol 29 pt 1 (1935–36). Bird, JM, 'The father of psychophysiology – Professor FL Golla and the Burden Neurological Institute' in Freeman, Hugh, and Berrios, German E (eds), *150 years of British psychiatry* vol ii (1996) p. 508.
155 Knight, Geoffrey, 'British contributions to neurological surgery' in *Medical Press* vol 225 (1951) p. 471.
156 Schurr, Peter H, *So that was life. A biography of Sir Geoffrey Jefferson* (1997) pp. 190, 208. PRSM vol 33 (1940).
157 Letter Edwards to Northfield and Stewart 2 December 1942, CM Section of Neurology 1942, K74.

158 PRSM vol 40 (1947).

159 *Ibid* vol 39 (1946).

160 *Ibid* vol 48 (1955).

161 GM Section of Neurology 1955, K76.

162 CM 18 July 1967.

163 CM Section of Neurology 1970–78, Ms/46/a1.

164 I am grateful to Dr F Clifford Rose for information.

165 Weir, Neil, *Otolaryngology. An illustrated history* (1990) p. 125.

166 CM British Laryngological, Rhinological and Otological Association 1906, I56.

167 Charter Symonds' speech, centenary meeting, Transacs vol lxxxviii (1905).

168 PRSM vol 4 pt 2 (1910–11). Hobday, Sir Frederick, *Fifty years a veterinary surgeon* (1938) pp. 55–56. Hobday was mistaken in remembering this as a meeting of the Comparative Medicine Section.

169 McBride, P, 'Sir Felix Semon – his work and its influence on laryngology' and Thomson, Sir St Clair, 'The history of rhino-laryngology' in *Journal of Laryngology, Rhinology and Otology* vol 28 (1913) pp. 113–29, 394–96.

170 CM Section of Laryngology 23 January 1919, K53.

171 *Ibid.*

172 Letter Dickinson to MacAlister 6 October 1913, MacAlister correspondence, folder 1/G13, Box 28.

173 PRSM vol 12 pts 1, 2 (1918–19) p. 258.

174 BMJ (i) 11 April 1953 pp. 838–39.

175 *Bulletin* 30 (1920). PRSM vol 12 (1918–19) p. 258 and vol 13 (1919–20) pp. 43–101. CM Laryngological Section 16 May 1919, K53. MacAlister correspondence 1920, folder 1/G13, Box 28.

176 *Bulletin* 35 (1922).

177 PRSM vol 21 (1927).

178 BMJ (ii) 10 November 1923 pp. 885, 888.

179 *Lancet* (ii) 10 November 1923 p. 1039.

180 CM Section of Laryngology 1921–22, K54. *Lancet* (i) 7 January, 1 April 1922 pp. 48, 662–63.

181 BMJ (i) 6 February 1943 pp. 173–75. PRSM vol 21 pt 1 (1927–28).

182 PRSM vol 18 pts 1, 2 (1924–25).

183 *Ibid* vol 24 pt 2 (1931).

184 CM Section of Laryngology 1921–32, K54.

185 PRSM vol 54 (1961).

186 PRSM vol 51 (1958).

187 Grant, J Dundas, 'The oto-laryngological societies of Great Britain and Ireland' in *Journal of Laryngology, Rhinology and Otology* vol 28 (1913) pp. 416–20. BMJ (ii) 8 July 1899 p. 93. Otological Society of the United Kingdom 1899–1907, I124.

188 *Royal Society of Medicine. Record of the events... op cit* pp. 141, 143–44.

189 Grant *op cit* p. 419.

190 CM Section of Otology 1907–23, K130.

191 CM 20 December 1927.

192 Otosclerosis committee, K135, Box 48.

193 PRSM vol 23 pt 2 (1930). Presidential address, PRSM vol 51 (1958).

194 PRSM vol 30 pt 2 (1937).

195 Report of the Committee for the Consideration of Hearing Tests (1929) K142, Box 48.

196 Fraenkel, GJ, *Hugh Cairns* (1991) p. 71.

197 PRSM vol 24 pt 2 (1931).

198 CM Section of Otology 1939–42, K131; 1942–43, K132.

199 PRSM vol 52 (1959), vol 66 (1973).

200 Presidential address, PRSM vol 47 (1954).

201 British Electro-Therapeutic Society 1902–07, I36. *Lancet* (i) pt 1 18 January 1902 p. 167.

202 Burrows, EH, *Pioneers and early years. A history of British radiology* (1986) p. 175.

203 *Royal Society of Medicine. Record of the events... op cit* p. 143.

204 Burrows *op cit*, p. 177.

205 BMJ (ii) 7 December 1907 p. 1670. PRSM vol 1 pt 1 (1907–08).

206 PRSM vol 3 pt 1 (1909–10).

207 Burrows *op cit*, pp. 162, 177.

208 PRSM vol 6 pt 1 (1912–13).

209 Burrows *op cit*, pp. 130–31, 183–84.

210 PRSM vol 2 pt 1 (1908–9), vol 5 pt 1 (1911–12), vol 7 pt 1 (1913–14), vol 8 pt 1 (1914–15).

211 *Ibid* vol 12 pts 1–2 (1918–19).

212 CM Section of Electro-therapeutics 17 November 1916, K33.

213 I am grateful to Professor Roger Berry for alerting me to his presidential address of 1985 in JRSM vol 79 (1986) and his address to the British Institute of Radiology in *British Journal of Radiology* vol 60 (1987) pp. 947–55.

214 PRSM vol 2 pt 1 (1908–09).

215 *Ibid* vol 8 pt 1 (1914–15).

216 CM Section of Electro-therapeutics 21 January, 17 March 1910, K33.

217 Minutes of special committees 1928, H5.

218 PRSM vol 11 pts 1–2 (1917–18), vol 19 pts 1–2 (1925–26).

219 Presidential address, PRSM vol 19 pts 1–2 (1925–26).

220 CM Section of Electro-therapeutics 19 December 1924, Letter MacAlister to Woodburn Morison 25 November 1925, K34.

221 CM Section of Electro-therapeutics, 4 December 1930, K34.

222 Speech by Watts Eden 15 April 1932, MS/78, Box 112.

223 *Lancet* (i) 20 April 1968 pp. 870–71.

224 Sections of Radiology and Physical Medicine 1931, MS/74/f1, Box 71.

225 PRSM vol 27 pt 2 (1934).

226 *Bulletin* 55 (1932), 59 (1934), 63 (1936). Finzi correspondence 1932, K175, K176, Box 49.

227 PRSM vol 37 (1943–44).

228 CM Section of Radiology 1944–45, K171. RSM, Annual Report of Council, CM 17 July 1945.

229 PRSM vol 44 (1951).

230 *Ibid* vol 46 (1953).

231 CM 15 April 1980. CM Section of Radiology 1980–84, Ms/74/a1. Information from Professor Roger Berry.

232 *Röntgen Centenary Congress. Programme and Abstracts* (1995).

233 BMJ (i) 20 April 1907 pp. 965–66.

234 Mair, Alex, *Sir James MacKenzie MD 1853–1925 general practitioner* (1973) p. 202. PRSM vol 1 pt 3 (1907–08).

235 PRSM vol 7 pt 3 (1913–14).

236 Therapeutical Society 1903–07, I144, 145.

237 PRSM vol 3 pt 3 (1909–10).

238 Dixon Memorial Lecture notes 1941, Box 82.

239 PRSM vol 28 pt 1 (1934–35).

240 *Ibid* vol 34 (1940–41). Dixon Memorial correspondence 1933–38, Box 50.

241 PRSM vol 20 pt 2 (1920), vol 27 pt 1 (1933–34).

242 Willcox, Philip HA, *The detective-physician. The life and works of Sir William Willcox* (1970) pp. 261–63, 270, 272, 315. Buckley and Potter, *op cit*, p. 56.

243 Report of the Indian Drugs Enquiry Committee 1930–31, K190, Box 49. Minutes of special committees 1933, H5.

244 Stevenson, Lloyd, *Sir Frederick Banting* (1947) pp. 314–16.

245 PRSM vol 34 (1940–41).

246 CM 20 October 1919.

247 GM Section of Therapeutics and Pharmacology 1907–08, K185. Section of Experimental Medicine and Therapeutics 1908–50, K188. CM Section of Experimental Medicine and Therapeutics 1943–54, K187.

248 PRSM vol 43 (1950).

249 CM Section of Experimental Medicine and Therapeutics 1954–64, K187.

# Chapter 8

# From Anaesthetics to Proctology

No LIMIT WAS PLACED on the number of Sections that could be constituted within the Royal Society of Medicine, and both the Society's Secretary MacAlister and Sir William Osler were keen to expand the original incorporation by the addition of other specialties. Their aim was to draw all branches of medicine into one organization, and with 39 Sections and 15 Fora in the Society in the year 2001 it may be said that their object has been fulfilled.

Three medical societies that were not prepared to join the RSM on its foundation in 1907 soon did so: the Society of Anaesthetists and the Society for the Study of Disease in Children in 1908, followed by the British Balneological and Climatological Society in 1909. Three years later Osler proposed a Section of Anatomy (hoping for the co-operation of the Anatomical Society of Great Britain) and another on Physiology (aimed at the Physiological Society); he also gave notice of his intention to found a Section of Medical History and Literature, and this was the only one of these suggestions to materialize (as the Section of the History of Medicine). Osler also seconded the motion put by the President, Sir Francis Champneys, for a Section of Ophthalmology and he supported Sir William Selby Church's suggestion for a Section of Tropical Medicine; the two new Sections, Ophthalmology and Tropical Diseases and Parasitology, were constituted in 1912.[1] MacAlister wanted to bring the Association of Registered Medical Women into the fold, a suggestion he made to Mrs Scharlieb in 1913 but the women declined the offer.[2] At the conclusion of the First World War, Sir Rickman Godlee proposed the establishment of at least two new Sections: one for Economics and Ethics and another to deal with Medicine in relation to War. Only the latter was formed; it was known as the War Section until it changed its name to the United Services Section in 1929.[3]

Three sub-Sections of the Section of Surgery were approved in 1913: urology, orthopaedics and proctology. Urology and Orthopaedics achieved the status of full Sections in the 1920s, followed by Proctology in 1939 (now Coloproctology). The new discipline of Comparative Medicine was recognized by the RSM in 1923 and 75 years later one of its members, Lord Soulsby, was elected President of the Society, the first veterinary surgeon to hold the office. Dr Norman Howard Mummery's proposal for a Section of Industrial Medicine (1925) and an application for a Section of Genetics (1932) were perhaps too far ahead of their time to gain the acceptance of the Council of the RSM.[4]

Twelve new Sections were established between 1908 and 1938, beginning with Anaesthetics and concluding with the last to be formed before the Second World War, Proctology. After the war, the introduction of the National Health Service and the increased specialization of the medical profession led to the proliferation of Sections, and in the last decades of the 20th century the multidisciplinary Fora added a new dimension to the Society's activities, as will be seen in Chapter 9.

## Section of Anaesthesia (Plate 48)
originally Anaesthetics

The Society of Anaesthetists – the first in the world – was planned in October 1892 and commenced business in 1893. The initiative lay with Dr John F Silk, and F Woodhouse

An invitation to a conversazione of the Society of Anaesthetists at 20 Hanover
Square in 1897; the Society met regularly in the north room on the ground
floor.

Braine was the first President. From 1899 the Society met in the north room at 20 Hanover
Square, for which it paid the RMCS a rent of ten guineas a year. The Society's *Transactions*
first appeared in 1898, and at the opening of the 20th century members of the Society
mounted a campaign for the proper instruction of medical students in anaesthetics.

Most members of the Society of Anaesthetists were in favour of amalgamation with the
other medical societies on certain conditions, chiefly that women be eligible for Fellowship
of the RSM (the first woman member of the Society of Anaesthetists had been elected in
1894 and by 1907 there were 13). Negotiations on this issue delayed the incorporation of
the Section until June 1908, when the Society of Anaesthetists was dissolved, handed over
assets of £112 19s 9d and became a Section of the RSM with Mr Richard Gill as its
President.[5] It pre-dated the Section of Anaesthetics of the BMA by four years.

The Section was quick to grasp the nettle, namely the regulation of practice.
FW Hewitt's proposals for legislation to make it an offence for anyone other than a
medical practitioner to administer an anaesthetic gave rise to serious discussion. Initially
Hewitt and Silk disagreed on the subject, as was their habit, but on a second occasion the
Section approved the motion for legislation to restrict the administration of anaesthetics to
legally qualified medical practitioners. Sir Frederic Hewitt's Parliamentary Bill to this effect
failed; he died in 1916 and the matter was postponed until after the war.[6]

## The chloroform controversy

Alfred Goodman Levy, a cardiologist investigating heart rhythms under chloroform anaesthesia, used the work of the Chloroform committee of the RMCS in 1864 (see pages
112–13) as the basis for a paper delivered to the Section of Anaesthetics in May 1914.
Levy's conviction that chloroform anaesthesia was perfectly safe provided it was given at
full strength continuously, had been aired in *Heart* (1912), and two years later he argued
his case in front of a Section meeting, receiving a spirited response.

Dr Joseph Blomfield, President of the Section, knew members would criticize the paper
and Richard Gill did so immediately. While the substance of Levy's paper was contro-

versial it did alert the profession to the dangers of the irregular administration of chloroform, though his views were challenged by many.[7]

## New apparatus

The demonstration of new apparatus was a regular feature of Section meetings and in November 1912 Dr HE Boyle and the surgeon George Gask demonstrated their new apparatus for the intratracheal insufflation of ether. Gask had approached Boyle earlier in the year enquiring if he was prepared to anaesthetize patients for intrathoracic operations. Boyle was cautious: 'This appeared to me to be rather a new departure'. He read all the papers by Meltzer, Elsberg and others, then with Gask devised a simple portable apparatus which was used for the first time in March 1912. It consisted of foot-bellows, two bottles (one for ether and one for water), a manometer and some tubing.[8] Six years later Boyle showed members another device, his 'nitrous oxide–oxygen–ether outfit'. Following his

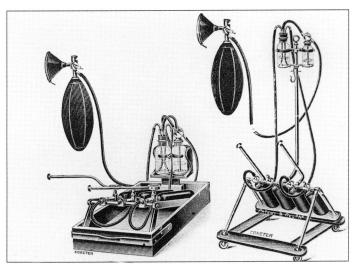

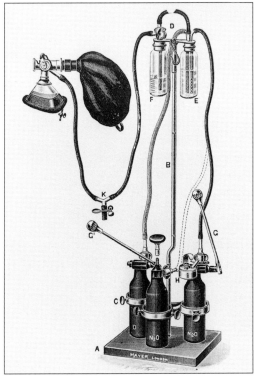

At a meeting of the Section of Anaesthetics in November 1919 Dr Geoffrey Marshall exhibited two types of portable gas–oxygen apparatus: a portable set and a combined set (above). Marshall, who as Sir Geoffrey was to be President of the RSM 1958–60, devised the apparatus to administer anaesthesia to casualties in the First World War. At the same meeting in 1919 Dr Francis Shipway showed apparatus for nitrous oxide, oxygen and ether (left); his modification of Marshall's apparatus combined easy control with portability.

success with this outfit (Boyle admitted that credit was due first to Dr James Gwathmey whose apparatus he had adapted), the British army ordered a large number of 'Boyle machines'.[9]

Boyle, who was anaesthetist to St Bartholomew's Hospital at the time, represented the RSM at meetings of the Canadian Society of Anaesthetists and the American Society of Anaesthetists in 1921, when he was described by the *American Journal of Surgery* as 'a very splendid and delightful type of English gentleman'. He was President of this Section from 1924 to 1925.[10]

Other members of the Section who demonstrated apparatus included Captain Geoffrey Marshall (later Sir Geoffrey and President of the RSM 1958–60) who described a portable gas–oxygen apparatus, as did Dr Francis Shipway.[11] Shipway was one of the first anaesthetists to appreciate the importance of temperature regulation during anaesthesia, a subject he explored in a paper to this Section on 'The influence of anaesthesia on the body temperature' in 1916.[12] He was elected President of the Section in 1925 and was knighted three years later, having anaesthetized King George V twice.

Dr RJ Minnitt of Liverpool is usually credited with popularizing self- or midwife-administered inhalation analgesia; his book on *Gas and air analgesia* was published in 1938. The seed had been sown by a discussion on the use of nitrous oxide and oxygen for obstetric pain relief at the RSM in 1933. Minnitt was inspired to search for a better solution and the following year he delivered a paper to the Section of Anaesthetics on 'Self-administered analgesia for the midwifery of general practice'. This was published in the *Proceedings* with an illustration of Minnitt's portable apparatus, which was an intermittent flow machine designed to deliver 50% nitrous oxide in air. Once it gained the approval of the Central Midwives Board, Minnitt's method was widely used in domestic and hospital midwifery.[13] When he was elected President of the Section in 1943 he chose as the subject of his address 'The history of gas and air analgesia for midwifery', and he was later awarded the Honorary Fellowship of the Society.

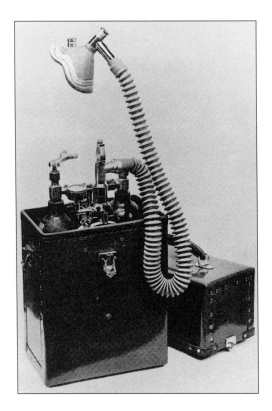

Dr RJ Minnitt's intermittent-flow machine for self- or midwife-administered analgesia was exhibited to the Section in 1934. Minnitt was President of the Section 1943–44.

## New ideas and techniques

With little anaesthetic experience between them and no precedent in this hazardous branch of the specialty, Ivan Magill and Stanley Rowbotham worked at the Queen's Hospital for Facial and Jaw Injuries in the years after the First World War. Their achievement with war injuries involving about 3,000 anaesthetics was reported to the Section in February 1921.[14] Magill was both innovative and inventive, as can be seen from his description of endotracheal anaesthesia and blind nasal intubation given to the Section in November 1928, and he also showed members the tube he had devised for endotracheal anaesthesia.[15] Magill was to be President of the Section in 1937 (see below).

At a Section meeting in April 1921 Dr RC Mackenzie Wallis and Dr C Langton Hewer announced a new general anaesthetic: 'a compound possessing powerful anaesthetic properties, which has no relation chemically to either chloroform or ether'. This was to be marketed commercially as ethanesal, a product that aroused brief and intense interest. Professor Storm van Leeuwen, a pharmacologist at the University of Leyden, reported his findings on commercially available ethers to the Section in 1924. Henry Dale, Dr Charles Hadfield and Boyle took part in the thought-provoking debate that followed. Boyle was quite satisfied with ethanesal; Hadfield, on the other hand, knew of complaints about its variable quality. 'No one questioned that ethanesal worked; it did, though for the "wrong" reason. The question was why it was thought that pure ether did not'.[16]

In 1941 MD Nosworthy's observations on 'Anaesthesia in chest surgery', with special reference to controlled respiration and war casualties, launched the idea of assisted respiration in chest surgery. He urged the anaesthetist to 'maintain an efficient tidal exchange by rhythmic squeezing of the breathing bag'. It has since been realized that this 'simple and curiously unscientific contribution has gone almost unremarked', although it forms the basis of most modern anaesthetic methods.[17]

## Anaesthetic committees

Concern about the purity of anaesthetic agents prompted the Council of the Section to suggest an investigation, and this initiative was welcomed by the Medical Research Council. The RSM/MRC committee began work in 1924, with Blomfield and Shipway representing the Section.[18] Hadfield reported the committee's work on nitrous oxide to the Section in 1926, generating a discussion, and the committee continued with tests on ethylene, acetylene, avertin and evipan. Later it investigated problems such as explosions and ether convulsions; Hadfield retired from the committee in 1945 to be replaced by Nosworthy, and the committee continued its work until 1956.

Sir George Newman of the Ministry of Health was concerned about the mounting number of deaths of patients under anaesthesia between 1911 and 1925 (an increase from 276 in 1911 to 442 annually) and he requested a report on the possible reasons from the RSM. Four members of the Section of Anaesthetics, two from the Surgical Section and one pathologist worked on this committee for two years before concluding that it was impossible to base a report of any value on the misleading and variable data available. It was therefore deemed wise not to proceed with the publication of the committee's report on 'Deaths during Anaesthesia'.[19]

At the request of the Mercantile Marine Department of the Board of Trade the Council of this Section investigated the Neuron System of Resuscitation in 1932. A preliminary report had been submitted by the RSM Council in October 1932 when a more detailed enquiry into this novel method of resuscitation was referred to the Section of Anaesthetics. There was a problem in finding victims for trials and the inventor of the method, Mr NG Pogose, was called upon to demonstrate his Neuron System on a stalwart friend in front of the Section's Council. After some hesitation Council members placed themselves in Pogose's hands and although they were suspicious of his 'ju-jitsu' trick of stimulating the

 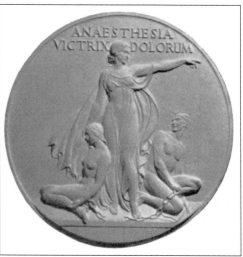

The Henry Hickman Medal was designed by TH Paget and was first presented to Dr Wesley Bourne in 1935. Hickman experimented on animals with carbon dioxide to induce suspended animation in the 1820s. On his death in 1830 a memorial fund was established.

phrenic nerves and applying retroclavicular pressure, they were intrigued. On the whole they decided in favour of the traditional Schäfer method of resuscitation.[20]

### Hickman Medal

The centenary of Henry H Hickman's death was approaching, and the possibility of a memorial medal to mark his early experiments in suspended animation was raised at a Section meeting in May 1929. Within a year £190 was forthcoming towards a medal for outstanding work connected with anaesthesia. Dr Cecil Hughes, Honorary Secretary of the Memorial committee and a past President of the Section, arranged that the fund was entrusted to the RSM on the understanding that the medal would be awarded on the recommendation of the Section. The first choice of designer for the medal, Eric Gill, declined the commission, so it went to TH Paget (who was paid 40 guineas). The inscription on the medal aroused strong feelings: Dr Still objected to 'Anaesthesia Conquers Pain' because 'it sounds exactly like a Bovril slogan or the advertisement of somebody's painkiller' and he proposed *Anaesthesia Victrix Dolorum* as a shade less deplorable. His suggestion was adopted and the medal was first awarded to Dr Wesley Bourne of McGill University in 1935.[21]

### Association of Anaesthetists, the Faculty and the Royal College

The President of the Section for 1930 to 1931, Dr HW Featherstone of Birmingham, assumed Hewitt's mantle with regard to the promotion of the status and training of anaesthetists. He gave no hint in his presidential address of his intention to found the Association of Anaesthetists of Great Britain and Ireland in 1932 but, as the historian of the Association points out, 'there is no doubt that it was as a result of his active Presidency and the contacts this brought with most of the leading anaesthetists of the day, that the need for action ... was impressed upon him'.[22] The purpose of the new Association was not to replace the Section of the RSM, whose work was restricted to the scientific and academic, but to complement it.

While Honorary Secretary to the Section, Dr Ivan Magill was the first to suggest a Diploma in Anaesthetics (1931).[23] He could not persuade the RSM to give official support to this proposal, nevertheless several members of the Section met to form the Association of Anaesthetists and to promote the qualification.

The introduction of a qualification in anaesthesia was a primary objective of the Association and in 1935 the Diploma in Anaesthetics was established. The Association played a prominent part in the foundation of the Faculty of Anaesthetics of the Royal College of Surgeons in 1948 when Dr Archibald Marston, a past President of the Section, became its Dean. In 1988 the Faculty developed into the College of Anaesthetists, becoming the Royal College of Anaesthetists by a charter of 1992.

*The 1930s and 1940s*

In 1936 Magill gave his paper on 'Anaesthesia in thoracic surgery' to a Section meeting: he recalled that six years previously he and Dr Langton Hewer had reported on four anaesthetics for lobectomy, but now he had experience of 128. 'Lobectomy, which was formerly regarded as a rare operation even in a chest hospital, now appears on the operation list with considerable frequency'. Magill also remarked that it was one of the virtues of the discussions at these meetings that results of scientific research could be explored 'notwithstanding the absence of finality': the RSM was the only body in the country which afforded such an opportunity, and Magill took full advantage of it.[24]

Magill's presidency of the Section (1937–38) inaugurated a period of large attendances at meetings, with a record number of 203 at one meeting in March 1946. On that occasion the current President, George Edwards, ordered the discussion to be prolonged indefinitely, the subject being 'A milestone in anaesthesia? – d-tubocurarine chloride' (derived from curare which was used as an arrow poison in South America). The basis of the discussion was a paper submitted by Dr Cecil Gray ('Gray of Liverpool') and Dr John Halton revealing the advantages and dangers of curare as an anaesthetic. Halton had first used d-tubocurarine chloride in November 1944, and when regular supplies became available in this country from April 1945 he and Gray began to realize its great possibilities. 'The road lies open before us, and with a grave and insistent warning to the inexperienced that we are dealing with one of the most potent poisons known, we venture to say that we have passed yet another milestone, and the distance to our goal is considerably shortened'. Much of their early work had been done in Professor Charles Wells' Department of Surgery at Liverpool, and he was convinced that the use of tubocurarine was a significant advance: he reported that patients 'not only wakened quickly but were unusually co-operative and were able to begin, almost at once, the limb movements and breathing exercises that were so vital to quick recovery and low morbidity'.[25]

Gray and Halton returned to the Section in April 1947 to discuss 'Further experiences with curare', by which time doubts had set in about its use: Dr Geoffrey Organe had found that results were not always all that could be desired, but Gray and Halton maintained that during two years of using d-tubocurarine chloride in over 2,000 cases there had only been one fatality. Most of those present at the meeting agreed that 'curarization' had come to stay. Curare did indeed revolutionize anaesthetic practice, and Dr Gray's part in this was acknowledged when he was awarded the Honorary Fellowship of the Society in 1979 (he had been President of the Section 1955–56).[26]

Another member of the Section who received an Honorary Fellowship was Sir Ivan Magill. He had advised the Emergency Medical Service during the Second World War and the Ministry of Health during the foundation of the National Health Service, ensuring the status of anaesthetists within the state system. He was made an Honorary Fellow in 1955, knighted in 1960 and his 90th birthday called for a special meeting of members of the Section, the Association and the Faculty in June 1978. Acknowledged as 'a world doyen of anaesthesia', Sir Ivan Magill continued to attend meetings of the Section of Anaesthetics until shortly before his death in 1986.[27]

## The 1950s and 1960s

The popularity of meetings of the Section continued into the 1950s under the presidency of Professor Geoffrey Organe (1949–50). For many years he was one of the world's leading figures in anaesthetics, and in this country he was President of the Association of Anaesthetists and a founder member of the Faculty in 1948. With two pharmacologists, William Paton (another member of the Section to receive a knighthood) and Eleanor Zaimis, Organe was involved with the trials of decamethonium – indeed he was one of the first human volunteers for the trials.

Organe's presidential address emphasized the pace of change and progress that faced anaesthetists: 'We must be experts in intravenous, intrasternal, spinal, epidural and local anaesthesia; we must be laryngologists, tracheologists and bronchologists and we must have something of the miraculous powers of guardian angels if we are to protect our patients against the onslaughts of some of the more radical surgeons'.[28]

Professor Robert Macintosh (later Sir Robert), a Fellow of the Society in 1925, President of the Section for 1953–54 and an Honorary Fellow in 1967, had introduced the Macintosh laryngoscope blade in 1943 and he too attracted a large following at Section meetings. He had been persuaded by Lord Nuffield to become the first Professor of Anaesthetics at Oxford University in 1937 – this was the first fully endowed chair in the subject anywhere in the world. His many achievements were remembered by those present at a symposium organized by the Section in October 1987 to celebrate his 90th birthday.[29]

The first female President of the Section, Dr Katherine Lloyd-Williams, was elected in 1956: her presidential address was on the anaesthetist's role in undergraduate training. She spoke with authority, for she was Dean of the Royal Free Medical School and later the first female Dean of the Faculty of Medicine in the University of London. One of her successors as President, Dr Aileen Adams, described Lloyd-Williams as 'one of the first and most distinguished in this field'.[30]

By the 1960s anaesthesia was on a plateau. WD Wylie's presidential address of 1963 defined the peaks of success achieved in the 1930s, the 1940s and 1950s when practical skill, scientific knowledge and the establishment of the NHS created a thriving specialty. With the increased specialization of medicine, this President expressed concern that the specialty of anaesthesia might be stifled by the narrow channels in which hospital clinical work tended to run.[31]

## Diversity of meetings

Dr TM Young's analysis of the subject matter of meetings from 1908 to 1995 found that the most popular topic was local anaesthesia: 'it is a credit to the Section's awareness of novelty that the first paper on extradural anaesthesia was read in March 1925, although the subject then lay fallow until re-presented by Massey Dawkins, who claimed the first recorded account in Great Britain of its use by the lumbar route' in 1945. Resuscitation, ether, nitrous oxide and anaesthesia in dental surgery have also been discussed regularly.[32]

There was a surge of interest in the history of anaesthesia in the 1980s with the first International Symposium on the subject at the Erasmus University, Rotterdam, in 1982. This was followed by the foundation of the Anaesthesia History Association in the USA (1984) and the History of Anaesthesia Society in Britain (1985). The Second International Symposium on the History of Anaesthesia was held in London in 1987 and the proceedings were published by the RSM (1989). The RSM Press also published *Essays on the history of anaesthesia* in 1996.

The 1990s opened with the presentation of shields bearing the Society's coat of arms to 16 surviving past Presidents of the Section. Several meetings of this decade focused on Europe (for example, the European laws on medical equipment, the European Diploma) and members enjoyed a meeting at Mainz in 1992, the first held outside the British Isles.

Joint meetings with other Sections and with the Association of Anaesthetists and the History of Anaesthesia Society commanded good attendances, and even the Section's ordinary meetings were attended by between 50 and 70 members. At the Annual General Meeting in 1995 the name of the Section was changed to the Section of Anaesthesia, and the first meeting under the new name was on 'Paediatric anaesthesia'.

The introduction of muscle relaxants, intermittent positive-pressure ventilation, new techniques, equipment and anaesthetic agents and more sophisticated monitoring allow anaesthetists to manage patients who would formerly have been considered ineligible for surgery. This poses a challenge, and a meeting on 'Anaesthesia for rare and difficult cases' held in 1995 focused on anaesthesia for paraplegics, in endo-bronchial laser surgery and carcinoid syndrome. The specialty is now one of the most scientific in hospital medicine while at the same time it demands a wide knowledge of medical diseases, drugs and medications.

## Section of Paediatrics and Child Health (Plate 49)
### originally for the Study of Disease in Children

The first book in English on children's diseases was written by Thomas Phaer in the mid-16th century and a precious, miniscule copy of the 1546 edition survives in the RSM Library. This early example notwithstanding, the medical profession in Britain was slow to focus on children. One of the first to do so was Dr John Clarke, a founder-member of the Medical and Chirurgical Society in 1805. He lectured on midwifery at St Bartholomew's Hospital and wrote on obstetrics and the diseases of pregnancy and children, yet he does not appear to have inspired any disciples.

Later in the 19th century other members of the RMCS helped to advance the treatment of sick children, notably Charles West, President of the Society from 1877 to 1879, who was supported by Bence-Jones and other Fellows in the foundation of the Hospital for Sick Children (Great Ormond Street), the first of its kind in the country. Important

*The boke of children* by Thomas Phaer (or Phayer) was the first book written in English on children's diseases (1545). This edition of 1546 was published with Phaer's *The regiment of life*, and is in the Society's Library.

contributions to the understanding of children's diseases were presented at the meetings of the RMCS, notably Sir Thomas Barlow's paper of 1883 on infantile scurvy and George Frederic Still's description of juvenile rheumatoid arthritis (Still's disease) in 1896. Professor Still's work was published in the Society's *Transactions* (1897, 1903) and he contributed further papers to the Clinical Section, the Therapeutical and Pharmacological Section and case reports to this Section.[33]

The first Society for the Study of Disease in Children was founded in 1900 by Mr AH Tubby and Mr Sydney Stephenson.[34] Among the 102 original members who were drawn from all over Great Britain and Ireland, were Robert Jones the orthopaedic surgeon, Dr Harold Stiles the plastic surgeon and the omniscient, omnipresent Dr Frederick Parkes Weber. The Society was dedicated to 'the more exact and scientific study of disease in childhood'; it held meetings at the children's hospitals, arranged an annual provincial meeting and a dinner, and by 1904 boasted 304 members. Special investigations were undertaken into the causes of 'precocious puberty' and the hospital treatment of children with tuberculosis.[35]

## Opposition to the RSM

The Society for the Study of Disease in Children at first declined to join the proposed union of medical societies, choosing to wait upon the decisions of the two wealthiest societies, the Medical Society of London and the Royal Medical and Chirurgical, before committing itself. The absence of the MSL from the union and the opposition of Robert Jones, Mr R Clement Lucas and Sydney Stephenson to the scheme made amalgamation seem unlikely. Jones was bitterly opposed to the dissolution of the Society and its replacement by a Section of the RSM; it has been suggested this was due to personal rivalry between himself and Tubby, and/or his own determination not to surrender the independent specialist society to the establishment.[36]

At a special meeting called in November 1906 the Society's members had their say: Stephenson urged his colleagues to 'refuse resolutely to have anything whatever to do with this wild-cat scheme. [Hear, hear] I ask you, gentlemen, not to barter your birthright for a mess of pottage and a mess, if I may say so, of extremely indifferent pottage'. Clement Lucas was in the chair and he recommended that the Society should decline to join the scheme, which he described as 'absolutely and hopelessly unsound'. Mr Milner Burgess had some fun quoting a ditty to illustrate the danger of being swallowed by a predator:

'There was a young lady of Niger,
Who smiled as she rode on a tiger.
They returned from that ride,
With the lady inside,
And the smile on the face of the tiger'.[37]

By 1908 it was clear even to the die-hards that the RSM was financially sound and flourishing, so the Society for the Study of Disease in Children agreed, 'not without some reluctance and misgivings' to become a Section of the RSM with 319 members, 'more than £800 and a small but valuable library'.[38]

The Section's first meeting was held on 23 October 1908 with Dr George Carpenter as Chairman of Council (this appointment was in the tradition of the defunct society, but the Section soon conformed by appointing a President). Mr Hugh Lett, Dr EI Spriggs and Mr HJ Stiles were the first Honorary Secretaries and the Council members came from as far afield as Cork and Bristol. The first paper was on toxaemia, the first general discussion on whooping cough and in June 1909 Dr Carpenter delivered the Wightman lecture on congenital heart affections.[39] Even Robert Jones was reconciled to the demise of the original Society: by 1911 he was taking an active part in the work of the Section and as President in1921–22 he introduced to it the custom of a presidential address (see below).

## The Section and its work 1908–26

The Section's meetings for each session were clearly divided between discussions opened by an authority in a special subject (such as infant feeding), clinical meetings for the exhibition of cases and specimens, and the reading of short papers. A provincial meeting was first held in 1910, when ladies were invited to accompany members to the Royal Portsmouth Hospital, and from 1923 meetings were held regularly at children's hospitals. During the First World War attendances fell to a low of 17 and the number of meetings was reduced to four for the session of 1915–16.

The Section perceived that it had a role outside the confines of 1 Wimpole Street and as early as 1909 applied pressure for the stricter enforcement of medical examinations of school children 'forthwith'. In 1925 the Section was galvanized into action after a long discussion with two other Sections on the control of tuberculosis and the milk supply. A subsequent resolution urged the Council of the RSM to press the government to re-enact the Tuberculosis Order immediately.[40]

## Mellanby and rickets

Perhaps the most controversial meeting of the Section took place in February 1920, when Dr Edward Mellanby took the floor. He had been researching rickets in children for the Medical Research Committee since 1914 and he presented his findings (based on experiments on dogs) to the Section. He dwelt on the importance of accessory food factors ('vitamines') in the feeding of infants and he demonstrated that the lack-of-food factor was a causation of rickets. Professor Noel Paton could not agree and criticized Mellanby's findings in the strongest terms. Paton deplored 'the present craze for Vitamines – a horrible name since we do not know that, even if they exist, they are amines, or what they have to do with life', and Dr Robert Hutchison agreed that vitamines were merely 'the latest dietetic stunt'.[41] Mellanby's researches were subjected to emphatic criticism from members of the Section but with the publication of his report on *Experimental rickets* the following year his conviction that rickets was due primarily to the deficiency of a fat-soluble vitamin in the diet gained acceptance, with the ultimate result that rickets was eradicated from this country.

## Rolleston's retrospective

The President for 1927–28, Dr John Davy Rolleston (who also served as President of the Clinical, Epidemiological and History of Medicine Sections), thought that the most important discussion of the Section to date had been on 'Congenital syphilis'.[42] This had absorbed two meetings in February/March 1921: Sir Humphry Rolleston (his brother) had opened the discussion and Sir Frederick Mott, Dr L Findlay, Dr Amand Routh, N Bishop Harman and Dr D Nabarro also took part.

Rolleston analysed the cases brought before the Section's meetings between 1908 and 1927, finding that those most frequently demonstrated were diseases of the nervous system (142 cases), congenital defects exclusive of congenital heart disease (127), alimentary disorders (63), diseases of the skin (51), congenital heart disease (45), ophthalmology (35) and acute infections (33). The opportunity to see and discuss such cases brought physicians, orthopaedic surgeons, neurologists, psychiatrists, dermatologists and ophthalmologists to the Section and its Presidents were as likely to be orthopaedic surgeons as paediatricians, while Rolleston himself had wide interests.

One such President was the orthopaedic surgeon Sir Robert Jones, a pioneer in the treatment of crippled children (as in the Robert Jones and Agnes Hunt Orthopaedic Hospital).

Strangely, he was never a President of the Orthopaedic or Surgical Sections but he was President of the Section for the Study of Disease in Children 1921–22, giving an address on 'The treatment of paralysis in children' in which he affirmed the 'inestimable value in bringing together the physician and the surgeon' both at the Section meetings and in the treatment of the paralysed child.[43]

As President of the Section in 1929 Sir Thomas Fairbank spoke on osteogenesis imperfecta, giving his reasons for regarding ante- and post-natal cases as due to the same disease. He had given his first papers to this Section before the First World War but once the Section of Orthopaedics was established most of his papers went in that direction (see pages 359–60).

## The British Paediatric Association

The specialty came of age with the founding of the British Paediatric Association in 1928 by Dr Donald Paterson, a forceful Canadian who was to be President of this Section 1942–43. Of the six founders who attended the inaugural meeting of the BPA in February 1928, all but Professor Still came to be Presidents (at different times) of this Section.

The very name of the Association established paediatrics, although the meaning and spelling of the word caused some misunderstanding. The *BMJ* insisted on the American spelling, 'pediatrics', to the intense irritation of its principal proponent in this country, Still, who wrote to the editor disclaiming any knowledge of 'pediatrics'.[44]

The BPA grew steadily in membership and influence. The work of the Association, the founding of the first chair of paediatrics in 1929 and the International Congress held in London in 1933 put the specialty on a firm footing. Sir Leonard Parsons, a past President of the Section, was able to report in his preface to *Modern trends in paediatrics* (1951) that 'the study of the child in health and disease has advanced in the last few years from a rather insignificant and certainly neglected section of medicine to become one of the major subjects of the medical curriculum'. The contents of this volume referred to the many contributions made by members of the Section and published in the Society's *Proceedings*.

## Prematurity and breast feeding

In response to a request from the Medical committee of Queen Charlotte's Hospital, the British Paediatric Association and the Section for the Study of Disease in Children set up a joint committee in 1937 to establish a standard definition of prematurity. The committee led by Dr NB Capon and Dr Alan Moncrieff reported succinctly: 'An immature or premature infant is one whose birth weight is 5½ lbs or less, regardless of the supposed period of gestation'.[45] This definition has since been abandoned; a baby is now regarded as premature if born before 37 weeks.

Towards the end of 1941 the Section took up the cause of breast feeding, which was out of favour at the time. Dr David Levi urged the Section to agitate for education and publicity on the advantages of breast milk; he wanted to see a campaign supported by the Ministry of Health and/or Education, with better information for medical students and films for school children and townswomen's guilds. The RSM refused to back Levi's publicity campaign because it exceeded the scientific function of the Section, so the issue was confined to discussion.[46]

Members of the Section were authorized by Council to collaborate with the Section of Obstetrics and Gynaecology in assisting Sir Joseph Barcroft's work on the respiration of the human baby in 1944.

## Dr Helen Mackay

The nutrition of infants and dietetic deficiencies of childhood were the special interests of Dr Mackay, whose reports on rickets (1919–22), nutritional anaemia in infancy (1931) and the comparison of breast-fed and artificially fed infants (1959) altered medical attitudes towards infant feeding. She was a regular supporter of the Section, serving as Secretary for 1933–34, and in the latter year she was elected the first female FRCP. Ten years later she was to be the Section's first female President.

In lieu of a presidential address Dr Mackay chose to open a discussion on 'The nutrition of the premature infant in the first month of life' (1944), and later in the session she presented cases of rickets at a meeting held at the Queen Elizabeth Hospital where she worked. She set the example for other women Presidents of the Section – Isabella Forshall, Beryl Corner and Victoria Smallpiece.

## Section of Paediatrics

At a Council meeting in November 1945 Dr Beryl Corner, who first presented a case to the Section in November 1937 and who was still taking an active part in the Section's discussions in December 2000, suggested that the Section should change its name to bring it in line with North America and some European countries. Members were then asked to state their preference for the title of Paediatrics or Child Health and of those who replied, 81 voted for Paediatrics and 47 for Child Health, so the name was changed to Paediatrics in 1946.[47] It was thought at the time that members would understand that the word paediatrics implied the same approach as in North America where it embraced all aspects of the medical care of children, from diseases to preventive medicine. But as Dr Corner has pointed out, time showed that this philosophy did not really develop in the United Kingdom; thus when the Royal College of Paediatrics was founded in 1996 it had to add the words 'and Child Health' to its title so as to make it abundantly clear that the College embraced all aspects of the medical care of children.[48] Likewise, the Section was to add Child Health to its title in 1999.

In 1946 Denis Browne held the presidency of the Section. He had worked at Great Ormond Street since 1922, and was the first London surgeon to confine his practice to paediatric surgery; his career led him to the presidency of the British Association of Paediatric Surgeons in 1954.[49] He gave papers to the Surgical, Physical Medicine and Endocrinology Sections as well as Paediatrics: one of 1949 illustrated his new method of treating congenital dislocation of the hip, involving nine months in an apparatus. Browne had treated 42 cases in children under four using this method and in all of these he obtained stable, painless hips.[50]

The Section's Council had recognized in 1934 that the clinical meetings were the most popular and therefore to be encouraged. Such meetings continued to be the Section's forte, providing an important platform for young paediatricians, for they could be sure of valuable critical appraisal, most likely from Dr Parkes Weber. He is remembered for his encyclopaedic knowledge 'and his comments could be completely devastating or the reverse for a young doctor'.[51]

A period of growth and development in paediatrics followed the establishment of the NHS and attendances at Section meetings reflected this: as many as 300 went with Dr Wyllie to see cases at Guy's Hospital and 220 were present at a discussion on congenital heart disease. Encouragement was given to physicians, surgeons and general practitioners to join the Section and the membership broadened, as did the style of meetings and the topics dealt with. In the 1950s the case histories, often illustrated, were invariably published in the *Proceedings* – as many as 30 a session, to the satisfaction of authors and readers eager to share unusual cases and problems.

## Children in hospital

In November 1952 the Section was shown a film by Dr John Bowlby and Dr James Robertson: 'A two-year-old goes to hospital', a heart-rending record of a normal little girl who went through a cycle of crying, withdrawal, breakdown, anxiety and rejection of her mother during an eight-day stay in hospital with limited visiting. At its conclusion, the President, Dr Winnicott, commented that it illustrated a very real problem: 'The effect of separation of small children from their mothers was so often serious, even producing irreversible changes'.[52]

This had not previously been recognized nor shown so graphically, and the film was to have effect. Dr Dermod MacCarthy, for one, was persuaded to allow unrestricted visiting of children in hospital even though many consultants considered the presence of mothers a nuisance. The welfare of children in hospital was the subject of an Official Report in 1959 and attitudes gradually changed, to the benefit of both children and parents.

### Dr DW Winnicott and Sir Peter Tizard

The child psychoanalyst Donald Winnicott had a lasting influence on the Section and on paediatrics generally. His address to the Section in 1953 conveyed his feelings about the relationship between paediatrics and child psychiatry, a debate that continues. Winnicott's paper was illustrated by 'squiggles', a game he devised to encourage his young patients to draw – 'a kind of projection test', which he found revealing. And in his concluding remarks Winnicott commended the concept of child health as 'presupposing an eventual growth of mutual understanding, one in which the child-psychiatrist can be understood by his paediatric colleagues'.[53]

Professor JPM Tizard (Sir Peter) was sure that Winnicott would 'be remembered long after all the rest of us have been forgotten' for his personal qualities, high intelligence, delicious wit, skill as a paediatrician and, chiefly, because 'he was a philosopher who altered the way in which we think about children in relation to the adults they are to become'.[54]

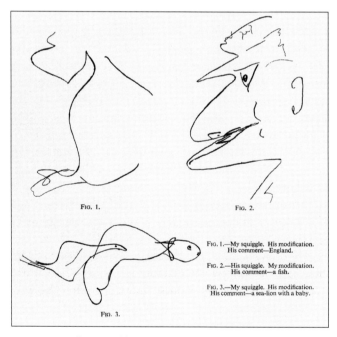

FIG. 1.

FIG. 2.

FIG. 1.—My squiggle. His modification. His comment—England.

FIG. 2.—His squiggle. My modification. His comment—a fish.

FIG. 3.—My squiggle. His modification. His comment—a sea-lion with a baby.

FIG. 3.

Dr DW Winnicott illustrated his presidential address of 1953 with squiggles.
His technique was to draw a squiggle, then his patient turned it into something. Then the patient (in this case a boy) drew a squiggle which Winnicott turned into something. Figure 1: Winnicott's squiggle; the boy's modification made it look like a map of England. Figure 2: the boy's squiggle modified by Winnicott – the boy saw this as a fish. Figure 3: Winnicott's squiggle, which the boy modified into a sea lion with a baby. 'As events turned out it was justifiable to understand from this drawing that the boy had a powerful maternal identification', Winnicott commented.

Tizard was President of the Section in 1980–81, having been President of the Neonatal Society, and he was shortly to be President of the BPA. He had been in charge of the neonatal unit at the Postgraduate Medical School, Hammersmith, from 1954, later occupying the foundation chair of paediatrics at Oxford. It has been said that he 'invented' neonatology at his research unit, to which he recruited a talented team. John A Davis wrote of Tizard's admiration of 'the paediatrician turned psychoanalyst Donald Winnicott, whose Boswell he would like to have been and with whom he was on terms of mutual friendship at a time when the rest of us chose either to spit in Winnicott's face or sit at his feet'.[55]

## The 1970s

In the 1970s all the Sections were urged to publicize their meetings more effectively, and the President of this Section invited a MP, an editor and an economist to engage in a discussion on 'The mass media and the child': Mrs Shirley Williams MP, Mr William Rees-Mogg of *The Times* and Professor Himmelweit of the LSE were brought together, and on other occasions Sir Keith Joseph and Mrs Margaret Thatcher also made their views known.

In October 1975 the President, Professor John L Emery, addressed the Section on 'Postneonatal mortality in Sheffield', where he worked at the Children's Hospital: 'the halcyon period of the immediate postwar years, when neonatal and postnatal mortality rates fell steadily in all social groups' was over, he announced. Emery was especially concerned about the postnatal death rate in this country, which lagged behind France, Japan and the Scandinavian countries, and he went on to present his studies on the home death situation, 'the so-called cot-death or crib-death ... There has probably been more nonsense written about these child deaths than about most other present situations in paediatrics', he stated, calling for the improvement of the primary home medical care of infants.[56] Emery's research into cot deaths, which established him as a leading authority on the subject and earned him the Honorary Fellowship of the RSM, revealed links between mortality and smoking, room temperature and prematurity, and he claimed that 80% of infant deaths were probably due to recognizable medical causes that had not been diagnosed while a further 10% were the result of infanticide or filicide.

On a lighter note, Professor Emery led a party of some three dozen members of the Section and their guests to a meeting with the Société Française de Pédiatrie in 1976, meriting a record in the Minutes which begins 'On arrival in Paris the party dined in some style at the Restaurant de Petit Seine'.[57] The scientific meeting took place at the Hôpital Antoine Béclère, Clamart, and the success of the trip prompted others to Denmark and Holland, and in 1978 a brave contingent followed Dr Hugh Jolly to Ulster.

Another satisfying event was the Section's successful nomination of the psychoanalyst Anna Freud for Honorary Fellowship of the RSM in 1978. She was delighted to follow in her father's footsteps and recalled that he had felt his Fellowship made him a full member of the British medical fraternity. Anna had fled to England with her father in 1938 and had founded the Hampstead Child Therapy Course and Clinic after the war, besides being a prolific author.

## Changes

For many years the Section was concerned about the mental trauma suffered by infants who were brought to the RSM to appear at clinical meetings, and the practice was stopped in 1981. Instead, members were asked to present undiagnosed and problem cases by means of photographs and the child's history, to a panel of experts. 'This turned out to be a form of paediatric "Call my bluff", mixed with a clinical pathology quiz. It produced an unusual and edifying session which was greatly enjoyed'.[58]

Since 1985 an annual symposium on 'Cystic fibrosis' has been organized by Professor TJ David, who has served as Honorary Secretary to the Section, as its President (1996–97) and as editor of the Society's *Journal*. With recent advances, cystic fibrosis has become more complex to treat due to the expanding range of drugs and an increasing array of complications. It was with these problems in mind that the first symposium on the subject was held at the RSM and the papers were published as a supplement to the *Journal* in 1986.

Like the Clinical and Dermatological Sections, this Section was dismayed by the decreasing number of case reports published in the *Journal*. The presentation of a case with the near-guarantee of its publication had always been a major attraction to junior hospital doctors who would then join the Society. In 1985 it was calculated that at least 270 cases annually were presented at the meetings of six Sections. The accompanying reports were valuable and this Section wanted to see an increase, not a decrease, in the number published.[59]

During the Presidency of Dr Thomas Stapleton (1985–86) the Section benefited from a presidential badge and a visit from HRH Princess Anne. She was invited to a meeting on 'Paediatrics and child health in China and Africa' organized by the President, who had international contacts. Her Royal Highness joined the overseas delegates for lunch – 12 paediatricians and obstetricians from China and 12 from African countries. Child health and care has since been one of the Princess's chief concerns.

## Section of Paediatrics and Child Health

The concept of child health, concerned not just with disease but with the preventive, social and developmental aspects of child health and welfare, was developed in the United Kingdom by Professor Charles McNeil in Edinburgh, where a chair in Child Life and Health was founded in 1931. Following the Beveridge Report of 1942 universities established departments of child health, and the mass evacuation of children during the war focused attention on many defects in the existing system of medical care for children, resulting in malnutrition, psychological disorders and developmental abnormalities. In 1996 the Royal College of Paediatrics and Child Health made it clear that it was concerned with all aspects of health in childhood as well as disease, and in 1999 the Section acknowledged the concept by changing its name accordingly.

There are now many sub-specialties of paediatrics which have to be balanced with general paediatrics in the Section's annual programme. 'Paediatric asthma', 'Diabetes' and 'Children and smoking' have recently been subjects for meetings, and on other occasions specialist interests were catered for by meetings with the Neonatal Society and the Faculty of Child Psychiatry. The annual meeting on cystic fibrosis is now one of the major UK meetings on the subject and commands papers from many specialties, and in the year 2000 a special meeting commemorated the centenary of the founding of the Section's predecessor, the Society for the Study of Disease in Children.

## Section of Rheumatology and Rehabilitation (Plate 50)
originally Balneology and Climatology

The British Balneological and Climatological Society owed its origin to Dr Samuel Hyde of Buxton in Derbyshire, formerly the editor of the *Journal of British and Foreign Health Resorts*, assisted by Dr Septimus Sunderland of London. The Society was established in 1895 'to further the development of those natural resources of climate and natural springs and the encouragement of good fellowship amongst men following that special branch of medical practice'. Dr Harry Lewis of Folkestone was the first President and Sir Edward Sieveking was persuaded to be an Honorary President.[60] Dr Robert Fortescue Fox remembered that the proceedings at the Society's Council meetings were discursive and

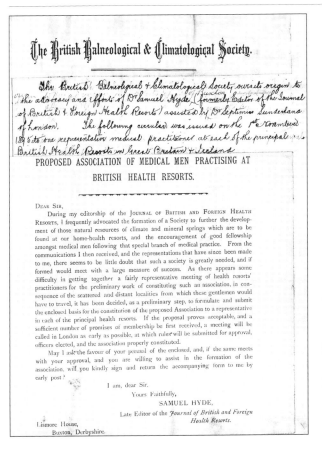

The British Balneological & Climatological Society.

PROPOSED ASSOCIATION OF MEDICAL MEN PRACTISING AT
BRITISH HEALTH RESORTS.

DEAR SIR,

During my editorship of the JOURNAL OF BRITISH AND FOREIGN HEALTH RESORTS, I frequently advocated the formation of a Society to further the development of those natural resources of climate and mineral springs which are to be found at our home-health resorts, and the encouragement of good fellowship amongst medical men following that special branch of medical practice. From the communications I then received, and the representations that have since been made to me, there seems to be little doubt that such a society is greatly needed, and if formed would meet with a large measure of success. As there appears some difficulty in getting together a fairly representative meeting of health resorts' practitioners for the preliminary work of constituting such an association, in consequence of the scattered and distant localities from which these gentlemen would have to travel, it has been decided, as a preliminary step, to formulate and submit the enclosed basis for the constitution of the proposed Association to a representative in each of the principal health resorts. If the proposal proves acceptable, and a sufficient number of promises of membership be first received, a meeting will be called in London as early as possible, at which rules will be submitted for approval, officers elected, and the association properly constituted.

May I ask the favour of your perusal of the enclosed and, if the same meets with your approval, and you are willing to assist in the formation of the association, will you kindly sign and return the accompanying form to me by early post?

I am, dear Sir,

Yours Faithfully,

SAMUEL HYDE,

Late Editor of the *Journal of British and Foreign Health Resorts.*

Lismore House,
Buxton, Derbyshire.

A circular launching the British Balneological and Climatological Society in 1895. The Society became the Section of Balneology and Climatology in 1909, developing into the Section of Physical Medicine (1931), and renamed the Section of Rheumatology and Rehabilitation in 1974.

conversational, with Hyde at the head of the table at Limmers Hotel or Hanover Square, 'a short sturdy figure with tightly-buttoned frock-coat, with ready smiles, gentle persuasive voice and unassuming manner, full of geniality and tact and sometimes conveniently deaf'.[61] Balneology, defined as the scientific medical study of bathing, and climatology, which is the scientific investigation of climatic conditions, were subjects of intense interest to the Victorian medical profession and the public and the popularity of health cures, water treatments, spas and resorts continued into the Edwardian era.

The RMCS had become involved with balneology and climatology through the publication of two authoritative tomes on the *Climates and baths of Great Britain and Ireland* (1895, 1902, see pages 115–16). Contacts had thus been forged between the RMCS and the spa doctors throughout the British Isles and this record of co-operation may have prompted proposals for amalgamation. In the normal course of events the Balneological and Climatological Society, being an occupational group with members dispersed nationwide, hardly fell into line with the mainstream London medical societies that formed the core of the RSM. When first approached about the amalgamation in 1905 the Balneological and Climatological Society had a membership of 380, three-quarters of whom were country Fellows who felt they were entitled to a reduced subscription if they joined the RSM because they were unlikely to enjoy the facilities of the Library and house in London.

The last issue of the *Journal of Balneology and Climatology* gives the flavour of the Society's interests: it featured Dr Ernest Solly's presidential address on 'The municipal management of health resorts', an advertisement for Ripon Spa and notes on December weather on the south coast.[62] There was no hint of the impending death of the Society, nor of its rebirth in October 1909 as a Section of the RSM.

At the last annual dinner of the Society, Dr Robert Fortescue Fox acknowledged 'the honour and advance that for the first time in this country the branch of therapeutics with which they were concerned was to be formally adopted and incorporated by the central body' – the RSM. This was recognition indeed, although he doubted if such a 'fellowship of goodly knights' would ever meet again.[63]

### The first sessions of the Section

Dr Leonard Williams was the Section's first President, assisted by a Chairman of Council, Alfred Street; the Council numbered 32 and there were 12 Vice Presidents. Williams thought too much emphasis had been given to science in the recent past and he attempted to redress the balance between science and empiricism. In addition to the presidential address, the meetings of the first session featured papers on 'The hygiology of Naples', 'The Chiltern Hills and Dales in certain of their natural and medical aspects' and 'Arthritis deformans'.

The last session before the outbreak of war was somewhat limp, with only five meetings: the President was Dr FA de T Mouillot of Harrogate and he spoke about his practice there. Dr Chippingdale put forward a claim for 'London as a health resort and sanitary city', promoting its salubrity and suitability for certain maladies, chiefly of the psychopathic or neuropathic nature.[64]

### Physical treatment of disabled soldiers

During the First World War the Section's War Disablement committee assisted the Army Medical Service by advising on which kind of case was likely to benefit from bath treatments and which resorts were suitable for the military wounded and invalids. Two reports recommended the use of various kinds of remedial baths and other physical treatments needed to prevent 'an army of cripples'.[65]

The Section also held a discussion on 'The physical treatment of medical disabilities induced by war', which was opened by Dr William Gordon, who had improvised a lamp to treat sciatica and leg pains associated with trench fever. The war brought a vast number of new and interesting cases for consideration, from nerve cases to trench foot, but Gordon regretted that the profession generally had not yet recognized 'the immense benefit disabled men derive from physio-therapeutics. The responsibility for the calamity does not lie at the door of the Royal Society of Medicine'. (Recognition for physiotherapists came in 1920 with a grant of a royal charter to the Chartered Society of Massage and Medical Gymnastics.[66])

Likewise, rheumatologists were soon to be encouraged. As the country struggled to its feet Ministry of Health Reports of 1924–28 revealed the high proportion of sickness absence caused by rheumatic disease, accounting for one-sixth in males and one-seventh in females of total sickness absence from work. Rheumatic disease was thus officially recognized as a major problem, and this provided a salutory stimulus to worldwide interest in rheumatoid arthritis and other diseases of the rheumatic group. Dr Fortescue Fox summoned a committee for the study of rheumatology, and in November 1925 a meeting was held at the RSM to consider 'The treatment of rheumatism in industry'. This was attended by Sir George Newman of the Ministry of Health, who spoke of the need for a national rheumatological service with out-patient clinics for physical treatment, and arthritic units at hospitals.[67]

The year 1930 saw the opening of the first rheumatism clinic – the Red Cross Clinic in Peto Place – and specific rheumatology units at hospitals began to be established. A committee of the Royal College of Physicians was established under the chairmanship of a past President of the RSM, Sir Humphry Rolleston, to study the classification and nomenclature of rheumatic disease in 1932 and when its report was published, Lord Horder and Dr William Copeman decided to take the matter further by founding the Empire Rheumatism Council in 1936 (later renamed the Arthritis and Rheumatism Council).

## The Section of Physical Medicine

Meanwhile, the Section of Balneology and Climatology had difficulty in maintaining cohesion among its members, scattered as they were from Torquay to Harrogate. The possibility of amalgamation with the Section of Electro-therapeutics was mooted in 1930, and in the subsequent reshuffle the Sections of Electro-therapeutics and Balneology and Climatology were superseded in 1931 by the Section of Radiology and the Section of Physical Medicine.

The title of Physical Medicine was not ideal, as the Honorary Secretary was the first to admit, yet for over 40 years none better could be found. The chief spokesman for the specialty, Sir Stanton Woods, defined physical medicine 'as that branch of the medical art whch employs physical agents in diagnosis and treatment – heat, electricity, massage, movement, gymnastics, games and productive occupation'.[68]

The need to treat and rehabilitate those wounded in the First World War, for example in the orthopaedic and remedial centres organized by Robert Jones, had given an impetus to occupational therapy and physical medicine, but with the closure of these centres in 1918 physical medicine fell into oblivion. The London Hospital was an exception, leading the way with a Department of Physical Medicine under the direction of Stanton Woods. He worked at the Hospital from 1911 and came to public notice when he was called upon as a specialist in physical medicine to treat King George V for emphysema in 1928, resulting in the recovery of the King and a knighthood for Stanton Woods.

The first general meeting of the Section of Physical Medicine was held at the recently opened Red Cross Clinic: GC Simpson spoke on 'Meteorological factors affecting health' and Sir Robert Jones gave a paper on 'Manipulation'. At the first Council meeting of the Section in June 1931 Stanton Woods made his presence felt, and he succeeded Dr FG Thomson as President the next year. Although Physical Medicine and Radiology were now two Sections they shared a dinner in 1932 when Dr T Watts Eden, the Society's President, spoke of the wide net cast by physical medicine and its valuable contribution to orthopaedic surgery. 'We are living in a drug-ridden age', Watts Eden lamented, 'we are pelted with advertisements from hoardings, from the half-penny post and even from our medical journals. Now while Physical Medicine does not exactly advise us, with Macbeth, to "throw physic to the dogs" it undertakes the all-important mission of proclaiming the healing virtues which reside in nature: in air and water and in changing climate, in light and electricity, in the companionship of the sea, the hills and the forests, and even in the glades of solitude'. Sir Robert Jones, replying on behalf of the guests, was brief – he understood that a jazz band was 'whetting its instruments of torture for the immediate use of the guests... Therefore, as one who firmly believed in scientific manipulation of the limbs for the development of the health of the body he would detain them no longer from indulging in the sanitary exercise which could only be enjoyed to the accompaniment of syncopated music'.[69]

Dr Frank D Howitt, a colleague of Stanton Woods and the first President of the Heberden Society, was an early supporter of the Section as its Honorary Secretary, and President for 1937–38. During the Second World War Howitt acted as consultant in physical medicine to the army and with a team of experts (including four who were later Presidents of the Section) established rehabilitation units at home and abroad. When in 1952 Howitt gave the Samuel Hyde Memorial lecture on 'The evolution of physical medicine' he recalled that those who came together under the banner of physical medicine at the RSM represented different facets of medical endeavour; some had specialized in clinical fields, others in particular forms of treatment based on applied anatomy, physiology or physics. 'Yet they felt that in Physical Medicine they had found an outlet, an expression and a platform for their work. And it was the primary duty of the new Section to integrate their endeavours and to find a common denominator'.

Howitt remembered early meetings on 'The effect of strains on children' and 'Physical education', and a debate on 'The need for the promotion of physical fitness' which took place 18 months before the outbreak of the Second World War and elicited much abuse for its militaristic flavour.[70]

The integration of the various interests within the Section proved difficult and the programme failed to satisfy everyone. There was rivalry between the specialist groups of rheumatology and rehabilitation: Howitt thought the two should be synonymous while Copeman stood for rheumatology alone and was anxious not to be associated with physical medicine. The subsequent introduction of the NHS had the effect of encouraging the feud. While Stanton Woods urged patience and co-operation, provincial members of the Section failed to appear at meetings and during the session of 1940–41 air raids so interrupted the business of the Section that only two meetings were held. Revival came in 1942–43 with an average attendance of 69 at meetings. The urgent need for the treatment and rehabilitation of the forces was uppermost in members' minds and Dr Philippe Bauwens was elected President, serving for double the usual time (1942–44).

### Dr P Bauwens

Dr Philippe Bauwens was in charge of the Electro-therapy Department of St Thomas' Hospital, where he pioneered electromyography. His presidential address, delivered at a time when plans were being laid for a state medical service, presented his ideas on the future of physical medicine. The statement was described by one editor as wise and appropriate and Lord Horder reinforced this; he later became President of the British Association of Physical Medicine and did more than anyone to set rheumatology and rehabilitation on the road to respectability.

Bauwens had strong views on the future of physical medicine and nothing good to say about the Section, which may possibly explain why the address was not published in the *Proceedings*. He spoke with derision about the union of the late Balneological Section with 'one of the divorced partners' of the old Electro-therapeutics Section, a union which 'remained from a scientific and other standpoints as sterile as chastity itself'. Efforts made in other quarters to enhance the position of physical medicine had proved equally disappointing. 'It must be admitted', Bauwens continued, 'that when we cast an unbiased mind back to physical medicine in pre-war days, we find ourselves thinking of something rather shapeless and unsatisfactory. As a group our interests and activities were strangely heterogeneous and a common factor in our aims was far from apparent. Indeed, physical medicine almost could have been described as a receptacle for all forms of therapeutic flotsam and jetsam which might remotely be termed physical'.[71]

### Physical medicine, rheumatology and rehabilitation

The increased demand for physiotherapy and rehabilitation, together with the reorganization of hospital care during the Second World War, gave wider recognition to the importance of physical medicine. The army instituted a Physical Development Centre in 1941 under the direction of physical medicine specialists, who also bore the main burden of the hospital rehabilitation of the wounded. Stanton Woods had presided over the first International Congress of Physical Medicine in 1936 and acted as adviser to the Ministry of Health during the war. The status of the specialty was further enhanced by the formation of the British Association for Physical Medicine in 1943, and in the following year the Diploma in Physical Medicine was established.

By 1952 almost every teaching hospital in England was staffed by a consultant physician in physical medicine and the future of the specialty looked bright, although Dr Howitt warned of its fragmentation if a separate specialty of rheumatology was recognized. This looked increasingly likely: the Empire Rheumatism Council had been inaugurated at the RSM in 1936, the year in which the Heberden Society was founded; the British League Against Rheumatism was established in 1946 and the British Rheumatism Association the next year. A leading light in these associations was Dr WSC Copeman, author of a *Textbook of the rheumatic diseases* (1948 with further editions). He saw 1948 as the *annus mirablis* of rheumatology, although others have cited 1949, the year the International Congress of Rheumatology was held in New York, at which it was announced that certain corticosteroids were able to reverse many acute manifestations of rheumatic inflammation.[72]

At the RSM good attendances at Section meetings reflected the attention now being given to physical medicine. This was confirmed by Stanton Woods who saw the Second World War as the turning point, bringing 'an ever-increasing appreciation of its importance by the medical profession and by the health and hospital authorities throughout the country ... There has been a complete re-orientation of physical medicine, a widening of facilities, organization and scope as to present almost a revolution in the treatment of disease'.[73]

In 1952 the first International Congress of Physical Medicine took place in London and the programme covered recent developments in physical medicine, rehabilitation and resettlement and rheumatic disorders. The word rehabilitation – Howitt referred to it as 'a clumsy, omnibus term'– caused confusion at first, only becoming generally recognized during the Second World War. The Section had begun to focus on the subject with a discussion on 'Rehabilitation in disease and injury of the chest' during the winter of 1942–43; this and other meetings attracted as many as 70, including a high proportion of members of other Sections. One of the highlights of 1946 was a summer meeting at the first civil centre for retraining the disabled at Egham. Squadron Leader CB Wynn Parry's suggestion for a symposium on RAF rehabilitation proved equally successful. Wynn Parry became President of the Section in 1968 and was instrumental in establishing the Diploma of Medical Rehabilitation in 1976.

*Lectures*

The Samuel Hyde lecture is a legacy from the British Balneological and Climatological Society and was first given in May 1911 by Fortescue Fox, who described himself as 'one of the old Balneological Guard'. His special interest was medical hydrology, defined as 'the science of waters, vapours, and mineral or organic deposits in connection with waters, as used in medicine both by internal administration and in the form of baths and applications'. He continued on this theme for three meetings.[74]

Two further lectures are organized by the Section in memory of Richard Kovaks and Ernest Fletcher. In 1953 Mrs Ina Kovaks of New York informed the Council of an endowment in memory of her late husband, who had been an Honorary member of the Section before his death in 1951. The fund was established in 1955 and was intended in the first place for the purchase of books on physical medicine for the Library; it was later extended to sponsor a lecture. As the Kovaks lecturer for 1961, Dr Bauwens spoke of Kovaks as 'the Boswell of physical medicine' (his book on *Electrotherapy and light therapy* was a classic). His widow also gave the Section a silver cigar box, and after her death a legacy increased the fund substantially, enabling the sponsorship of a visiting Fellow from the UK and the USA in alternate years.

The third lecture commemorates Dr Ernest Fletcher, who had devoted most of his life to the study of chronic rheumatic disorders. After his death friends at the Charterhouse Rheumatism Clinic collected £500, which was entrusted to the RSM in 1963. Dr Morris Ziff was the first to hold this lectureship, coming from Texas to address the Section in December 1964.[75]

## Section of Rheumatology and Rehabilitation

Dr Copeman, a medical historian as well as a rheumatologist, maintained that rheumatic diseases had been recognized since the fifth century BC. More recently, in the history of the RSM and its antecedent the Medical and Chirurgical Society, Benjamin Brodie had presented his first paper on 'Diseases of the joints' to the MCS in 1813, the preliminary to his seminal work of 1818 (see pages 30–31). A modern renaissance of rheumatology dawned in 1928 with the Ministry of Health Reports on Chronic Rheumatism, yet the subject did not come of age until after the Second World War. Dr Howitt had suggested that the Section's name should be changed to include rheumatology and rehabilitation in 1946, but the Council of the RSM did not encourage a change in the Section's name nor did the proposal for a new Section of Rheumatology gain approval, despite the fact that Lord Cohen, President of numerous societies and councils, promoted rheumatology.

The advances were such as to necessitate the rewriting of nearly all the chapters of Copeman's *Textbook of rheumatic diseases* in 1964, yet the chasm widened between rheumatologists, who had an increasing number of effective drugs to call upon, and those who were more interested in the machinery of physical medicine and rehabilitation. The Section strove to reconcile the differences by adjusting its objectives in 1964 'to advance the study of the causation, diagnosis and treatment of the rheumatic diseases, and those locomotor disorders to which physical methods of treatment contribute and to develop this along scientific lines'. The President for 1963–64, Dr R Michael Mason (commemorated in the Michael Mason Medal of the British Society for Rheumatology) proposed the name of the Section should be adjusted to Physical Medicine and Rheumatology. He had reviewed the Section's programme over the last five years and had analysed the diagnostic categories of patients referred to physical medicine consultants: the figures indicated that 80.9% of patients were suffering from rheumatic disease. But Mason's attempt to change the Section's name evoked 'unreasonable passions', the Section's Honorary Secretary, Dr George Kersley, recalled. Doomed to failure in 1964, it was nevertheless 'this Section which a few years later proved to be the vanguard of change by becoming officially the Section of Rheumatology and Rehabilitation in 1974'.[76]

With the prospect of joining the EEC looming, the Section's Council resolved that 'our medical house must be put in order' and when a Specialist Advisory Committee on Physical Medicine changed its name to Rheumatology, Dr DRL Newton, the Section's President for 1972–73, thought it was high time for a change in the Section's title to reconcile Rheumatology and Rehabilitation. Accordingly, in 1973 the Section's objectives were redefined: 'to advance the scientific study of rheumatology, which is that branch of medicine concerned with the diseases of connective tissue and disorders of the musculo-skeletal system' and 'to advance the scientific study of rehabilitation which is the restoration to optimum function of people suffering from disability particularly of the locomotor system'.[77]

The British Association for Physical Medicine likewise changed its name to the British Association of Rheumatology and Rehabilitation, and in 1984 fused with the Heberden Society to form the British Society for Rheumatology, while the Medical Disability Society took rehabilitation under its wing. These two societies represent the two disciplines which at the RSM remain in one Section, 'living together in happy biosis with some overlap, but each recognized as a reputable clinical teaching and research entity'.[78]

The fields of immunology and molecular biology have led to a rapid increase in the understanding of rheumatological disorders and new drugs have become available, yet osteoarthritis remains a common rheumatological disorder and 2% of people worldwide suffer from rheumatoid arthritis. This all provides a rich source for papers and the Section's millennium meeting took as its theme 'The seven ages of rheumatology'.

## Section of Psychiatry (Plate 51)

This was the first Section to be formed *de novo* after the amalgamation in the sense that before the formation of the Section of Psychiatry in 1912 all the Sections derived from pre-existing medical societies. Once psychiatry showed the way, the Section of the History of Medicine followed in the autumn of the same year and the precedent had been set for others.

The initiative in setting up the Section of Psychiatry was taken by the Council of the RSM in response to prodding from Sir Henry Morris (President of the RSM 1910–12) and Dr Frederick Mott, the psychiatric pathologist. Both echoed Lord Haldane who, as Chairman of the Royal Commission on University Education in London, had remarked that in a recent work on psychiatry he found German, French and American writers quoted but only one Englishman. This led him to conclude that 'the English profession does not stand very high as an authority in psychiatry'. Mott confirmed that the subject had in recent years been neglected in this country and that he had personally wondered if a Section of the RSM might correct this.[79]

In March 1912, at a meeting for those interested in establishing the Section held at 15 Cavendish Square, Mott suggested that it should be organized on the same lines as the Neurological Section (of which he was currently the President) and he conveyed the hearty approval of Dr Henry Maudsley for the proposed section.[80] Mott and Maudsley were already plotting what was to be the Maudsley Hospital and Maudsley was elected an Honorary corresponding member of the Section, attending a meeting at the Claybury laboratory where Mott was the Director, in December 1916.[81]

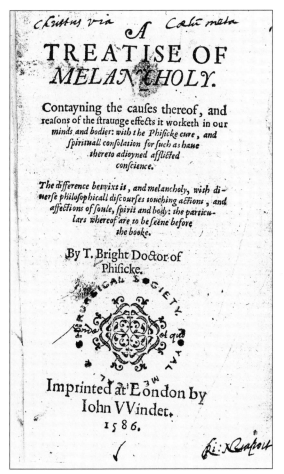

The first book on psychiatry in English was written by Timothy Bright, physician to St Bartholomew's Hospital, in 1586. Bright's *Treatise of melancholy* gave the first comprehensive description of depression in English. Bright's work was quoted by Robert Burton in the *Anatomy of melancholy* (1621) and was probably used by Shakespeare as a source for Hamlet's melancholia. Bright is also known as the inventor of shorthand, 'an arte of short, swift and secret writing by character' (1589).

The Section was at first described as being for the study of mental diseases, the Council of the RSM having some difficulty with the pronunciation of the word 'psychiatry'. A lexicographer was consulted, who advised that if the Society was going to adopt the term it should settle the pronunciation itself.[82] The aim of the Section was to bring English contributions on mental diseases to the same high standard as those on neurology, an objective that may well have originated with Mott, who had the interests of both Sections at heart. The Section of Neurology of the RSM was particularly strong at this time, supported by Gordon Holmes, Henry Head, Victor Horsley, Wilfred Harris and N Bishop Harman and its example appeared enviable to psychiatrists.

The annual gathering of the Section of the British Medical Association was not in a position to foster the scientific study of mental disease consistently, and the Medico-Psychological Association was in disarray. The latter had been wooed by the RMCS in 1870 and 1907, but with few London members and interests focusing on asylum administration, the Medico-Psychological chose to remain independent although many of its members were interested in joining the Section of Psychiatry of the RSM. Ultimately, the Medico-Psychological Association evolved into the Royal College of Psychiatrists, but while it was labouring through a difficult phase it fell to the Section of the RSM to promote psychiatry in this country by attracting psychiatrists, psychologists, criminologists and neurologists to its meetings with a view to spreading knowledge of mental disease.

Eighty-five founder-members elected the genial Sir George Savage as the first President of the Section. Then aged 70, Savage was at the top of his profession, yet his recommended treatment of Virginia Woolf (rest, food and a baby) illustrated the limited perception of psychiatrists in the early years of the 20th century. Dr Mott and Dr R Percy Smith were Vice Presidents and Dr RH Cole and Dr Bernard Hart were the Honorary Secretaries as the Section swung into action in the summer of 1912. The officers decided that the work of the Section would be divided between the discussion of special subjects at meetings at 1 Wimpole Street and practical meetings in laboratories and hospitals – the first took place at Bethlem in December.[83]

### Rows and Orr

Richard G Rows and David Orr had translated *Modern problems in psychiatry* from the Italian in 1909, and together they presented their work on the influence of toxins on the nervous system to the Section in January 1914. In the same session Rows' ambitious paper on 'The importance of the personality in mental disorders' was published in the *Proceedings*.[84] He recounted his interviews with two women suffering from religious delusions, and Rows concluded that in both cases there was 'a predisposing factor in the abnormal psycho-sexual development and in both the breakdown occurred after an emotional shock'. Rows was one of the first in this country to seize on the work of Freud and interest in his paper was such that discussion was postponed to a special meeting.

### Repercussions of the Great War

The Great War produced an orgy of neuroses as cases of shellshock reached a peak of 16,000 in 1916 with the battle of the Somme. Rows, Orr, Hart and Maurice Craig led the investigation into shellshock at the Maghull Military Hospital from 1914 and their work gave rise to several papers and discussions at the RSM. The subject was debated at a meeting of the Sections of Psychiatry and Neurology in January 1916 when Mott explained that shellshock was generated by the explosion of heavy ammunition such as large shells, mines, aerial torpedoes, 'whizz-bangs', trench mortars and bombs.[85] Mott was President of the Section from 1914 to 1916 and later wrote *War neuroses and shell shock*. Sir Maurice Craig of Guy's Hospital was the author of *Psychological medicine* (1912) and was to be President of the Section from 1928 to 1929.

The work of these men in the treatment of shellshock and war neuroses in the military hospitals during the First World War established their reputations in civilian as well as military psychiatry. In the long term their achievement was to bring fresh insight to mental disorders and their treatment, stimulating a reassessment of insanity and the reform of 19th-century lunatic asylums and lunacy laws.

### Jung and Freud

Dr William McDougall's presidential address of 1918 reviewed the present state of psychology and he paid tribute to the advances made by Carl Gustav Jung, who himself addressed a meeting of the Section in July 1919, one of his first public engagements after the war. Jung apologized that his paper on the problems of psychogenesis was not comprehensive, 'but the point I wish to make is that in psychiatry we have a field for psychological research which is wide and not yet cultivated'. Jung's paper was well received. 'The dour old Scot McDougall' was said to have remarked afterwards, 'Well, Switzerland has at last justified her existence'.[86]

According to his biographers, Jung returned to London in 1939 to give a paper on 'The psychogenesis of schizophrenia' and to take part in a discussion at the RSM on 'The symbolic life', when he was confronted by a bishop. He 'showed both sides of his enigmatic personality. On the platform he was tigerish; uncompromising and witheringly sarcastic; but when the session was over he was all broad smiles and geniality and marched out of the hall arm-in-arm with the gaitered divine'. He was awarded the Honorary Fellowship of the Society in this year.[87]

The Society had acknowledged the influence of Sigmund Freud's work in awarding him an Honorary Fellowship in 1935 and his daughter Anna was to be honoured likewise (see page 315). Freud *père* died in London in 1939, having undergone treatment for cancer administered by Dr Neville Finzi, a leading radiologist and founder of the Section of Radiology (see page 286). After Freud's death the Section of Psychiatry held a memorial meeting when Ernest Jones, who was to write three volumes on Freud's life and works, led the tributes. A past President of the Section, Professor Edward Mapother, spoke of Freud's fertile and penetrating mind: 'he brought to psychology and psychiatry more of the imagination of the great artist than of the solid objectivity and rigid logic of the scientist'.[88]

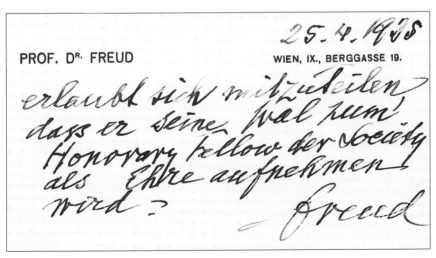

Professor Sigmund Freud accepted the Honorary Fellowship of the RSM in 1935.
This represented the first official recognition in this country of Freud's work; the
honour came shortly before his 79th birthday.

## Legislation and education

In the 1920s the Section became preoccupied by proposed changes in the law regarding the insane. The debate commenced in 1924 when the President Dr TB Hyslop declared that insanity was incapable of definition, and continued until 1927 when Dr R Langdon-Down's presidential address reviewed the work of the Royal Commission on Lunacy and Mental Disorder and urged the government to adopt a progressive attitude.[89] Like-minded psychiatrists, civil servants and MPs helped to shape the Mental Treatment Act of 1930, which transformed the position of psychiatry in this country by legalizing admission to mental hospitals without certification. The Act was to have another beneficial effect in establishing the first psychiatric clinics.

The Section also took up the question of the education of medical students in psychology, described in the 1930s as 'almost nothing'. Dr Bernard Hart used his presidential address of 1931 to urge that psychology should be raised to a level with other scientific disciplines.[90]

## Cyclothymia

The National Council for Mental Hygiene, this Section and the Royal Medico-Psychological Association formed a committee to investigate cyclothymia, apparently as the result of a joint discussion held by the Sections of Psychiatry and Neurology in February 1930. Sir Edward Farquhar Buzzard opened with an address on the milder forms of manic-depressive psychosis, prompting Dr H Crichton Miller to substitute the word cyclothymia as more appropriate. Dr Neill Hobhouse admitted that cases were not recognized by the profession in general and he hoped that the adoption of the word cyclothymia would 'mark a step in the fulfilment of the object which inspired this discussion', namely the diagnosis and treatment of manic-depressive psychosis. Dr Helen Boyle, one of the first women to work as a psychiatrist in this country, took part in this discussion. She was the founder of the Lady Chichester Hospital in Hove and she had outlined her ideas for 'The ideal clinic for the treatment of nervous and borderline cases' in a paper of 1922, which members discussed over two meetings.[91]

As for the subject of cyclothymia, the committee's report was pronounced negative in 1932 and was not published.[92]

## Maudsley men

Sir Frederick Mott, as he became in 1919, was instrumental in founding the Section and the Maudsley Hospital. Advances in psychiatry in this country were to centre on the Maudsley, which opened in 1923 as a treatment centre for the mentally sick. Mott and Dr Miguel Prados y Such from Madrid were already producing important results in the pathological laboratory, and in 1921 they presented their studies in dementia praecox to the Section: Mott's work on the pathology of dementia praecox is probably his most important contribution to psychiatry.[93]

The first Medical Superintendent of the Maudsley was Professor Edward Mapother, who set rigorous standards for his staff. As President of the Section in 1933 he pleaded for the development of research in psychiatry and he did his utmost to stimulate this. The emigration of German psychiatrists was just beginning and Mapother invited Dr Mayer-Gross to the Maudsley, where he was joined by the neuropathologist Dr Alfred Meyer from Bonn. When Professor FL Golla became Director of the Maudsley he too encouraged or invited researchers and scientists to join him, establishing the Hospital's reputation for research and teaching. These 'Maudsley men' inspired many meetings of the Section with their papers.

Golla was himself President of the Section from 1939 to 1940 and was to be followed by several of the Maudsley team. Among them stood Professor Aubrey Lewis, whose term in office (1946–47) brought Dr Eysenck to a meeting to speak on 'The measurement of personality' – his personality theory was soon to achieve publicity with the publication of *Dimensions of personality* (1947). Later in this session a meeting was held 'to discuss the social distinctions of the adult homosexual and some of the reasons for it, and to point out our ignorance'. No statistics could be relied upon because no systematic sociological enquiry had been made... 'we need and need badly a fact-finding investigation'. Dr EA Bennett referred to Ernest Jones's claim that 'psychoanalysts are able to obtain a large portion of cures' and the discussion went so far as to consider homosexuality as a crime.[94]

The stream of Maudsley men continued with the presidencies of Professor Desmond Curran (1951–52) and Dr Mayer-Gross, a world authority on schizophrenia, in 1954. There soon followed a succession of three – Sargant, Stengel and Slater. Sargant has gone down in Munk's Roll as the most important figure in postwar psychiatry; Stengel was an authority on the problems of suicide, while Slater has been acclaimed as the founder of psychiatric genetics in Britain; he was made an Honorary Fellow of the RSM in 1976. Another of the school, Dr Denis Hill, was elected President in 1964 and was later knighted; Dr Wilfred Warren joined the Maudsley after the War and was President of the Section in 1970.

## *Sargant, Slater and Hill*
During the Second World War Dr William Sargant and Dr Eliot Slater worked at the Sutton Emergency Hospital (later called Belmont), where the first 1,000 admissions included some 150 men with acute hysterical loss of memory, a condition rare in peace-time. It was found that prompt injections of sodium amytal brought the memory back but if these soldiers were returned to duty their symptoms recurred. Sargant and Slater's findings on 'Amnesic syndromes in war' were published in the Section's *Proceedings* for 1941, and Sargant later reported that their recommendations that such unstable patients should be discharged from the army were followed.[95]

Also at Sutton Emergency Hospital was Dr Denis Hill, a fellow-member of the Section with Sargant and Slater. Hill set up a large and efficient department at the Hospital for investigating brainwave activity, and during an ebb in the tide of military casualties he and Sargant undertook research into the relation between low blood sugar levels and violence. One of their cases, who had stabbed his mother to death, made legal history when on the medical evidence provided by Hill and Sargant, the jury delivered a verdict of guilty but insane.

In a second case the Judge ruled that the brainwave records shown by Hill and Sargant were not relevant, an opinion shared by Dr Norwood East of the Prisons Medical Services and President of this Section 1943–44. This session was dominated by the medico-legal debate surrounding the two trials with which Hill and Sargant were associated. Norwood East gave his presidential address on 'The state, the criminal and the psychiatrist', and this was followed by a joint meeting of the Section with the Medico-Legal Society when the President held forth on 'Criminal responsibility and medical culpability'. At the next meeting of the Section Dr Hill presented his paper on 'Cerebral dysrhythmia and its signif-icance in aggressive behaviour'. He showed abnormal records of brainwaves, sometimes approaching very near to epilepsy or showing actual epilepsy, taken from people who had recently been hanged for murder. Dr Alfred Meyer and Sargant spoke in the discussion; then, 'at a crisis in the debate', Norwood East 'so lost his nerve as even to accuse Dr Hill of distorting the brainwave evidence. This shameful scene provoked a state of almost tempo-rary war between Sir Norwood East and some of the doctors engaged on brainwave research'. Some 20 years later Sargant reported that the relevance of Hill's brainwave research to crimes of violence was generally accepted.[96]

## ECT

Dr Lothar Kalinowsky of Berlin introduced electro-convulsive therapy to Britain through the pages of the *Lancet* in December 1939, and on the 30th of that month Professor Golla, Dr W Grey Walter and Dr GWT Fleming presented an account of the first ECT trials in England. The Section responded quickly, organizing a meeting for 9 January 1940 at which Kalinowsky, Golla, Grey Walter and Fleming discussed 'Electrically induced convulsions', followed by WH Shepley and JS McGregor on 'The clinical applications of electrically induced convulsions'. The latter described the apparatus and techniques as modifications of those first devised by the Italian Cerletti in 1938. The advice of Kalinowsky was also acknowledged, and in his comments Kalinowsky emphasized the harmlessness of ECT.[97] Dr RK Freudenberg, who was to be President of the Section 1965–66, spoke of the 'curability' of mental disorder by ECT. The *Lancet*, however, advised caution before 'electrically induced convulsions are allowed to become the fashionable method of treating severe psychoses',[98] and the public was even more suspicious about what was perceived to be a violent treatment.

### The Second World War and its aftermath

As Professor Edward Mapother stressed at a meeting on 'Nervous disease in the fighting services' (1936), neuroses had been one of the largest medical problems of the Great War, far larger than official figures conveyed, and would probably be so again.[99]

He predicted correctly, and several Section meetings held between 1939 and 1945 concentrated on war neuroses. Other papers dealt with the effects of wartime industrial conditions on mental health; Dr Aubrey Lewis raised the question of whether a man with 'effort syndrome' should be in the army, and Sargant and Slater presented their findings on wartime amnesic syndromes (see above). Group therapy was becoming acceptable and in 1943 Lt Joshua Bierer reported on 'A new form of group psychotherapy' – this was his experiment in helping patients to run clubs and hence form relationships. Three years later Bierer founded the Marlborough Day Hospital in London, which led to the recognition and expansion of day-care for the mentally ill.[100]

The emigration of psychiatrists from Germany and Austria brought a rich intellectual tradition to British psychiatry, represented in the Section by Meyer, Mayer-Gross, Freudenberg, Stengel, Guttman and Strauss. Keen to foster British psychiatry, the Section joined members of the Royal Medico-Psychological Association on a committee to advise on the future of psychiatry and all its branches in this country. When Dr Erwin Stengel, founder of the Department of Psychiatry at Sheffield University, gave his presidential address in 1957 on the teaching of the subject in Britain, his verdict was that the standard was variable, and at Sheffield at least *in statu nascendi*. Doubtless at his invitation, Anna Freud gave a paper during this session, divulging the research studies being carried out at her Hampstead Child Therapy Clinic. This had grown steadily under her leadership and research there was breaking new ground.[101]

### Anglo-American Symposium

In September 1949 the Section organized an Anglo-American Symposium to discuss the problems arising from recent developments in psychosurgery, neurophysiology and physical treatments in psychiatry. The fourth International Neurological Congress had recently taken place in Paris and Dr Sargant saw this as the opportunity to divert eminent American colleagues to London on their way home from Paris. Sir Henry Dale, President of the RSM at the time, confessed that having opened the symposium he had not intended to take any part in the meetings, 'but he had found the whole atmosphere of the discussion so intensely stimulating' that he had sat through the whole 'rare feast of knowledge and ideas'. Among the speakers were Professor Golla and Dr JR Rees of the Tavistock Clinic.[102]

## A Royal College and the British Association

The quest for a royal college of psychiatrists was launched in the 1960s amid strong feelings. In March 1963 John G Howells advanced a resolution advocating a college, and this was the major issue at a special meeting of the Royal Medico-Psychological Association held at the RSM in November. 'The meeting was full of excitement', Howells wrote, 'the ebb and flow of argument, and the decisive interventions were memorable'. Dr Sargant appealed against a break with the Royal College of Physicians; another past President of the Section, Desmond Curran, campaigned against the proposed college in the medical press and a future President, Denis Hill, promoted a Faculty instead. Surprisingly, in view of the opposition, the vote was in favour of a college, subject to postal ballot. The committees entrusted to petition the Privy Council for a college and to formulate by-laws and examinations included a heavy quota of Presidents of the Section of Psychiatry: Stengel, Slater, Sargant, Roth, Warren, Skottowe and Shapiro. Their efforts eventually met with success and the Royal College of Psychiatrists was incorporated in 1971.[103] The stormy meeting at 1 Wimpole Sreet had proved productive.

While the Royal College was in gestation there were moves afoot to found a society, association or academy of psychopharmacology. The discovery of LSD in 1943 and the introduction of chlorpromazine in 1954 initiated the psychopharmacological era, with British scientists embarking on research and trials in different centres. There was no existing association to further psychopharmacology, improve standards and develop policy so it was proposed to establish an academy to fulfil this function. The proponents and opponents faced each other at two meetings at the RSM in November 1974, leading to the formation of the British Association for Psychopharmacology. The new Association held its first clinical meeting, which 'floundered rather' at the RSM.[104]

## The later decades of the 20th century

The influence of the Maudsley Hospital was enduring, as Professor Stengel stressed in 1963: 'the importance of the Maudsley and its responsibility as a training centre cannot be overrated'. The first President of the 1970s, Dr Warren, was a 'Maudsley man' and other distinguished Presidents of this era included Dr Freudenberg, Dr Desmond Pond, Dr Martin Roth (who as Sir Martin returned to address a meeting in 1980) and Dr Felix Post, who specialized in geriatric psychiatry.

By the end of the 1960s an anti-psychiatry movement was under way and attendances at Section meetings began to fall. At one Council meeting in January 1973 23 resignations were registered (the subscription to the Society had recently been increased). Although the Section possessed a membership of over 500 sometimes only 10 people attended a meeting, and its future hung in the balance. The problem was identified as alternative attractions – particularly in London, where a wealth of lectures and courses were offered.[105] There was little support from younger psychiatrists and 'anti-psychiatry' was even proposed as a subject for discussion in 1974.

The situation continued to deteriorate and in 1980 the Medical Services Secretary, Dr Bennette, calculated that the Section was about half the size it had been 10 years before. Changes in the programme and the efforts of Dr TL Dunn brought membership numbers up to 460 in 1984, and four years later an essay prize was instigated to encourage trainees. By 1991 Dr Dunn was pleased to report good attendances at meetings on philosophy, community care, political issues and child psychiatry; all-day and joint meetings were also successful. Guest speakers were popular, and in the first year of the new millennium the Section managed to entice Professor Roy Porter of the Wellcome Trust and Professor Kay Jamison from Johns Hopkins Medical School to a meeting on 'The law and mental illness'.

## Section of the History of Medicine (Plate 52)

Four years before his death, Sir William Osler put it on record that he had completed 10 'extraordinarily happy' years as Regius Professor of Medicine at Oxford. Reflecting modestly on his achievements, he continued, 'I have not done much in the profession here, but I have done 3 useful things, or better, helped to: (1) The Association of British Physicians. (2) The Quarterly Journal of Medicine. (3) The Historical Section of the Roy. Soc. Medicine'.[106]

The history of medicine was already arousing interest at the RSM before Osler founded the Section. Dr Joseph Frank Payne was personally interested in the subject and had in 1907 obtained approval from the Council for one meeting in each session to be set apart for papers or discussions on the history and antiquities of medicine, the exhibition of books, manuscripts, works of art, instruments or other objects.[107] Following Dr Payne's initiative a meeting devoted to medical history took place at the RSM on 19 June 1907, when Mr D'Arcy Power gave a paper on Dr Bayley and his works (1529–92), accompanied by the exhibition of Bayley's *Treatise on the preservation of eyesight*; Dr FW Cock showed Dr Richard Mead's 18th-century watch and various other medical antiquities were exhibited to 21 Fellows, Osler among them.[108]

Long before this, however, a collection of antique obstetrical instruments formerly belonging to the Chamberlen family were shown in 1818 to a meeting of the Medical and Chirurgical Society (see pages 99–100). The history of the instruments, including the midwifery forceps with which the name is associated, provided the subject of a paper given by Dr Robert Lee in 1861, considered to be of sufficient merit to warrant publication in the *Transactions*.[109]

Sir D'Arcy Power claimed that the History of Medicine Section had its roots in discussions he had with Osler *circa* 1900, when they had toyed with the possibility of establishing a society for the study of the history of medicine, 'to be called the Freind Society and we hoped that Dr Payne would become its President [John Freind was the first in this country to chronicle medical history in his *History of physick* (1725–26)]. The project failed and it was not until Sir William Osler came to Oxford that it was possible to revive it'.[110]

### Sir William Osler founds the Section (Plate 53)

It took Osler to launch the History of Medicine Section in 1912, as recalled by Dr Raymond Crawfurd, President of the Section from 1916 to 1918. 'I doubt if it would ever have come into existence but for his quickening influence: he acted like a magnet in gathering together a company of original members'. Osler was the Section's first President and his presence in the chair was 'a sure draw'. He contributed some papers personally but his chief faculty lay in extracting papers from apparently unproductive sources.[111]

Osler planned the Section carefully, sending out 168 private letters to ascertain the number likely to join. MacAlister was impressed: 'You are really the finest quality of terra cotta brick! If other people who suggest things would do as you do, I might possibly live a few years longer'. Sir Richard Douglas Powell, on the other hand, was not in favour of Osler's proposal for a new Section: 'I think the History and Literature of Medicine ought to form part of the present Medical Section of the RSM. It seems to me a mistake to multiply the Sections by too many subdivisions. Indeed Medicine is already so divided that the Medical Section is really starved for interesting papers and I am told that attendances at this section are poor. Why not have an occasional paper or address on History in its proper place, the Section of Medicine?'.[112]

Osler was not to be deterred. He recruited support for his Section from Sir Francis Champneys, President of the RSM from 1912 to 1914, from Dr Crawfurd, recently Dean of King's College Medical School and later knighted, Sir Thomas Clifford Allbutt,

Sir Ronald Ross, Sir William Selby Church, Sir Henry Morris and Professor Richard Caton. The organizing committee met twice in October, and about 160 attended the first meeting on 20 November 1912. Osler then expressed his hope that the Section would be a meeting-ground for scholars, students and 'all those who feel that the study of the history of medicine has a value in education'. In 1913 he reported to one of his Baltimore friends that 'our new Section in the History of Medicine is going to be a great success ... I was very anxious to have Allbutt or Norman Moore as President but the younger men would have neither of them, & insisted that I should be elected: I am sorry in a way as I am afraid Moore was rather hurt but I have had a nice talk with him about it'.[113]

Osler's approach to medical history was a broad one. At the inaugural meeting of the Section he spoke on 'A Down survey manuscript of William Petty' (a 17th-century legal record/survey of Ireland); in May 1918 he gave a paper about 'The first printed documents relating to modern anaesthesia'. At the conclusion of his talk on anaesthesia, during which he emphasized the achievement of Dr WT Morton in 1846, he presented the first printed documents relating to the administration of anaesthesia to the Society. The pamphlets, Morton's report in *The Boston Medical and Surgical Journal* of 18 November 1846, his account of the inhalation of sulphuric ether (1847) and a fifth edition of *Letheon* (1847) had been obtained from Morton's son, and they are inscribed with Osler's notes and quotes.[114]

Osler encouraged others to submit papers on subjects that ranged from Rabelais to the portraits of William Harvey. He introduced occasional lectures and the publication of monographs such as the lectures of Professor Morris Jastrow of the University of Pennsylvania. Jastrow was invited by Osler to give a lecture on 'The medicine of the Babylonians and Assyrians', and this attracted 70 Fellows and 39 visitors to a meeting in October 1913. Jastrow was impressed by the 'most remarkable group of physicians and other scholars' from London, Oxford and Cambridge assembled at the meeting by Osler; 'it was as though he wanted to ensure the continuity of research by encouraging the next generation to go on – in every field'.[115]

The lack of scholarship of some papers soon came in for criticism, to which Osler responded, 'We cannot make medical historians in a couple of years'. He admitted that perhaps the material presented to the Section lacked research; however, 'I do not think there is much that could be called folk-lore or gossip' and he looked forward to the time when real scholars might become associated with the Section.[116]

Osler was still badgering friends to submit papers to the Section in the autumn of 1919. He died that December and at the next Section meeting D'Arcy Power, the current President, gave a short eulogy on Osler and his approach to history: 'To his urbanity and friendliness we owe it that the Section is more like a family than an integral part of a great scientific Society; to his wide culture that we admit – as is shown this evening by our papers – subjects which are germane to but are not actually a part of the history of medicine'.[117]

Osler had presented Morton's articles and valuable works by Harvey and Rösslin to the Library. After his death it was revealed that he had bequeathed to the RSM a collection of Dr William Withering's letters in the 'hope that some member of the Historical Section with [sic] edit them carefully'. The letters are preserved in the Society's manuscript collection[118] and in 1986 Dr Ronald Mann published a facsimile of the letters, *William Withering and the foxglove* (the Library also possesses a first edition of Withering's *Account of the foxglove*, Plate 47).

## Presidents

Many well-known authors and medical historians followed in Osler's footsteps as Presidents of the Section: Professor Charles Singer (1920–22), Sir Humphry Rolleston

(1930–31), Sir St Clair Thomson (1933–35), Sir Walter Langdon-Brown (1939–40), Dr EA Underwood (1948–50), Sir Zachary Cope (1954–56), Dr WSC Copeman (1964–66). True to the Oslerian tradition, academics and experts in many fields have been called upon to deliver papers to the Section, from T Wilson Parry on 'Prehistoric trephined skulls' (1921, 1936) to Terence Cawthorne, an ear surgeon and President of the RSM from 1962 to 1964, who gave papers on 'The last illness of Oscar Wilde', 'Goya's illness' and 'Julius Caesar and the falling sickness'. Cawthorne was elected President of this Section in 1968 but died before delivering his address, which was presented posthumously: 'Toulouse Lautrec. Triumph over infirmity'.[119]

## Lean years

The initial success of the Section did not continue unbroken. Referring to JD Rolleston's work for the Section as its Honorary Secretary (1915–18) and President (1924–26), Dr AP Cawadias remembered these were lean years. 'History of medicine was considered at that time as a hobby of the retired and dilettante. Even when I started my rather long work as secretary in 1928 attendance and interest were so poor that I was told that the Council of the Society considered the suppression of the Section. It was men like John Davy Rolleston, Charles Singer, Sir Arthur MacNalty, RO Moon, Herbert Spencer, Arnold Chaplin, Frederick Parkes Weber, who persisted in maintaining it in the middle of a general indifference'.[120]

Charles Singer, who rose to be Professor of the History of Medicine at London University, served as the Section's editorial representative for 23 years (1918–41) when he fought hard to maintain a high standard in the published papers. He also kept a strict eye on lengthy, dull presentations: at one meeting when a foreigner whose English was not good persisted in talking for over an hour, Singer produced a miniature set of traffic lights and switched the signal to red.[121]

In March 1932 the Section held a meeting in honour of Sir Archibald Garrod to discuss the history of the introduction of biochemistry in medicine. The President of the Royal Society, Sir Frederick Gowland Hopkins, was present and he identified Justus Liebig and Sir Archibald as the two fathers of biochemistry. Garrod expressed his appreciation of Dr W Langdon-Brown's paper 'dwelling specially on its wit and its thread of satire' but he objected to the phrase 'introduction of biochemistry into medicine', preferring to regard biochemistry as a branch of medicine.[122]

## Jubilee meeting and volume

Exceptionally, the History of Medicine Section published its *Proceedings* separately bound as annual volumes from 1913 until 1939. The jubilee of the Section in 1962 justified a supplement to volume 56 of the *Proceedings* of the RSM containing papers about some distinguished members of the Section and an 'Evaluation of the work of the Section in fifty years'. Dr Douglas Guthrie, Lord Cohen, Cope and Copeman reviewed their favourite papers and looked at the future prospects for the Section. Cope reflected that over the last 50 years he knew of only one or two surgeons under the age of 50 who had read a paper before the Section: 'it might not be a bad idea if the Section would attract some of the younger surgeons to deal with the evolution of surgery during the past century', he suggested.

Dr Copeman, who personally did a great deal to promote the history of medicine, commented on the 'astonishing recent increase of interest in historical medicine which now extends well beyond the confines of our Section and Society', referring to the founding of the Society of Apothecaries' Faculty of the History of Medicine and Pharmacy in 1959. He attributed the birth of the latter to 'the influence which this Section has exerted upon medical thought over the past half century' and expressed the hope that a chair in medical

PLATE 30:  At the official opening of 1 Wimpole Street on 21 May 1912 King George V and Queen Mary signed the Obligation Book.

PLATE 31:  A conversazione was held to celebrate the opening of the new building in May 1912.

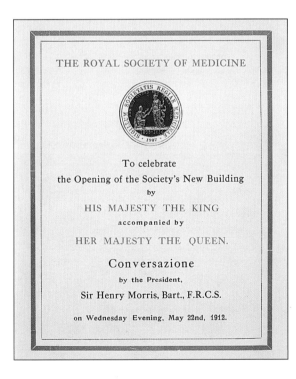

THE ROYAL SOCIETY OF MEDICINE

To celebrate
the Opening of the Society's New Building
by
HIS MAJESTY THE KING
accompanied by
HER MAJESTY THE QUEEN.

Conversazione

by the President,
Sir Henry Morris, Bart., F.R.C.S.

on Wednesday Evening, May 22nd, 1912.

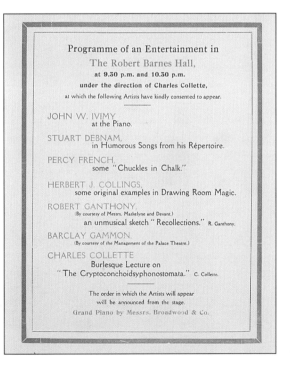

Programme of an Entertainment in
The Robert Barnes Hall,
at 9.30 p.m. and 10.30 p.m.
under the direction of Charles Collette,
at which the following Artists have kindly consented to appear.

JOHN W. IVIMY,
at the Piano.

STUART DEBNAM,
in Humorous Songs from his Répertoire.

PERCY FRENCH,
some "Chuckles in Chalk."

HERBERT J. COLLINGS,
some original examples in Drawing Room Magic.

ROBERT GANTHONY,
(By courtesy of Messrs. Maskelyne and Devant.)
an unmusical sketch "Recollections."  R. Ganthony.

BARCLAY GAMMON,
(By courtesy of the Management of the Palace Theatre.)

CHARLES COLLETTE,
Burlesque Lecture on
"The Cryptoconchoidsyphonostomata."  C. Collette.

The order in which the Artists will appear
will be announced from the stage.
Grand Piano by Messrs. Broadwood & Co.

PLATE 32: *Opposite page* The presidential badge and chain of office presented by Sir St Clair Thomson in 1927. The badge in silver-gilt and enamel was designed by Martin Travers and executed by Basil Allen. The elaborate early 17th-century chain is believed to have come from the Percy Marquand collection. A new chain of office was presented to the Society by Sir David Innes Williams, President 1990–92.

PLATE 33: *Opposite page* The Grant of Arms to the Society, 1927.

PLATE 34: The coat of arms designed by Martin Travers, 1927. The crest is composed of three sprigs of the herb all-heal. The green and red divisions of the shield represent physicians and surgeons respectively. The serpent of Moses denotes healing. The supporters are the Saints Cosmas and Damian, who have been associated with medicine and surgery since the third century. The motto from Martial, *non est vivere sed valere vita* (it is important to enjoy good health to live fully) was inherited from the Medical and Chirurgical Society.

PLATE 35: The first presidential robe was presented in 1931 by Lord and Lady Dawson of Penn (right, above); it was modelled on the robe worn by the Rector of Padua University. The current robe (below) was designed on more conventional lines by Ede and Ravenscroft and was first worn in 1959.

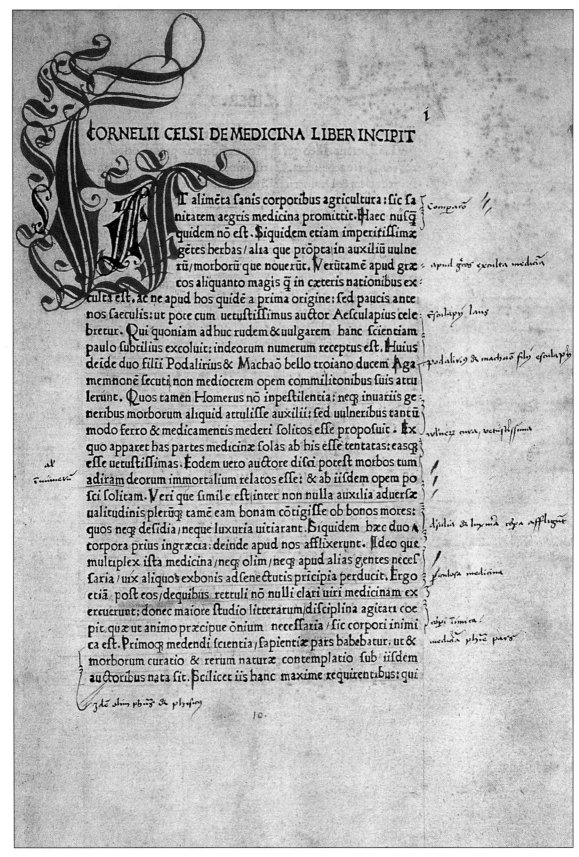

PLATE 36: A copy of *De medicina* by Celsus (1478). It was written *c.*30 AD and was the first classical treatise on medicine to be printed.

PLATE 37: The Section of Surgery's presidential badge with its large cornelian cabochon was made by Eve Fawcett and presented by Mr Alan Pollock in 1980.

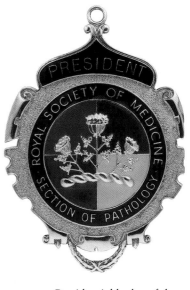

PLATE 38: Presidential badge of the Section of Pathology, designed by Toye, Kenning and Spencer, 1993.

PLATE 39: The Section of Odontology's presidential badge was presented by Carl Schelling in 1931.

PLATE 40: The presidential badge of the Section of Neurology was the idea of Dr Bickerstaff (1962) and was made by Garrards in 1963. It features the first British neurologist, Dr Thomas Willis, who fought for King Charles I in the Civil War and was Sedleian Professor of Natural Philosophy at Oxford before coming to London in 1666. The design incorporates plants with neurological connections: *Strychnos nux vomica*, *Papaver*, *Nicotiana* and *Atropa belladonna*.

PLATE 41: The President's badge of the Section of Obstetrics and Gynaecology was purchased with a donation from Professor Newell Philpott and was made by Garrards under the direction of Mr E Cope and Dr Davies, 1965.

PLATE 42: Portrait of Samuel Cartwright, the first President of the Odontological Society in 1856, by John Wood (1858).

PLATE 43: A miniature of Sir St Clair Thomson, President of the Section of Laryngology 1911–12, President of the Society 1924–26 and of the Section of the History of Medicine 1933–35. He presented the badge and chain for the President of the Society and was instrumental in securing the Grant of Arms.

PLATE 44: The presidential badge for the Section of Laryngology was presented by Sir William Milligan in 1922. The motto *sine amicitia vitam esse nullam* emphasizes the need for friendship among those working together. The centre medallion represents the profile of Manuel Garcia.

PLATE 45: The presidential badge of the Section of Otology was presented in 1927 by Mr HJ Banks-Davis, President 1917–18.

PLATE 46: The presidential badge of the Section of Radiology was purchased in 1968 with a legacy from Dr Neville Finzi, who had been President for 1943–44.

*Digitalis purpurea.*

PLATE 47:  A plate from Dr William Withering's *Account of the foxglove and some of its medical uses* (1785). Withering found that digitalis (taken as 'foxglove tea') had a stimulant action on the heart and proved effective against cardiac dropsy. He wrote in his preface that 'The use of the foxglove is getting abroad and it is better the world should derive some instruction, however imperfect, from my experience, than that the lives of men should be hazarded by its unguarded exhibition or that a medicine of so much efficacy should be condemned and rejected as dangerous and unmanageable'. Digitalis entered the *Pharmacopoeia* in 1809.

PLATE 48: The presidential badge of the Section of Anaesthesia was presented by past Presidents in 1953.

PLATE 49: Dr Keith Lovel presented the presidential badge for the Section of Paediatrics; it was designed by Toye, Kenning and Spencer, 1986.

PLATE 50: Dr Basil Kiernander, President of the Section of Physical Medicine 1958–60, presented the silver badge for his successors to wear.

PLATE 51: The presidential badge of the Section of Psychiatry was purchased in 1984.

PLATE 52: The presidential badge for the Section of the History of Medicine was initiated by Dr W Hartson, President 1973–75. It was made by Kim Southam and donated by Maurice Newbold and officers of the Section in 1976.

PLATE 53: Portrait of Sir William Osler. A copy by Philippa Abrahams of the painting by Stephen Seymour Thomas (1908) was commissioned by Dr Alex Sakula and presented to the RSM in 1989.

PLATE 54: The Section of Ophthalmology's presidential badge was presented by Frederick Ridley, President of the Section 1963–65.

PLATE 55: Drawings by Ida Mann for her paper with BD Pullinger on 'Mustard gas lesions of the eyes of rabbits and men', 1941. Her attention had been drawn to cases of delayed mustard gas keratitis by a previous paper in the *Proceedings* by TJ Phillips. Hitherto no records were known of the state of the eyes between exposure to mustard gas and the onset of recurrent ulceration years afterwards. The figures show cases soon after exposure (top), progressing to cases seen 23 years after exposure (figures 5 and 6).

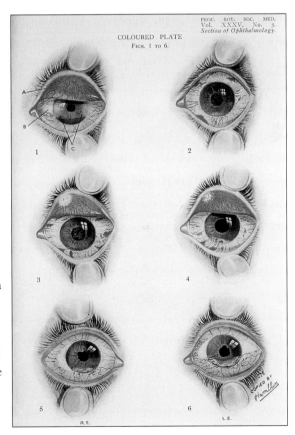

PLATE 56: The United Services Section's presidential badge was purchased with funds left over from a symposium held in the aftermath of the Falkland Islands campaign. The badge was first worn by Professor HHG Eastcott, President 1981–83.

PLATE 57: The Section of Urology's Council resolved to purchase a presidential badge of office in 1985 and commissioned Nigel Bumphrey to design it; Dennis McQuoid was the engraver (1986).

PLATE 58: Dr Basil Helal, President of the Section of Orthopaedics 1991–92, initiated the presidential badge which is inscribed 'Donated by Orthofix SRL 1992'.

PLATE 59: The presidential badge presented by Professor and Mrs G Pampiglione in 1976. Pampiglione was President of the Section of Comparative Medicine 1970–71 and 1984–85.

PLATE 60: The Section of Coloproctology's presidential badge depicts John of Arderne, the 14th-century surgeon who wrote a treatise on *fistula-in-ano*. The Section resolved to commission a badge in 1959 and it was made in 1961 to a design by Mr Henry Thompson, a past President.

PLATE 61: 'The keystone' presidential badge of the Section of General Practice was presented by Dr EP Scott in 1954.

PLATE 63: The presidential badge of the Section of Occupational Medicine features Bernardino Ramazzini, who in the early 18th century described the diseases associated with certain trades. It was engraved by Leslie Durbin under the direction of Dr VSG Murray and Dr WM Dixon and was first worn by Dr FG Taylor, President 1988–89.

PLATE 62: The presidential badge of the Section of Pharmaceutical Medicine and Research recalls the Section's origin as the Library (Scientific Research) Section. The badge was presented jointly by Allen and Hanbury's Ltd and Glaxo Laboratories Ltd in 1968.

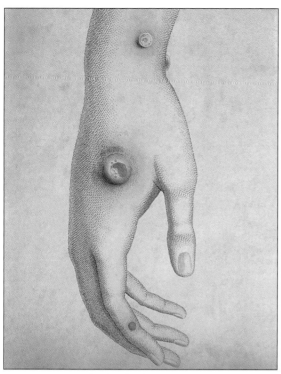

PLATE 64: The hand of Sarah Nelmes, from *An enquiry into the causes and effects of the variolae vaccinae, a disease discovered in some of the western counties of England, particularly Gloucestershire and known by the name of The Cow Pox* by Edward Jenner (1798). Jenner inoculated a healthy eight-year-old with matter from the sore on the hand of Sarah Nelmes, a dairymaid who was infected by her master's cows.

PLATE 65: Portrait of Dr John Elliotson by James Ramsay, 1836. During Elliotson's term as President (1833–35) the Society was incorporated as the Royal Medical and Chirurgical Society.

PLATE 66: The Accident and Emergency Section's presidential badge was purchased with Section funds in 1989.

PLATE 67: The presidential badge for the Section of Clinical Forensic and Legal Medicine was presented in 1989. It is inscribed with the names of Dr Neville Davis, Dr A Haidar, Dr SE Josse, Dr R Moffat and Dr S Steinberg.

PLATE 68: The presidential badge for the Section of Sports Medicine was donated in 1995 by Dr Ahmad A Marvasti in memory of his father, Dr GH Alim Marvasti, a well known surgeon of Iran.

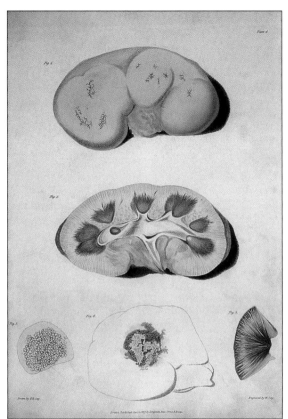

PLATE 69: The large white kidney from the post mortem on Henry Izod aged 25, from Dr Richard Bright's *Reports of medical cases* vol i (1827). Bright's study of kidney disease led to the eponymous title, Bright's disease.

PLATE 70: An illumination from an antiphonal of *c*.1460–70 by Girolamo da Cremona and a collaborator, possibly Andrea Mantegna. It depicts the Saints Cosmas and Damian (the supporters in the Society's coat of arms) who amputated the patient's gangrenous leg (shown in the foreground) and replaced it with the leg of a Moor. This is believed to be the first recorded instance of transplant surgery.

PLATE 71: The presentation of the Richard T Hewitt Award to Sir Richard Doll in 1999. He is seen here with Dr Richard Wilbur (*left*) and Lord Soulsby (*right*), in front of the portrait of Hewitt by Leonard Boden.

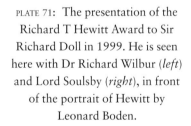

PLATE 72: Queen Elizabeth II, accompanied by the President Sir John Walton (later Lord Walton) and the Duke of Edinburgh at 1 Wimpole Street on 2 July 1986 when the Queen reopened the building after redevelopment.

PLATE 73: *Opposite page* Top: The new interiors of 1 Wimpole Street were designed by Elsom, Pack and Roberts. This shows the conservatory with the sculpture in steel, 'Civilization' by Dr Ismond Rosen who presented it to the Society in 1987.

PLATE 74: *Opposite page* Bottom: The Library, looking towards the reading room and showing the glass engraving commemorating Dr Robert Willan, presented by the British Association of Dermatologists.

PLATE 75: The main hall (the rooms on the far side have since been renamed the Porritt Suite after Lord Porritt, President 1966–67).

# ELIZABETH THE SECOND

by the Grace of God of the United Kingdom of Great Britain and
Northern Ireland and of Our other Realms and Territories Queen,
Head of the Commonwealth, Defender of the Faith:

## TO ALL TO WHOM THESE PRESENTS SHALL COME, GREETING!

WHEREAS His late Majesty King William the Fourth did by Royal Charter dated 30th September 1834 (hereinafter referred to as "the original Charter") constitute a body corporate by the name of The Royal Medical and Chirurgical Society of London (hereinafter referred to as "the Society"):

AND WHEREAS His late Majesty King Edward the Seventh was pleased by Royal Charter dated 29th May 1907 (hereinafter referred to as "the Supplementary Charter") to confirm the incorporation of the Society and to change the name of the Society to The Royal Society of Medicine and to alter the constitution thereof:

AND WHEREAS the Society has submitted unto Us in Our Council an humble Petition representing that it is desirable for the purposes of the Society and the furtherance of its objects that the original and the Supplementary Charters should be amended and extended and praying that We should be graciously pleased to grant the Society a further Supplemental Charter for this purpose:

NOW THEREFORE KNOW YE that We, having taken the said Petition into Our Royal Consideration, and being minded to accede thereto, have of Our especial grace, certain knowledge and mere motion granted and declared and do by these Presents for Us, Our Heirs and Successors grant and declare that:—

1. The original Charter shall be amended as follows:—
   (a) delete the words:
      (i) "notwithstanding the Statutes of Mortmain";
      (ii) "the yearly value of which shall not exceed in the whole the sum of Two thousand pounds computing the same respectively at the rack rent which might have been had or gotten for the same respectively at the time of the purchase or acquisition thereof";
      (iii) "and that not more than two thirds of the Fellows who have formed the Council of the preceding year shall be re-elected members of the Council at such annual meeting";
   (b) after the words "have been approved by the Council" insert:—
      "The Council may, whenever they think fit, elect to put a proposed resolution (other than a Special Resolution) to the vote by means of a postal ballot rather than at a Meeting of Fellows. A resolution so put and passed by a two-thirds majority of those voting shall be as effectual as if it had been validly put to and passed by a Meeting of Fellows by such majority.

PLATE 76: The Supplemental Charter of 21 October 1998 with Letters Patent of 10 February 1999 provides for a postal ballot of Fellows when necessary, for simplified procedures in any future changes and for specific powers of investment.

history and pharmacology might be established in one of our great universities. 'Such a consummation in the near future would, I am sure, delight the spirits of our Founder Members, for we should have "arrived"'.[123]

Since these hopes were expressed, the history of medicine has become a flourishing academic discipline in the United Kingdom and the integration of the subject into the university system has been a key achievement, for which the Wellcome Trust deserves major credit. Between 1971 and 1998 academic units in the history of medicine were established by the Trust at the universities of Cambridge, Oxford, Edinburgh, Glasgow, Manchester, East Anglia and at University College, London. The Trust also supports university awards and its History of Medicine Library is unsurpassed.[124] According to a recent survey by the Institute of Historical Research there are 113 teachers with interests in medical history at British universities, including our 'great universities'. The spirits of the founder-members of the Section must be gratified.

## The 1990s

The GMC's recommendations of 1993 on undergraduate medical education were broadly favourable to special study modules in subjects such as the history of medicine: 'It is hoped that the student of tomorrow may be drawn towards some of these other disciplines and that opportunities to study, for example, a language or to undertake a project related to literature or the history of medicine, may be offered'.[125] Following this up, the Section organized a symposium on 'The history of medicine and tomorrow's doctors' in 1997, and encouragement was given to students by the Norah Schuster Prize, offered for an essay in the history of medicine. Dr Norah Schuster, an Honorary Fellow of the Society who died in 1991, was the first woman to take the pre-clinical course at Cambridge and obtain a first-class degree in the Natural Science Tripos; she was later the first woman President of the Association of Clinical Pathologists. She was a Vice President of this Section for many years and an Honorary member who was remembered fondly as 'an elegant, intelligent lady sitting in the front row of many scientific and subsequently historical meetings. She had an intriguing trace of eccentricity when wielding an ear trumpet but always had a sharp and pertinent question or comment'.[126]

The history of medicine in this country is not primarily associated with medical schools and this has been identified as an area of potential expansion. The dissemination of the subject to wider audiences has met with remarkable success, however, and in this the Section has played a part. In the year 2000 it was the largest Section of the Society and its meetings hold wide appeal, for the good reason that every specialty has its history and its heroes.

## Section of Ophthalmology (Plate 54)

The development of specialist eye hospitals, most notably the Royal London Ophthalmic Hospital – universally known as Moorfields – encouraged ophthalmologists to found the Ophthalmological Society of the United Kingdom, a Society that had its roots in the earlier Moorfields Club. Sir William Bowman was the obvious choice as first President of the Society and his address at the inaugural meeting of June 1880 stressed the need to avoid narrowness and exclusiveness; he wanted to include those who worked in all disciplines of ophthalmology.[127] This accorded with the principles of the RSM, yet the Ophthalmological Society of the United Kingdom chose to remain independent, eventually developing into the College of Ophthalmologists in 1988 (now a Royal College).

Initially, the Society failed to reply to MacAlister's proposals for amalgamation and when it became clear that its members were divided on the question it declined to join the RSM. A special meeting to discuss the possibility was attended by 95 members in 1909, when George Mackay and Edward Nettleship led the vanguard in favour of union with the

RSM, but a decision was postponed. The Secretary of the RSM was confident that minor problems could be overcome and in March 1912 he organized a conference between representatives of the RSM and the Ophthalmological Society.[128] His confidence was misplaced, for on 11 July the Ophthalmological Society decided against joining the RSM. Nevertheless, relations remained cordial: the Society was pleased to accept MacAlister's offer to house the Bowman Library and it held a successful Annual General Meeting at 1 Wimpole Street in 1913.[129]

Meanwhile the RSM was determined to add a Section of Ophthalmology to its roll and on 26 July 1912 a total of 92 names were enlisted. Sir George Anderson Critchett, surgeon oculist to the King, was elected the first President of the Section, with Edward Nettleship, who held the prestigious post of Curator to Moorfields Eye Hospital, as a Vice President and Leslie Paton as Honorary Secretary.

## Early papers and discussions

There was clearly room for both the Ophthalmological Society and the Section and many ophthalmologists belonged to both. A total of 140 members were admitted to the Section in October 1912 and during this first session there were as many as nine or ten papers at each meeting, presented to audiences of some 50 members and guests. The first important discussion, on 'Disease of the pituitary body', was held jointly with the Section of Neurology in March 1913 and these two Sections frequently shared expertise for mutual benefit. Dr Gordon Holmes and Leslie Paton of the National Hospital, Queen Square, were leaders in the field of neuro-ophthalmology and they were staunch supporters of both Sections, providing stimulating and original papers.

The discussion on 'Disease of the pituitary body' was opened by a Fellow of the Royal Society, Professor Schäfer, followed by cases and specimens shown by Gordon Holmes, Mr N Bishop Harman, Dr FE Batten and Mr HJ Parsons (who as Sir John was to be President of the RSM from 1936 to 1938 and the only ophthalmologist to be so). This galaxy attracted an audience of 131 and a second evening was allocated to allow Garrod and Langdon-Brown to have their say.

The discussion of February 1914 likewise ran over two evenings, there being much interest in the use of 'Salvarsan in ophthalmic practice'. This was opened by Mr William Lang, soon to be President (whose name is commemorated in the Lang Medal), with contributions from E Treacher Collins and Dr Alexander Fleming.[130]

## William Lang

Lang was on the staff of Moorfields Eye Hospital from 1884 and on his retirement in 1912 he instituted a research scholarship. His daughter was the instigator of the lectureship for the Section of Ophthalmology, of which Lang had been President for the years 1916–18. His address to the Section on 'The aetiology and treatment of iritis' referred to his preoccupation with focal sepsis. Sir Anderson Critchett, JG Turner and Ernest Clarke contributed their expertise but Leslie Paton thought the emphasis of the discussion was biased: 'we owe to our President the recognition of pyorrhoea as a very potent source of iritis. Possibly it is in his honour that speakers tonight have laid a disproportionate stress on it as the most important cause' – Lang's figures for 200 cases of iritis found pyorrhoea accounted for 37%.[131]

After Lang's death his daughter gave £10,000 (anonymously) to the Section to advance ophthalmology and this was capped by £1,000 in 1979. Consequently the Ophthalmology Fund was established to give a prize, travelling scholarships and an honorarium to a lecturer. The inaugural lecture was given by Sir Stewart Duke-Elder in 1965 who spoke on 'Moorfields and British ophthalmology', arguing that the development of the specialty in England depended essentially on the school of Moorfields Eye Hospital. After the lecture Duke-Elder was pleased to receive the Lang Medal (members of the Section had subscribed

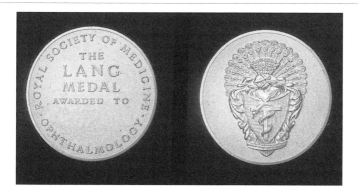

The Lang Medal was first presented to Sir Stewart Duke-Elder in 1965, in memory of William and Basil Lang. Mr William Lang (left below) had been President of the Section 1916–18; his son Basil Lang (right) died young.

to this as a mark of respect to William and his son Basil) and he graciously donated the honorarium to the Society's funds.

At the same meeting the President of the Section, Frederick Ridley, presented the badge of office worn by his successors (Plate 54). Ridley particularly disliked the meaningless description of Ophthalmology Fund lecture ('a barbarous title') and soon engineered its change to the Lang lecture.[132]

## Myope classes

N Bishop Harman, the School Medical Officer for London from 1902 to 1911, was responsible for reforming the education of myopic children. His initiative to improve the education and integration of children with defective sight was revealed to the Section in 1913.[133] Four years previously he had launched an experiment with the first myope class for elementary schoolchildren not suited to the ordinary curriculum. He stressed the need for the careful examination of the children's eyes, specified the class size, the curriculum and even designed the lighting, schoolbooks and desks (see page 336).

By 1915, in a paper on 'The education of children with defective vision', Bishop Harman reported that there were then five myope classes established in London and more in the provinces, Scotland and America, where he became quite a celebrity on this account.[134]

N Bishop Harman, ophthalmic consultant to the London School Board, persuaded the authorities to institute special classes for children with defective sight. They were known as myope classes and the children were equipped with special desks designed by Bishop Harman, seen here in use during an arithmetic lesson.

## Definition of blindness

Harold Grimsdale, surgeon to the Westminster Ophthalmic Hospital for 24 years, drew the Section into a discussion on the definition of blindness. This arose because of a Bill before Parliament to provide technical education, employment and maintenance for the blind – the proposed legislation bristled with complications such as the just administration of pensions for the blind, the education of blind children and the criteria for blindness.

In the first place it was found that the certification of blindness throughout the country was in a state of chaos: it was possible for the same patient to be considered sighted by the Pensions Officer and blind by the authority compiling the Blind Register.

Bishop Harman, Leslie Paton and Priestley Smith applied their minds to the problems and the Section's report was published in the *Proceedings* for 1914–15. 'Blindness is, strictly speaking, the inability to distinguish light from darkness', it began, while recognizing that this definition could not be strictly adhered to. Then there was the question of the examination of the blind by qualified ophthalmologists and the need to know the cause of blindness. The Section's report was forwarded to the Committee on the Welfare of the Blind, which expressed high appreciation of the valuable assistance this gave to the framing of recommendations.[135]

## Experiences of war

Mr Priestley Smith was President of the Section for the first two years of the First World War. He was already well known for his studies on glaucoma and was a past President of the Ophthalmological Society. He was also an inventor: at a meeting in 1914 he showed members a trench periscope he had devised from a wooden rod and two mirrors. Lt Colonel Elliot was not impressed: he thought it would be of little use unless it was binocular.[136]

Cases of gunshot wounds with visual disorientation and a Grenadier guardsman who suffered a bullet wound at the battle of the Marne, impairing his sight, were demonstrated in the 1915–16 session and Mr WT Lister (Sir William, a nephew of Joseph Lister) and Dr Gordon Holmes presented a paper subsequently given publicity in the *Medical Press* and the American and British journals. The two colleagues had been working with the British Expeditionary Force at base hospitals in France for 18 months and their observations on 'Disturbances of vision from cerebral lesions' presented facts 'that have an important bearing on the cerebral localization of vision and more particularly on the representation of different regions of the retina in the cortex'. In thanking the authors for their paper Sir Anderson Critchett seemed overwhelmed by its content and he spoke of the extraordinary opportunities 'this terrible war' afforded for increasing the knowledge and experience of ophthalmologists.[137]

## Glass eyes and slit lamps

During the First World War the Section advised the authorities on the number of ophthalmologists required in the London hospitals (insufficient and needing reorganization). It also put pressure on the government to encourage the production of glass eyes in England. This was prompted by a letter from Mr MS Mayou, a founder-member of the Section who wrote to the Council pointing out the serious shortage of glass eyes in this country; he believed there was only one man in England making artificial eyes 'in which the eye is absolutely copied from the patient'. The Council took this up with the Ministry of Munitions who claimed there were six other manufacturers in the country and that production of glass eyes totalled 180 a week. Unconvinced, the Section's committee on artificial eyes pressed the Ministry 'to leave no stone unturned until the supply of glass eyes is equal to every demand', war injuries having created an unforeseen need for the product. German manufacturers excelled in artificial eye production but understandably the committee was opposed to the German monopoly and suggested that French experts might be called upon.[138]

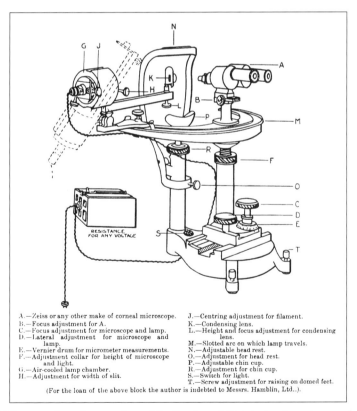

A.—Zeiss or any other make of corneal microscope.
B.—Focus adjustment for A.
C.—Focus adjustment for microscope and lamp.
D.—Lateral adjustment for microscope and lamp.
E.—Vernier drum for micrometer measurements.
F.—Adjustment collar for height of microscope and light.
G.—Air-cooled lamp chamber.
H.—Adjustment for width of slit.

J.—Centring adjustment for filament.
K.—Condensing lens.
L.—Height and focus adjustment for condensing lens.
M.—Slotted arc on which lamp travels.
N.—Adjustable head rest.
O.—Adjustment for head rest.
P.—Adjustable chin cup.
R.—Adjustment for chin cup.
S.—Switch for light.
T.—Screw adjustment for raising on domed feet.

(For the loan of the above block the author is indebted to Messrs. Hamblin, Ltd..).

MS Mayou, a founder-member of the Section of Ophthalmology, invented the
Mayou operating lamp and slit lamp. At a meeting of the Section in December
1926 he exhibited his improved version of the slit lamp (see overleaf).

Mayou was known for his version of the slit lamp, which he exhibited to the Section in 1926. T Harrison Butler had first demonstrated a slit lamp ('this valuable addition to our methods of examination') at a meeting in 1924 – he and Dr Ida Mann were among the first to introduce the instrument to British ophthalmologists. The lamp was the brainchild of Professor Gullstrand of Sweden and it was to revolutionize the examination of the eye: it shone a thin slice of intense light on the eye and its path could be observed through a binocular microscope. Dr Mann described the experience as 'like cutting a microscopic section through live tissue and many things undreamt of were revealed'.[139] Moorfields Hospital acquired its first instruments in 1923 and 10 years later Bishop Harman demonstrated a hand slit lamp at a Section meeting.[140]

## Council of British Ophthalmologists

After the First World War came the move to establish an association to promote the interests of ophthalmologists and deal with the administrative, political and public aspects of the specialty. E Treacher Collins, a founder-member of the Section and President of the Ophthalmological Society at this time, was chiefly responsible for founding the Council of British Ophthalmologists at a meeting held at the RSM in May 1918. Two other prominent members of the Section, Sir Anderson Critchett and Sir John Parsons, took leading parts in establishing the Council and it was largely due to Parsons that the Council dissolved in favour of a Faculty. Four representatives of the Section agreed to serve on the Council, which leapt into action with reports on the teaching and examination of medical students in ophthalmology, and on distant vision. Nurtured by the Section, the Council of British Ophthalmologists was the precursor of the Faculty of Ophthalmology founded in 1945 and an ancestor of the Royal College of Ophthalmologists.

## Dame Ida Mann

Miss Mann, as she was on her admission to the Section in 1921, advanced to the Council before the end of the decade. She maintained that she attended all the meetings of the Section in the 1920s, for she was determined to learn and to make her mark. She was supported by her two 'chiefs', Leslie Paton (a founder-member of the Section) and Frank Juler who was President 1942–44. By her own account, the status of the Ophthalmological Society of the UK had fallen in international medical circles through having become too clinical, which may explain the popularity of the Section meetings: Sir William Lister, Tudor Thomas, Sir John Parsons, Macdonald Critchley and Ernest Clarke could all be found there in the 1920s. Clarke gave a paper on his special subject, 'Refraction work', to the same meeting that saw the debut of Miss Mann with a demonstration of models illustrating the development of the human eye. This went towards her book on the subject published in 1928.

In 1927 Mann was appointed to the honorary staff of Moorfields Eye Hospital (the first female to secure the post) and she was later the first female Professor at Oxford. Meanwhile she was making her name as the scientist of the ophthalmic world with a stream of papers and demonstrations. In October 1926 she presented to the Section her new theory of antenatal inflammation as the most likely explanation for macular coloboma: 'I was lucky enough to adumbrate future discoveries, as when, dealing with macular coloboma (a condition in which the region of most acute vision, the macular lutea, is defective) I demolished the older theories which blamed atypical development, in favour of an intra-uterine infection ... This is now known to be an odd and unusual inflammation, toxoplasmosis, more common in domestic animals than in man, so I was justified'.[141]

A year later, Mann's paper on 'Retinal differentiation in man' was read, a rehearsal for the Arris and Gale lecture she gave to the Royal College of Surgeons in 1928. Dr Mann was the first woman to hold the office of Honorary Secretary to the Society in 1940 and after the war she joined forces with Sir Stewart Duke-Elder and Sir John Parsons to promote the Institute of Ophthalmology. She emigrated to Australia in 1949 and was awarded the DBE in 1980.

## Sir James Tudor Thomas

The 1920s also saw the emergence of JW Tudor Thomas at Section meetings, giving his views on miners' nystagmus, demonstrating an experiment in keratoplasty and showing sterilizers for drop bottles and prismatic spectacles. Among the papers he gave to the Section was the description of 'Corneal transplantation on an opaque cornea' upon which his fame is founded. He described the case he had operated on at Guy's Hospital on 15 November 1930 as 'the first practical application to man of certain principles formed on the basis of experimental work on corneal transplantation'. The patient made a slow recovery and two years later he could count fingers 33 inches away from his face.

In December 1934 Tudor Thomas demonstrated his 15th successful corneal graft and the patient's sister attended the meeting to testify to the remarkable improvement in her brother's sight, appearance and vivacity – he could now write, and cross the road outside Victoria Station. Triumphs such as these encouraged other eye surgeons: BW Rycroft adapted Tudor Thomas' technique with equal success (Sir Benjamin Rycroft was elected President of the Section in 1959).[142]

Tudor Thomas conceived the idea of a registration bureau for the collection and use of donor material, and this was under way at the Central London Ophthalmic Hospital before the outbreak of the Second World War, with Tudor Thomas in charge of the corneo-plastic department. An eye bank was established at East Grinstead for casualties of the war, and in 1952 the Corneal Grafting Act allowed the Ministry of Health to set up eye banks throughout the country.

Patrick Trevor-Roper (President of the Section 1978–80) was instrumental in setting up the eye bank at Westminster Hospital in the hope that it would supply donor material for corneal grafting in London, and this led to the formation of the British National Eye Bank in 1968. Eye banking now provides a safe supply of transplant material which can be routinely requested, and the development of microsurgery, fine sutures, needles and viscoelastic substances have transformed corneal transplantation.

## Sir Stewart Duke-Elder

Another famous name in ophthalmology appears in the Section's records from 1928: that of Duke-Elder, who later served on the Council and as a Vice President though never as President. Ida Mann and Duke-Elder were bitter rivals at the start of their careers, competing for every job and prize, and she remembered him as 'wild, witty and more like a leprechaun than anything else'.[143]

Duke-Elder's paper of January 1928 on 'Factors controlling the intra-ocular pressure' was recognized immediately as a piece of original research. His audience at the meeting included Treacher Collins, Mayou and Sir John Parsons, the elder statesman of ophthalmology, who was pleased to hear that the work he and others had done 'in the days of darkness' had not been shattered by Duke-Elder. Parsons even went so far as to say that Duke-Elder's research was 'an advance which redounded to the honour of British ophthalmology', throwing new light on the subject.[144]

Sir Stewart Duke-Elder's *magnum opus* was his *Textbook of ophthalmology*, published in seven volumes between 1932 and 1954. His wife, Phyllis, an ophthalmologist herself and later Dame Phyllis, was often seen at work in the RSM Library during the 1930s, checking references and writing abstracts for her husband.[145] Duke-Elder was Director of the Institute of Ophthalmology for 17 years and he was instrumental in establishing the Fellowship examination in ophthalmology of the Royal College of Surgeons (1947).

## FW Edridge-Green

Edridge-Green made his original study of colour blindness in 1889 but it was many years before his thesis was taken seriously, and 1930 before he gave a paper to the Section on 'The detection of colour blindness'. Another meeting heard his 'Theory of vision', which he claimed had the approval of the International Medical Congress, meeting in Budapest. The audience at the RSM were unconvinced and some had difficulty in following his reasoning. His ideas were still being viewed with scepticism in 1988 when the Edridge-Green lecture posed the question 'Colour vision: did Edridge-Green get anything right?'. His bequest of £3,000 to found this lectureship gave Edridge-Green recognition that he had struggled hard to obtain in his lifetime.[146]

## Contact lenses

Mr A Rugg Gunn gave the Section an early introduction to the fitting of contact lenses in November 1931, explaining a method that was similar to that used in the clinics of Professor Heine of Kiel and Professor Ergellet of Jena.[147] The member – and President – who did most to advance contact lenses in this country was Frederick Ridley, whose address of 1963 traced the history of contact lenses to Dr Josef Dallos of Budapest (1933). Dallos' work attracted British attention and Ida Mann, Williamson-Noble and Rugg Gunn studied his methods, returning to London to establish the first contact lens centre in England at 18 Cavendish Square in 1937.

As a young man Frederick Ridley worked with Dr Alexander Fleming on lysozyme, providing material for a paper to the Section on 'Lysozyme and its relation to infection of the human eye' in 1928. During the war Ridley began to take an interest in contact lenses and his paper of 1946 told of 'Recent developments in the manufacture, fitting and prescription of contact lenses'. The wearing of plastic contact lenses in this country was in its infancy and Ridley thought this review of the case histories of 200 consecutive patients who desired to wear 'Dixey lenses' (made of transpex) was probably the first of its kind.

Under the NHS the demand for contact lenses escalated, and Ridley's work at the contact lens department of Moorfields gained an international reputation. It was therefore to be expected that Ridley returned to the subject in his presidential address of 1963. He anticipated exciting advances, a further huge demand and the perfection of a soft, flexible material so that 'at some future time we may be able to say of contact lenses "Fit them and forget them"'.[148]

## War injuries to the eye

The first Section meeting of 1940 was on 'Gas injuries to the eye', referring to injuries inflicted by mustard gas, which was first used by the Germans in 1917. Some of the early cases had been treated by Sir William Lister, Mr Charles Goulden and Mr MH Whiting at Boulogne; although victims seemed to recover, they were subject to corneal ulceration 10–15 years later.

The discussion of January 1940 presented for the first time the research conducted by Flight Lt Walker and Wing Commander Livingstone. Their experiments on rabbits showed that great improvement followed dosages of ascorbic acid, and their work was published in full in the *British Journal of Ophthalmology* in February. Dr Ida Mann, working at the Imperial Cancer Research Fund laboratory in Oxford, seized on the subject and in 1941 she and her colleague Dr BD Pullinger told the Section about their findings on mustard gas lesions of the eyes of rabbits and men (Plate 55).[149]

Meetings were few and far between in 1940 and 1941, resuming with a joint discussion between the Sections of Ophthalmology and Neurology on 'War injuries' in 1942, and another on 'Burns to the eyelids' led by Surgeon Rear Admiral Cecil Wakeley, a volcano of energy at any meeting. After the war members heard Professor Arnold Sorsby speak on

'Penicillin in ophthalmology', discussions and papers on the new antibiotics and the requirements of industry in respect of eye casualties.

## Sir Harold Ridley

In the 1950s the Section was fortunate to elicit contributions from the prolific author and a Vice President of the Section, Eugene Wolff, who spoke at the symposium on 'The visually handicapped child' in 1968, and from Harold Ridley, Norman Ashton and Patrick Trevor-Roper.

A paper by Trevor-Roper on 'The influence of eye disease on pictorial art' warranted several rare colour plates in the *Proceedings* for 1959: works by Holbein (astigmatic with a vertically compressed eye?), Cézanne (myopic), Guercino ('the squinter') and Turner (senile cataract), to name but a few, illustrated the author's narrative.[150] The subject generated his book on *The world through blunted sight* (1970).

Ridley developed the idea of implanting a plastic lens in the eye in place of an extracted opaque one and he first performed this feat in November 1949, to the incredulity of colleagues and disapproval of traditionalists. Once accepted, Ridley's work led to the development of safe and effective modern intra-ocular lenses. These have transformed the quality of vision restored to patients after cataract operations. Implantation of these lenses coupled with modern microsurgical techniques has meant that visual rehabilitation is now rapid and of good quality. The original lenses were made of perspex and this substance has stood the test of time although alternative materials are now available, such as silicone which is used for folding lenses.[151]

Ridley was made an Honorary Fellow of the Society in 1986, the 50th anniversary of his first intra-ocular implant was celebrated in 1999 and he was soon to be knighted in recognition of the fact that there are between two and three million people worldwide who owe their sight to him.

## Professor Norman Ashton

Professor Ashton took an active part in Section meetings for 20 years before being elected President in 1971, the same year that he was made a Fellow of the Royal Society. As he remarked, the presidency was 'a cachet of lower calibre, but very distinctive, especially for a non-ophthalmologist' – he was first and foremost an ophthalmic pathologist and had occupied the exalted position of Curator/pathologist/librarian to Moorfields. Ashton also worked at the Institute of Ophthalmology for 30 years, his main research being diseases of the retinal blood vessels such as diabetic retinopathy, hypertensive retinopathy and most notably the retinopathy of prematurity. He made the key discovery that excessive oxygen given for breathing problems associated with premature birth can cause an obliteration of retinal blood vessels, disorganized growth and scarring. His observations led to the careful control of oxygen given to premature babies.[152]

In 1971 Ashton with Dr Alec Garner took the subject of retrolental fibroplasia further, correcting some misconceptions and in the same year he gave his address 'On ocular basement membranes with special reference to the retina' – which, strangely, was not selected for publication in the *Proceedings*. It was Professor Peter Tizard, the paediatrician, who spoke on Ashton's special subject, 'The retinopathy of prematurity', elaborating on Ashton's work of 1953 with his own views on the modern management of oxygen therapy in the newborn.[153]

Professor Ashton was made an Honorary Fellow of the RSM in 1979.

## A survey of the Section

Debates and symposia were introduced into the Section's annual programme in the 1960s – on 'The visually handicapped child', for instance; the motion 'This house despises the use of the Graefe knife' was also debated. In the autumn of 1966 the Section organized an ophthalmic tour to Ethiopia to investigate the extent and nature of eye disease. As a result a pilot survey of eye disease in one province was drawn up, and of course those members joining the tour gained valuable experience.[154]

Mr H Vernon Ingram succeeded as President in 1965, although he was based in Newcastle where he nurtured the department of ophthalmology and established a chair in the specialty at the university. Vernon Ingram is chiefly remembered for the development of the ruby laser ophthalmoscope, one of the first instruments used in this method of eye treatment. His address to the Section drew attention to this latest laser ophthalmoscope, and he pointed out the advantages of laser therapy – little recognized in 1966.[155]

The presidency of Professor Ashton helped to sustain the Section at a time when others languished, and in 1975 a survey revealed that the membership stood at 335. Practising eye surgeons made up 50%, pathologists, juniors and so forth comprised 18%, 2% were service members, 20% were retired eye surgeons, and 'others (physicians etc)' accounted for 10%. All the Sections were encouraged to increase their membership and this proved fruitful for the ophthalmologists; the Council reported in 1977 that its membership drive had been highly successful.[156]

The presidential address, the Lang lecture, the Edridge-Green lecture and the Registrars' meeting all still have regular places in the Section's calendar and in recent years the programme has been enlivened by provocative debates ('And so this house bids farewell to the general ophthalmologist'), the occasional quiz and a squint forum. Updates on contact lenses, new procedures in corneal surgery, research in glaucoma and a demonstration of telemedicine have alerted members to the unremitting advances in ophthalmology.

## Section of Tropical Medicine and Parasitology
originally Tropical Diseases and Parasitology

The Society of Tropical Medicine and Hygiene was founded by Sir James Cantlie in 1907 with Sir Patrick Manson as its first President and Professor Ronald Ross as Vice President. Cantlie, who already produced the *Journal of Tropical Medicine*, had attempted to form the Society in 1899 when his enquiries brought unfavourable replies. The general opinion was that a Section of Tropical Medicine under the auspices of the RMCS or the Epidemiological Society would be preferable to yet another medical society.[157]

At a second attempt the Society of Tropical Medicine and Hygiene was founded in January 1907, just a few months before the amalgamation of 15 other medical societies in the RSM. Despite overtures from MacAlister, the Society refused to join the RSM and the correspondence is peppered with hints of friction between the two: MacAlister expressed his regret in 1909 that 'an unfortunate contretemps should have led to the severance of the societies'.[158] Relations simmered for four years until at a special Council meeting of the RSM in 1912 Sir William Selby Church and Sir William Osler recommended that a Section of Tropical Medicine be constituted, with or without the Society dedicated to that subject, and a conference was arranged in the hope of building bridges.[159] A major obstacle in the way of amalgamation was that the Society of Tropical Medicine and Hygiene charged no entrance fee; 'We would also lose our individuality and the control of our Transactions, and missionary members who now pay 10/6d would have to pay 1 guinea'.[160]

The refusal of the Society of Tropical Medicine and Hygiene to join the RSM puzzled MacAlister, who was determined to have tropical medicine represented within the Society. Writing to the editor of the *BMJ* in July 1912 he drew attention to the steps the Council of the RSM was taking to form Sections of Ophthalmology and Tropical Medicine. 'In the formation of these Sections nothing antagonistic is intended towards existing societies for the study of these subjects. Leading members of both societies are co-operating . . .'.[161]

But the Society of Tropical Medicine and Hygiene still refused to be drawn into the RSM. Its Council feared that its prestige and individuality would be lost within the larger organization and that its foreign members would not benefit from amalgamation.[162] The success of this Society, comprising 603 members in 1912, and difficult relations with its leading men spelled doom for the new Section of the RSM. Naturally enough, MacAlister invited Sir Patrick Manson to join the Section, but Manson told Sir William Leishman that he had declined 'and at the same time intimated my opinion that the formation of such a Section was a mistake and not in the interest of Tropical Medicine, I did all I could to discourage it'.[163]

### An unsteady start

Nevertheless, the Section of Tropical Diseases and Parasitology was constituted in 1912, and MacAlister continued to woo the Society of Tropical Medicine and Hygiene in an effort to breathe life into the Section. The response remained negative. 'We fought the matter out last July', Dr Low wrote in 1913, 'and in that fight won. The RSM then, to my mind, behaved in a very underhand manner, and I am perfectly sure if they had won they would have treated us with scant respect. After failing to establish a section of their own, they now, by more diplomatic means, appeal to us again to open the whole question. I am perfectly certain in my own mind that if our Society proposes to amalgamate with the RSM it will split us asunder and ruin us absolutely'.[164]

Although the Section of the RSM was formally constituted in 1912, the refusal of the large and vigorous Society of Tropical Medicine to combine with it spelt failure. Without having held any meetings the Section was suspended and any subscriptions paid in anticipation were returned in 1914.[165]

### Section of Tropical Medicine and Parasitology

After the First World War MacAlister made enquiries as to whether the Section should be actively constituted or wound up, and decided on the former. The name was changed to Tropical Medicine and Parasitology in 1921 and under the Presidency of Sir Leonard Rogers a programme was arranged. Rogers had recently retired from the Indian Medical Service and was pleased to avail himself of the RSM Library, where he spent his time studying the literature of leprosy: his paper of 1922 was a study for his forthcoming book on *Leprosy* (1925).

MacAlister invited Professor WJR Simpson to the first scientific meeting of the Section and a discussion on 'Amoebic dysentery' attracted Dr P Manson-Bahr, Professor Dudgeon and Sir George Buchanan. MacAlister claimed that the Section wished to work in harmony with the Royal Society of Tropical Medicine and Hygiene, yet it was not until 1927 that the embargo forbidding Council members of the Royal Society of Tropical Medicine from taking office in the Section of the RSM was lifted.[166] The opening of the London School of Hygiene and Tropical Medicine two years later detracted from the work of the Section, which limped on until a general meeting of its members voted for its dissolution in 1936: 'It is felt that the abolition of this Section will simplify the work on Tropical Medicine which is being done in London'.[167]

The RSM's contribution to tropical medicine did not end there, however: 35 years later the Society commenced publication of *Tropical Doctor*, a journal devoted to medical practice in the tropics and aimed at doctors in remote areas of developing countries. The initiative lay with Dr Hugh Clegg as Director of the Society's International Office in 1967 and it was a new venture for the RSM, which had previously confined its publishing activities chiefly to the *Proceedings*. The continuation of the series consistently over 30 years is a testimony to its usefulness.

## United Services Section (Plate 56)
### originally the War Section

In his presidential address to the Society in 1918 Sir Rickman Godlee suggested a new Section 'to deal with matters connected with medicine and surgery in relation to war'. The Steering committee appointed to take the matter further was chaired by Sir Humphry Rolleston, Godlee's successor as President, and included Sir David Bruce and Sir William Leishman. The first meeting to organize the Section was held at 1 Wimpole Street on 13 March 1919: 12 people committed themselves to be founder-members, including Surgeon Rear Admiral Sir Robert Hill, who was to be the Section's first President.[168]

### The War Section

Initially the proposed section was referred to as War Medicine and Surgery, or Naval and Military Medicine, but by the end of July 1919 the Section had been officially established as the War Section, 'for dealing with all questions affecting Medicine and Surgery in connection with the Naval, the Military and the Air Forces of the Empire'. Sir William Norman, Director General of the Medical Department of the Navy, and Sir John Goodwin of the Army Medical Service then proposed that the United Services Medical Society should be invited to amalgamate. The Secretary of that Society had some difficulty contacting members, given that many were overseas; one application to transfer to the War Section was received from Lt Colonel Albert Hamerton in Baghdad, Mesopotamia. Pending that Society's response, the organizing committee oversaw arrangements. This committee was formed by representatives of the Admiralty, the War Office, Air Ministry, India Office, South African Medical Service, Canadian Army Medical Corps, New Zealand and Australian medical services and the Colonial Office. Fair representation of the services was to be a characteristic of the Section, in the election of its Presidents in rotation, and in the Council. Similarly the three Honorary Secretaries were drawn from the three main services and when meetings were arranged they were allocated equally to the three forces.[169]

The Section's first general meeting was held on 10 November 1919, at which the President, Sir Robert Hill, gave credit to Sir Humphry Rolleston, Sir Rickman Godlee,

Sir Rickman J Godlee, whose valedictory address as
President of the RSM proposed the formation of a
Section devoted to war medicine, 1918.

Mr CH Fagge, Sir John Bland-Sutton, Colonel William Pasteur and Sir John MacAlister 'for the conception of creating a War Section'. He anticipated that meetings would provide opportunities for many happy reunions and hoped that if the need should arise, the Section would be able to provide a skeleton medical organization. The lack of such a scheme in the Great War of 1914–18 had meant that at its beginning there was considerable disorganization of medical services and specialist talents were lost. Ophthalmic surgeons had found themselves in charge of medical wards and Hill told how one well-known dentist, whose practice was normally besieged by eager patients, had been found slung over the side of a minesweeper in Scapa Flow, put to work as a painter.

A more serious note was struck by the President's analysis of casualties at the Battle of Jutland and by other papers of the first session on 'Gas poisoning', 'Scurvy in the navy' and 'Prevention of disease on active service'.[170]

It had been left to the Secretary of the RSM, MacAlister, to approach the United Services Medical Society about amalgamation, and in May 1920 that Society agreed to the terms. Major EM Middleton, of the Royal Army Medical College and Secretary to the United Services Medical Society, replied on behalf of his Society, disclosing that the latter possessed funds of some £200 to £250 and about 300 members. In the event the USMS transferred additional sums to the RSM, and good relations with the RAMC paved the way for a conversazione at the College in 1922.[171]

The Section settled down to a programme of six meetings a year with each medical department of HM Forces being responsible for organizing two of them. The list of original members of the Section ran to 172, but many of them had addresses abroad or out of London, which doubtless accounted for disappointing attendances at meetings. When only six came to one meeting in May 1922 it was time to review the situation. The problem was identified as absence of members abroad and it was suggested that the admission fee to the Section might be abolished. Instead some variety was provided by meetings at the laboratories of the Royal Army Medical College, Millbank. During Sir John Goodwin's presidency papers were limited to 30 minutes duration and in the subsequent discussion speakers were permitted no more than five minutes each. A demonstration of advances in chemical warfare was called for (evidently impractical) and Air Commodore D Munro gave an illuminating address on the possible uses of the aeroplane in the medical services in future warfare (1923).[172]

### United Services Section

In 1928 there was renewed anxiety about poor support for the Section, so its activities were advertised in the naval and military medical journals and a change of name was suggested which might broaden its appeal. The title of Services Section was the first option but United Services Section was preferred, so the Section altered its name in 1929 and redefined its aims: 'to bring together medical men serving in His Majesty's Forces and other men interested in their work, for the advancement of medicine as applied to the services in peace and war, and for the promotion of good fellowship among them on the lines of their common scientific interests'.[173]

Attendances continued to decline, to the extent that on being nominated President-elect in March 1938 Air Commodore HE Whittingham questioned whether the Section should continue. He was over-ruled and took the post of President. The outbreak of the Second World War gave the Section a sense of purpose, and its Council resolved that 'urgent matters' must take priority at meetings. This was not to be: many members went abroad on active service and the Section was suspended between 1940 and 1948. For the interim a series of highly successful Inter-Allied Conferences were held at the RSM (1942–45) and when the Section was revived in 1948 under the presidency of Sir Henry Tidy it was resolved that its meetings should be in the spirit of those conferences.[174]

Sir James Watt by Leonard Boden. Watt was a Vice President of the United Services Section in the 1970s and President of the RSM 1982–84.

## Recovery

In the aftermath of the Second World War the Section addressed the problem of the future of disbanded Medical Officers of the forces, specifically the need for postgraduate courses and the difficulties a general duties Medical Officer faced in an increasingly specialist profession. Sir Henry Tidy oversaw the discussion on the prospects for the general duties officer, the general practitioner of the forces who was described as a 'Jack-of-all-trades, master of none'; 27 speakers voiced their concerns.[175]

Tidy, Sir Gordon Gordon-Taylor and Sir James Watt will be remembered for their work towards the postgraduate training of Medical Officers in the services, which enabled them to compete on equal terms with their civilian counterparts for NHS appointments. These three exceptional members of this Section were to be honoured by election as Presidents of the Society. Watt is also remembered for organizing a series of colloquia on complementary medicine, encouraged by the Prince of Wales and held under the auspices of the RSM (see pages 472–73). He is an outstanding naval historian and was made an Honorary Fellow of the Society in 1987 and an Honorary Member of the Section in 1997.

Sir Gordon Gordon-Taylor's term as President of the Section (1950–51) brought an influx of new members: Gordon-Taylor had been at Passchendaele in the First World War, in the Second (aged 61) he held the rank of Surgeon Rear Admiral and he had recently been President of the RSM (1944–46). Meetings of the early 1950s dealt with 'The prevention of venereal disease in the services', 'The treatment of wounds in war' and 'Fitness for service in tropical climates', at which members shared their experiences during the last war. The Section has always been dedicated to good fellowship and in 1952 the first annual dinner was given at the RAMC mess and judged to be successful and to be repeated. This spirit of camaraderie had a beneficial effect on the Section membership which rose to a record of over 200 in 1953, having doubled over the previous four years.[176]

## Reflections on papers presented to the Section[177]

The medical branches of the three Services have each made unique and seminal contributions to the advancement not only of medical and surgical practice, but also to the physiological measurement in humans during their quest to fly higher, dive deeper and expose themselves to the dangers of heat, cold, noise, irradiation, chemicals and bacteria. Clearly such topics are not discrete and it would be an over-simplification to attribute all medical problems of personnel serving on sea, land and air to the Royal Navy, British Army and RAF respectively. Overlap occurs and many topics reflect areas of mutual interest such as the career structures of Medical Officers, fitness to serve, evacuation of the wounded, problems of atomic, bacterial and chemical warfare and even aviation medicine.

The subject matter of the many excellent papers that appeared in the *Proceedings* between 1919 and 1978 illustrated some very specific medical demands reflecting the changing face of warfare and the quotidian medical needs of service personnel. Sadly, with the cessation of the *Proceedings* in 1978 some papers have been lost.

Each of the three medical branches will be remembered for its particular expertise. Sir James Watt's paper 'Doctors in the wars' pointed out that 'in the past lessons have been learned only to be forgotten, then relearned through painful experience in the succeeding campaign'.[178] In the Royal Navy several generations have made outstanding contributions to our knowledge of diving and sub-marine escape: 'Recent research of deep-sea diving' (1931); 'Sub-marine escape from one hundred fathoms' (1966) and 'Recent advances in underwater medicine' (1971). Sir Sheldon Dudley, Medical Director General during the Second World War presented important papers on fever and hygiene in the navy. Motion sickness, hypothermia, drowning and survival at sea have also been subjects of papers. Life in the navy must have been considered ulcerogenic, as some of the seminal work on H2 antagonists was conducted on serving personnel by Drs RH Hunt and JJ Misiewicz and Sir Godfrey Milton-Thompson.

The army has always had the largest medical branch and has led the field in tropical medicine, hygiene and the prevention of infectious diseases, wound care and delayed suturing, casualty evacuation and triage organization for catastrophes and conflicts world-wide. For example, papers have dealt with 'Ambulance transport in undeveloped countries' (1931), 'Milestones in achievement in army hygiene' (1934), 'Problems in the evacuation of the multiple injured casualty' (1970) and 'Injury in terrorist wars – a military surgical team in Belfast' (1995).

The RAF has tackled all the major issues of flying, and surprisingly, introduced the artificial kidney to the United Kingdom in the late 1950s. The names of Sir Archibald McIndoe and George Morley are synonymous with plastic surgery in the RAF, McIndoe having set up the unit at East Grinstead where Battle of Britain pilots were given reconstructive surgery. Papers of special interest to the RAF included 'Psychomotor response in relation to flying' (1924), 'Respiration in high flying' (1937), 'Clinical problems of orbital flight' (1963) and 'Post traumatic renal failure'. Two recurrent topics affecting all three services have been the threat of nuclear attack, the problems of psycho-neurological breakdown in service personnel such as shellshock, neurasthenia and battle fatigue, and the counselling of released hostages. Ironically, it was members of the Section of Psychiatry who took the first faltering steps in the understanding of war neuroses in the First World War, and Macdonald Critchley contributed much to naval psychiatry during the Second. The problem has continued to express itself in many guises to the present day: post-traumatic stress disorder following physical or mental trauma and some of the aspects of Gulf War illnesses may be part of the same continuum.

Since the inception of the tri-service concept in 1985, colloquially known as the 'Purple Option' (a reference to the blend of uniform colours), demarcation lines have been less distinct. Thus a new level of co-operation is evident, as seen in recent papers where Medical Officers work alongside each other in a tri-service capacity.

The decrease in the membership of the Section reflects in some measure the shrinking Defence Medical Services. The 1983 poll listed 276 members of whom 90 were serving:

31 with the Royal Navy, 36 with the British Army and 23 with the RAF. Of the 83 civilians, 79 were ex-servicemen and three were overseas members. Meetings presently attract an average of between 40 and 50 participants, but with a depressing shortage of junior service MOs; this is attributed to the loss of the serving officers' concessionary subscription and to the increasing disruption of service life by training rotations and cross-appointment within the three services.

## Wars, rebellions, campaigns and expeditions
Since the Second World War symposia have discussed the medical problems encountered in Korea, the Falkland Islands and the Gulf War. Other presentations included an account of 'Severe malaria among British troops in the East African Campaign' (1928), 'The problems of medical care during the 1931 Burma Rebellion' (1933), and of medical support in Kurdistan (1991), Rwanda (1995) and Kosovo (2000).

The conflict in the Falkland Islands called for a symposium and dinner in 1983, arranged on the joint initiative of the President of the Section and the President of the Society, and held at the Royal College of Surgeons. It aimed to mark the contributions made by the medical profession during the campaign and to discover what lessons might be learned. In all 34 short papers were presented by officers of the three services, under the headings of 'Maritime medical support', 'War at sea', 'War on land', 'Casualty evacuation' and 'Operational clinical problems'. The symposium was attended by 354 people and many others had to be turned away. There were displays and exhibitions, and at the end of the first day nearly 200 participants dined at Fishmongers' Hall. Admiral of the Fleet Lord Lewin spoke after dinner and the orchestra of the Royal Marines entertained the company – each musician had seen active service in the Falklands as a stretcher-bearer.[179]

## Guest lecturers and visiting Professors
At the Annual General Meeting and dinner it has been the custom over the last few years to invite a guest speaker. This has often enlivened the occasion, except perhaps for Ludovic Kennedy's talk on 'Euthanasia'. Other contributions came from the retired Chaplain of the Fleet, the Rt Rev Noel Jones, Bishop of Sodor and Man, who spoke on 'Body and soul', Esther Rantzen on 'Protecting children' and Lt Colonel Alan Hawley on 'Refugees in Rwanda'.

The Burroughs Wellcome visiting Fellowship allowed the Section to invite eminent Medical Officers from abroad, with the added advantage of solving the problem of finding a guest speaker for that year. Colonel Norman Rich, Dr Donald Trunkey, Professor Ben Eiseman and Professor Craig Llewellen have been invited, and two guest lecturers made a strong impression: Field Marshal Lord Carver who spoke on 'Morale in battle – the medical and the military' in 1989, a compassionate examination of stress and fear in battle with its attendant psychiatric syndromes.[180] And in 1992 Sir Hugh Beach addressed the Section on 'The next decade – what are the armed forces for?'.

## The 'Away Day'
A successful addition to the programme since the mid-1980s, the 'Away Day' evolved from Open Days when the Section visited service and Ministry of Defence establishments. Some memorable visits have been to the Royal Naval Hospital Haslar, the Institute of Naval Medicine, Royal Naval Air Station Culdrose, the Royal Army Medical College, and Porton Down. The closure of many such centres has threatened the viability of the Away Day as an annual event and the possibility of civilian venues has been raised.

## Medals and prizes
The Chadwick Prize and Medal, named after the social reformer Sir Edwin Chadwick (1800–90) allowed the trustees 'if they saw fit, once in every five years, to present a sum of

£100 and a Gold Medal' to a worthy naval or army officer. Despite that condition, in 1995 it was awarded to an RAF Officer, Wing Commander Harold Whittingham, later Sir Harold and Section President, for his services to aviation. Surgeon Captain Sheldon Dudley received the award in 1930 and Colonel NP McArthur in 1935. No further record of this prize being awarded has been found.

In 1992 Bayer Diagnostic sponsored a prize to encourage research among service Medical Officers in training grades. Two papers from each service are short-listed and judged by the President and service Deans, and the winner is awarded £100 with £50 for the runners-up. Bayer discontinued their grant in 1999 but the meeting continues.

### Envoi

The papers presented to the Section and its annual programme reflect fairly accurately the changing medical requirements of the Defence Medical Services over the years. It is axiomatic that the DMS have to be prepared for war and for the increasing demands produced by peace-keeping roles, man-made or natural catastrophes and conflicts. These demands have concentrated efforts and fostered a philosophy of mobile expedition strategies and a move towards highly trained Field Surgical Trauma teams (FSTs) that can be mobilized quickly and act effectively. The Medical Officer of the 21st century is versatile and capable of being a general duties doctor, and is also skilled in advanced life support and acute trauma. The Section must move with the times and this may mean the acceptance of non-medical health carers and mergers with Sections or Fora with similar agendas. It is interesting that at a recent meeting of the Catastrophes and Conflicts Forum almost 60% of the participants had a service connection.

With the end of the Cold War the threat of nuclear warfare has declined, but the developing sophistication of weaponry in the new millennium presents terrifying possibilities: the death-dealing blast of explosion and the flesh-wrenching cut of hard steel will be superseded by the more potent, invisible chemical and bacteriological killers. The role of mass vaccination of service personnel against such terrors and the aetiology and pathogenesis of some facets of Gulf War illnesses remain *sub judice*. It is a sobering thought that such topics may well set the future agenda of the United Services Section. Whatever path the Section follows its aim is the protection, health and welfare of our servicemen and women.

## Section of Urology (Plate 57)

The 18th-century anatomist William Cheselden and the surgeon Sir Henry Thompson vie for the title of father of British urology: Cheselden expounded 'the high operation for the stone' in 1723 (although he later abandoned this technique in favour of the lateral operation), and Thompson, who was a Vice President of the RMCS in 1888, was renowned for lithotrity.[181] William Coulson wrote an authoritative book on *Lithotrity and lithotomy* in 1853 and Henry Morris, who as Sir Henry was to be the second President of the RSM, was a pioneer of renal surgery in the 1880s; yet none of these masters can be said to have established the specialty of urology. There was, of course, St Peter's Hospital for Stone, established in 1860 by an ill-assorted group of founders 'for the treatment of stone in the bladder and other diseases of the urinary tract' who met with opposition from colleagues. In the mid-19th century urology was still associated with venereology, so was not considered respectable, and the medical establishment objected to the specialist hospitals because they diverted funds and expertise. These factors were sufficient to stifle the development of urology in the Victorian age.

### Proposal for a sub-Section

The first steps towards recognition for the specialty were taken in the second decade of the 20th century largely through the initiative of Mr Edwin Hurry Fenwick. His path to fame

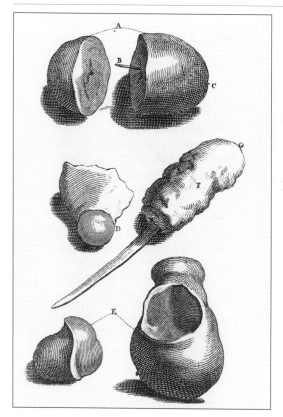

A copy of William Cheselden's *Treatise on the high operation for the stone* (1723), dedicated to Dr Richard Mead and signed by the author, was presented to Benjamin Brodie by William Prout in 1829 and given to the RMCS by Charles Hawkins in 1867 'with the hope that the Society will not part with it'. This illustration shows (top) a stone taken out of a five-year-old boy with the head of a large needle upon which the stone was formed. Middle left, part of a stone formed on the side of a musket bullet shot into the bladder of a soldier at the siege of Lille. Middle right, a stone formed on a bodkin in a woman's bladder. Below, two stones with a polished joint successfully removed from a patient.

started with the Jacksonian Prize for his essay on 'Tumours of the bladder' in 1887; he was one of the first in this country to practise cystoscopy, and he was quick to appreciate the value of X-rays in urinary surgery. Fenwick was joint President of the International Association of Urology, which held its second Congress in London in 1911, and two years later he petitioned Sir Francis Champneys, the President of the RSM, for a Section of Urology. Colleagues preferred to see a sub-Section of Surgery in the first instance and that Section approved the creation of three sub-Sections simultaneously – for urology, orthopaedics and proctology.[182]

Mr Edwin Hurry Fenwick, who took the initiative in promoting urology as a specialty before the First World War. He petitioned for a Section of Urology in 1913.

The decision had been taken but the organization was lacking, so for the session of 1913–14 papers on 'Ureteral calculi' and 'The kinked ureter' were presented to the Surgical Section and published as part of that Section's *Proceedings*. The Great War then intervened and it was not until 1920 that urology re-emerged, this time as a full Section of the RSM.

## The Section starts work

The credit for giving urology full Section status goes to Mr Walter Spencer, President-elect of the Section of Surgery. An organizing committee was appointed in 1919 and the inaugural meeting of the Section of Urology was held on 17 March 1920.[183]

Sir Peter Freyer, a colleague of Fenwick's at St Peter's Hospital, was the ideal figure to head the new Section and his elegant presidential address acknowledged Spencer's influence in favour of the Section. This 'marks a distinct and healthy advance in the attitude of the surgical world in England and particularly in London, which until recently looked askance at the idea of urology being a distinct specialty', Sir Peter commented. Recording the progress of urinary surgery over the previous 45 years, he could not resist mentioning 'my operation of total enucleation of the prostate' first carried out in 1900, since when he had completed 1,674 similar operations.[184] He expressed some surprise that urology had achieved the status of a full Section and he hoped that members would foster progress: 'I believe that the formation of this Section, by creating a healthy and friendly rivalry in your efforts, and by co-ordinating your work, will have a vast and favourable influence in continuing the progress of recent years'.[185]

Sir Cuthbert Wallace and Sir Thomas Horder (Lord Horder, as he was to become) added weight to the Section as Vice Presidents; AR Thompson, who had established the first department in genito-urinary surgery at St Thomas', was one of the first Council members, as was Dr W Langdon-Brown; JW Thomson-Walker and Cyril Nitch were the Honorary Secretaries.

The presentation of papers and cases commenced in October 1920 with Sir Thomas Horder's 'On the treatment of subacute nephritis by kidney decapsulation'. At the six meetings of the Section in this first session Victor Bonney (who was perfecting the Wertheim hysterectomy at the Chelsea Hospital for Women), Zachary Cope (who as Sir Zachary was to be President of the Section of Surgery 1939–40), Thomson-Walker, SG MacDonald, RH Jocelyn Swan, Philip Turner, Frank Kidd (co-founder and editor of the *British Journal of Urology* from 1929) and Dr Alfred Webb-Johnson (later President of the RSM) were in evidence. There was no sign of Fenwick and Sir Peter Freyer died within the year.

## Prostatic surgery: Sir John Thomson-Walker and Terence Millin

Sir Peter Freyer's former assistant, JW Thomson-Walker, took centre stage in 1921 with his modification of Freyer's operation. His paper on 'The prevention of urinary obstruction after prostectomy' gave credit to Freyer, passing quickly on to the subject of post-operative obstruction 'with a view to discussing whether some modification of the original operation is not necessary in order to meet this sequel shown by experience to occur'. Thomson-Walker cited 15 cases; he claimed his operation took only 15 minutes longer than Freyer's and he believed it to be superior in that shock was diminished because haemorrhaging was controlled.[186] By 1930 he had performed over 2,000 prostatectomies and if he had not improved on Freyer's mortality figures he claimed fewer complications during convalescence. Thomson-Walker was an internationally acclaimed authority on urinary tract stone and was knighted in 1922. On his retirement from St Peter's in 1932 the Section invited him to give an address: he chose to talk on 'Some changes and problems in urology'. At the same time a dinner was given in his honour, and he was presented with cufflinks engraved with the Society's crest (purchased with what remained of the dinner fund).[187]

When Walter Galbraith spoke on 'Modern trends of prostatic surgery' in his presidential address of 1947 he claimed that Thomson-Walker's method had proved too complex for the average surgeon, who continued to use the simpler Freyer method. Galbraith placed more emphasis on Terence Millin's achievement: 'He described an extra-vesical method of prostatectomy which he named retropubic prostatectomy'. This, a procedure that was relatively safe and simple to learn, was the subject of Millin's paper of 1946, which had inspired comments from 10 leading urologists and earned the congratulations of Mr HP Winsbury-White.[188] Within two years of its introduction Millin, who had previously been an exponent of transurethral resection and the Millin resectoscope, reported a series of 1,700 cases operated on by the new technique by 16 surgeons, with an overall mortality rate of 5.3%. This was seen as a revolution by Galbraith and one that had been set in motion by the Section's meeting of January 1946.[189]

Millin was also interested in the treatment of incontinence, opening a discussion on its surgical treatment in January 1939, to which Victor Bonney and EW Riches contributed. Millin spoke sympathetically about the anguish incontinence caused and he was to continue the theme in his presidential address of 1948 on 'The ureter, the gynaecologist and the urologist', in which he emphasized the need for team work. 'Our two specialties cannot remain watertight compartments when it is the patient we are endeavouring to make watertight', he began.[190] Yet 20 years later Thomas Moore was still lamenting the unsatisfactory state of female urology, namely that a woman was usually referred to a gynaecologist with no training in urology, or possibly to a urologist with no training in gynaecology.[191]

## Changing nature of the Section

Dr E Cuthbert Dukes, who had been attending meetings of the Section since the 1920s and who was the first pathologist to be its President (1956–57), provided an account of the development of the Section during that period from 'behind the scenes'.[192] Dukes spoke from personal experience and knowledge of the main players; he had also been President of the Sections of Proctology and the History of Medicine and was elected an Honorary Fellow of the Society in 1967. To urologists he is best known for his book on urine examination (1929), the museum he established at St Peter's Hospital and his classification of bladder tumours.

Dukes' review of the Section's development named Thomson-Walker as the chief founder of the Section and Freyer as the figurehead, while Sir Thomas Horder, the second President, provided an invaluable link with general medicine (he later became so involved with institutions and organizations that his early contacts with urology tend to be overlooked). Dukes also praised Dr Walter Langdon-Brown for the broad vision he brought to the Section (Langdon-Brown was at different times President of the Sections of Urology, Therapeutics and Pharmacology, History of Medicine and Endocrinology). With Dukes he took a leading part in a somewhat negative discussion on 'Urinary antiseptics' held jointly with the Sections of Pathology and Therapeutics and Pharmacology in 1929. After considering members' reports and opinions, both Dukes and Langdon-Brown agreed that the antiseptics did no good. The discussion had been unproductive: 'the reason was it was a disappointing subject' and Langdon-Brown was left bemused, under the impression that 'there must be something in the climactic [sic] conditions of America which rendered urinary antiseptics more effective than in this country'.[193]

According to Dukes' account, the character of the Section changed after the presidency of Langdon-Brown (1923–24). Under his successors, Mr Cyril Nitch, Mr Jocelyn Swan, Sir Girling Ball, Mr Frank Kidd and Mr Swift Joly the control of the Section passed into the hands of urological surgeons. The founders had encouraged a broader view and the influence of Horder and Langdon-Brown had ensured that the medical aspects of urology were kept well to the fore; the attendance book confirms that initially a strong group of consulting physicians and some pathologists came to meetings regularly. With the supremacy of the urological surgeons, pathologists, radiologists and physicians rarely attended. It was only in the 1950s that a strong group of younger pathologists began to take an active part in the Section's life, especially at the clinico-pathological meetings. This encouraged Dukes, who anticipated a more varied audience at future meetings because advances in urology were leading to the discovery of undeveloped territories in medical knowledge where many others besides urologists wished to stake a claim.

Among the presidential addresses of the period 1920–57 Dukes singled out Swift Joly's on 'The pathology of calculus disease of the urinary tract', the preliminary to *Stone and calculus disease of the urinary organs* (1929), which became a standard reference book. Dukes also spoke kindly of the general surgeon/pathologist Sir Henry Wade, the first President from north of the Tweed (1937–38), and he praised the long service of Mr A Clifford Morson. He had joined the Section in 1920 and had served on the Council for 30 years, as President for 1933–34 and he was still assisting the editorial committee in 1956.

Over and above the initiative and work of its founders and Presidents, Dukes was convinced that 'the chief incentive to the foundation of this Section was the pressing need of the urological patient … This anonymous individual has played a more important part in the development of urology than any President, Secretary or Councillor. But for him we should not exist! … We come here to these meetings for many different reasons, such as to meet old friends, to enjoy each other's company and to receive instruction and edification. But deeper down, perhaps subconsciously, we come for the same reasons which inspired the Founders and original members of this Section, namely because we know that here in the fresh invigorating atmosphere of the public forum, we can discuss the urological patient objectively, without so much as a passing thought for hospital estimates or priorities or any such thing. It is a fine tradition. We have inherited this freedom from our predecessors. We must preserve it, both on the stage and behind the scenes, and hand it on unsullied to our successors'.[194]

*Business*

At the Section's first Council meeting in June 1920 it was decided that papers should be limited to 20 minutes and that ideally they should be selected to deal with the medical and surgical aspects of the same subject. The second meeting of every session was to be a clinico-pathological one and there was to be one provincial meeting a year. The Council made a point of inviting well-known speakers such as Professor Jurasz from Poland and Dr O Lowsley from New York to give papers and in 1936 R Ogier Ward asked Solly Zuckerman (Beit Research Fellow at Oxford), who spoke on 'The endocrine control of the prostate'.

The Section's Council rebuffed an approach from the British Social Hygiene Council in 1933, making it quite clear that the Section was not interested in gonorrhoea and that the subject of venereal disease was outside its scope: the perception that urology was associated with venereal disease did not enhance the status of urologists and the Section sought to dispel the connection.

The first overseas meeting, with the Dutch Urological Society, took place in Holland in 1934. Ladies might accompany members but only one lady per member was permitted at the banquet. Overseas meetings became a regular event after 1982, when the first 'Uroski' meeting took place in Austria. There were 71 participants and the meeting was judged a great success, academically and socially. Similar sorties were to be arranged to Europe, Colorado, Egypt, with a change of scene in the year 2000 when a meeting was held in Cape Town.

In the 1930s the Annual General Meeting was the most important event in the Section's calendar, extending over two days with a meeting at the Royal College of Surgeons, papers, demonstrations of operations at London hospitals and a dinner. Shortly after the AGM of 1936 the Council reluctantly accepted the resignation of one of the founder-members, Cyril Nitch, who retired to the country. He wrote, 'The work of the Section and the many kindnesses I received from its members is one of the most pleasant recollections of my professional life; added to this is the pleasure and pride in seeing the infant which Thomson-Walker and I "wet-nursed" grow into such a vigorous and intellectual adult. Floreat!'.[195]

### The Second World War

Horace P Winsbury-White was President of the Section at the outbreak of the war. He was editor of the *British Journal of Urology* and possessed 'a zest for the female urethra and its many diseases'.[196] As President he invited Dr Ernst Sklarz to show his new method of endovesical photography to the Section, and he instigated discussions on 'Urinary incontinence and radiotherapy in urology'. His most enduring contribution was the foundation of the Winsbury-White lectureship (see pages 355–56).

John Everidge and TE Hammond succeeded Winsbury-White, followed by GE Neligan, summoned unexpectedly in 1941 when the President-elect, Sir Alfred Webb-Johnson, was elevated to the Presidency of the Royal College of Surgeons. Neligan was able to give the Section the benefit of his experiences in two wars at a discussion on 'Injuries to the genitourinary tract' in 1941.

The senior Honorary Secretary, Mr ED D'Arcy was killed in action, as was Mr R Fowler Ward, and some meetings were cancelled during the war, although not the annual dinner. A past President, Sir Hugh Lett, was called upon to talk about 'Forty years in urology' in 1941; he was President of the Royal College of Surgeons in May 1941 when it was bombed with the loss of much of the museum's collection.

One aspect of the war affecting many members of the Section and their patients was the poor quality of English catheters, the only ones available. Millin and Morson urged the Council to encourage British manufacturers and to take the matter up with the Royal College of Surgeons.

Towards the end of the war meetings revived, with discussions on the complications of sulphonamide therapy, the use of penicillin in urinary diseases and the effects of stilboestrol.[197]

### The British Association of Urological Surgeons

When a White Paper was published in 1944 as a preliminary to the proposed state medical service R Ogier Ward, who had been President of the Section 1935–36, was consulted as the representative of urology. He was struck by the fact that no organization could speak for urologists and on his return from overseas he consulted Sir Alfred Webb-Johnson and Sir Ernest Rock Carling; they confirmed his opinion that an association of urologists was essential if urology was to obtain a footing in the NHS. Colleagues were summoned to EW Riches' house in December 1944 to consider the matter – all of these seven founders of what was to be the BAUS were past Presidents of the Section of Urology. They circulated a wider group of surgeons, pointing out that an association was necessary to promote urology and, moreover, that 'in the immediate future one of its most important functions would be to represent to those responsible for the development of the medical services of the country, the ideals of urology'.[198]

The BAUS was officially constituted in 1945 with Ogier Ward as its first President, supported by 12 officers and Council members who were at one time or another Presidents of this Section. The new Association was soon invited to joint meetings with the Section and relations were good. In their different ways both the Association and the Section promoted urology, a branch of surgery which the Ministry of Health's Statement on Consultant Services of 1950 still did not recognize as a specialty.

The opening of the Institute of Urology and its growing reputation under the Directorship of JD Fergusson, the efforts of the Specialist Advisory Committee to establish higher surgical training in urology and of course the continuing activities of the Section and the BAUS helped to raise the status of urology in the 1950s and 1960s.

In 1963 the Section's Council gave a more precise definition of its aims: 'to advance the study of urology and promote a high standard in the specialty by the exchange of ideas at regular meetings',[199] and the following year Howard G Hanley struck an optimistic note in his presidential address. He thought that the years of open and sometimes underground struggle by a few dedicated men were beginning to bear fruit and that urology would be a specialty in the near future. He identified the difficulties as not enough work, opposition from colleagues, little financial reward and lack of facilities in the hospitals, all of which could be overcome. 'It is obvious therefore that if we really wish to see urology established as a specialty in Britain today the effort and drive must come from ourselves – from the periphery'.[200]

## Winsbury-White lectures

HP Winsbury-White was a Fellow of the Society from 1921 until his death in 1962. He bequeathed to the RSM £1,000 to found a lecture on a medical subject and the first was given by Professor Chester Winter of Ohio State University in the session of 1964–65. In 1967 the honour went to Mr JD Fergusson, who had collaborated with Winsbury-White on the second edition of his *Textbook of genito-urinary surgery* (1961). Fergusson's presidential address of 1962 was 'On the conservative management of prostatic cancer' – this was his special subject and he was one of the first to advocate oestrogen therapy. His paper cited 467 cases, but he admitted that the results were difficult to assess. 'Nevertheless, when we remember that just over 30 years ago, before the introduction of endocrine

Horace P Winsbury-White, President of the
Section of Urology 1938–39. He bequeathed a
legacy of £1,000 to establish a lecture.

methods, most patients died of prostatic cancer within 18 months, we can feel assured that conservative management of this description carries at least some benefit'. Fergusson placed more faith in the procedure of implanting radioactive material into the pituitary, a technique he pioneered.[201]

Fergusson's Winsbury-White lecture of 1967 referred to its founder and to the complex advances urologists must grapple with: chemotherapy, hormones, electrolytes and the use of physical agents, to say nothing of organ transplantation.[202]

### Recent years

Howard Hanley thought that recognition of urology as a specialty was imminent in 1964. The new techniques and procedures certainly encouraged specialist training and this was eventually recognized by the NHS.

At Section meetings members reported their personal triumphs. In 1960 LN Pyrah brought up to date results of his rectosigmoid bladder operations, and Sir Eric Riches discussed his experience of 14 colocystoplasty cases: 'long, tedious and must be very meticulous. When doing it I am always reminded of the Song of the Shirt, "Stitch, Stitch, Stitch" but I feel that I shall go on with it'.[203]

In his address of 1968 Thomas Moore anticipated more frequent renal transplantations, improved laboratory techniques and the possible freezing of semen, and in 1971 GF Abercrombie reported a new operation for nephro-ureterectomy which he had carried out 14 times on 10 patients.[204]

Urology was even spawning sub-specialties, notably paediatric urology. OL Addison had first addressed the Section on this 'quite undeveloped subject' in 1936. Meredith Campbell's book on *Paediatric urology* was published the next year, and in 1955 the BAUS devoted a session to it. The chief protagonist of paediatric urology at the RSM was David Innes Williams, whose presidential address of 1969 was on 'The ureter, the urologist and the paediatrician'.[205]

The problems of infertility come within the urologist's sphere, and in 1978 Mr William Hendry suggested that a new Section of Andrology be formed; the Council also toyed with the idea of changing the Section's name to Urology and Andrology. This was rejected (the British Andrology Society and the Society for the Study of Infertility were to advance this cause) but in the 1990s the Section held a combined meeting on 'Aspects of andrology', and Hendry devoted his presidential address to 'Iatrogenic damage to male reproductive function' (1994).

The preface to the second edition of *Urology* by Professor John Blandy and Mr Christopher Fowler (1996) asserts that urology had at last achieved the status of a recognized specialty: 'since the first edition [1976] the battle to establish urology as a separate specialty in the British Isles has been won and today it is accepted that Higher Surgical Training in the specialty should begin as soon as the young surgeon has finished Basic Training in the Common Trunk of Surgery-in-General'.

The campaign opened by E Hurry Fenwick at the RSM in 1913 had at last achieved success.

## Section of Orthopaedics (Plate 58)

By 1894 there was a nucleus of British surgeons sufficiently devoted to orthopaedic practice to found the British Orthopaedic Society, which held its first meeting at the house of the RMCS in Hanover Square in 1895. Its members were mostly surgeons working at the National Orthopaedic Hospital and there was conflict between some strong and forceful personalities: 'Tubby and Openshaw seldom met; and if they did meet one or other was almost certain to boil with rage. Muirhead Little was too passive to succeed as peacemaker. The Society died a natural death and the *Transactions* ceased publication in

1898'.[206] Alfred Tubby and TH Openshaw were later reconciled, and together with E Muirhead Little were founder-members of the sub-Section of Orthopaedics of the RSM in 1913 (see below).

The Royal National Orthopaedic Hospital in Great Portland Street (an amalgamation of three London orthopaedic hospitals) provided new opportunities and facilities for orthopaedic surgeons when it opened in 1909. The first hospitals and homes for the treatment and care of cripples had been established and by 1912 three London hospitals (Charing Cross, St Bartholomew's and Guy's) had set up orthopaedic departments. William Macewen's classic *The growth of bone* appeared in 1912, accompanied by the enlarged edition of Tubby's *Deformities including diseases of the bones and joints*. Thus stimulated and encouraged, and with the prospect of recognition for orthopaedics at the forthcoming International Medical Congress, members of the defunct British Orthopaedic Society rallied in May 1913 to launch an orthopaedic sub-Section of the Surgical Section of the RSM.

## A sub-Section

The Council of the sub-Section of Orthopaedics met in July 1913, shortly before the first appearance of an Orthopaedic Section at the International Medical Congress meeting in London. Mr E Muirhead Little, son of the 'father of London orthopaedics', WJ Little, was elected the first President of the RSM's Section. AS Blundell Bankart and E Rock Carling were the first Honorary Secretaries and Sir Robert Jones, Tubby, Openshaw and Jackson Clarke, who had all belonged to the British Orthopaedic Society, were Council members; there were 59 members of the sub-Section altogether. In his presidential address Muirhead Little lamented the fact that the British Orthopaedic Society had 'felt compelled to perform hara-kiri some dozen years ago', for he felt sure that if it had survived orthopaedics would have constituted one of the original Sections of the RSM.[207]

The presentation of papers and cases commenced in November with contributions from Paul B Roth and Mr HAT Fairbank (Sir Thomas). Roth was a particularly keen member and his striking appearance and provocative personality doubtless commanded attention. Mr C Max Page, RC Elmslie, Tubby, Blundell Bankart and Laming Evans also showed cases and apparatus at meetings during this session, but attendance was disappointing – there were never more than 15 at a meeting.[208] Nevertheless, the papers and cases presented were printed as an appendage to the *Proceedings* of the Surgical Section and as such they formed the first collection of orthopaedic papers published in this country.

Shortly before the outbreak of war in 1914 members petitioned for a full Section, but were unsuccessful: the Section of Surgery found the idea 'very undesirable' and MacAlister reported that the RSM Council was equally unsympathetic.[209]

In view of the 'exceptional circumstances' of 1914–18 the leaders of the Section dispersed: Tubby to Egypt and Jones to France. The officers and members of the Council were then re-elected, with Muirhead Little retaining the presidency until 1920.

## Sir Robert Jones

In 1910 Robert Jones had presented his paper 'On fractures in the neighbourhood of joints' to the Surgical Section, laying down the principles of mobilization of elbow injuries and his condemnation of passive movement. This was later cited as an interesting landmark in prewar orthopaedic literature and one of the classics.[210] As Inspector of Military Orthopaedics in the First World War Jones persuaded the War Office to reserve 400 beds at the military hospital at Alder Hey for wounded soldiers needing orthopaedic surgery, and the Hammersmith Infirmary at Shepherd's Bush was put to similar use. Jones personally toured France demonstrating the Thomas splint (named after his uncle, Hugh Owen Thomas, who had trained him) and this became a permanent part of war equipment in this war and the next. As a result of his efforts Jones was knighted in 1917, having placed British orthopaedics on a firm footing. He was, and is, the acknowledged giant of orthopaedics and he gave the specialty a definition: 'the recognition and practice of definite principles of treatment, whether operative, manipulative or educational, which lead to the restoration of function in nerves and muscles and in deformed or disabled limbs'.[211]

At the end of the war Jones applied his mind to establishing a network of country orthopaedic hospitals, which were to form the bedrock of orthopaedic practice until the 1960s. A great number of surgeons retained an interest in bone and joint surgery after the war, and the specialty was recognized by the foundation of the British Orthopaedic Association in 1918. This initiative originated with three members of the sub-Section: Openshaw, Jones and Muirhead Little put their names to the circular calling a preliminary meeting, and at the inaugural meeting all but two of those present were members of the Orthopaedic sub-Section of the RSM.

## A full Section

It was not until 1919 that proceedings of the sub-Section recommenced with DE Laming Evans' 'Case of coxa vara after reduction of congenital dislocation of the hip'. He was elected President the next year, when his address focused on 'Congenital dislocation of the hip'.[212] The experience of the war gave members plenty to discuss; meetings were well attended and the specialty looked set to expand. Therefore in May 1921 Laming Evans and Muirhead Little began campaigning for a full Section of Orthopaedics, only to meet with opposition from general surgeons who refused to countenance the subdivision of surgery. The Section of Urology had set a recent precedent, however, and the general surgeons were defeated by the orthopaedic surgeons' insistence that 'surgery can no longer be treated as a whole'. The petition proposing the new Section was tactfully worded and cautious, placing the traditional emphasis on the treatment of deformity to which opponents of specialism could hardly object: it defined orthopaedics as 'the surgery of congenital and acquired deformities of the extremities and spine'. Thus despite objections from the Surgical Section, the orthopaedic specialists had their way and the full Section of Orthopaedics first met on 7 February 1922 with Dr Laming Evans continuing as President. He was given a hearty vote of thanks for his address and praised for the energy and courtesy that had resulted in the formation of the Section.[213]

## Scoliosis

The activities of the full Section began with meetings on scoliosis, traumatic spondylitis and recent advances in orthopaedic surgery. A record number of 80 Fellows, members and visitors attended one meeting in March 1922 to hear Mr D McCrae Aitken speak on the use of remedial exercises as applied to scoliosis. This paper was the first published for the full Section in the *Proceedings*, and McCrae Aitken's studies on scoliosis were to appear in print over many years; he was elected President of the Section in 1929.

As a practical outcome of the meeting, Laming Evans suggested the formation of a committee jointly with the Chartered Society of Massage and Medical Gymnastics and the Ling Association to investigate scoliosis. This seems to have culminated in a conference to consider the use of physical exercises in the treatment of curvatures of the spine, when RC Elmslie, McCrae Aitken, AS Blundell Bankart and Dr F Barrie Lambert represented the Section.[214]

## The interwar years

The work of orthopaedic surgeons in the First World War enhanced their standing, as TH Openshaw acknowledged in October 1922: 'The status of an orthopaedic surgeon has been considerably enlarged during the war. There was a time when it was as much as anybody's reputation was worth to be known as an orthopaedic surgeon'. Sir Harry Platt went even further, stating that in these interwar years orthopaedic surgeons became 'the darlings of the gods'.[215]

The war had drawn attention to traumatic disabilities, and in 1922 Openshaw led a discussion on 'Traumatic spondylitis'. The session continued with contributions from Naughton Dunn and Blundell Bankart on spastic paralysis, and Rowley Bristow recounted a case of the unsatisfactory transplantation of hamstrings which would have to be 'undone'.

The advance of orthopaedics continued, fostered by Fairbank, Elmslie, Bristow, Trethowan, Aitken, Bankart and Laming Evans who 'set an example by regular atten- dance, bringing members of their teams. The latter were encouraged to show the cases under the care of the chief. An attendance of 20 or so grew rapidly, until the Section was one of the most popular at Wimpole Street'.[216]

A Rocyn Jones, who tackled 'The evolution of orthopaedic surgery in Great Britain' in his presidential address of 1937, reported that ever since its formation the Section had provided 'a ready forum for the consideration of difficult clinical cases or of those of unusual interest'. During each session at least two meetings were devoted to a 'full dress discussion of some orthopaedic problem' and occasionally a foreign surgeon was invited to expound upon his special subject – Albee, Scudder and Smith-Peterson, for instance.[217] Dr MN Smith-Peterson of Boston spoke to a meeting of 73 Fellows, members and visitors in March 1929 on 'The diagnosis and treatment of low back pain' (he was soon to be famous for his hip operation). Later in the year Professor Fred Albee, President of the American Orthopaedic Association and the author of *Orthopaedic reconstructive surgery* (1919), gave an address on 'Original surgical applications of the bone graft', and was duly elected the first corresponding member of the Section.

From 1928 onwards the first female members of the Section were in evidence: Erna Jebens and Maud Forrester Brown. The latter was the first female orthopaedic surgeon working in London, at the Battersea Hospital, and she became a member of the Section's Council in 1935.

## Sir Thomas Fairbank

HAT Fairbank was a familiar figure in the RSM Library and at meetings for nearly 40 years, and was elected an Honorary Fellow in 1951. As President of the Section in 1924 he

Sir Thomas Fairbank, President of the Section of Orthopaedics 1924–25 and an Honorary Fellow of the Society from 1951.

spoke on 'Some affections of the epiphyses', a subject of topical interest at a time when attempts were being made to classify Schlatter's knee, Kohler's disease and other epiphyseal abnormalities.[218]

Fairbank gave several papers, which were always well illustrated, and he invariably drew the younger generation into the proceedings. In the early days most of the patients shown at the meetings had undiagnosed conditions and as knowledge of orthopaedics increased surgeons sent cases with end-results of treatment. 'Fairbank enjoyed both, and so often demonstrated some child with fantastic abnormality of bone and he always managed to show radiographs of every bone that mattered'.[219]

Perhaps Fairbank's most impressive contributions to surgical literature were on diseases of the skeleton and congenital dislocation of the hip. He took an early opportunity to present his views on the latter to the Section in 1922 (unpublished), and 17 years later he held forth once more 'On the routine treatment of congenital dislocation of the hip': 'The first essential is early diagnosis', he declared, and he went on to summarize the indications for open reduction, or exploration of the joint or the 'shelf operation'. Platt added his experience of 386 dislocations; as Rocyn Jones noted, their conclusions derived from very considerable experience.[220]

On Sir Thomas Fairbank's 80th birthday in 1956, the *Journal of Bone and Joint Surgery* published a special birthday volume, and this is a rich source of information about the work of the Section and its members. St JD Buxton referred to Fairbank's foundation of the country branch of the Great Ormond Street Children's Hospital at Tadworth in Surrey, which provided many patients for clinical meetings at the RSM; their records were later published in Fairbank's *Atlas of general affections of the skeleton* (1951). A Rocyn Jones' contribution to the birthday volume was based on his presidential address to the Section, and Norman Capener's paper on 'The hand in surgery' was a version of his unpublished address of 1950 (see page 362).[221]

### Sir Harry Platt

One of Sir Robert Jones' last pupils, Harry Platt, became President of the Section in 1931. He was also a founder and President of the British Orthopaedic Association and the first orthopaedic surgeon to be President of the Royal College of Surgeons (1954–57). His address, 'Observations on bone tumours', was one of several scientific contributions to the *Proceedings*; latterly he was diverted to the subject of the teaching of orthopaedics, presenting his ideal scheme of postgraduate training to the Section.[222]

Platt also delivered the Robert Jones Memorial lecture in 1942, reminding the audience that Jones had been 60 at the end of the Great War when he embarked upon perhaps the most strenuous period of his life. Inspired by the host of children he had seen at Jones' clinics, Platt's main theme for this lecture was 'Congenital dislocation of the hip', and he made modest reference to the children's orthopaedic hospital he himself had established on the shore of Lake Windermere.[223]

Platt's ideas, practical and academic, fostered the expansion of services in the NHS from 1948 and reached the printed page in his *Selected Papers* of 1963. His influence was as wide as it was long – he lived to be a hundred.

### 1939–45 and after

During the interwar years Sir Robert Jones' pupils had dominated the orthopaedic scene, and the major responsibility for organizing the orthopaedic requirements of civilians throughout the country and orthopaedic services during the Second World War fell to these same men.

Thomas Fairbank was Orthopaedic Adviser to the Emergency Medical Service and other past Presidents of the Section worked as regional advisers, notably GR Girdlestone and

Harry Platt; W Rowley Bristow advised the British army, and a future President, Reginald Watson Jones, was in charge of orthopaedics for the RAF.

The largest meeting of the Section to date took place in October 1939, when 350 Fellows, members and visitors gathered to hear Dr Joseph Trueta on 'The organization of hospital casualties during the bombing of cities' (based on his experience in Barcelona during the Spanish Civil War). Trueta had devised the closed-plaster method of treating compound fractures in that war, and his book on *The treatment of war wounds and fractures* (1939) proved useful to British surgeons.

Meetings of the Section continued as far as war-time conditions allowed, and clinical meetings were held at the emergency hospitals if possible. Hence members visited Botley's Park War Hospital, Chertsey, where Rowley Bristow was working, the RAF Hospital at Ely and the Orpington Emergency Hospital. At the Wingfield-Morris Orthopaedic Hospital, Headington, Oxford, they saw 24 cases of peripheral nerve injury 'arranged' by the expert in the field, Professor Seddon.

Constantine Lambrinudi, who had already been struck by coronary thrombosis, was elected President in 1941. He was renowned for his drop-foot operation and procedures for claw toes and *pes cavus*. He chose a new subject in 1939, 'The intramedullary fixation of forearm fractures with Kirschner wires': 'the use of intramedullary wires in the treatment of fractures has, so far as I know, not previously been described'. Lambrinudi had tried it three times with success and he explained and illustrated these cases, before and after operation. It was some years before his technique gained credibility and it is now acknowledged as important in the management of fractures.[224] Lambrinudi's presidential address on 'The role of orthopaedics in medical education' was given at the Orpington Emergency Hospital in 1941: 'During the last war it required all the persuasive genius of Robert Jones before orthopaedic surgeons were given a fair trial; in this one there are not enough to go round'. Lambrinudi called for the re-orientation of the teaching of orthopaedics and he would doubtless have taken this further had he not died in 1943.[225]

Other contributions to meetings came from Archibald McIndoe on skin-grafting; Blundell Bankart told of his intrepid operations, Dr Royal Whitman of New York declared that orthopaedics was now an important and progressive branch of surgery (1943) and Dr Sterling Bunnel of San Francisco gave an address on 'Hand surgery in the war'.

With the advent of peace, Professor Seddon's work on peripheral nerve grafting operations and muscle transplantation was announced to the Section. In 1940 at the age of just 36 he had been appointed Nuffield Professor of Orthopaedic Surgery at Oxford, where he developed the peripheral nerve injury unit. On coming to London as Director of the Institute of Orthopaedics in 1948 he was elected President of the Section and his address was on 'Peripheral nerve repair' – a preview of his report to the Medical Research Council. 'Hitherto peacetime peripheral nerve surgery has suffered from being nobody's business', he stated. He discouraged hasty primary care: 'patients with nerve injuries can always be dealt with at leisure and with the degree of technical skill denied them in the past'.[226]

Section meetings after the war were well organized and well attended. Denis Browne gave a paper on 'Congenital hip dislocation' (see page 313) to an audience of 200, and George Perkins' presidential address was on 'Flat foot and instability'. Demonstrations were staged to show a rotating wooden frame or turning bed and a sitting–standing invalid chair connected to a power plug. The clinical meetings 'led to various and lively discussions on such problems as Calvé's disease of the spine, amputation of toes for deformity with metatarsalgia, [and] congenital bowing of the tibia'. Another meeting was held at Lord Mayor Treloar's Cripples' Hospital when Sir Thomas Fairbank gave an appreciation of its first Medical Superintendent Sir Henry Gauvain, who had died not long before. Gauvain had been President of the Sections of Electro-therapeutics and Paediatrics of the RSM (see pages 284–85).[227]

## The 1950s

The 1950s opened under the presidency of Norman Capener, whose address on 'The hand in surgery' was illustrated by the artist and sculptor Barbara Hepworth. Capener had organized the Princess Elizabeth Orthopaedic Hospital at Exeter and a range of orthopaedic services throughout the county, and at the meeting he demonstrated his Exeter splints and other ingenious instruments.[228]

The mid-point of the 20th century was judged by the *Journal of Bone and Joint Surgery* to be an appropriate juncture to take stock of the progress of orthopaedic surgery over the last 50 years. H Osmond-Clarke undertook a review of the achievements in Britain, covering in 55 pages the leaders, the societies and the journals between 1900 and 1950. He reported that the Section of the RSM continued to flourish: 'it plays an important and very active role in providing a forum for discussion and debate and for the presentation of difficult and interesting clinical problems'. The leading figures in orthopaedics over the last 50 years were well represented in the Section and Osmond-Clarke wrote of 'the remarkable spell of Robert Jones, the lofty, ascetic Tubby, the pugnacious Openshaw, the forceful Hey Groves, the earnest but irascible Laming Evans, the equable and thoughtful Elmslie, the restless and exuberant Trethowan'. These men erected the edifice of orthopaedics in this country, not least through the Section meetings.[229]

Many orthopaedic surgeons were still dissatisfied with the teaching of their specialty in this country. Philip Wiles, who was the first surgeon in Britain to design and insert a total hip replacement as early as 1938, outlined the many difficulties that had yet to be overcome in the teaching of orthopaedics, in his presidential address of 1952. Nor was his successor, H Jackson Burrows, afraid to speak his mind about the shortcomings of the medical curriculum. Jackson Burrows used his presidential address to air his views without

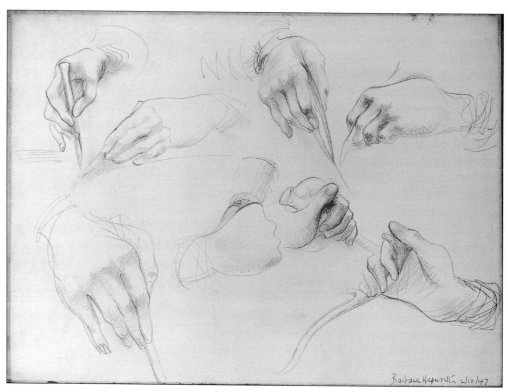

Barbara Hepworth's Study of Surgeon's Hands (1947) illustrated many points made by Norman Capener in his presidential address on 'The hand in surgery', 1950. Capener organized a regional service for south-west England based at the Princess Elizabeth Orthopaedic Hospital, Exeter, where Hepworth sketched surgeons at work.

fear of debate or contradiction, firstly on the subject of unnecessary treatment. 'More than half the boys leaving public schools have lost their tonsils, and as many as four in five their foreskins', and he went on to speak of the evils of wedges and 'remedial exercises' for children, and of the need for a new Society for Leaving the Poor Little Blighters Alone. More seriously he drew attention to the insatiable demand for orthopaedic training, the need for original research, postgraduate study and special orthopaedic departments.[230]

Sir Reginald Watson-Jones had been active in the Section from the age of 27, and by the time he was elected President in 1955 he was an international figure. He was in the vanguard of orthopaedics in this country and is perhaps best known as the founder and editor of the British volumes of the *Journal of Bone and Joint Surgery* (from 1948). He wrote the standard textbook *Fractures and joint injuries* (1940) and was also responsible for establishing accident services after the Second World War.

## The development of artificial joints

The orthopaedic problems that loomed so large to Sir Robert Jones and his protégés – tuberculosis of the bones and joints, war casualties and the crippling aftermath of rickets – were disappearing by 1950. New challenges then faced orthopaedic surgeons and the new age of implants had begun. The complete substitution of the damaged hip joint by a prosthesis was to be the life work of John Charnley.

While he was still working at the Manchester Royal Infirmary, Charnley accepted an invitation to participate in the Section's symposium on 'The use of metal in bone surgery' in May 1957. This was opened by Mr GK McKee of Norwich who illustrated the first artificial hip joint, derived from a lag screw. He had been using vitallium screws and stainless steel plates since 1942, and in February 1948 he presented ten cases of cup arthroplasty of

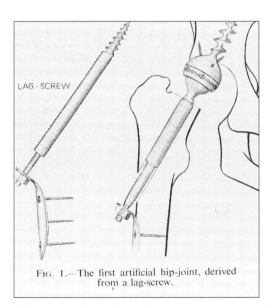

FIG. 1.—The first artificial hip-joint, derived from a lag-screw.

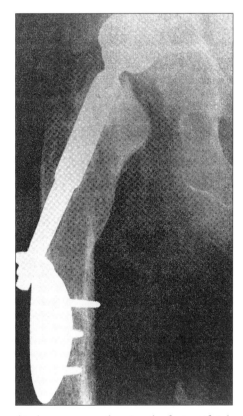

Illustrations from GK McKee's paper on the use of metal in bone surgery showing the first artificial hip joint derived from a lag screw, and an X-ray taken two years after insertion. McKee's paper was presented at a symposium in 1957.

the hip to the Section.[231] McKee persevered with total hip replacement over a long period, while others, including Charnley, nursed reservations. Charnley's comments at the Section's symposium in 1957 were limited to the mechanical factors, the simple stresses and strains put on the artificial hip joint. He doubted if a satisfactory metallic prosthesis was viable and spoke about impossible problems.[232]

Charnley returned to the RSM to take part in another symposium in December 1958, this time on 'The treatment of fractures of the shafts of long bones'. By this time he was dreaming of a centre for hip surgery at Wrightington Hospital, and once this was established he embarked on painstaking trials to test the wear of plastics against steel.

The symposium organized by the Section in 1958 was opened by Mr William Gissane, who had reviewed Charnley's book on the *Closed treatment of common fractures* (1950) and who set up the Birmingham Accident Hospital. In the discussion Charnley, who was beginning to abandon fracture work to concentrate on arthroplasty of the hip, was less confident than Gissane: 'our understanding of the basic processes which govern fracture repair are far from complete'.[233]

It was not until 1961 that Charnley publicized his new operation in the *Lancet*: 'Arthroplasty of the hip; a new operation'. The paper was amply illustrated and clear; although the technique in its present form had only been in use for 15 months (97 hips).[234] But Charnley's triumph proved hollow, for it became clear after some 300 operations that the plastic he was using (PTFE or Fluon) was not a suitable material for hip replacements. From 1962 Charnley was persuaded to try polyethylene, which proved successful. As a result of his pioneering work the hip replacement evolved as an excellent operation, becoming generally available by the early 1970s. Charnley was knighted in 1977; at the time of his death in 1986 he was still pursuing improvements and new ideas.[235]

Charnley's arthroplasty of the hip was the beginning of artificial knee, shoulder and elbow joints, all leading to increased specialization, improved techniques and materials. Professor Renato Bombelli of Italy and Robert Mathys of Switzerland reported persistently good results with the cementless fixation of implants to the Section in 1981 at a day-long meeting that aroused great interest.[236]

## Recent Presidents and meetings

Arthur L Eyre Brook's survey of the British orthopaedic scene in the early 1970s highlights the contributions of several Presidents. Karl Nissen (President 1962–63) is described as 'a Francophile from New Zealand' known for his work on digital neuroma and osteoarthritis of the hip. Denys Wainwright (President 1967–68) of Stoke-on-Trent was also known for his work on osteoarthritis of the hip and on fractures, and as a teacher at Liverpool University. JS Ellis (President 1971–72) was the first Professor of Orthopaedic Surgery at Southampton University; FC Dwyer (President 1974–75) did much to popularize osteotomy of the os calcis for many disabilities of the foot; FG St Clair Strange of the Seabathing Hospital at Margate was President 1965–66.

George Lloyd-Roberts (President 1976–77), who was guaranteed to enliven any gathering, dominated children's orthopaedics for some 30 years. His obituary made special mention of his classic papers on problems of the hip and foot in children – his address to the Section had been on 'Children's feet'.[237]

Two years after Lloyd-Roberts' presidency Mr A Graham Apley took his turn in the chair. He was a skilful educator and the author of *System of orthopaedics and fractures*, first published in 1959 and in its seventh edition by 1993. This broke new ground by virtue of the ample illustrations, and it became an essential tool for orthopaedic surgeons and those wishing to understand the structure and function of the musculoskeletal system, its diseases and its responses to trauma. Apley was a brilliant speaker and during his presidency the number attending meetings averaged 70; he was made an Honorary Fellow of the Society in 1995.

Joint meetings with the Section of Plastic Surgery proved a success and distinguished foreign speakers attracted much interest. The Section was fortunate to be able to call upon Mr JA Fixsen to serve as President for 1997–98, a surgeon of international repute whose programme focused on 'Bone tumours' and 'Gait disorders', and a symposium on 'The management of leg length inequality' was held; his paper on 'Problem feet in children' was published in the *Journal* for 1998.

Clinical meetings ceased in 1973, since when the pattern has remained largely unchanged except for the dropping of the free paper sessions in 1996. An important object of the meetings has been to give trainees the opportunity to present their work and many have cut their teeth on the rostrum in the Barnes Hall. In recent years it was felt that the quality of papers declined, so trainees' papers from specific units have been read instead. It has been the custom to alternate town and country Presidents, although meetings outside London occur only once every two years. 'Should we perhaps travel a little more?' Mr Brian Reeves asked in his presidential address of 1998, 'we could easily become, with all the demands on our time, a London Section of a National Society'.[238]

## Section of Comparative Medicine (Plate 59)

In his presidential address to the Section in 1926 Sir D'Arcy Power traced the origins of comparative medicine to ancient Greece. His imagination conjured up Hippocrates for the Section's first President or Patron, and he thought 'Aristotle would have joined our Section at once' and the first candidate for Honorary membership 'must certainly have been Mago, the Carthaginian, who was known as the "Father of Agriculture"'. D'Arcy Power, a leading medical historian, was gratified to see the two streams of human and veterinary medicine united at last in the new discipline of comparative medicine.

According to D'Arcy Power, a society for comparative medicine had been discussed by Sir Thomas Clifford Allbutt and Sir Berman Sims Woodhead at Cambridge 'many years ago', and the advantages of such a society had been evident at meetings of the old Pathological Society where medical members had learnt much from the contributions of veterinary surgeons. 'The project of forming a Society of Comparative Pathology was talked about, the usual objections were raised', and no one came forward 'as an active spirit to call it into existence' until 'the veterinary side of the profession took up the matter', namely Professor Hobday.[239]

### Professor Hobday founds the Section

Professor Frederick Hobday, veterinary surgeon to the King (and duly knighted in 1933), was a vigorous representative of his profession, keen to advance the education and status of veterinary surgeons. He brought many colleagues into the RSM, recruiting them at meetings of the National Veterinary Medical Association, and in February 1921 he opened his campaign to bring comparative medicine under the auspices of the RSM in a lecture on 'Observations on some of the diseases of animals communicable to man'. Clifford Allbutt, Regius Professor of Physic at Cambridge, regretted that he was unable to be present since this was a subject which he had been pursuing for many years.[240]

Hobday used the lecture to promote comparative medicine as a new specialty: 'The students of human medicine nowadays have become specialists and sub-divided specialists; and the students of veterinary medicine also, but there is room even yet for a still further specialism – viz, for those who will bridge the gap between the two, and specialize in comparative medicine'. As a result of the lecture a combined meeting was organized on 14 February 1921 between the RSM and the Central Branch of the National Veterinary Medical Association, followed in March by another meeting on 'The eradication of

Sir Frederick Hobday, founder of the Section of
Comparative Medicine and its President
1924–26.

Sir Thomas Clifford Allbutt, first President
of the Section of Comparative Medicine
1923–24.

tuberculosis from man and animals'. This time Allbutt was one of the main speakers, along with Sir John McFadyean, Hobday and Dr Inman.[241]

Thus the ground had been prepared by the time Hobday wrote to the Secretary of the RSM, MacAlister, on 24 February 1923 suggesting that a new Section be established 'where graduates of the two branches, medical and veterinary, will meet to discuss some of the knotty problems which are common to man and animals'.[242] Hobday claimed that 61 members of the veterinary profession who were Fellows of the RSM supported the founding of the Section, moreover he had the backing of Allbutt. The Council of the RSM agreed that a Section of Comparative Medicine and Pathology might be constituted, whereupon 11 Fellows of the Section of Pathology objected, with the result that Pathology was omitted from the title.[243]

An organizing committee met on 29 June 1923 under the chairmanship of the President of the RSM, Sir William Hale-White, when Hobday formally proposed the formation of the Section of Comparative Medicine. It was decided that initially the Section would function under the same regulations as the Section of Medicine, that it would have a President taken in alternate years from human or veterinary medicine and that the Council of the Section should be made up of equal numbers from the two branches of medicine.

The meeting to establish the Section followed quickly. There were 40 members present, and it was decided by a small majority that the first President of the Section should be a medical man: Allbutt was elected and Hobday was to follow as the first veterinary President in 1924. As usual, an Obligation Book was opened which the members of the Section had to sign, indicating their acceptance of the rules of the Section and their willing-ness to support and promote its activities.

## The proceedings commence

The first scientific meeting of the Section took place on Wednesday 24 October 1923, when the presidential address was given by Sir Thomas Clifford Allbutt. Sir Thomas welcomed members and congratulated the new Section and the RSM as a whole: 'Your Society now shares with Cambridge University the honour of being first in the field to recognize that disease has to be studied as a biological whole' (the Institute for Research in the Pathology of Animal Diseases was established at Cambridge in 1923). Allbutt anticipated that animals would benefit from the work of the Section, industries and possibly governments, 'and we may learn more about diseases that affect animals and humans'.[244] These remarks came in the wake of outbreaks of rabies in England between 1918 and 1922, and there had recently been a mass slaughtering of cattle with foot and mouth disease – the Ministry of Health was urging investigation and remedies.

Allbutt's address was followed by a paper given by Hobday entitled 'Cryptorchidism in animals and man' illustrated with pictures and specimens from over 1,200 cases. The meeting was attended by 62 Fellows, members and visitors. Hobday wrote of the value of these meetings, 'at which the discussions bring out the respective, varied and sometimes contrasting objects for which the human and the veterinary healers exercise their skill'.[245]

The Section was just three years old when its President Sir D'Arcy Power spoke about its origins (see above) and acknowledged the influence of Allbutt, the energy of Hobday and the zeal of the Secretaries in making the Section a success: 'And it remains for all of us to maintain and even to enhance its position by contributing to our knowledge and taking part in the discussions. The work of the section embraces a vast field extending on the one side to the most difficult problems of human medicine and on the other to the interrelation of human and veterinary science, showing thereby that the processes of disease are identical whether they occur in men or in animals'.[246]

From the outset the Section had as its objective the bringing together of persons from many different specialities who had a common interest in comparative medicine. The purpose was always to maximize the usefulness of discoveries in human medicine as they may be applied to diseases of animals and to make the best use of observations on animals to the better understanding and relief of human diseases.

## Presidents[247]

Many distinguished men and women from veterinary and human medicine have served on the Section's Council and as President. Professor Alexander Fleming was elected President in 1942; he was to be a Nobel prizewinner and was awarded the Gold Medal of the RSM in 1947. Three eminent members of the Section have been awarded the Honorary Fellowship of the Society: Sir Thomas Dalling (President 1938–39), Dame Olga Uvarov (who had qualified as one of the first female veterinary surgeons in 1934 and was President of the Section 1967–68) and Professor Lord Soulsby of Swaffham Prior (President 1993–95). The last-named went on to become the first non-medical President of the RSM in 1998. Another name that should receive special mention is that of the neurologist Professor G Pampiglione, twice President of the Section and its untiring supporter from the 1960s to the 1980s. He presented the President's badge of office, a magnificent gold medallion fashioned from an antique shoe buckle (Plate 59). Others who have been President of the Section twice are the veterinary surgeons Mr Kenneth Burns and Mr Hugh Platt; since 1989 all Presidents have held office for two years.

## Variety of meetings

The Section usually holds five or six meetings in each session and they cover a very wide range of subjects. The first session of 1923–24 featured Professor Hobday (see above), Professor E Mellanby on 'Nutritional diseases in animals' and Thomas WM Cameron on

'The pig and human disease'. RT Leiper and Cameron demonstrated pathological results in helminthic infections in animals, and FAE Carew's illustrated paper was on 'The bull-dog calf', a contribution to the study of achondroplasia.[248]

By the 1940s the meetings had come to take the form of discussions on broad subjects, such as 'The control of diseases of cattle inimical to man' (this continued for all five meetings of the 1941–42 session), 'The span of life' (1947) and the presentation of individual papers.

The Section has often held joint meetings with other Sections, and latterly has also held meetings with other bodies such as the Royal Society of Health and the British Small Animals Veterinary Association. In recent years it has been the practice to hold a meeting in which a group of papers on the same topic are presented. Some indication of the diversity of the subjects covered at the Comparative Medicine meetings can be gathered from the following examples: influenza, tuberculosis, malaria, salmonella, Gumboro disease, genetic manipulation of viruses, sleep, rabies, acupuncture, radiology, embryo transfer and organophosphorus toxicity. It is the tradition that the June meeting takes the form of a visit, usually to a medical or veterinary research institute, although one of the most enjoyable was to Charles Darwin's house and the (then) Royal College of Surgeons Museum at Downe.

In 1955 the Section Council decided to initiate a Section Dinner after the March or April meeting, which has proved very popular; in 1971 the Honorary Secretary was instructed 'to arrange a dinner, including wines, at a price of about 50 shillings' (£2.50), a reminder of the degree of inflation since that time. In those days informal Council dinners usually followed the short evening meetings and speakers were invited to dine with the Council; these were very agreeable occasions held in the upstairs dining-room of the old building.

It used to be the practice to publish the presidential address of the Section in the *Proceedings* (later the *Journal*) of the RSM. Over the years a large number of meeting reports, summarizing the main points of the meetings, have also been published, together with some full-length papers submitted by the speakers. Unfortunately pressure on space in the *Journal* has tended to curtail this activity.

### Members and non-members
One of the distinguishing features of the Section is that it is not career-orientated. The members, who number about 300, are mainly doctors, veterinary surgeons and scientists who have a common interest in comparative medicine. They are usually specialists in a discipline of their own and attend Section meetings for general background interest rather than for improving their performance at work. Most of the meetings of the Section, however, include a great deal of solid, scientifically based information of educational value to both specialists and generalists, and as with other Sections attendance can earn Continuing Medical Education points for those who are eligible. Each meeting tends to attract a different audience. For example, a meeting on 'Immunodeficiency viruses in people and animals' is likely to appeal to an audience of some Section members and many non-Section members. The same Section members might then come to the next meeting on, for example, 'Poisons recognition and avoidance', but the non-Section members at that meeting would differ from those at the previous meeting. This creates some difficulty in attracting an appropriate audience, and suitable colleges, institutes and organizations have to be targeted with publicity about forthcoming Section meetings.

The introduction of detailed financial accountability in many organizations has had the effect of making it more difficult for staff to justify absence from work to attend a Section meeting, especially if its subject is unlikely to contribute directly to the improved performance of customary duties. This particularly affects younger people, who are less able to cover their travel costs, and has been exacerbated by the introduction of charges for attendance at some meetings. This has not been helpful to the Section; even so, it continues to have an active and enthusiastic Council that puts forward exciting proposals for forthcoming meetings. So long as there are men and women who appreciate the stimulus of discussion outside the confines of their own specialty and who are pleased to venture at times into the intellectual fields of other disciplines, the successful future of the Section of Comparative Medicine can be predicted with confidence.

## Section of Coloproctology (Plate 60)
### originally Proctology
The history of the Section of Coloproctology might be traced to John of Arderne (or simply John Arderne), the 14th-century father of British proctology, whose image is depicted on the Section's presidential badge.[249] While the specialty may have medieval – and older – roots, its representation by a society and subsequently by a Section of the RSM begins with the formation of the British Proctological Society in December 1912. The event was marked by a dinner at Pagani's Restaurant and the absence of any Minutes. Of the 15 founder-members, nine were or had been on the staff of St Mark's Hospital for Cancer, Fistula and other Diseases of the Rectum, including the President, Mr Frederick Swinford Edwards, and the Honorary Secretary, Mr JP Lockhart-Mummery.

The reasons for establishing the British Proctological Society at this juncture are not stated. The American Proctologic Society had been founded in 1899 and as yet there was no British parallel, although there had long been two London hospitals specializing in diseases of the rectum and colon – St Mark's and the Gordon. Possibly London proctologists were aware of the intentions of urological and orthopaedic colleagues to attach

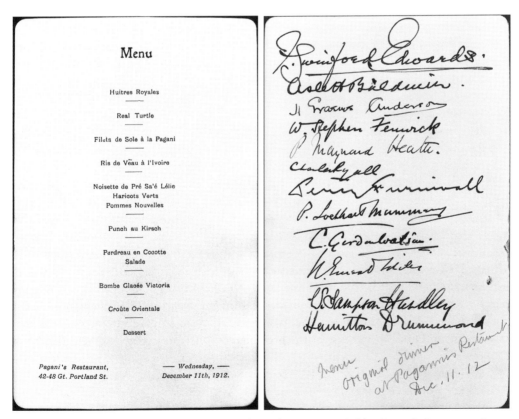

The foundation dinner of the British Proctological Society was held at Pagani's Restaurant in December 1912. The BPS was officially inaugurated in February 1913, soon joining the RSM as a sub-Section of Surgery. The menu was signed by founder-members.

themselves to the RSM and looked for equal recognition from that Society and from the International Congress of Medicine being planned for 1913. Swinford Edwards, remembered as the scholarly President who introduced the injection method for piles to this country, retired from St Mark's in 1913 and may have sought to realize longstanding hopes for a society devoted to his specialty. Lockhart-Mummery, younger and ambitious, had recently popularized Professor Strauss's sigmoidoscope and was writing *Diseases of the rectum and anus*. To him the foundation of a proctological society was part of a crusade and his book, published in 1914, announced that surgery of the rectum was as much a specialty as gynaecology, ophthalmology or laryngology.

Harold Dodd, a later President of the Section, commented that the 'healthy rivalry' between St Mark's and the Gordon Hospitals, the publication of *Diseases of the anus and rectum* by DH Goodsall and WE Miles (1900, 1905) and Lockhart-Mummery's Jacksonian prize essay on 'Diseases of the colon' (1909) stimulated the foundation of the sub-Section of proctology in 1913.[250]

## Sub-Section of Proctology

The foundation of the British Proctological Society did not escape the notice of the Secretary of the RSM, John MacAlister, who was determined to draw specialist medical societies into the larger Society. The first item on the agenda at the inaugural meeting of the British Proctological Society in February 1913, held at the RSM's new building in Wimpole Street, referred to a letter from MacAlister suggesting that instead of being a separate society, the BPS should become a sub-Section of the Surgical Section of the RSM. The proposal was deferred for three months, and in May the BPS agreed unanimously to disband and be incorporated within the RSM under the leadership of the same officers – Swinford Edwards, Percy Furnivall, Lockhart-Mummery and Sampson Handley.[251]

It has been suggested that this liaison came about because the RSM 'was attempting to improve its position, in particular in relation to the BMA, by absorbing specialist groups'

Founders of the Section of Proctology: left, F Swinford Edwards, President 1913–19, 1924–25; right, JP Lockhart-Mummery, President 1919–20, 1926–27, 1937–40.

such as urologists, orthopaedic surgeons and proctologists.[252] It is certain that MacAlister and Professor Osler sought to absorb medical societies within the RSM, and since 1907 the Society had thus expanded, but it is unlikely that this had any bearing on relations with the BMA.

The sub-Section first met on 15 October 1913 and declared its object to be the promotion of the surgery of the rectum and colon. There was soon an influx of nominations for membership from well-known surgeons such as James Berry, E Rock Carling and Charters Symonds, and meetings were organized for the session of 1913–14 when several cases were presented by Aslett Baldwin, Sampson Handley and Lockhart-Mummery, whose paper on 'Haemorrhagic proctitis' was published in the *Proceedings*. From the foundation of the sub-Section in 1913 until his resignation in 1952 Lockhart-Mummery was its indefatigable promoter and its President three times. When he eventually tendered his resignation, the Council noted 'his great services to the Section which he was in a large measure instrumental in forming'.[253] His son, Sir Hugh, was a worthy successor and President of the Section 1966–67. With another President of the Section, Mr Basil Morson, he gave an influential paper distinguishing Crohn's diseases of the colon from ulcerative colitis and he was associated with the present President, Professor Heald, in the introduction of stapling devices. The Section held an all-day memorial meeting in honour of Sir Hugh in 1990.

Swinford Edwards was re-elected President for the first six years of the sub-Section's life (reappearing in 1924) until 1919 when Lockhart-Mummery served his first term, succeeded in 1920 by 'the surgically immortal Ernest Miles' (famous for his abdominoperineal excision). Miles' presidential address was the first to be published in the *Proceedings* and it opened with a tribute to the work of members in generating new interest in the study of proctology. Miles detected signs that the medical schools had begun to realize the subject deserved a place in the curriculum. 'When this comes about men will no longer go out into the practice of their profession with next to no knowledge of rectal complaints and the day will have passed when an early carcinoma of the rectum will remain undetected for want of a timely rectal examination. Let us hope that in the near future we shall no longer see so large a proportion of cases of rectal cancer that have passed beyond the stage of operability'. This brought him to his main subject: the question of how soon a colostomy should be performed in inoperable cases of carcinoma of the rectum – as one of his successors commented, in 1955 the subject would scarcely have arisen because the operability rate had increased from 35% in 1913 to over 90% by then.[254]

During the First World War meetings were held 'circumstances permitting'. As soon as the war was over the Council resolved (on the proposal of Mr Anderson and Sir Charles Gordon-Watson) that 'all Germans should be expelled from this Society' – a resolution that was not condoned by the RSM. Gordon-Watson was elected President in 1921, when he set in motion the first of five petitions for the up-grading of the sub-Section to a full Section.[255]

### Special discussions

From time to time during the interwar years the sub-Section organized a special discussion on a particular problem to which guest speakers were invited – Sir Arthur Keith and Sir Berkeley Moynihan, for example. In 1923 the esteemed Sir Humphry Rolleston, President of the Royal College of Physicians, Regius Professor of Physic at Cambridge and a past President of the RSM, opened the discussion on 'Ulcerative colitis'. He recalled that its recognition was largely due to the work of Sir William Hale-White, a President of the RSM. The Section of Medicine had debated the subject in 1909 when Lockhart-Mummery inaugurated the clinical study of colitis by describing the first stigmoidoscope observations ever made of this condition. In 1909 the disease had a mortality of over 50%; by 1923 Lockhart-Mummery's figures showed a decline to 15.7%.

The subject of ulcerative colitis was raised again in 1933. Rolleston's belief that the condition was not a specific disease was refuted by surgeons such as Lionel Norbury and ETC Milligan, and in 1934 Lockhart-Mummery claimed that mortality had decreased to 10%. The most effective treatment remained a matter for debate: Norbury argued for surgical treatment and WB Gabriel recommended the injection of olive oil, while Dr Arthur Hurst, a gastroenterologist, disagreed with both. At a full discussion in 1953 attended by Richard Cattell of the Lahey Clinic, Boston, it was agreed that the colon should be removed in severe cases. The only physician participating in that debate was Dr Francis Avery Jones, who was to give his presidential address on 'Colitis' in 1966, by which time trials on the new drugs had been undertaken; Avery Jones recommended corticosteroids for moderate and severe cases of colitis, and sulphasalazine for milder cases.[256]

The title of one of John of Arderne's 14th-century treatises, *Fistula-in-ano*, was the subject for discussion at the annual meeting of the sub-Section in 1929, when Lockhart-Mummery argued that infection might pass along the glands through the wall of the anal canal. He took the lead in a joint discussion on the same subject with the Urological Section in 1932.

As President in 1927 Sir Charles Gordon-Watson spoke on the radium treatment of cancer of the rectum. He was a bold and heroic operator and one of the last adherents of the clamp and cautery method of treating piles. In the 1920s he became interested in the possibilities of radium treatment, visiting Paris and Brussels to observe foreign techniques. In 1927 he spoke as a proselytizer for radium in the treatment of cancer of the rectum, recommending small doses over a long period, whereas Lockhart-Mummery favoured large doses for short periods. By 1930 Gordon-Watson had decided that 'the percentage of failures in operable growths did not justify treatment by radium in preference to surgery in the present state of our knowledge'. Hedley-Whyte, President in 1946, remembered Gordon-Watson's 'enthusiasm in the later twenties with radium, and how we followed him, and like him, were disappointed'.[257]

*The Charter of Proctology*
Professor G Grey Turner gave his presidential address of 1925 on 'The relationship of proctology to greater medicine'. He was no specialist and was as successful in the treatment of the cleft palate as in uretero-colonic transplantation. Looking back over the previous 25 years Grey Turner found that diseases of the anus and rectum had been overshadowed, firstly by abdominal surgery and secondly by the overcrowding of the hospitals which necessitated the relegation of important cases to the waiting list. Nevertheless, a small band of surgeons and the special hospitals had sustained the specialty, as had the sub-Section, although Grey Turner found fault with its title because it indicated 'a more limited field than we would wish'.

Grey Turner's address was seized upon by members of the sub-Section as a Charter for Proctology. He made several points regarding the teaching and practice of proctology and it coincided with a bid to give the specialty full Section status. In spite of being among the most active departments of the RSM, the Council of the sub-Section complained that it had no representation on the Society's Council and was limited to a small number of pages in the *Proceedings*. Furthermore, it was argued that proctology had amply justified its existence as a separate entity. The Surgical Section did not agree.[258]

The proctologists made another attempt at Section status in 1930 with a statement that revealed the sub-Section comprised 56 members, with the high average attendance of 49 at meetings. Dissatisfaction was expressed with the 'ridiculous situation' whereby membership of the sub-Section was limited to those already members of the Surgical Section – proctological meetings were attended by pathologists and physicians but should they wish to join they had first to join the Section of Surgery. 'We have also suffered in rather more acute form from the editorial supervision of our proceedings', which had to be submitted to the Surgical Section; authors of papers complained of sweeping excisions and alterations by editors. This statement was rejected by the Surgical Section: it had opposed the formation of Orthopaedics as a separate Section and objected even more strongly to a separate Section of Proctology, 'only harm can follow the increasing isolation of those surgeons who are especially concerned with a special department ... there will be no limit to the multiplication of such Sections'.[259]

Four years later Lockhart-Mummery and Sir Charles Gordon-Watson pointed out the injustice of the situation. The sub-Section had by then existed for 21 years, during which time six new full Sections had been inaugurated. Their point was ignored, until eventually Lockhart-Mummery's petition of 1938 met with success. As President for the third time he called a special meeting of the sub-Section in November 1938 and Professor Grey Turner used his influence with the Surgical Section (he had been its President for the previous two years), securing its co-operation in granting full Section status to Proctology. This was agreed in June 1939.[260]

## Section of Proctology

Lockhart-Mummery, WB Gabriel, Lawrence Abel, ETC Milligan, Cuthbert Dukes and RS Corbett saw the Section through the years of the Second World War, contributing papers on 'War wounds of the large intestine', and giving demonstrations and organizing clinico-pathological meetings at St Mark's Hospital, although by 1942–43 there were only three meetings in the session. Gabriel, dubbed the 'Archangel Gabriel', was known for his radical operative procedures and for refusing to use blood transfusion. Lawrence Abel, working at the Gordon Hospital, was Gabriel's rival. He introduced the meticulous technique used by TE Jones of Cleveland and showed that peritonitis may occur from infection spreading inwards from the abdominal wound. The Australian surgeon ETC Milligan (who belonged to the Moral Rearmament Movement and endeavoured to make converts among patients and colleagues) and one of his successors, Clifford Naunton-Morgan (President 1948–49 and 1963–64), were known for transforming haemorrhoidectomy into a surgical art-form.

Dr E Cuthbert Dukes, President from 1943 to 1944, was also to be President of the Sections of Urology and History of Medicine in the 1950s. He is revered by proctologists for his work on the pathology and biochemistry of rectal disease and his address was on 'The surgical pathology of rectal cancer'; his classification of rectal carcinoma was to be adopted throughout the surgical world and this Section nominated him for Honorary Fellowship of the RSM in 1966. During Dukes' presidency the Section's AGM had to be postponed 'owing to the imminence of the opening of the Allied Invasion of Europe' and because several members had been ordered to duties outside London. The Council Minutes also record the election of a past President, Sir Gordon Gordon-Taylor, as President of the RSM in 1944. The Section has provided several Presidents of the Royal College of Surgeons, from Sir Edward Muir to Sir Barry Jackson, but only one President of the RSM.

## A national association?

With the NHS coming into operation, the future of specialist hospitals such as St Mark's hung in the balance. Official enquiries revealed that the surgeons of St Mark's relied on the Proctological Section of the RSM for the interchange of ideas: 'We cannot think of any better way' of achieving co-operation.[261] Harold Dodd, however, wanted to see a national association of proctologists established, and in 1948 he put it to the Section's Council that an association should be founded 'to build up proctology throughout the country in the same way that the Association of Urologists is safeguarding urology' (the British

Association of Urological Surgeons was founded in 1945). Lionel Norbury, ETC Milligan and Ronald Raven supported Dodd, forming a committee 'to advance the science of proctology and assist in the diffusion of knowledge and training in the subject',[262] but it was another 40 years before the Association of Coloproctology of Great Britain and Ireland came into being (see below).

Dodd was still trying to rally colleagues in 1955, using his presidential address to supplement Grey Turner's Charter of Proctology with dictates on the surgeon's qualifications: mental, physical and spiritual fitness ('Good literature should be on our desks and at the bedside, the Book of Books being amongst them'), judgement, surgical technique and teamwork.[263]

## Joint meetings

There was much to be learnt from American proctologists, who had organized a society 13 years before the British, and members of the American Proctologic Society paid an official visit to St Mark's Hospital in 1914. Shortly before the Second World War delegates from that Society were entertained by the Section in London and during the war the Inter-Allied Conferences held at the RSM cemented friendships. In 1949 members of the Section travelled to a meeting of the American Society and this led to regular combined meetings, most notably in 1959 when the diamond jubilee of the American Society was celebrated by a three-day meeting with the Section in London. Henry Thompson was the current President, HE Lockhart-Mummery opened a symposium on 'Ulcerative colitis', and Oswald Lloyd-Davies, Sir Heneage Ogilvie and Ronald Raven gave papers, balanced by those from their American colleagues. Harold Dodd gave the meeting historical perspective in a paper that underlined the distinctive work of past Presidents of the Section on carcinoma of the rectum – 'spirited men like WB Gabriel and Lawrence Abel'. He mentioned Lloyd-Davies' apparatus that enabled two surgeons to work simultaneously at the perineum and abdomen and he referred to the 'courageous initiative' of Raven. 'What other qualities did these past Presidents have which fitted them for the grisly problem of carcinoma of the rectum?' he questioned. They were first-class surgeons as well as proctologists, they were keen students who wrote and spoke creditably, they were physically fit and they also had to be travellers – 'some of them were among the first to obtain the degree of BTA, now a necessity for British surgeons, it stands for Been To America'.[264]

Joint meetings were also arranged with the French Proctological Society in Paris (1967) and with Greek proctologists (1968), together with a tripartite Anglo-American-Australian meeting (1974, now organized every five years) and in 1975 the RSM's Annual Report made special mention of the highly successful European meeting that brought together not only proctologists from 11 European countries but also participants from the USA, Brazil, Mexico and Venezuela. In the late 1970s, when many Sections were weak and complaining about inadequate funding, the success of the Section of Proctology's joint meetings was held up as an example to others.

From 1982 'Teach-Ins' were launched in the provinces. The first was held at Birmingham General Hospital and 51 registered for the day. Other successful teaching days were held at Manchester, Cardiff, Oxford, Nottingham and Southampton, and by 1987 they yielded an annual profit of £1,000.

## Section of Coloproctology

A change of name for the Section was discussed regularly from 1962 onwards; it was initially prompted by the wish to attract more physicians, pathologists and radiologists to meetings. Dr F Avery Jones brought the matter up again in 1966, generating 'a lively discussion including classical witticisms from Mr Reilly'. The Council was wary of a current proposal for a new Section of Gastro-enterology and decided not to make any changes for the present.

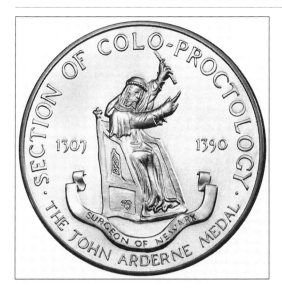

The John of Arderne Medal, introduced in 1983 and presented for the best paper by a trainee during the session.

In 1973 HE Lockhart-Mummery proposed the Section's name should be changed to the Section of Diseases of the Colon and Rectum. Finally in 1981 a change was advocated because of confusion abroad, where proctology has a different connotation. After considering various options, the Section voted for Coloproctology and this was ratified by the RSM in 1983. The design of the John of Arderne Medal was adjusted accordingly and in generous mood the Section went on to establish the Salmon lecture in honour of Frederick Salmon, founder of the Fistula Infirmary (St Mark's Hospital) in 1835, and to support travelling fellowships.[265]

## Association of Coloproctology of Great Britain and Ireland

One school of thought found that the Section had disadvantages in that its activities meant there was little need to establish a national proctological society and journal that might have been beneficial to the growth of proctology in Britain. Far from discouraging a wider association, the Section had endorsed the idea in 1948 and took more positive action in the late 1980s, even proposing that the Section should change its name to the British Association of Proctology.

In the 1980s the Section was one of the most successful, due mainly to an enthusiastic membership committed to the advancement of the clinical, scientific and teaching aspects of coloproctology. Although the membership was predominantly from the south of England and the Midlands and meetings centred on Wimpole Street, the Section was the only voice for coloproctology in the country. This was satisfactory when dealing with purely academic matters, but the prospect of a specialist register and other changes proposed in a White Paper caused the Council to reconsider the role of the Section *vis-à-vis* the body of British coloproctology. It was felt that this Section of the RSM was a very valuable forum for discussion, the presentation of research and for education in coloproctology but, as Professor Irving pointed out, it was not the role of the RSM to be engaged in training since that was the remit of the Royal Colleges of Surgeons.

The Royal College of Surgeons of England was at this time mulling over the place of sub-specialties within general surgery, especially in relation to the proposed change in the Fellowship examination, and with this in mind Professor M Keighley (President 1996–97) and Mr Philip Schofield (Professor Schofield, who was President 1993–94), produced a paper on the experience and training required in a consultant with a special interest in colorectal surgery, forwarded to the College in 1986.

Two years later Schofield's paper on the future of coloproctology in the United Kingdom suggested that the formation of a British society of coloproctology was inevitable. It would have wider powers than the Section, geographically, politically and in training and standards, and Schofield maintained 'it was essential that the Section should initiate such a society in order that it should not itself be weakened'. The Honorary Secretary, Mr RJ Heald, pointed out to the Society's Council in 1989 that the Section comprised the most significant group of coloproctologists in the country and they wished to become a national association. The RSM Council was not amenable to the initiative, even though Heald (who as Professor Heald was to be President for 1999–2000) received 48 letters supporting a new body of coloproctology.[266] In the face of objections from the Society's Council, the Section appointed a working party to advance the proposed British association, confident that sooner or later the Royal College would recognize coloproctology as a specific specialty. Thus in March 1990 the Association of Coloproctology of Great Britain and Ireland was inaugurated with the current President of the Section, Mr Geoffrey D Oates, as its first President.[267] The objectives of this multi-disciplinary association are to promote the interests, standards and training in coloproctology. It brought the British coloproctologists in line with American, Australian and European colleagues and left the Section free to pursue its academic role.

1 The Anatomical Society and the Physiological Society were approached by MacAlister, see letter MacAlister to his brother 23 July 1912, folder 3/G8, Box 23 and MacAlister to Bayliss 21 October 1912, folder 3/G9, Box 24. Section of Tropical Diseases and Parasitology, Regulations and Constitution 1912, 1921, K198, Box 49.

2 MacAlister correspondence 1913 folder 2/G11, Box 26.

3 *Bulletin* 26 (1918). Section for Naval and Military Medicine approved 13 March 1919, H3. MacAlister correspondence 1920, 1921 folder 8/G18, Box 31. *Bulletin* 30 (1920).

4 CM 16 December 1924. *Bulletin* 55 (1932).

5 Society of Anaesthetists correspondence 1892–1908 I4, Box 42. Much of the information for the history of this Section is based on Young, TM, *A short history of the Section of Anaesthetics of the Royal Society of Medicine and the Society of Anaesthetists* (1998) and Boulton, TB, 'The organization of the specialty of anaesthesia' in Atkinson, Richard S and Boulton, Thomas B (eds), *The history of anaesthesia* (1989) pp. 159–162.

6 *Lancet* (i) pt 1 30 January 1909 pp. 319–20. Howat, DDC, 'Sir Frederic William Hewitt' parts 1 and 2 in JMB vol 7 February 1999 pp. 5–10, vol 7 May 1999 pp. 63–68.

7 Lawrence, Christopher, 'Experiment and experience in anaesthesia: Alfred Goodman Levy and chloroform death' in Lawrence, Christopher (ed), *Medical theory, surgical practice* (1992) pp. 263–94.

8 PRSM vol 6 pt 1 (1912–13).

9 *Ibid* vol 11 pts 1–2 (1917–18).

10 Atkinson and Boulton *op cit* pp. 209–10.

11 PRSM vol 13 pt 1 (1919–20).

12 PRSM vol 9 (1916).

13 PRSM vol 27 pt 2 (1934). O'Sullivan, Ellen P, 'Dr Robert James Minnitt 1889–1974: a pioneer of inhalation analgesia' in JRSM vol 82 (1989) pp. 221–22.

14 PRSM vol 14 (1920–21).

15 *Ibid* vol 22 (1929), vol 29 pt 1 (1935–36).

16 PRSM vol 17 pt 1 (1924). Atkinson and Boulton *op cit* p. 211.

17 PRSM vol 34 (1940–41). For the organization of the specialty see Atkinson and Boulton *op cit* Chapter 8.

18 Howat, DDC, 'Joseph Blomfield 1870–1948' in Barr, Marshall, Boulton, Thomas B, and Wilkinson, David J (eds), *Essays on the history of anaesthesia* (1989).

19 Deaths during Anaesthesia committee 1927–28, H4, H5.

20 Report signed by Charles Hadfield, 9 December 1932. MS//04/f5, Box 63.

21 Hickman Medal correspondence 1928–31, M17, Box 82.

22 Boulton, Thomas B, *The Association of Anaesthetists of Great Britain and Ireland 1932–1992. The development of the specialty of anaesthesia* (1999) p. 17.

23 CM Section of Anaesthetics 6 November 1931, K1.

24 PRSM vol 29 pt 1 (1935–36).

25 *Ibid* vol 39 (1945–46).

26 *Ibid* vol 40 (1946–47). I am most grateful to Dr Aileen K Adams for comments such as this and for a copy of her article in the *Journal of the Royal College of Physicians of London* vol 33 no 1 (1999) pp. 65–69.

27 Lee, KG, 'The life and work of Sir Ivan Whiteside Magill KCVO' and Pallister, WK, 'Sir Ivan Whiteside Magill (1888–1986) and tracheal intubation' in Atkinson and Boulton *op cit* pp. 601–9.

28 PRSM vol 43 (1950).

29 JRSM vol 81 (1988) pp. 426–28.

30 *Ibid* vol 88 (1995) pp. 519–23.

31 PRSM vol 57 (1964).

32 Young, TM, *op cit* p.11. The papers referred to were given by FS Rood 6 March 1925 and by Massey Dawkins 5 January 1945.

33 For a profile of Still and list of his published work see 'In memoriam. George Frederic Still 1868–1941' in *Archives of Disease in Childhood* vol xvi (1941) pp. 147–65. Still was not a Fellow of the RSM.

34 Obituary of Colonel AH Tubby, BMJ (i) 1 March 1930 p. 419. Biographical information and personal papers of Tubby, Contemporary Medical Archives Collection GC/87/4, Wellcome. List of members, Society for the Study of Disease in Children 1906–07, MS66/I2, Box 71.

35 Society for the Study of Disease in Children 1900–08, I11, 12.

36 Cooter, Roger, *Surgery and society in peace and war. Orthopaedics and the organization of modern medicine 1880–1948* (1993) p. 45. Waugh, William, *A history of the British Orthopaedic Association* (1993) p. 7.

37 Society for the Study of Disease in Children 1905–08, I18, Box 42.

38 Letter MacAlister to President RSM 25 June 1908, folder 1/G7, Box 22. Amalgamation correspondence 1905–08, I18, Box 42.

39 PRSM vol 2 pt 1 (1908–09).

40 GM Section for the Study of Disease in Children 1908–32 MS/66, K145.

41 PRSM vol 13 pts 1, 2 (1919–20).

42 Presidential address, PRSM vol 20 pt 2 (1927).

43 *Ibid* vol 15 pts 1–2 (1921–22).

44 BMJ (ii) 10 November 1928 p. 867.

45 *Bulletin* 63 (1936). Report of Joint Committee on Prematurity 22 January 1937, K150, Box 48.

46 GM Section for the Study of Disease in Children 1941, K146, CM 1942, K144.

47 CM Section for the Study of Disease in Children 1945–46, K144.

48 I am grateful for information from Dr Beryl Corner.

49 Williams, David Innes, 'Denis Browne and the specialization of paediatric surgery' in JMB vol 7 August 1999 pp. 145–50.

50 PRSM vol 41 (1949).

51 Information from Professor John Emery.

52 PRSM vol 46 (1953).

53 Presidential address, PRSM vol 46 (1953).

54 *Ibid* vol 74 (1981).

55 Munk's Roll vol ix (1994) p. 520.

56 PRSM vol 69 (1976).

57 GM Section of Paediatrics 1962–90, Ms/66//b1.

58 Letter from Professor John Emery, PRSM vol 74 (1981).

59 JRSM vol 79 1985 pp. 541–43.

60 British Balneological and Climatological Society 1895–1909, I5, 7.

61 PRSM vol 4 pt 1 (1910–11).

62 British Balneological and Climatological Society I10, I10A Box 42.

63 *Ibid* I7.

64 PRSM vol 3 pt 1 (1909–10), vol 4 pt 2 (1910–11), vol 7 pt 1 (1913–14).

65 *Bulletin* 20 (1915). PRSM vol 10 pt 1 (1916–17).

66 PRSM *Ibid*.

67 Storey, Geoffrey O, T*he history of physical medicine* (1992) p. 18.

68 Woods, Sir Robert Stanton, 'Physical medicine' in Dunn, CL (ed), *The Emergency Medical Services* (1952) pp. 366–87.

69 Speeches by Watts Eden and Jones, 15 April 1932, MS/78, Box 112.

70 PRSM vol 45 (1952).

71 Bauwens, P, 'Planning for the future of physical medicine' in *British Journal of Physical Medicine and International Review* January 1942 vol 5 no 1 pp. 152–57.

72 Copeman, WSC, *A short history of the gout and rheumatic diseases* (1964).

73 Woods *op cit*.

74 PRSM vol 4 pt 2 (1910–11).

75 Kovaks and Fletcher Lectures MS/78/g1, Box 63.

76 CM Section of Physical Medicine 1964, K156A. Kersley, George D, and Glyn, John, *A concise international history of rheumatology and rehabilitation* (1991) pp. 101–02.

77 CM Section of Physical Medicine 1973, K156A.

78 Kersley and Glyn *op cit* p. 103.

79 *Bulletin* 14 (1912).

80 Proposed Section of Psychiatry, K170, Box 48.

81 Collie, Michael, *Henry Maudsley. Victorian psychiatrist* (1988) p. 76.

82 CM 19 April 1912. *Bulletin* 14 (1912).

83 CM Section of Psychiatry 1912, K165.

84 PRSM vol 7 pt 3 (1913–14).

85 *Ibid* vol 9 pt 3 (1915–16).

86 *Ibid* vol 12 pt 3 (1918–19). Brome, Vincent, *Jung* (1978) p. 184.

87 McLynn, Frank, *Carl Gustav Jung* (1996) p. 419. Brome *op cit*.

88 Berrios, German E, and Freeman, Hugh (eds*), 150 years of British psychiatry 1841–1991* (1991) p. 225.

89  PRSM vol 18 pt 3 (1924–25) and vol 21 pt 1 (1927–28).

90  *Ibid* vol 25 pt 2 (1932) and vol 25 pt 1 (1931–32).

91  *Ibid* vol 15 pt 3 (1921–22).

92  Sub-committee on cyclothymia, K169, Box 48. PRSM vol 23 pt 1 (1929–30). CM 8 November 1932.

93  BMJ (i) 19 June 1926 pp. 1063–66.

94  PRSM vol 40 (1946–47).

95  *Ibid* vol 34 (1940–41).

96  *Ibid* vol 37 (1943–44). Sargant, William, *The unquiet mind* (1967) pp. 190, 194.

97  PRSM vol 33 (1939–40).

98  *Lancet* (ii) 30 December 1939 pp. 1232–33, 1353–55, 1373.

99  PRSM vol 29 pt 1 (1935–36).

100 *Ibid* vol 37 (1943–44).

101 *Ibid* vol 51 (1958).

102 Supplement to PRSM vol 42 (1949) p. 93.

103 Howells, John G, 'The establishment of the Royal College of Psychiatrists' in Berrios and Freeman, *op cit* p. 124.

104 Wheatley, D, and Healy, David, 'The foundation of the British Association for Psychopharmacology' in *Journal of Psychopharmacology* vol 8 no 4 (1994) pp. 268–78.

105 Report of working party on future policy of Section of Psychiatry September 1976, MS/72/f1.

106 Cushing, Harvey, *The life of Sir William Osler* vol ii (1925) p. 478.

107 Report of Council 1 March 1907, Transacs vol lxxxx (1906–07) p. lxxxvii.

108 Transacs vol lxxxx (1906–07) p. 415.

109 GM 17 March 1818, B3. Transacs vol lxv (1862) pp. 1–24. The instruments were later presented to the Royal College of Obstetricians and Gynaecologists.

110 'Proceedings of the Section of the History of Medicine' 14 January 1920 in Supplement to PRSM vol 56 (1963) p. 45.

111 Cushing *op cit* p. 324.

112 *Ibid*. Letter Douglas Powell to Osler 3 August 1912, MacAlister correspondence folder 3/G9, Box 24.

113 Cushing *op cit* pp. 339, 344. History of Medicine Section 1912, Box 82.

114 L.9.c.16, 17, 18, Box 59.

115 Cushing *op cit* p. 378. Mann, RD, 'The contributions in the Proceedings of the Section of the History of Medicine that relate to the Renaissance and earlier periods of the history of medicine' in JRSM vol 86 1993 pp. 472–76.

116 Cushing, *op cit* pp. 444–45.

117 'Proceedings of the Section of the History of Medicine' in Supplement to PRSM vol 56 (1963) p. 45.

118 Ms 534.

119 PRSM vol 63 (1970).

120 'Proceedings of the Section'... *op cit* p. 29.

121 Charles Singer Memorial Meeting 7 March 1962, PRSM vol 55 (1962).

122 Bearn, Alexander, *Archibald Garrod and the individuality of man* (1993) p. 143. BMJ (i) 19 March 1932 pp. 523–24.

123 Supplement to PRSM vol 56 (1963) pp. 30–40.

124 Information kindly supplied by Professor Roy Porter.

125 GMC, *Tomorrow's doctors* (1993) p. 10.

126 Obituary by Mr Harvey White, CM 16 July 1991.

127 Hulke, JW (ed), *Collected papers of Sir William Bowman* vol ii (1892) p. 40.

128 MacAlister correspondence 1912–13, folder 3/G8, Box 23 and G17, Box 30. MacAlister to President of Ophthalmic Society 20 July 1912, folder 3/G19, Box 32. Bulletin 14 (1912). Conference 28 March 1912, H3.

129 Letter Lawford to MacAlister 26 April 1913, MacAlister correspondence folder 3/G11, Box 26.

130 PRSM vol 7 pt 3 (1913–14). GM Section of Ophthalmology 1912–14, K121.

131 PRSM vol 10 pt 3 (1916–17).

132 Lang lecture and Medal M23, Box 55.

133 PRSM vol 6 pt 3 (1912–13).

134 *Ibid* vol 8 pt 3 (1914–15).

135 CM Section of Ophthalmology 1914–15, K119. PRSM vol 8 pt 3 (1914–15). Definition of Blindness, K124,125, Box 48.

136 PRSM vol 8 pt 3 (1914–15).

137 *Ibid* vol 9 pt 3 (1915–16).

138 CM Section of Ophthalmology 1917–18, K119.

139 Buckley, Elizabeth I, and Potter, Dorothy U (eds), *Ida and the eye* (1996) p. 100.

140 PRSM vol 17 pt 3 (1923–24).

141 *Ibid* vol 20 pt 1 (1926–27). Buckley and Potter *op cit* pp. 94, 107.

142 PRSM vol 26 (1932–33), vol 28 pt 1 (1934–35).

143 Buckley and Potter *op cit* p. 96.

144 PRSM vol 21 pt 1 (1927–28).

145 BMJ (i) 15 April 1978 p. 993.

146 PRSM vol 23 pt 1 (1929–30).

147 *Ibid* vol 25 pt 1 (1931–32).

148 *Ibid* vol 39 (1945–46), vol 57 (1964).

149 *Ibid* vol 33 (1939–40), vol 35 (1941–42).

150 PRSM vol 52 (1959).

151 I am grateful for information from Mr Larry Benjamin.

152 Obituary, *The Times* 26 January 2000.

153 PRSM vol 64 (1971), vol 65 (1972).

154 Ophthalmic tour 1966, MS/58/f1, Box 63.

155 PRSM vol 59 (1966).

156 CM Section of Ophthalmology 1963–77, MS/58/a1.

157 Cantlie, Neil, *Sir James Cantlie* (1939) p. 152. Archives of the Royal Society of Tropical Medicine and Hygiene, WTI/RST, Wellcome.

158 Letter MacAlister to Carnegie Brown 8 October 1909, Archives of the Royal Society of Tropical Medicine *op cit*, Box 7, WTI/RST/DI, Wellcome.

159 Section of Tropical Diseases and Parasitology, constitution and regulations 1912, 1921, K198, Box 49. Tropical Medicine Conference 14 May 1912, H3.

160 Letter Secretary of Society of Tropical Medicine and Hygiene to Ross 10 May 1912, Box 7 *op cit*.

161 Draft letter MacAlister to editor BMJ, 23 July 1912, MacAlister correspondence Folder 1, G8, Box 23.

162 MacAlister correspondence 1912 folder 1/G8. *Lancet* (ii) 16 November 1912 p. 1395.

163 Letter from Manson 13 November 1912, H3. Letter Manson to Leishman 2 October 1912, Box 7 *op cit*.

164 Letter Low to Leishman 20 January 1913, Box 7 *op cit*.

165 Section of Tropical Diseases and Parasitology K197–8, Box 49.

166 Letter Prout to Balfour 3 February 1927 *et seq*, Archives of the Royal Society of Tropical Medicine *op cit* WTI/RST/D3.

167 *Bulletin* 63 (1936).

168 *Bulletin* 27 (1919).

169 Correspondence, foundation etc. War Section 1919, MS/84/f1, Box 71. CM War Section 1920–53, K203.

170 Presidential address, PRSM vol 13 pt 3 (1919–20).

171 MacAlister correspondence 6 June 1919, 28 May, 15 June 1920, 12 March, 10 September 1921, folder 8/G18, Box 31. Correspondence War Section/United Services Section 1919–20, MS/84/f1, Box 71.

172 CM War Section 1919–25, K203.

173 *Ibid* 1928–29.

174 CM War Section 10 September 1932, 14 March 1938, 25 October 1939, K203.

175 PRSM vol 42 (1949).

176 GM United Services Section 1 October 1953, K204.

177 The major part of the history of this Section was contributed by Dr Campbell Mackenzie and Diana Berry, to whom I am most grateful.

178 JRSM vol 77 (1984) pp. 265–67.

179 RSM, *Annual Report 1982–83*.

180 JRSM vol 82 (1989) pp. 67–71.

181 Dunsmuir, WD, and Kirby, RS, 'Sir Henry Thompson: the first British urologist (1820–1904)' in JMB November 1995 pp. 187–91.

182 CM 15 April 1913. MacAlister correspondence 1913 folder 2/G11, Box 26 and folder 2/G12, Box 27.

183 *Bulletin* 30 (1920–21). GM Surgical Section 22 July 1919, MS/82, K179.

184 PRSM vol 14 pt 3 (1920–21).

185 *Ibid*.

186 *Ibid*.

187 CM Section of Urology 1932–33, K199. Presidential address, PRSM vol 50 (1957).

188 PRSM vol 39 (1945–46).

189 Presidential address, PRSM vol 41 (1948).

190 *Ibid* vol 32 pt 2 (1939), vol 42 (1949).

191 *Ibid* vol 62 (1969).

192 *Ibid* vol 50 (1957).

193 PRSM vol 22 pt 2 (1928–29).

194 Presidential address, PRSM vol 50 (1957).

195 CM Section of Urology 1920–36, K199.

196 Winsbury-White lecture 1967, PRSM vol 61 (1968).

197 CM Section of Urology 1938–41, K199, 1941–46, K120.

198 Blandy, John, and Williams, JP, *The history of the British Association of Urological Surgeons 1945–1995* (1995) pp. 17–18. Pyrah, LN, *The development of urology as a surgical specialty in the United Kingdom* (1987) 3 vols, typescript, RCS.

199 CM Section of Urology 23 May 1963, K120.

200 Presidential address, PRSM vol 58 (1965).

201 *Ibid* vol 56 (1963).

202 PRSM vol 61 (1968). Winsbury-White lecture, MS/86/G1, Box 63.

203 PRSM vol 53 (1960).

204 *Ibid* vol 62 (1969), vol 65 (1972).

205 *Ibid* vol 29 pt 2 (1935–36), vol 63 (1970).

206 *Journal of Bone and Joint Surgery* vol 30B February 1948 p. 204.

207 PRSM vol 7 (1913–14).

208 GM sub-Section of Orthopaedics 1913–22, K128.

209 CM Section of Surgery 9 July 1914, K177. CM sub-Section of Orthopaedics 1914, K127.

210 Griffiths, DLl, 'Some classics of British orthopaedic literature' in *Journal of Bone and Joint Surgery* vol 32B November 1950 pp. 676–93.

211 Clarke, H Osmond, 'Half a century of orthopaedic progress in Great Britain' in *Journal of Bone and Joint Surgery* vol 32B November 1950 p. 620.

212 PRSM vol 13 pt 3 (1919–20), vol 14 pt 3 (1920–21).

213 GM Surgical Section 18 May 1921, K179. GM sub-Section and Section of Orthopaedics 1913–22, K128. CM 20 June 1922, *Bulletin* 25 (1922).

214 CM and GM Section of Orthopaedics 1922, K127, K128. PRSM vol 15 pt 3 (1921–22).

215 PRSM vol 16 pt 3 (1922–23). Platt, Sir Harry, *Selected papers* (1963) p. 124

216 *Journal of Bone and Joint Surgery. Thomas Fairbank birthday volume* 38B (1956) p. 13.

217 PRSM vol 31 pt 1 (1937–38).

218 *Ibid* vol 18 (1924). A chronological list of Fairbank's contributions to surgical literature is published in the *Journal of Bone and Joint Surgery. Thomas Fairbank birthday volume op cit* pp. 18–21.

219 *Journal of Bone and Joint Surgery* (1956) *op cit.*

220 PRSM vol 32 pt 2 (1939). PRSM vol 31 (1937).

221 *Journal of Bone and Joint Surgery* (1956) *op cit.*

222 PRSM vol 37 (1943–44).

223 *British Journal of Surgery* vol 30 (1942–43) pp. 291–304.

224 PRSM vol 33 (1939–40).

225 *Ibid* vol 35 (1941–42).

226 *Ibid* vol 42 (1949).

227 *Journal of Bone and Joint Surgery* vol 30B (1948) pp. 211, 384–86. GM Section of Orthopaedics 1947–48, K128.

228 *Journal of Bone and Joint Surgery* (1956) *op cit* pp. 128–51.

229 Clarke, H Osmond, *op cit* pp. 620–75.

230 PRSM vol 46 (1953).

231 *Ibid* vol 41 (1948).

232 *Ibid* vol 50 (1957).

233 *Ibid* vol 52 (1959).

234 *Lancet* (i) 27 May 1961 pp. 1129–32.

235 Waugh, William, *John Charnley: the man and the hip* (1990).

236 CM Section of Orthopaedics 1980–81 MS/62/a2. PRSM vol 75 (1982).

237 Brook, AL Eyre, 'British orthopaedic surgery' in *Clinical Orthopaedics and Related Research* vol 88 October 1972 pp. 283–309. BMJ vol 292 15 February 1986 p. 490. PRSM vol 70 (1977).

238 Presidential address, 1998. I am grateful to Mr Reeves for a copy.

239 Power, Sir D'Arcy, *Selected writings 1877–1930* (1931) pp. 256–64.

240 MacAlister correspondence 4 August 1921, folder 8/G18, Box 31. Rolleston, Sir Humphry, *Sir Clifford Allbutt* (1929) pp. 92–93, 253–54.

241 PRSM vol 14 pts 1–2 (1920–21).

242 CM Section of Medicine 20 December 1921. CM 20 March 1923.

243 CM 17 April, 19 June 1923.

244 *Bulletin* 37 (1923), 39 (1924). PRSM vol 17 (1923–24).

245 Hobday, Sir Frederick, *Fifty years a veterinary surgeon* (1938) p. 56.

246 Power *op cit* p. 263.

247 I am grateful to Dr Anthony Cullen for his contribution to this Section.

248 PRSM vol 17 pt 2 (1923–24).

249 Presidential address, PRSM vol 47 (1954).

250 PRSM vol 49 (1956).

251 CM sub-Section of Proctology 1913, K161.

252 Granshaw, Lindsay, *St Mark's Hospital, London* (1985) p. 180.

253 PRSM vol 7 pt 3 (1913–14). CM Section of Proctology 1952, K162.

254 PRSM vol 14 pt 3 (1920–21), vol 49 (1956).

255 CM sub-Section of Proctology 1914–22, K161.

256 PRSM vol 26 (1933), vol 33 (1940), vol 46 (1953), vol 59 (1966).

257 *Ibid* vol 21 (1927), vol 23 (1930), vol 40 (1946–47).

258 CM sub-Section of Proctology 1925, K161.

259 Statement from President of sub-Section to RSM Council (1930) Ms/14/f2, Box 71.

260 CM sub-Section/Section of Proctology 1938–40, K161.

261 Granshaw *op cit* p. 210.

262 CM Section of Proctology 1948, K161.

263 PRSM vol 49 (1956).

264 PRSM Supplement to vol 52 (1959).

265 CM Section of Proctology 1966–82, Ms/14/a1.

266 CM 17 January, 18 April 1989.

267 CM Section of Proctology 1986–91. Letter from RS Lane, JRSM vol 84 (1991) p. 57.

# Chapter 9

# From Endocrinology to Primary Health Care

IN 1948 THE MEDICAL SCENE in the United Kingdom was revolutionized by the introduction of the National Health Service. This was the culmination of many years of thought and planning. A preliminary move had been made as early as 1911, with the passing of the National Health Insurance Act, and a second step was taken after the First World War when the Dawson Report presented the first systematic scheme for a comprehensive state medical service. This was the vision of Lord Dawson of Penn, President of the Royal Society of Medicine (1928–30) and of the Royal College of Physicians (1931–38) and twice President of the BMA.

The Beveridge Report of 1942 presented proposals for a national health scheme for all members of the community, and when peace came three years later the Labour government was in a position to carry out the party's longstanding commitment to a state health service. The National Health Act was passed in 1946 and after lengthy negotiations between the government and the medical profession the National Health Service came into operation in July 1948.

The NHS worked better than its critics had predicted. One of its strengths was the provision of comprehensive consultant and specialist services as new facilities were provided at hospitals. In this way the NHS acted as a springboard for the development of specialties and the recognition of new ones: technological advances coupled with the expansion of medical care nationwide triggered increased specialization, and this was to be mirrored in the creation of new Sections of the RSM.

The first Section to be formed after the close of the Second World War was Endocrinology, representing a relatively new specialty. The Section had been suggested informally in 1944 and it was constituted two years later, before the NHS was operational. There was then a gap of four years before the formation of the Section of General Practice – a preliminary to the foundation of the College of General Practitioners in 1952. With a major hospital rebuilding programme under way in the 1960s and 'high-tech' developments in renal dialysis, cardiovascular surgery and transplantation advancing fast, came a flurry of five new Sections, ranging from Occupational Medicine to Plastic Surgery. Between 1961 and 1985 the Council of the RSM was inundated with no less than 19 applications for Sections that were not approved. Eight new Sections were indeed inaugurated; some materialized at a later date and two were to be disbanded in the 1980s. As medicine developed and changed there was (and is) constant pressure to found new Sections and Fora, while others may outlive their usefulness.

Enthusiasm for new Sections such as Occupational Medicine, Clinical Immunology and Allergy, and Plastic Surgery, combined with sustained interest in the Sections of Endocrinology, Laryngology, Otology, Radiology, Proctology and Urology detracted from the activities of the more general Sections, and by 1972 this caused grave concern. The President of the RSM called the Presidents of the Sections together to discuss the problems and a Working Party addressed the difficulties. Although many of its recommendations were deferred, some changes were implemented without delay: the Section of Medicine was re-incorporated as Medicine, Experimental Medicine and Therapeutics, the Section of

Epidemiology was extended to embrace Community Medicine, the Library and Lay Section was reconstituted and the Open Section was inaugurated.

By no means all the problems were solved. In the 1980s inflation soared, the redevelopment of 1 Wimpole Street was prolonged, Sections expressed dissatisfaction with changes in the publication of their proceedings, communications between Sections and the Society were weak and attendances at meetings disappointing. A survey of attendance at the meetings of the 32 Sections during the session of 1981–82 revealed that the Section of Surgery was the largest with a membership of 610, of whom 13% usually attended meetings. The next largest, the Clinical Section with 535 members, had an average attendance of 11%. The Sections of Epidemiology and Community Medicine, General Practice, Pathology and Neurology each had an average attendance of 10% of their membership and over the previous three years only nine Sections had managed to increase their membership numbers: Clinical Immunology and Allergy, Dermatology, Endocrinology, Laryngology, Occupational Medicine, Otology, Proctology, Radiology and Urology. Of these, Clinical Immunology and Allergy, with 208 keen members, boasted an average attendance at meeetings of 52%, including guests.[1]

In order to stimulate interest the Sections were encouraged to organize symposia rather than short meetings, to hold more imaginative and joint meetings, to employ better publicity and to seek funding from pharmaceutical companies so as to offer hospitality at meetings. In the long term this policy was successful, with the exception of two Sections – Medical Education, and Medicine, Experimental Medicine and Therapeutics – which were forced to disband through lack of support. From 1982 the formation of multidisciplinary Fora to discuss and investigate particular subjects generated fresh, outside interest from professions supplementary to medicine, bringing an important new element to the Society's work. And in 1986 the opening of the enlarged and refurbished facilities at 1 Wimpole Street heralded the rejuvenation of the Sections and the life of the RSM generally.

## Section of Endocrinology

This, the first Section to be constituted after the Second World War, was the brainchild of Dr Raymond Greene and it had strong support from Sir Walter Langdon-Brown, a pioneer endocrinologist, Regius Professor of Physic at Cambridge and an Honorary Fellow of the RSM.

The earliest British contributions to endocrinology have been traced to Dr Thomas Willis and Dr Richard Lower in the late 17th century, 'both of whom hinted at the possibility of some mechanism of inner secretions'. In his presidential address on 'The development of British endocrinology', Dr PMF Bishop maintained that Willis was the first to recognize diabetes mellitus and the first to envisage a hormone. His associate Lower experimented with blood transfusion, published a ground-breaking treatise on the heart, *Tractatus de corde* (illustrated on page 31) and was Court physician to Charles II.[2]

After the deaths of these two brilliant men, however, endocrinology made few advances until the mid-19th century. In 1855 Claude Bernard introduced the concept of internal secretions, and Thomas Addison's monograph *On the constitutional and local effects of disease of the supra-renal capsules* was published. Addison was President of the RMCS, the antecedent of the RSM, for 1849–51 and although the Society's Council refused to publish his paper it has since been judged a milestone in endocrinology (see pages 43–44).

The RMCS can certainly take credit for publishing in its *Transactions* the papers by Thomas Curling on 'Sporadic cretinism with absence of the thyroid' (1850), work on the same subject by C Hilton Fagge (1871) and William Ord's paper on 'Myxoedema' (1878). Sir William Gull gave his classic description of myxoedema to the Clinical Society (the forerunner of the Clinical Section) in 1873 and having been a longstanding member of the

RMCS he was elected a Vice President in 1874. In the early 20th century Sir Edward Sharpey-Schäfer guided the growth of endocrinology: he had worked on the Society's scientific committee on suspended animation and his authoritative report on the Schäfer method of resuscitation of the drowned was published by the RMCS in 1904 (see page 112).

One of Sharpey-Schäfer's colleagues, Professor T Swale Vincent, opened a controversial discussion about current attitudes to endocrinology at a meeting of the Section of Therapeutics and Pharmacology in 1923 (before the Section of Endocrinology came into being, this Section included endocrinology among its interests). Vincent spoke of a crisis in endocrinology that threatened its existence as a respectable specialty: 'There is no subject upon which so much utter nonsense has been talked as upon internal secretion'. Professor G Murray, who in 1891 had successfully treated myxoedema with sheep's thyroid glands, agreed that the enthusiasm of speculative writers had given rise to a great deal of ephemeral literature which was of no value and possibly harmful. Vincent's 'cold douche of scepticism' generated suspicion of endocrinology and in this climate a proposal to found a Section devoted to endocrinology failed, thwarted by a petition signed by 78 Fellows and 33 other individuals in 1928. They protested that endocrinology had a place in the work of practically every Section of the RSM and that therefore a special Section was unnecessary.[3]

The wrangles of these years took time to resolve: Langdon-Brown's book on *The endocrines in general medicine* (1927) and Sir Humphry Rolleston's work on *The endocrine organs in health and disease with an historical review* (1936) helped to establish endocrinology as a maturing science. In the following year the *BMJ* proclaimed that 'The intense work carried out over the last decade has gone far to remove the disfavour into which endocrinology had fallen… solid achievements have been made. Possibilities are daily becoming realities'.[4] Thus endocrinology was poised to expand as a scientifically based field of medicine after the Second World War.

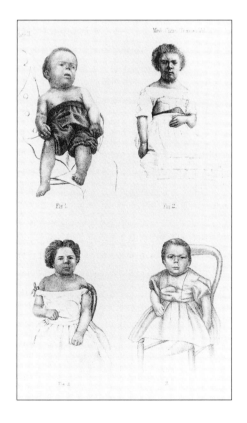

Dr Charles Hilton Fagge's paper to the RMCS in 1871 described 'Cases of sporadic cretinism' (a condition of thyroid deficiency). Building on this and the work of another Fellow of the Society, Thomas B Curling, Dr William Ord coined the word myxoedema in 1877 (see page 148). Illustrations from Hilton Fagge's paper of 1871 show, Figure 1, a child aged eight, under three feet tall with a stunted body and cretinous face; Figure 2 is a girl of 16 who suffered a change of features to cretinous type after measles; Figure 3 shows a 20-year-old idiot with peculiar cretinous conformation, two feet four inches tall, and Figure 4 a deaf and dumb 12-year-old with cretinous features, three feet in height.

## The formation of the Section

The prime mover behind the formation of this Section, Dr Raymond Greene, was the brother of the author Graham and of Sir Hugh Carlton Greene of the BBC. The doctor of the family, Raymond Greene helped to establish New End Hospital in Hampstead as a leading centre for the study and treatment of thyroid disease. Greene's approach to Sir Walter Langdon-Brown in November 1944 with a proposal for a Section of Endocrinology ran parallel to plans to form a society for endocrinology, and the relationship between the Society and the Section was to be a continuous theme.

Greene thought a Section of the RSM would serve a useful purpose by the 'reporting and publication of the very large number of rare and interesting cases which come the way of every hospital endocrinologist' and it would provide a place for discussion, very necessary for endocrinologists who tended to work in isolation. Within three days Langdon-Brown replied positively although he expected there would be some opposition: 'even a sub-Section would be something', he wrote.

With Langdon-Brown behind him, Greene canvassed Dr SL Simpson, who saw the proposed Section as a step towards the foundation of an Institute of Endocrinology in London; Professor Solly Zuckerman was more concerned with the proposed society for endocrinology, while Dr Bishop was keen to see a Section established so long as 'hot air merchants' were avoided, together with 'the type of consultoid who has already brought the subject a good deal of bad repute'. He trusted that Greene would make a careful choice of subjects and speakers for meetings to ensure that the Section gained a reputation for orthodoxy and not hot air or quackery.[5]

The Secretary of the RSM, Mr George Edwards, encouraged Greene in his initiative and the Section was formally proposed by Mr LH Broster in April 1945. The application was signed by 20 Fellows and four non-Fellows, who asked for the creation of the Section on the grounds that the Society did not provide for this increasingly important subject. A sub-committee reviewed the matter, encountering opposition to the proposed Section from the Clinical Section and the Sections of Pathology and Experimental Medicine, the main reason being that a Section of Endocrinology would trespass on their territory. Greene, Broster (who recruited support from provincial endocrinologists) and Dr H Gardner-Hill advanced their cause energetically, however, and in October 1945 the Council sanctioned the new Section. The founder-members held a meeting and dinner at the Café Royal in December to elect officers, and the Section was formally constituted on 25 January 1946.

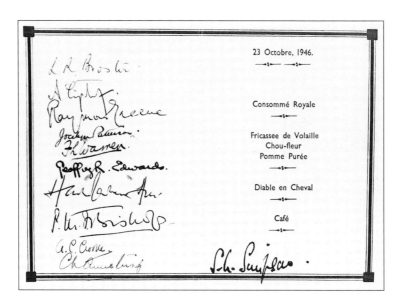

23 Octobre, 1946.

Consommé Royale

Fricassee de Volaille
Chou-fleur
Pomme Purée

Diable en Cheval

Café

The first dinner of the Section of Endocrinology was held at the United University Club in October 1946. Founder-members of the Section signed the menu.

## Sir Walter Langdon-Brown

Sir Walter Langdon-Brown, who was a past President of the Sections of the History of Medicine, Urology and Therapeutics and Pharmacology, accepted the presidency of the Section of Endocrinology even though he was suffering from Parkinson's disease. His illness allowed him to write an address on 'The birth of modern endocrinology' but did not permit him to attend the inaugural meeting of the Section in May 1946, so Greene read the address on his behalf. The Council expressed deep regret that Langdon-Brown was absent and put it on record that 'the inception of the Section was largely due to the prestige of a pioneer in endocrinology and to a distinguished Fellow of the Society'.[6] Langdon-Brown acted as 'a catalyst between the laboratory and the ward' and this led him to take an interest in endocrinology not as a specialty but as a tool for the better understanding of medicine as a whole. 'For this reason he gave his support to the formation of a Section of Endocrinology of the Royal Society of Medicine'.[7]

Langdon-Brown's address congratulated those who had worked so hard for the public recognition of the status of endocrinology, 'of which this Section is an outward and visible sign'. He traced the birth of modern endocrinology to the Clinical Society's committee on myxoedema and to Murray's treatment of endocrine deficiency with sheep's thyroids in the late 19th century. He made no mention of Brown-Séquard's work on internal secretions, emphasizing instead the contributions of Rolleston, Sharpey-Schäfer and Oliver, and he referred to Bayliss and Starling's discovery of secretin in 1902 – 'full of theoretical interest but has proved disappointing therapeutically'. He attached greater significance to Starling's 'hormone theory' presented in 1905: 'The foundation of a scheme of this sort led to a great increase of interest and research in the whole field of endocrinology'. As an aside Langdon-Brown mentioned the simile for which he is remembered, 'I ventured to call the pituitary gland "the leader of the endocrine orchestra" although it later transpired that the hypothalamus held the still more important rank of conductor of that orchestra'.[8]

Sir Walter Langdon-Brown supported the proposal to found the Section of Endocrinology in 1944 and was the first President of the Section in 1946; he died before the end of that year.

Langdon-Brown omitted to mention the previous attempt to found a Section of Endocrinology in 1928, nor did he refer to the American Endocrine Society founded in 1917 or to the nascent Society for Endocrinology, inaugurated three months after the Section. He was merely content to see the Section established before his death in October of the same year.

### 'West Endocrinology'

The question in the minds of those at the inaugural meeting of the Section was whether or not the Section would flourish. A 'peripatetic correspondent' to the *Lancet* claimed that many had been against the formation of the Section from the beginning and its detractors dubbed it the Section of West Endocrinology. The author stressed that because endocrinology had 'a finger in every pie' it had to be a correlating, organizing branch of medicine. The endocrinologist of 1946 needed 'the imperturbable conviction of a Murray or Banting, the careful fact-weighing logic of a Cushing, the undiminished enthusiasm of a Langdon-Brown, the collector's pride and knowledge of a Parkes Weber. In a word, the endocrinologist should be one of the scholars of the profession. I am afraid there won't be many of us'.[9]

On the contrary, when the Section commenced business in October 1946 with a discussion on 'The overactivity of the adrenal cortex', 150 were present. Discussions or the reading of papers alternated with the presentation of clinical cases and with joint meetings, for example with the Section of Obstetrics and Gynaecology on 'The use of oestrogens in gynaecology' in 1947.[10] The succession of Sir Henry Dale as President of the RSM in 1948 gave the Section confidence – Dale had worked with Starling at University College and was a joint Nobel prizewinner in 1938 for studies of the chemical transmission of nervous impulses.

### The Section and the Society for Endocrinology

According to Dr Bishop, President of the Section in 1954, all resentment and resistance to the new Section disappeared almost immediately and the Section was on good terms with the Society for Endocrinology from the beginning. The Section and the Society held joint symposia, and representatives from both approached the Medical Research Council with the suggestion that it should consider providing facilities for laboratory investigations such as urinary hormone assays to clinical departments unable to have these carried out in their own hospitals. As a result the MRC set up a clinical endocrinology committee which among other things, published a standard method of determining urinary 17-ketosteroids.[11]

The Section and the Society also co-operated on a committee, chaired by Mr Broster, to consider how to encourage progress in endocrinological research (1950–52). Joint meetings of the two associations attracted between 250 and 300 Fellows, members and visitors, and combined meetings with the Society for the Study of Fertility, the British Diabetic Association and the London Thyroid Club were also popular in the 1950s.

### Whither endocrinology?

Dr Bishop's review of British endocrinology in 1954 looked to the past and to the future, posing the question: 'whither endocrinology?'.[12] At this time endocrinology had not yet acquired a status comparable to neurology, psychiatry or paediatrics. The number holding appointments as endocrinologists on hospital staffs could be counted on the fingers of one hand, and there was a serious lack of recruits. The virtue of the Section was that it attracted not only physicians who had already established themselves as endocrinologists but also younger Fellows of the RSM who attended the meetings because they wished to broaden their medical education. Bishop was convinced this was the way forward: 'we want to collaborate not to insulate, to co-operate not to isolate', and he urged the expansion of the endocrine aspects of the major branches of the medical sciences so as to provide gynaecological endocrinologists, endocrine paediatricians and endocrinologists in thyroid clinics and fertility clinics, for dermatology, rheumatology and urology. Unless consultant posts were created soon, Bishop argued, endocrinology in this country would wither.

The situation was soon to change: Professor Russell Fraser (President of the Section 1956–57) became famous for his work at the Postgraduate Medical School, Hammersmith, and on the wider stage an International Endocrine Congress was held in London in 1964. Gordon Wolstenholme, a member of this Section and later Honorary Secretary of the RSM 1964–70 and (as Sir Gordon) its President from 1975 to 1977, was keen to draw the Section into membership of the International Society of Endocrinology. This was an unprecedented step and the Council at first refused to subscribe until Lord Cohen of Birkenhead, a forceful President of the Society, proposed the motion from the chair and it was carried *nem con*.

Before the end of the decade the Section's Council had approached the Royal College of Physicians, campaigning for official recognition of Clinical Endocrinology and Metabolism as a specialty. This was during the presidency of RI Bayliss and it fell to him to draft the memorandum, which met with success in 1968. In drawing up the specialist training programme of 1970 the Royal College acknowledged the Section of Endocrinology at the RSM 'as the strongest body of clinical endocrinologists in Great Britain'.[13]

In view of the activities of the International Society of Endocrinology (to which the Section was affiliated), the Society of Endocrinology of the USA, a European Association, the Society for Endocrinology, postgraduate courses in the subject at Hammersmith and Edinburgh, not to mention the activities of the more general medical associations and societies, it is remarkable that there was still room for the Section of the RSM. Even during the 1970s, when several Sections were experiencing difficulties, the Section maintained a full programme with two meetings a session for clinical cases, two meetings for short papers, one jointly with the Society for Endocrinology, a provincial meeting and an AGM with a guest speaker and dinner.

In 1985 the Clinical Endocrinology Trust and the Section founded a visiting professorship to enable an eminent endocrinologist from overseas to spend a few weeks lecturing in this country, and a second scheme funded by the Trust subsidized the subscriptions of six young Fellows of the RSM.

Symposia rather than short evening meetings were favoured in the 1980s (this made the travelling more worthwhile) and by the 1990s the major events in the annual calendar were two three-day joint meetings, one with the Society for Endocrinology and the other with the British Endocrine Societies. Gradually these large societies tended to eclipse the Endocrine Section of the RSM, where the list of resignations lengthened as the 1990s advanced.

## Close to collapse

The Section celebrated its golden jubilee in November 1996 with anniversary lectures and a champagne reception and buffet at the Royal College of Physicians.

The past might be celebrated but the Section's future was uncertain. It had a deficit of £1,094, recent meetings had been poorly advertised and attended, there was dissatisfaction with the current organization of both the Society and the Section. In January 1997 it was proposed that the Section should leave the RSM and join the Society for Endocrinology because the latter was the central focus for endocrinology in Britain. When the proposal was put to the vote only 83 of the 485 Section members replied: 48 were in favour of defecting and 35 were against. In a subsequent ballot, however, the majority of members expressed the wish that the Section should *not* be abolished, although not one of them was willing to serve as President, Secretary or Council member. In these circumstance the Section failed to present an academic programme for the sessions between 1998 and 2000, but was not disbanded. It survived under the care of a Steering committee and resumed meetings in January 2001.

## Section of General Practice (Plate 61)

The morale of general practitioners was poor when the National Health Service came into operation in 1948; earlier that year 84% of them had voted against its introduction. In its initial phase the state health service generated further frustration and discontent among GPs because the system appeared biased in favour of the development of hospital care, at the expense of GPs who faced a heavier work-load and felt isolated. A leader in the *Lancet* of January 1950 urged a change of emphasis: 'The alternative – the only alternative – is to make a big positive effort to raise the level of prestige of general practice. This can still be done'.[14] The point was taken up by the *BMJ*: 'The amount of money being spent on hospitals, specialists, eyes and teeth obscures the most important problem of modern medicine – the status of general practice. General practice is at the crossroads. The general practitioner sees himself being elbowed out of the hospital, finds himself more isolated than ever before from his colleagues in specialist and consulting practice, is plagued with paper work, and sees little prospect of obtaining those pleasant conditions of work so alluringly offered to him by the propagandists for the National Health Service during the years before July 1948'.[15]

Articles such as these fuelled correspondence from unhappy general practitioners, overstretched and seeking recognition for their special skills. The problems were aired at the BMA meeting in the summer of 1950 when there was recurrent defiance of the platform that tended to obscure all else: 'Clearly most minds were painfully occupied with thoughts of the falling prestige of the practitioner', the *Lancet* commented.[16]

### The Section is formed

In these uneasy circumstances a Section of the RSM was formed in 1950 to give general practice official recognition as a specialty. Dr GM Kerr and Dr Geoffrey Barber petitioned the Council for the new Section, supported by the signatures of 74 specialists (Fellows of the RSM) and 78 general practitioners, of whom 13 were Fellows. The petition expressed growing concern over the present standard of work of the general practitioner: opportunities to keep up to date were few and those that existed had drawbacks. 'The Royal Society of Medicine can offer the great advantages of its all-embracing scope, its accepted authority and stimulating atmosphere to assist in upgrading the standard of general practice and it would render great service by taking such a significant lead whilst at the same time complete its own scope by catering for all members of the medical profession'. The Council was receptive on the understanding that the Section would concern itself solely with medical knowledge under the conditions of general practice, and that the proposed Section 'would strictly avoid any suspicion that its discussions embraced any matters concerned with the political and ethical as distinct from the technical and scientific aspects of general practice'.[17]

The *BMJ* was enthusiastic: 'This promises to be an excellent departure from tradition and will no doubt be welcome to the many general practitioners who will be able to take advantage of it'. The objects of the Section were to narrow the widening gap between specialists and family doctors, to provide for the general practitioner an active link with currently accepted ideas and to keep alive the academic or scientific attitude to medicine and its allied branches. At meetings of the Section GPs were able to hear the latest views on subjects related to their daily work expressed by leading specialists 'and the Society provides that encouraging atmosphere where discussion can range freely over the science and practice of medicine... The sponsors of this venture and the Royal Society of Medicine are to be congratulated on starting what should be a most interesting and educative Section. It is to be hoped that similar enterprise will be shown by those medical schools and universities where the problems of general practice still receive too little attention in the curricula'.[18]

There were 160 founder-members of the Section, 86 of whom attended the inaugural meeting on 22 November 1950. Not a single Fellow of the RSM had raised an objection to the proposed Section and its launch was smooth. Dr George Abercrombie was elected the first President, with Barber and Kerr as Honorary Secretaries. Through the Section and the College, Abercrombie was to play a quietly effective role in restoring morale to a portion of the medical profession that had been shaken by the impact of the NHS. As Dr John Hunt (himself one of those who joined the Section at its start) testified, Abercrombie 'did a great deal for the new Section which earned him later the Honorary Fellowship of the Royal Society of Medicine'.[19] For his part, Abercrombie paid homage to Dr Kerr as chiefly responsible for founding the Section. Kerr was to be an energetic President of the Section in 1957, circularizing some 5,000 doctors in the London area to tell them about the advantages of the Society and the Section.

The first Vice Presidents of the Section were Dr William Pickles and Dr JD Simpson, and Sir Wilson Jameson was a leading figure on the Council. No fewer than seven members of the first two Councils were on the Steering committee for the College of General Practitioners. Indeed the historian of the Royal College of General Practitioners described the formation of the Section 'as a dress rehearsal for the foundation of the College, with colleagues who were later to found the College already working successfully together'. Another account describes the Section as 'a seed bed in which many of the essential ideas of the College were tried out'.[20]

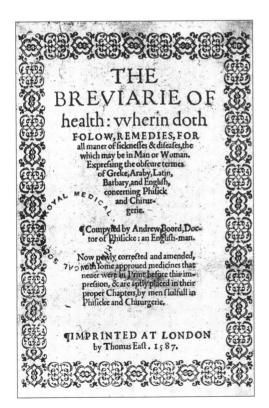

*The breviarie of health* by Dr Andrew Boord (first printed in 1547), a pioneer work on family medicine. Arranged alphabetically, it was the prototype of the modern family health manual.

The Society's Council reported in July 1951 that the Section had completed a successful first year with a series of interesting meetings culminating in a highly enjoyable dinner at Claridges.

## The Royal College of General Practitioners

There had been several moves to establish a college of apothecaries or general practitioners in the mid-19th century, all of them unsuccessful. A century later, following the introduction of the NHS and the Collings Report, the idea began to circulate once again – according to Lord Hunt's recollections, Dr Geoffrey Barber and Sir Wilson Jameson hatched a plan for a possible new college during a conversation outside the Mitre in Oxford. The publication of the Cohen Report on *General practice and the training of the general practitioner* (1950) focused attention on the academic plight of GPs and at the AGM of the Medical Practitioners Union in 1951 a resolution was passed to urge the foundation of a college.

'What part was the new Section of General Practice of the Royal Society of Medicine going to take?' Dr Hunt questioned. 'Before our first letter appeared in the journals we had written to the President, Lord Webb-Johnson, among others, telling him what we were doing. He replied "I feel very strongly that to found a college would be a great mistake"'. Hunt also wrote to Abercrombie, President of the Section, suggesting a meeting to discuss a possible college with other GPs, 'But after careful and sympathetic consideration, and after consultation with the executive of the RSM, this request was turned down because it was thought that such a meeting might be too "political". That was a disappointment because "political" was the one thing we hoped we were *not*!'. Although Hunt failed to obtain official support from the RSM, there was close liaison between the Section and the

Left, Dr John Hunt (later Lord Hunt) and right, Dr George Abercrombie, founder-members of the Section of General Practice and also members of the Foundation Council of the College of General Practitioners.

Steering committee for the college and Hunt spoke highly of the success of the Section in the continuing education of GPs. In planning the college he had the example of the Section before him, and he learnt lessons of more than historical interest by studying reports of previous attempts to found a college; these he pored over 'on many evenings in 1953 in the basement of the library of the Royal Society of Medicine'.[21]

Despite opposition from three Royal Colleges and the President of the RSM, the College of General Practitioners was born in 1952, gaining the prefix Royal in 1967 and becoming a fully fledged Royal College of General Practitioners by a charter of 1972.

Close relations between the Section and the College were maintained and the Section provided five Presidents of the College, the first being Dr Pickles (1953–56), who was followed by Abercrombie (1959–62), Hunt (1967–70, who became Lord Hunt of Fawley in 1973), Dr JP Horder (1979–82) and Dr Stuart Carne (1988–91). Abercrombie, Hunt and Horder were also Presidents of the Section, and other Presidents who worked hard for the College were Dr Richard Scott, Dr A Talbot Rogers, Dr Barber, Dr Robin Pinsent, Dr John Woodall and Dr Donald Crombie.

## The Section at work

The proceedings of the Section began appropriately with a discussion: 'What is general practice?'. This was opened by Dr Barber, and concluded with a reminder that it was each member's responsibility to bring to the Section 'notes of the pattern of common diseases so that we can learn by discussion, in the same way as our colleagues in other Sections of this Learned Society'. Meetings on 'Influenza', 'The acute abdomen' and 'Headaches' followed.[22]

Abercrombie's presidential address took the form of a paper on 'An occasional obstetrician', which Hunt found full of interest. Hunt's own first paper to the Section was about a diagnostic unit he had set up in London during the five years after the war, independently of the NHS. This failed to reach the pages of the *Proceedings* but was published by the *BMJ* with an illustration of Hunt's diagnostic bag, which he described as an ordinary thin music case containing essential equipment.[23]

Following the foundation of the College in 1952, a revival of confidence among GPs was reflected in the activities of the Section. A badge of office for the President was presented by Dr EP Scott, members enjoyed a joint meeting with the local Clinical Society at Ipswich with an excellent lunch at the Great White Horse, and the annual May meeting became a highlight with a guest speaker and buffet supper. Talks by Hardy Amies on 'After my fashion' (1958) and by Dame Ninette de Valois on 'A career as a dancer' (1959) made a welcome change to discussions on 'Piles' and 'Common lung infections', and attracted members' wives to the AGM.

Drs Robin Pinsent, Donald Crombie and Peter Higgins, all of them to be Presidents in due course, attended meetings regularly, travelling (as Dr Horder remembers) in Crombie's ancient Rolls Royce from Birmingham and Staffordshire. Pinsent earned the admiration of the Section for delivering his valedictory address as President in 1960 with oesophageal speech, having undergone a laryngectomy. Both he and Crombie played an extremely important part in the start of the research effort of the College and Higgins became the first Professor of General Practice at Guy's Hospital.

The 1960s brought recognition of general practice from academia with the foundation of the first chair in General Practice at Edinburgh University. Nevertheless, GPs were discouraged by government policy: the Minister of Health, Enoch Powell, launched a programme of hospital redevelopment which, coupled with an ever-increasing number of new drugs, had a profound impact on family practitioners and by the mid-1960s many were leaving the NHS. As medical knowledge and technologies expanded, the large new hospitals gained more political muscle and funding, to the detriment of general practice.

GPs demanded a new contract, achieved by the Family Doctor Charter of 1966. Discussions at Section meetings often addressed members' concerns and echoed their predicament – 'The general practitioner in a changing world' and 'State medicine in Britain, past, present and future', for example.

## Albert Wander lecture

In 1961 the trustees of the Dr Albert Wander Charitable Fund notified the RSM of a gift of £1,000 to found an Albert Wander General Practice lecture, the first of which was given by Dr RE Hope-Simpson in June 1964. His subject, 'The nature of herpes zoster', drew on his study of all cases occurring in his practice over a 16-year period. As a preface Hope-Simpson paid tribute to Dr Albert Wander, the founder of a pharmaceutical house in Berne. 'A man of wide cultivation, actively devoted to the sciences, keenly interested also in the arts and literature, he was a Doctor of Philosophy and was awarded an Honorary Doctorate in Medicine by the University of Berne and another in Philosophy by the University of Zurich'. The success of Wander's pharmaceutical firm provided the financial basis for wide philanthropy and the Albert Wander lecture continues to be a regular feature of the Section's calendar.[24]

## Forum for GPs

After the example of a postgraduate course run by the Section of Oncology, the Section of General Practice organized a study course in September 1977 under the title of 'New perspectives: a forum for general practitioners', which was given Continuing Medical Education accreditation and later Postgraduate Education Allowance approval. Thirty-five chairmen/speakers appeared at the first forum and 46 GPs from all over Britain registered. The first course, held during the presidency of Dr Margaret Pollack who was a well-known paediatrician, lasted five days and its success resulted in plans for a second forum. The series proved so popular that by 1983 numbers had to be restricted; the 20th forum was held in September 2000.

## Integration not fragmentation

The 'years of growth' in general practice *circa* 1968–77 were followed by 'the happy years' *circa* 1978–87.[25] Conditions of employment and the administration of practice premises improved, morale recovered and academic departments at universities and medical schools were established. Dr John Fry and others defined the role, knowledge and skills required of GPs, who joined the Section in increasing numbers. Membership reached 330 Fellows, 32 members and four Honorary members in 1965, increasing to 408 in 1978–79. The forum for GPs was consistently popular but from the beginning of the 1980s attendance at the Section's meetings declined, in line with the experience of some of the older Sections. The Society's house was being redeveloped, and problems of communication between the governing body of the RSM and its members caused disquiet. Many of the recommendations for change made by the Working Party in 1973 awaited implementation, and the role and function of the RSM came into question.

Such issues were addressed by Dr Luke Zander who, as President of the Section for 1980–81, outlined changes he wished to see such as informal catering after meetings and improved communications within the Society and with the laity. His valedictory address to the Section in 1981, 'Integration not fragmentation in health care – is there a role for the RSM?', echoed the ideals of the founders of the Society in its emphasis on the importance of maintaining unity in an age of increasing specialization. Zander went on to suggest that the RSM should establish Forums (or Fora) related to a specific topic. An example had already been set by a multidisciplinary three-day conference organized by this Section with the Section of Obstetrics and Gynaecology in the spring of 1981 on 'Pregnancy care for the

1980s'. This had attracted GPs, a few obstetricians, psychologists, educationalists and sociologists and was an unqualified success.

Zander presented his ideas to the Council of the RSM while he was still President of his Section and the first three Fora were soon operational (see page 439 *et seq*).

## Dr John Fry

The outstanding member of the Section in recent years was Dr John Fry, President 1962–63 and who agreed to serve a second term in 1988–89 during which, by the exertion of considerable effort, he revived the Section at a low point. In a valedictory address after his first term as President, Fry spoke on 'Coronary heart disease in general practice', based on his practice records. The keeping and analysis of records was Fry's strength, and he possessed a remarkable gift in being able to assimilate a large number of facts and reproduce them in a logical way.

As a GP in Kent Fry collected and collated data about every patient, using this as the basis for over 50 books and numerous articles. This made him an internationally renowned pioneer of research into the content of general practice and the role of the GP, giving good reason for his election as an Honorary Fellow of the RSM in 1989. After his death in 1994 publishers gave books to add to the general practice and primary health care shelves of the RSM Library, where a plaque records Dr Fry's lasting influence.

## The effects of reforms

National Health reforms caused anxiety among GPs and Section meetings often mirrored their concerns. As the NHS moved into the 1990s GPs faced administrative upheaval with the introduction of the internal market and the Patient's Charter, so it was appropriate that the Albert Wander lecture for 1991 focused on 'The new contract – at the sharp end'. At another meeting of that session a senior civil servant from the Department of Health elaborated on the government's new contract: 'he assured us that they were not out to get us', as many had supposed.[26] Dr Martin Godfrey's valedictory address was entitled 'The NHS

Dr John Fry, President of the Section of General Practice 1962–63 and 1988–89, is remembered by a plaque in the Library.

reforms from the sidelines' (1991) and at the end of the decade, when it seemed that new NHS proposals would radically alter the traditional role of the GP, overtones of despair could be detected at meetings on 'The future general practitioner: tools for survival' and 'Cost-effective prescribing: meeting the challenge or breaking the bank'.

Over the 50 years of its existence the Council of the Section has generated a full programme, and with over 1,000 members the Section is one of the largest of the RSM. Future policy is to develop more educational activities, with variation in the frequency and style of meetings in order to provide greater stimulus for research and professional development in general practice overall. The Section also aims to move towards the challenge of revalidation with personal and practice development plans as tools of continuing education.

## Section of Pharmaceutical Medicine and Research (Plate 62)
originally Library (Scientific Research)

The formation of a Library was one of the main objectives of the Medical and Chirurgical Society on its foundation in 1805. Commencing with donations from members and expanding with purchases at home and abroad, the Society's Library was a major attraction to the medical societies that amalgamated to form the RSM in 1907, and once established at 1 Wimpole Street the Society's medical Library became known as the best in Europe.

The Library was renowned but its use was restricted, and in the 1930s its club-like atmosphere was still very apparent. Fellows subscribing to the Society expected and received personal attention from the staff, and outsiders could only access the Library at second hand through the influence or introduction of a Fellow. This state of affairs became increasingly unsatisfactory after the Second World War: there were those working for pharmaceutical companies, government departments, universities and industry who needed regular access to the Library, which was in need of regular additional income. A grant from the Wellcome Trust had funded the extension of the Library to a second floor in 1953 but it was clear that if the collection and Library services were to be maintained, the annual income of the Society must be raised. A solution to both problems was found in the creation of a Section composed of members who paid to use the Library.

Therefore the Library (Scientific Research) Section was inaugurated in 1956 to provide individuals who were not Fellows access to the Library 'for the cultivation and promotion of scientific research in furtherance of the objects of the Society'. The Section was targeted primarily at nominees of firms in the pharmaceutical and allied fields and within the first year more than 30 organizations had joined, bringing an increase in the Society's income of over £2,500. Admission to the Section cost 10 guineas, supplemented by an annual subscription of 100 guineas for a Grade I member entitled to borrow eight items, 50 guineas for a Grade II member (entitled to four items) and a reading membership cost 10 guineas a year.[27]

A reception at 1 Wimpole Street attended by over 50 representatives from the pharmaceutical industry helped to launch the Section, which had substantial support from the Association of British Pharmaceutical Industry. The first members to enrol were sponsored by Glaxo Laboratories, Boots and Roche Products. The Section's first President was Professor CG Rob, supported by Sir Francis Walshe, Mr EG Muir, Dr Geoffrey Organe, Dr Basil Kiernander, Sir Clement Price Thomas and Professor A Kekwick as Vice Presidents and Dr HM Walker as Honorary Secretary.

*Library expansion*

The creation of the new Section, bringing nominees from the pharmaceutical industry, medical publishers, government departments and private societies to the Library, forced it to widen its scope. These readers needed books on subjects previously regarded as border-line; chemical and pharmacological textbooks and directories, dictionaries, indexes and reference books were now in demand and the Library expanded accordingly, adding nearly 200 new titles to its periodicals list between 1956 and 1958, and some 1,400 new books in the year 1956–57. The Librarian, Philip Wade, welcomed the institution of the Section as a significant innovation: he believed the RSM Library should serve both the Society and the nation and the founding of the Section was a positive step in making the collection more useful to a wider readership. Wade gave two addresses to the Section that made it clear that the new Section represented a development in the public value and importance of the RSM Library.[28]

## Meetings and papers

For the first two years there were no meetings for members of this Section, who were content with the use of the Library and its services. Meetings began modestly in 1958 with a discussion about users' expectations from a medical library and two films. An anonymous well-wisher provided sherry, and it became the custom to hold a party after meetings. Over the next few years the papers at meetings were roughly divided between matters of library interest (copyright, its history, methods of reproducing medical literature) and pharmaceutical content (advertising of pharmaceutical products, the discovery of iodine) and films (Antarctic expeditions were popular).

In April 1960 Mr LW Frohlich of New York, the founder and chairman of a pharmaceutical advertising agency, gave an influential paper to the Section – the first for this Section to be given space in the *Proceedings*. Frohlich spoke about the excellent relationship between the physician and the pharmaceutical industry in the United States and drew attention to the astonishing growth of the pharmaceutical industry since 1910. In the last 10 years alone, over 400 chemicals had been developed and introduced and this in itself posed a challenge to the medical profession.[29]

## A broader outlook

Dr Basil Kiernander, a founder-member of the Section and a past President of the Section of Physical Medicine, was elected President of the Library (Scientific Research) Section in 1966 and on his initiative the Section introduced meetings of general interest.

At Kiernander's suggestion the scope of this Section was broadened so as to cover librarianship, medical communication and other subjects. This gave the Section freedom to organize a meeting on 'The impact of television on medicine', which was opened by Lord Hill of Luton and Dr Charles Fletcher, at which Mr Chapman Pincher and Dr Terence Cawthorne spoke before an audience of 109 in April 1967. Subjects for other meetings ranged from 'Euthanasia' to 'Medicine and the press', many of them foreshadowing the discussions held by the Open Section in future years.

Dr Gordon Wolstenholme succeeded as President of the Section in 1968, although Kiernander frequently took the chair. Both men were involved over a long period with major policy-making committees of the RSM and their ideas for opening up the Society to the non-medical world and for broadening the scope of meetings were first felt at the Library (Scientific Research) Section.

## The Stevens Lecture for the Laity

Mr A Edwin Stevens was a member of the Library (Scientific Research) Section who in 1971 refused nomination to its Council due to pressure of business. Stevens was the founder of the company Amplivox, which designed and developed the world's first wearable hearing aid. Stevens more than compensated for his absence from the Council by founding a series of lectures for the laity, which are still given annually at the RSM.

The Society's Council had appointed a committee to discuss lectures for the laity in 1967, the idea being that the Society could make a positive and responsible contribution on the broad front of health education by initiating lectures that would bring the medical profession and the public into a closer relationship. For the meanwhile the question of funding such lectures dampened enthusiasm. Running concurrently there were tentative plans for a Lay Section of Medicine, although the Council's Annual Report for 1969–70 warned that such a departure from tradition presented difficulties and dangers as well as advantages.

When Mr Stevens came forward with the promise of £2,000 a year to fund lectures for a trial period of three years the offer was readily accepted and the funds were promptly applied to lectures for the laity. The first Stevens lectures were given in 1970 by Sir Michael Woodruff who spoke on 'The one and the many': two lectures on ethical questions relating to the practice of medicine. The success of the lectures persuaded Mr and Mrs Stevens to give a permanent endowment of more than £50,000, so the lectures continue. They bring together influential members of the medical profession and other disciplines to consider topical matters of wide medical and social significance and of common concern.

The Stevens lectures for the laity, many general interest meetings of the Library (Scientific Research) Section and the Christmas lectures for young people brought doctors and the public into closer contact at the RSM. The formation of the Library and Lay Section, superseded by the Open Section three years later, represented the rational extension of the policy.

## Library and Lay Section

The Library (Scientific Research) Section had shown the way by including the laity in discussion meetings of the late 1960s and it came to regard 'lay medicine' as its province. There was therefore some anxiety when in 1969 plans surfaced for a new Section of the Society to be devoted to lay medicine, because this was likely to encroach on the activities of the Library (Scientific Research) Section. When the proposal was debated at a Council meeting, Dr GE Paget suggested that the threat of a new lay section could be avoided by a fusion with this, the Library (Scientific Research) Section, 'to bring appropriate people into association with the Society'.

This was a controversial issue, and it went before the Society's Council three times before it received a majority vote giving formal approval to the Library and Lay Section in 1971. Sir Geoffrey Organe, the last President of the Library (Scientific Research) Section continued in the same office for the newly named Section.[30] The first meeting of the Section under its new name brought Professor Colin Buchanan of Imperial College, Mr G Holmes of the Noise Abatement Society, Dr M Aubert of the French Institute of Health and Medical Research and Mr Eldon Griffiths MP together to debate 'Health aspects of the environment'.

## Library (Scientific Research) Section revived

The expansion of the library and information services and the development of medico-lay contacts were such that the two aspects outgrew combination within one Section. On the recommendation of the Wolstenholme Working Party the two functions of the Library and Lay Section were separated so that each could thrive. Thus in October 1974 the Library (Scientific Research) Section was revived to fulfil its former role in providing library facilities to the pharmaceutical companies and others. At the same time 37 lay members, 29 Fellows and three Honorary Fellows of the Library and Lay Section transferred to form the core of the new Open Section (see page 419).

Thereafter the reconstituted Library (Scientific Research) Section catered almost exclusively for employees of pharmaceutical companies who made use of the Library and who met three times a session.

## Pharmaceutical Medicine and Research

The debate about a change of name to Pharmaceutical Medicine began in 1984 and the alternative title of Medical Information and Pharmaceutical Research was considered in 1988; it was felt that the existing title was cumbersome, did not help to attract new members or acknowledge the current interests of the Section. The last published paper from the Library (Scientific Research) Section was given at a meeting in January 1994 and by October of that year the Section had changed its name to Pharmaceutical Medicine and Research.

The aims of the renamed Section were defined as the development of an interactive forum on pharmaceuticals, the pharmaceutical industry, research and related technologies. Under the new title it was hoped to bring together pharmaceutical scientists, regulatory agencies, clinicians, scientific and allied health personnel.[31]

Over the next six years there was steady growth in the membership of the Section of Pharmaceutical Medicine and Research; Professor Peter Stonier succeeded Mrs Charlesworth as President in 1995, and was then succeeded by Miss Doreen Hepburn in 1996.

Early in 1998 a merger with the Forum on Clinical Pharmacology and Therapeutics was proposed by Mr Adrian Marston (junior Vice President of the RSM). It was considered that the objectives and interests of the Forum, which had been formed 10 years previously, were broadly similar to those of the Section of Pharmaceutical Medicine and Research and the merger was approved in April 1998.

## Lectures

The merger brought with it two eponymous awards that made funds available to cover expenses and honoraria for lecturers: the Henry Barnes Lecture Fund awarded £300 annually and the WE Dixon Memorial Fund presented an annual award of £400.

The first Henry Barnes lecture was awarded to Professor KW Donald in 1970. Dr Henry Barnes had initially left money in his will for a lecture on advances in clinical medicine, and the money became available after the life interest of his daughter had expired in 1963. The fund was inherited by this Section following the abolition of the Section of Medicine, Experimental Medicine and Therapeutics and was re-established in 1997. Professor Rolf Bass of the Human Medicine Evaluation Unit at the European Agency for the Evaluation of Medicines delivered the first lecture in May 1999 taking as his theme 'European pharmaceutical regulation into the millennium'.

The WE Dixon Memorial lecture was established following the death in 1931 of Professor Walter Dixon, a past President of the Section of Therapeutics and Pharmacology and a Fellow of the Royal Society. The lecture was delivered every three years on therapeutics and pharmacology and the first award was given to Sir Henry Dale in 1934 (see page 291). It was held in abeyance from 1983, however, and on being transferred to the Pharmaceutical Medicine and Research Section in 1997 it became an annual lecture. Dr David Horrobin, of Laxdale Ltd, Stirling, was the first recipient in January 2000, when he spoke on 'Innovation in drug discovery'.

## Into the new millennium

In October 1999 John Ferguson was elected President, leading the Section into the new millennium and giving support and organization to several Society meetings held during his term of office. In May 2000 Dr Roger Bolton succeeded Dr Ferguson as President of a strong Section.

## Section of Occupational Medicine (Plate 63)

During the 1960s there was a flurry of proposals for new Sections, reflecting the many new specialist departments being established at the hospitals. Dr AS Grimble of Guy's Hospital proposed a section of venereology in 1961, Dr John Fry suggested a section of medical care based on the example of the New York Academy of Medicine and neurosurgeons wanted their own section, while Dr JF Moorhead's proposal for a section of nephrology, rejected in 1969, was conceded 25 years later.

Two new Sections were inaugurated almost simultaneously in 1964: Occupational Medicine and Measurement in Medicine, the former being the senior by two weeks. The experience of two World Wars in the organization of a workforce in munitions factories and in the rehabilitation of the armed forces, for instance, had led to a broader appreciation of work-related health problems. In planning the future state medical service in the 1940s the BMA and the Royal College of Physicians visualized occupational health as part of the new scheme, but this was not to be the case. Nonetheless, the postwar years of high employment and relative stability encouraged the expansion of health care at work, stimulating units of the Medical Research Council and the creation of university departments of occupational health.

As early as 1925 N Howard Mummery had proposed a Section of Industrial Medicine, a proposal that was rejected by the Council of the RSM – with some justification, in view of the fact that when the Association of Industrial Medical Officers was founded in 1935 it attracted just 21 members. By 1963, however, the Association had a membership of over 1,000, providing a measure of the increased numbers working in this field, particularly during the Second World War, which saw the transformation of industrial toxicology and surgery into occupational health.

Since the War a period of full employment provided a further motive for the development of occupational health as a scientific discipline, for with manpower in short supply the care of the worker was essential. The armed services, the National Coal Board and some private companies such as Imperial Chemical Industries and Shell had established

Bernardino Ramazzini's *Diseases of workers*, first published in 1700 and translated into English in 1705, was the first treatise on occupational medicine. This edition of 1716 lists the diseases of 53 groups of workers, from miners of metals to soap-makers.

their own health research units, yet only three universities and one Institute in the British Isles offered postgraduate courses in occupational health.[32] Such was the demand to advance knowledge in the specialty that a new Section of the RSM was amply justified.

Informal discussions about the formation of the Section took place in 1963 between the Society's officers and Dr CM Fletcher (President of the Section of Epidemiology and Preventive Medicine), Sir Austin Bradford Hill (a past President of that Section), Dr JJ O'Dwyer (Principal Medical Officer of Unilever and a past President of the Association of Industrial Medical Officers), Dr RH Scott (Chief Medical Officer of Shell) and Professor RSF Schilling (Professor of Occupational Health at the London School of Hygiene and Tropical Medicine). Having considered the activities of existing groups such as the Association of Industrial Medical Officers, the Association of Certifying Factory Surgeons and the Occupational Health Society, it was concluded that the need for a Section of Occupational Medicine of the RSM was real. The proposal was submitted to the Society's Council in November 1963.[33]

## Inauguration speeches

At the inauguration of the Section on 12 October 1964 the President of the Society, Sir Terence Cawthorne, thanked Professor Schilling for the historical background to the Section, which began with the Italian Bernardino Ramazzini whose book of 1700 described the diseases of 42 occupations. Ramazzini gave essential advice to the profession: 'When a doctor visits a working-class home he should be content to sit on a three-legged stool, if there isn't a gilded chair, and he should take time for his examination and to the questions recommended by Hippocrates, he should add one more – What is your occupation?'.[34]

Milestones in British occupational medicine were marked by Percival Pott's observations on chimney-sweep's cancer, James Lind's recommendations on the prevention of scurvy in the navy and Robert Willan's work on skin disease in the 18th century. Thackrah's research on the diseases of the working population of Leeds and the appointment of Dr Legge as the first medical inspector of factories in 1898 were other historical landmarks mentioned by Cawthorne. On the death of Donald Hunter in 1979 the Section's Council added his name to the list of those who had made an outstanding contribution to occupational medicine, a just tribute in view of the publication of the ninth edition of *Hunter's diseases of occupation* in 2000.

This, the 28th Section of the RSM, aimed to serve doctors in industry and commerce, the services, universities, schools and other educational establishments so that those with a special knowledge of the relationship between sickness, injury and conditions of work might exchange information and experience. Research in occupational medicine and toxicology was to be encouraged and it was hoped that the Section would provide opportunities to assist in the training of those employed in the medical care of people at work. It was also anticipated that the meetings would result in a better working relationship between doctors in industry, academic medicine and the NHS. The Council planned to cover occupational health in the home and in sport as well as in industry and this gave the Section a wider perspective than the Association of Industrial Medical Officers.[35]

Professor Melville Arnott of the University of Birmingham, President of the Section 1967–68 and knighted soon afterwards, also spoke at the inaugural meeting. The Section appealed to him because he was anti-specialist and he regarded occupational medicine as an opportunity of bringing to bear upon problems of disease the resources of all the relevant divisions of medicine. He was particularly interested in 'farmer's lung', he saw many cases of severe anaemia traced to jewellery enamelling and in Birmingham urological problems were common in workers in the rubber industry (chemicals applicable to the industry were associated with carcinoma of the bladder).

The first President of the Section, Sir Austin Bradford Hill, was one of the first medical statisticians and was known to doctors throughout the world (he was currently Professor Emeritus of Medical Statistics, University of London). Bradford Hill's address of January 1965 was on 'The environment and disease: association or causation?'; he cited investigations conducted by himself and Dr Richard Doll on the association of smoking with lung cancer.[36] Bradford Hill, who counted Rowland Hill of penny-post fame and Professor Leonard Hill among his relations, was an Honorary Fellow of the RSM at the time of his death in 1991 aged 93.

The next meeting of the Section in May 1965 was held jointly with the Section of General Practice on the subject of 'Sickness absence': the trend was upward, Professor Morris of the Medical Research Council revealed. Other meetings covered 'Asbestos and asbestosis', 'Backache in industry', 'Occupational tumours of the bladder' and 'Trawler fishing and the Dogger Bank itch'.

### Trawlermen and the Dogger Bank itch

An occupational health unit at the London School of Hygiene and Tropical Medicine opened in 1956 under the directorship of Dr Richard Schilling who brought it to maturity as an Institute in 1968. Schilling was an influential educator in occupational health, he worked energetically as editor of the *British Journal of Industrial Medicine* from 1950 and he was active in the discussions that prefaced the inauguration of the Section of Occupational Medicine of the RSM.

Professor Schilling's presidential address of October 1965 on 'Trawler fishing: an extreme occupation' revealed his experiences during six days at sea with the Lowestoft fleet. He spoke of the high incidence of fatal accidents, skin disease and the poor general health of the fishermen, who reminded him of what he had seen among soldiers during the retreat from Dunkirk in 1940. Schilling concluded that trawler fishing was the most dangerous of occupations and the substance of his address went towards an article in the *Guardian* in December. This criticized the lack of preventive measures on the trawlers and disclosed unpalatable facts about the occupation, generating protests from trawler-owners and a reprimand from the authorities for causing alarm. Schilling's comments were given more credence after the loss of 58 men in vessel casualties, followed by the loss of three trawlers in 1968. A Board of Trade Committee of Enquiry into Trawler Safety was appointed and its report was described as 'one of the most sweeping indictments of any British industry of the present century'. Its recommendations were ignored.[37]

Schilling had agreed to undertake the voyage with the Lowestoft fleet in order to investigate a skin condition affecting trawler crews and leading to a manpower shortage in the fleet. In his research he was assisted by one of his former students, Dr Molly Newhouse, a determined lady with 'the characteristics of a benign but fearsome ferret... One of her outstanding achievements was to persuade more than 94% of a sample of 478 trawlermen to be examined for skin disorders as they disembarked after their voyage to the Dogger Bank in the North Sea'. Dr Newhouse later presented the results of her survey to the Section: 19.7% of the trawlermen suffered from occupational skin diseases, the most serious of which the men called Dogger Bank itch. This was caused by contact with sea chervil brought up in the nets that trawled the area.[38]

### Meetings and membership

From the outset the Section's Council planned joint meetings with the Association of Industrial Medical Officers and with other Sections of the RSM. The pattern was for two meetings a session with the Society of Occupational Medicine (as the Association was renamed) and joint meetings whenever possible. This change of name for the discipline, from industrial to occupational medicine, came about 'because the study of work, health and people covers all occupations', as Dr Leslie Norman commented in his presidential address of 1966. He had served 30 years in the field, most recently with London Transport, which in 1966 employed 74,000 workers whose medical care was in the hands of 10 full-time physicians and 41 nurses and advisers.

During his career Norman had seen 'an advance in the kind of doctors who enter industrial work'; they were beginning to establish a position among medical colleagues and in this the Section was instrumental. 'The formation and progress of this Section places occupational medicine alongside the other specialties of medicine. This position we shall maintain and develop'.[39]

Norman's confidence was borne out by the membership figures for the Section, which had increased from 176 founders in 1964 to 229 members by May 1966. Of these, 53% were whole- or part-time workers in occupational medicine, 23% were consultants (14 physicians, 13 psychiatrists, 10 dermatologists, 11 others), 9% were employed by HM Forces and 5% worked in non-occupational government departments and units.[40]

Jointly with the Society the Section hosted the Michael Williams lecture in 1969, founded in memory of Dr MHC Williams who as Medical Officer to ICI had been responsible for the medical supervision and employment conditions of some 15,000 people. He had also been active in the field of cancer prevention through the International Union Against Cancer before he was killed in a car accident at the age of 44 (1961). Initially a Society lecture, the Michael Williams lecture was later offered to Sections and the first time it was allocated to specific Section (Occupational Medicine) it was given by Professor Robert Case who had been associated with Williams in an investigation of the chemical industry.

## Schilling's disciples

Professor Schilling took the post of Director of the new occupational health unit at the London School of Hygiene and Tropical Medicine in 1956, and this was soon a department offering the first full-time course in occupational health. Schilling's influence was paramount at the School and in the Section, to which he recruited colleagues and students. Two physicians attending the first course of Schilling's department, Dr Molly Newhouse and Dr Suzette Gauvain, were strong supporters of the Section; so too was another of Schilling's disciples, Dr PJ Taylor, who had made his name with a classic study of sickness absence at an oil refinery. Like Taylor, Gauvain was an Honorary Secretary of the Section for many years before being elected President in 1975 when she chaired the important symposium on vinyl chloride (see below), and she served on the Council until 1980, the year of her death from a cerebral tumour. A colleague of Schilling, Dr JC Gilson, Director of the Pneumoconiosis Research Unit, served as President for 1968–69 and was a strong supporter of Schilling's department, which became the TUC Centenary Institute of Occupational Health in 1968.

Schilling himself was made an Honorary Fellow of the RSM in 1976; he was still taking part in Section meetings in the early 1980s and his autobiography of 1998 put a strong case for a new government policy for occupational health services.

## Vinyl chloride

A letter from Dr Newhouse to the Section's Council inspired a special meeting on the hazards of exposure to vinyl chloride in industry. On receipt of the letter, Dr Gauvain suggested that the subject deserved a whole day and this was to be the Section's first symposium, to which members of the Pathology and Oncology Sections were invited in September 1975. As President, Dr Gauvain opened the meeting: 'The story of vinyl chloride, when it comes to be written, will be seen as a watershed in the history of occupational medicine, forcing us to take a new attitude to occupational hazards and react quickly to first evidence of harm'.

Alarm bells had been rung in January 1974 when ICI announced it was taking steps to inform government departments, the TUC, its employees and customers of the facts relating to the death in 1972 of a worker who had subsequently been found to have died of angiosarcoma of the liver after 20 years' exposure to vinyl chloride. The news that a chemical widely used in the manufacture of plastics could be carcinogenic caused panic, prompting investigations, and a code of practice was issued by the Health and Safety Executive.

The purpose of the Section's symposium was to review British experience of the environmental, clinical, epidemiological and pathological effects of exposure to vinyl chloride and to exchange information. Gauvain also called for the consideration of what the future might hold in the way of carcinogenic risks: 'we can, I believe, regard the experience we have gained throughout the world with vinyl chloride as a pilot study on a newly discovered carcinogen'. ICI was represented at the meeting, radiologists told of their findings on four patients who had been involved in the production of polyvinyl chloride and the papers and discussions were given an unprecedented 35 pages in the Society's *Proceedings*.[41]

## Initiatives

Dr Gauvain's other initiatives included a dinner after her presidential address on 'The importance of an occupation' (unemployment was rising) and she took steps to attract a younger membership by organizing a meeting on 'Careers in occupational medicine', followed by a sherry party. This was praised by the Society 'for it successfully initiated a new style of meeting at which young doctors and student members were given the opportunity to see and hear about the scope of a subject, enabling them to judge more clearly whether they would want to work in this branch of medicine'.[42]

The major concerns of occupational health in the 1970s lay with the adverse effects of chemicals and with the new challenges presented by the oil industry in the North Sea where 18 commercially viable oil fields had been discovered by 1974. Dangers to oil workers and divers were promptly addressed by Section meetings on 'Off-shore medicine' and 'Oil rigs and diving', and one meeting was planned in Aberdeen.

Recent publicity in the media persuaded Dr JS McLintock, who was with the National Coal Board, to review coal workers' pneumoconiosis in 1976: statistics from the Department of Energy showed that 36,929 miners and ex-miners were receiving industrial injury pensions on account of being diagnosed with pneumoconiosis.

In 1979 'Human health and environmental toxicants' was the subject of an Anglo-American conference sponsored by the RSM, the RSM Foundation and the Faculty of Occupational Medicine and attended by the President and members of this Section.

## Changing problems

The emphasis in occupational medicine has shifted regularly since the Section was formed: the preoccupation of the 1950s and 1960s with occupational respiratory disease was superseded by concern for the effects of monotonous work in semi-automated manufacturing. Then came an increasing awareness of the adverse health effects of exposure to carcinogenic, mitogenic and teratogenic substances. The problems of the 1980s centred on the biological and neuropsychological effects of chemicals and challenges posed by new technology, with papers on 'New patterns of work', 'Repetitive strain injuries' and a symposium on 'Health care workers – who cares?' (as the largest employer in the country, the NHS was somewhat belatedly beginning to show concern for the health of its workers). A report of the meeting in the RSM *Journal* commented 'the size of the meeting and the quality of the papers and discussion showed that this sector of occupational medicine, neglected for so long but now its biggest growth point, is well on its way to maturity'.[43]

The Section experimented with a series of current practice seminars from 1983, held in the early evenings. They lasted a few years but there were too many competing meetings organized by the Society of Occupational Medicine, the Faculty, the Section and postgraduate establishments. In these circumstances the Council was advised to arrange fewer, longer and good-quality conferences and symposia.

A symposium 'On the need for occupational physicians' held in 1986 emphasized the scope then covered by this specialty, ranging from toxicology and environmental hygiene to industrial psychology, from first aid and casualty surgery to rehabilitation and aviation and diving medicine. The traditional industrial diseases had declined in recent years, although noise remained a widespread problem and new hazards arose from chemicals, visual display units and biotechnology. The conclusions of the meeting were that a gradual increase in the number of occupational physicians was needed, with a change in their functions to fewer routine examinations, and better training of part-timers.[44]

The 1990s began with an all-day meeting on 'Computers', and papers on 'Women at work' conveyed the warning that by 2000 they would constitute 50% of the work force and their medical needs would have to be catered for. Meetings on 'Chemical burns', 'Air quality', 'Stress management', 'Post-traumatic stress syndrome', 'Working round the clock' and 'The effects of global warming' expressed some of the anxieties felt by the British workforce and their medical advisers in the last decade of the 20th century. Such problems, and doubtless a quota of unforeseen hazards, will engage the attention of the Section as it approaches its 40th anniversary.

## Section of Measurement in Medicine

Dr Percy Cliffe, who established the Department of Clinical Measurement at the Westminster Hospital, was the instigator of the Section of Measurement in Medicine, first proposed under the title Measurement and Instrumentation for Clinical Medicine in February 1964. Cliffe was one of the Section's first Honorary Secretaries, its President for 1975–77 and its first Honorary member. His success in establishing the Section and

Dr Percy Cliffe, founder of the Section of
Measurement in Medicine and its President
1975–77.

The Ellison–Cliffe Medal bears the profiles
of Dr Carice Ellison and Dr Percy Cliffe,
founders of the lecture.

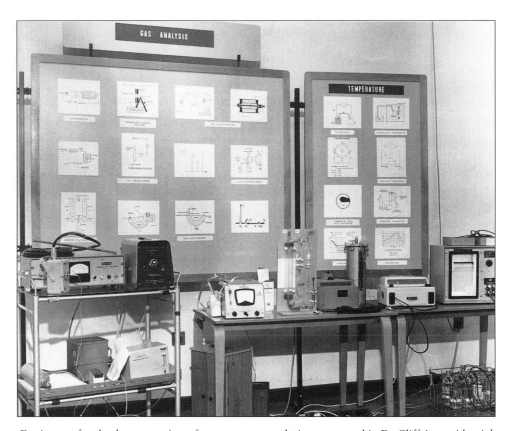

Equipment for the demonstration of measurement techniques, as used in Dr Cliffe's presidential
address of 1975 and in subsequent educational courses at London hospitals and
nationwide.

encouraging its growth was warmly acknowledged (he served the Society and the Section
in many capacities for almost 30 years).[45] Cliffe and his wife, Dr Carice Ellison, donated a
substantial sum to the RSM to establish the Ellison–Cliffe lecture – as Dr Ellison recalled,
the RSM appealed to her husband because of its wide spectrum of interests. 'He always felt
that science had a lot to offer medicine and vice versa; but that specialist jargon, on both

sides, often led to defensive anxiety and poor communication. From this he conceived the idea of setting up an annual lecture designed to bring doctors and scientists together in a setting that would be comfortable to both'.[46] The subject of the first Ellison–Cliffe lecture was 'Genetics and cancer', presented by Sir Walter Bodmer in October 1987, and in 1996 the Ellison–Cliffe Charitable Trust was registered to perpetuate the lecture and eventually provide for a travelling fellowship under the aegis of the RSM.

The Section was founded to provide a meeting-ground where physicians and surgeons could discuss and assess technological developments that might be used to advance knowledge of the diagnosis and treatment of disease and to assist in training those with clinical responsibilities in the techniques of instrumentation and measurement; all this was at a time when great interest was being shown by specialists in the increasing use of instrumentation in medicine.

Instead of the usual presidential address, and in keeping with his maverick personality, Dr Cliffe organized and led a full-day symposium with illustrated working models on clinical measurement (the day made a tidy profit for the Section). Cliffe's own department had been responsible for the design and manufacture of both kidney dialysis and cardiac by-pass machines in the pioneer days of the late 1950s and early 1960s. The Council of the RSM hoped that the Section would keep these developments and their applications under constant review, thus making a positive contribution to medical progress.

*Inauguration*
Sir Aubrey Rumball, Professor RHS Thompson and Mr Myles L Formby recommended the proposed Section to the Society's Council, which harboured reservations about the name. This was altered to Measurement in Medicine in March 1964, and within a month the 25 sponsors of the Section were joined by 55 other Fellows who indicated their support and at the inaugural meeting of October 1964, 146 founder-members enrolled.

After the election of Sir George Godber of the Ministry of Health as President and the appointment of the officers, a discussion was held on the aims, objects and future meetings of the Section.[47]

In his presidential address of 1970, Professor Max Hamilton recalled that there was much preliminary debate as to whether statistics should be included in the aims of the Section. 'This was a decision of great importance because it meant that the Section was concerned not only with measurement and its problems but also with the interpretation thereof i.e. the drawing of inferences from measurements. For this reason, the Section is not merely a haven for "gadgeteers". That this was meant seriously is demonstrated by the fact that, of the first four Presidents of the Section, only one can be said to be directly concerned with the use of equipment for measuring physiological functions'. Hamilton was himself a psychiatrist and in emphasizing the potential value of the Section he quoted Lord Kelvin, who 'once said that until a phenomenon can be measured it cannot be understood'. Hamilton expected that by 'the promotion of free discussion the Section would help to spread a sophisticated understanding of quantitative methods in the world of medicine. Therein lies its importance'.[48]

Lord Cohen of Birkenhead, President of the RSM and of the GMC, opened the Section's inaugural meeting by welcoming the 29th member to 'the comity of our Sections'. After a historical whirlwind that swept through Arab techniques of measurement to the school of biometricians in the late 19th century, Cohen expressed his confidence that the new Section would break down barriers. 'The specialties diverging from their mother-stem will converge in this Section. Here we all seek to find how techniques so valuable in other fields can be harnessed to the needs of medicine and surgery... Here colleagues in many fields, physicists, chemists, mathematicians, engineers and others can meet and help us with their specialized knowledge and skills to devise measuring instruments and techniques more rapid, more accurate and more appropriate to our special needs. In short there lies behind the concept of this Section a desire for a synergy and symbiosis of doctors, scientists and technologists for their mutual advantage'.

Sir George Godber's presidential address of January 1965 mentioned recent changes that justified the Section, the purpose of which should be 'the discussion and promotion of measurement in all the fields of the other Sections'. Accordingly, the next meeting concentrated on 'Measurement in the intensive care of heart disease', followed by meetings on 'Measurement in psychiatry', 'Measurement in ophthalmology', 'Measurement in forensic medicine' and 'Measurement of the quality of life'.[49] Thus the development of measurement in medicine touched all specialties, and in the late 1960s clinical measurement was introduced into the final examination for anaesthetists.

### Engineering and nuclear medicine

Lord Cohen had spoken of the benefits that would accrue by harnessing physicists, chemists, mathematicians and engineers to the Section; engineering in medicine was making great strides in the 1960s, and the Council of the RSM floated the possibility of a Section devoted to it. The Section of Measurement in Medicine raised objections, claiming it would overlap and duplicate a field already covered by this Section. To settle the point the Council resolved that the programme must be targeted at those concerned with all aspects of engineering in medicine, thus negating the need for a rival Section.

Engineering in medicine meant computers, and when Dr Richard Doll, then teaching medical statistics and epidemiology at University College Hospital Medical School and already famous for his publications on cancer, was elected President in 1967 he gave his address on 'Hospital records in the computer age'. He predicted with certainty that 'computers have a great deal to offer medicine' and that they would eventually transform its practice.[50]

The Section also embraced the measurement aspects of nuclear medicine, and indeed in 1971 considered adding Nuclear Medicine to its title (this was a reaction to a proposal from Dr William Greig for a Section of Nuclear Medicine).

### Meetings

By the 1970s meetings were being held both at London hospitals and occasionally 'out of town', while at the RSM there were joint meetings with the Royal Statistical Society, the Association of Medical Advisors to the Pharmaceutical Industry and the Breathing Club; during Dr Cliffe's presidency a postgraduate course was also introduced on Monday evenings.

Mr JA Dormandy was another dynamic President of the Section (1979–81): his proposal for a joint meeting with the Section of Pathology on haemorheology snowballed into the 'European meeting on clinical haemorheology' held at Kensington Town Hall in 1981. This in turn stimulated the founding of one of the first Fora of the RSM (see page 440).

The organization of many meetings with outside associations and co-sponsorship of a conference at the University of Sussex in 1982 complicated the Section's finances and there were several errors and misunderstandings. The Section claimed that information from the Society's finance office was inadequate, and the unfortunate result was a deficit to the Section of £2,869 in March 1988.

Five meetings were planned for the 1989–90 session, one of which had to be cancelled due to lack of response. The reality was that the ascendancy of the Section had passed. At the time of its foundation few doctors measured anything in scientific terms; Dr Percy Cliffe set the example, others followed his lead and the Section flourished. As the importance of instrumentation became recognized the specialties diverged, so that gastroenterologists measured gastric acidity, vascular surgeons measured blood flow, neurologists measured action potential and so on. 'None of these specialists had the remotest interest in the activities of the others, so that the logical basis for the Section fell away, and very few people attended the meetings. This resulted in the financial deficit in 1988. In spite of the unpromising situation, it proved quite difficult to disband the Section and the proposal to do so was firmly resisted'.[51] A possible name change to Measurement and Technology in Medicine was considered but the purpose and effectiveness of this was questioned. The Section's Council eventually agreed to disband in 2000 and a final meeting was held in January 2001 on 'Numbers and medicine 1600–2000', an appropriate finale. After nearly 40 years of enormous scientific and medical advances the Section, almost inevitably, became the victim of its own success.[52]

## Section of Clinical Immunology and Allergy

The British Society for Immunology, the British Allergy Society and the Antibody Club together persuaded the Council of the RSM to found the Section of Clinical Immunology and Allergy. A joint letter from the Secretaries of the three societies received a positive response and the 30th Section of the RSM was born in 1965.

Dr EJ Holborow (speaking for the British Society for Immunology), Dr J Morrison Smith (British Allergy Society) and Dr G Hamilton Fairley (the Antibody Club) claimed that the membership of those societies 'which jointly represent a considerable and probably a major portion of those in this country working mainly in the field' was in favour of co-operating in a Section of the RSM on the understanding that the societies did not dissolve but continued their individual activities in parallel. They each published a well known journal, held on to their funds and did not wish to be subsumed, but of course their members would gain 'by coming in amongst a wider field and those who were not pure immunologists would have the opportunity of attending meetings on that subject held by the Section'.

The British Allergy Society had been founded in 1948 and included botanists and non-clinicians among its 150 members. The British Society for Immunology was believed to have 500 members and it met three or four times a year, while the Antibody Club, organized by Hamilton Fairley, was said to have 140 members. Hamilton Fairley of St Bartholomew's Hospital was a distinguished contributor to Symington's *Scientific foundations of oncology* (1976) and he seems to have taken the lead in forming the Section, framing its objectives and *raison d'être*. His case rested on the recent expansion of knowledge in immunology, which impinged on a wide variety of clinical problems, particularly hypersensitivity diseases, autoimmune diseases, tissue transplantation, blood diseases and malignant disease. He hoped that the Section would bring together physicians, surgeons, immunologists and pathologists so that experimental findings could be communicated rapidly to clinicians, and so that clinicians could discuss the clinical problems requiring further laboratory investigation. It would thus bridge the gap between those concerned with clinical medicine and those concerned with the scientific aspects of immunology and in this way advance the knowledge of both. These notes, penned by Hamilton Fairley, were adopted for the Section's regulations with minor amendments.[53]

Several of those who wrote indicating their wish to be founder-members of the Section stressed its potential value as a bridge between the ward and the laboratory and as a welcome means of ready and rapid communication. As the first President of the Section, Professor RG White, said: 'one of its important functions will be to bring forth the news from the back-room boys of immunology and allergy to their clinical colleagues'.[54]

### Inauguration

The inaugural meeting of the Section held on 18 October 1965 was attended by 176 founder-members and was opened by the President of the RSM, Lord Cohen. He defined the Section's primary concern with 'a scientific discipline of the widest biological implications, namely the study of the body's reaction to foreign substances. To this were now being brought not only more accurate clinical observation and correlation and the older pathological techniques but also, because of the chemical structures of antigens and antibodies, all the tools of the highest precision'.

At the same meeting Sir Ronald Bodley Scott named Edward Jenner as the father of immunology and 1798 as the natal year of the specialty (Plate 64). After a pause of 80 years came the 'two astonishing decades which saw the full flower of bacteriology [1880–1900]. The very word "immunity" was not used in the sense we are using it this afternoon until 1880. It was in this year that Pasteur showed that fowls could be protected against fowl cholera by inoculation with attenuated organisms'. Bodley Scott reminded his audience of the work of Nuttal, Roux, Ehrlich, Landsteiner and the Austrian paediatrician Clemens von Pirquet, who devised the term 'allergy' in 1906 to describe the altered reactions that can develop when the body is exposed to specific foreign substances on more than one occasion. The decade that preceded the formation of the Section saw an upsurge of interest in autoimmune disease, the implications of which had been revealed by Sir Macfarlane Burnet. Another field assiduously cultivated by the immunologist in recent years was tissue transplantation, a domain established by Medawar in 1943. In concluding, Bodley Scott paid homage to the energy and determination of the enlightened sponsors of the Section. He was confident that it would bring together those interested in the many faces of immunology and make a special contribution to fascinating problems.[55]

Among the original members of the Section were Professor J Dacie (a future President of the RSM), Professor CD Calnan (the first Professor of Dermatology at London University) and Miss Edith Whetnall (after whom a lecture is named). Those who had promoted the formation of the Section, Hamilton Fairley and Morrison Smith, took the posts of Honorary Secretaries and Holborow was on the first Council.

*Subjects of meetings*

The programme started modestly in January 1966, and two further meetings in the year completed the session. The subjects of the first meetings were 'The significance of gastric antibodies', and 'Pulmonary hypersensitivity reactions to inhaled antigens' with papers on 'Farmers' lung', 'Bird fanciers' lung' and 'Fog fever in cattle'.

Dr White, whose presidential address dealt with the activity of adjuvants and presented his own tentative ideas on how antigens were handled by the cells of the body, was succeeded by Dr RS Brice Pearson in 1967. Asthma was his subject, and he had experience of 611 asthmatic patients over a period of seven years at King's College Hospital. He concluded that the prognosis was good in patients seen before the age of 30; after that age the outlook was less good.[56]

'Drug allergy' and 'Deficiency syndromes' were discussed at other meetings and the Section organized joint meetings with the Section of Experimental Medicine and Therapeutics on 'Autoimmune haemolytic anaemia' (1968) and with the Oncology Section on 'The immunotherapy of human cancer' (1971).

The presidency of Dr Deborah Doniach in 1969 brought new members into the Section; she was associated with Professor Ivan Roitt in the discovery of thyroglobulin autoantibodies in Hashimoto's thyroiditis, which helped to open the concept of a relationship between autoimmunity and human disease (1956). Roitt, the author of *Essential immunology* (1971, and in its ninth edition by 1997) was President of the Section in 1973 when he addressed the Section on 'Cell-mediated cytotoxic reactions'. He had also had his say at a meeting the previous year planned under the title of 'Immunology and the NHS' but diluted to 'The role of immunology in clinical medicine'. During this debate Roitt addressed the issue of the NHS and the specialty, urging a clear-cut and significant commitment on the part of the Health Service to accommodate developments in immunology and to encourage trainees.[57]

The research being done by 'the back-room boys' was important and the Section arranged meetings at the Medical Research Council's Rheumatism Research Unit at the Canadian Red Cross Memorial Hospital, Taplow, and at the Royal Postgraduate Hospital, Hammersmith. The Council was worried that meetings were becoming 'too academic' in 1975, so took steps to remedy this; a few years later the size of the Council was increased to 21 in order to represent all the relevant departments and fields of interest. From 1970 onwards research in immunology and allergy expanded greatly and dozens of new journals were launched. Immunology brought together cell biologists and immuno-chemists, genetics and molecular biology, and Professor AB Kay saw the need to educate members of the Section 'who may not be aware of the enormous power of molecular biological techniques for their own research'. He organized an all-day educational meeting in 1986 at which each speaker took time to outline the methodologies and applied them to their own particular research field.

### AIDS

In December 1983 the Section devoted a meeting to the 'Immunology of Acquired Immune Deficiency Syndrome': 'a stimulating day of clinical and scientific discussion introduced by Dr Anthony Pinching who dedicated the meeting to "our patients"'. Twelve speakers from the UK, the USA and Europe reviewed the current data and described much new and unpub-lished work. The relevance of the meeting (as reported in the *Journal*) 'was highlighted by the increase in the number of UK AIDS cases in late 1983 from thirteen (June) to thirty (December) with about 300 cases in Europe and 3000 in the USA'. Those attending the meeting stood to learn from the experience of workers in America, where AIDS was already established and Professor John Humphrey thanked the speakers for sharing information that 'would inform workers in Europe where the syndrome has only surfaced recently'.[58]

By 1986 about 21,000 cases had been diagnosed worldwide and the figure was to escalate, with dire predictions for the future. Dr Pinching devoted his presidential address to 'The challenge of AIDS' (1987), and the next year an all-day meeting explored the 'Natural history and therapy of HIV infection and AIDS'.

### Fluctuating attendance

Half-day meetings on 'Antibody genes' and 'Hepatitis B vaccine' proved successful and profitable in the early 1980s, and half- or whole-day meetings became the norm. 'All meetings were well supported by high attendance figures and in most cases sponsorship had been obtained', the Council reported in 1984.

By the late 1980s the situation had changed and the Section needed new blood. The active members of the Council and Vice Presidents had become outnumbered by the less active, so non-attending Council members were invited to retire and younger Honorary Secretaries were sought. Attendances had improved by 1989, the year Dr Seymour Klebanoff of Seattle was invited to give a special lecture on 'Phagocyte function'. Meetings for the last decade of the 20th century focused on new developments in the immunology of skin disease, tropical disease, rhinitis and what was new in rheumatoid arthritis, and the Section took a critical look at the current preoccupation with chronic fatigue syndrome.

## Section of Medical Education

All the Sections were concerned with medical education in the broadest sense and the purpose of all meetings was and is educational. Furthermore, various aspects of medical education, especially the need for adequate training and recognized qualifications for the specialties, were regular topics for presidential addresses.

With the publication of several official reports in the 1940s and 1950s, medical educa-tion came under particular scrutiny and the work of a Royal Commission on Medical Education during the 1960s generated anxiety. Articles in the press on 'Medical education at the cross roads' and 'The turmoil of medical education' drew attention to current problems and in this atmosphere the College of General Practitioners rallied its resources to defend the future of its members. At the RSM a proposal for a Section of Medical Education led to deliberations with the Deans of medical schools and representatives of the Association for the Study of Medical Education. The President, Lord Cohen, was in favour and 209 Fellows wrote in support of the proposed Section; another six expressed qualified approval and three opposed it. The views of the academic world swayed the Council and the Section was established in August 1966 followed by the inaugural meeting on 5 October under the presidency of Professor Sir Brian Windeyer, a past President of the Section of Radiology. The object of the Section of Medical Education was 'to discuss all aspects of medical education and teaching methods', with the emphasis on 'all'.[59] Despite objections on the grounds that the Association for the Study of Medical Education was already established and successful, the Section managed to recruit 344 founder-members.[60]

Sir John Richardson, President-elect of the RSM, gave the inaugural address on 'Some basic considerations in medical education', prefaced by the observation that the new Section 'must have an appeal of some sort to every member of the Society, since all have been taught and all should continue to be taught one way or another until they cease to practise medicine. This prolonged education throughout the whole of our professional lives is the underlying principle upon which the thinking of this Section, will, I believe, inevitably be based'.[61]

Continuing education in medicine is the premise upon which all Sections, indeed the Society, rests, and the successful pursuit of this goal led ultimately to the demise of the Section devoted exclusively to it.

The first medical book with anatomical illustrations: a woodcut from Johannes de Ketham's *Fasciculus medicinae* (1513 edition) depicting Petrus de Montagnana at his desk. He has been identified as Bartholomew de Montagnana, Professor at Padua in the 15th century and a popular teacher who attracted as many as 300 doctors to his lectures, establishing the reputation of Padua as a medical school.

*Meetings*

Section meetings for the first session on 'Vocational training in general practice' and 'Specialist training' were given ample space in the *Proceedings*, being of wide interest. Sir Brian Windeyer gave a valedictory oration on his experiences as Dean of Middlesex Hospital Medical School where in 1966 over 1,800 candidates competed for 100 student places.[62] The Report of Lord Todd's Royal Commission on Medical Education (1968) fuelled discussion and the Section was addressed by Todd in person that year. The presidency of Dr John Fry (1976–77) was inspirational; his address on 'Learning by doing' referred to his own practice where over 25 years he had halved the referral rate of his patients to consultant departments. He pinpointed the chief reasons for the reduction as his own wider experience and knowledge of the common diseases and an increasing awareness 'of the limitations of my consultant colleagues'.[63]

Topical issues such as 'Medical education and the Common Market' aroused interest, but meetings on 'Teaching ward rounds' and 'Higher diplomas' were less rewarding and no more than 30 members made the effort to attend. Within a year of its formation the Council had noted the problem of low attendance and the situation deteriorated until in the last decade of its existence only 4 or 5% of the membership came to meetings and no more than five new members joined annually. These difficulties were compounded by wider issues in the early 1980s, when many Sections registered poor attendances and unease about the lack of communication between the Sections and the Society. One anonymous member of this Section took it upon himself to write 'A Retort' expressing his dissatisfaction with the management of the Society 'run by a remote and faceless mandarinate icily disdainful of mere members'.[64]

The Section was failing to attract new members or a sufficient number to meetings and its last President, Dr MD Buckley-Sharp, reported in February 1983 that the membership was ageing and declining; the Section had lost or was about to lose the services of six long-standing and highly esteemed members. Therefore the Council reached the conclusion that the Section should be abolished, in the expectation that the Forum approach would prove more valuable for the discussion of medical education.[65] The Section of Medical Education was extinguished in 1983, and the following year saw the launch of a Forum on Medical Communication, where some of the subjects that interested members of the defunct Section could be aired.

## Section of Plastic Surgery

The first President of this Section, Mr Patrick Clarkson, was a protégé of Sir Harold Gillies, to whom the birth of plastic surgery in this country is attributed. 'This remarkable man, who had no orthodox training in plastic surgery, in a period of about five years established the principles and practice of the repair of mutilations of the face and lost features including the major tissue transfers by tube pedicle and those repairs needing epithelial inlay'.[66]

Gillies had taken part in a discussion on the treatment of injuries of the face and jaw at the RSM in 1916, when his work on the victims of the First World War was just beginning. Many years and a knighthood later, he showed members of the Clinical Section a case of lipodystrophy of the face improved by the insertion of fat grafts, and in 1959 he tried to convince members of the Surgical Section of the advantages of rapid reconstruction of the breast after cancer surgery. In the years between these papers the British Association of Plastic Surgeons was founded, the *British Journal of Plastic Surgery* was launched and the rapid postwar expansion of the specialty took place; in view of all these, the formation of a Section devoted to it was overdue.

The initiative for the Section came from Clarkson supported by the British Association of Plastic Surgeons, which submitted to the RSM a formal, corporate request. The

The founders of British plastic surgery, *c.*1948: left to right, Mr Rainsford Mowlem, Professor Pomfret Kilner, Sir Harold Gillies, Sir Archibald McIndoe.

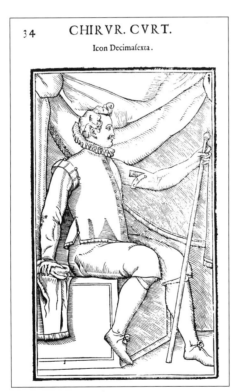

Reconstruction of the upper lip was carried out in the late 16th century and described by Gaspare Tagliacozzi in *De curtorum chirurgia per insitionem* (1597). Tagliacozzi was a surgeon of Bologna whose work in remodelling and repairing the nose, ears and lips was opposed by the Church.
A copy of his book is in the Society's Library.

Association claimed that 30 of its members who were Fellows of the RSM wished to see a Section established, and another 15 had pledged to seek election to the Fellowship if the Section was formed. The main reasons for the request were the need for suitable conditions for the presentation of clinical cases and a desire for the exchange of opinions with other specialists, neither of which the Association could provide. The Council of the RSM was considering several proposals for new Sections at this time and was wary of the dangers of duplication and of the fragmentation of the Society, but with a hard core of members guaranteed and more likely to follow, the Section of Plastic Surgery was approved in September 1967.[67]

Sir Harold Gillies was made an Honorary Fellow of the RSM in 1959 but neither he nor Sir Archibald McIndoe, his cousin and pupil, lived to see the Section of Plastic Surgery established. Nevertheless, Gillies' influence lived on in Clarkson, Richard Battle and Christopher Holborrow, who were founder-members of the Section. Patrick Clarkson had advocated the creation of the Section for many years and he was elected its first President at the inaugural meeting on 5 December 1967. He had trained under Gillies before being sent to command the maxillo-facial unit treating casualties of the Second World War in Tunisia, and he later dealt with those disfigured in the battle at Monte Cassino in Italy. In more peaceful times he established the Children's Burns Unit at Guy's Hospital and founded the Hand Club. Burns and hand surgery being his main interests, his presidential address reviewed 'Recent progress in the treatment of burns', and this was followed by a meeting on 'Congenital deformities of the hand'.

## Variety of meetings

Section meetings in the West Hall at 1 Wimpole Street were designed to appeal to orthopaedists, neurologists, urologists, paediatricians and ophthalmologists as well as plastic surgeons concerned with surgery of the entire body, which might involve transplantation, genetics, speech pathology, wound healing or human embryology and development. The broad scope of plastic surgery was reflected in the papers presented to the Section in the 1970s, ranging from malignant disease of the head and neck to burns dressings, and the trials and tribulations of cosmetic surgery.

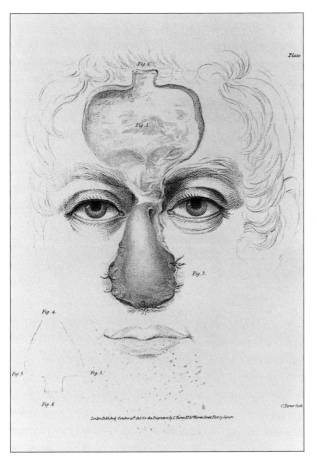

In 1816 Dr JC Carpue, one of the first members of the Medical and Chirurgical Society in 1805, published an account of two successful operations for restoring a lost nose from the integuments of the forehead. In this case Carpue performed a successful operation on an army officer who had been given mercury to treat venereal disease and this had caused the loss of his nose. Carpue's operations marked the re-introduction of major reconstructive surgery into western medicine.

Members were introduced to the history of the specialty in 1976 with papers tracing the development of pedicle flaps back to *circa* 600 BC, and proceeding century by century to the advances in anaesthesia for plastic surgery. Richard Battle gave a masterly account of the development of the specialty during and between the two World Wars – he had been the first plastic surgeon sent abroad with the British Expeditionary Force in 1939. He recalled that when in 1936 he had voiced his desire to specialize, he had been told not to bother because there were already four plastic surgeons in the country (Gillies, McIndoe, Kilner and Mowlem). By the 1970s, 'Thanks to the foundation in 1948 of the National Health Service which held on to the regional plastic centres, there are now centres giving plastic surgery cover to every area in the country'. This session offered further variety with a meeting on 'Plastic surgery and the mentally unstable' and an all-day meeting at St Andrew's Hospital, Billericay.[68]

*Success*

Membership of the Section continued to consist to a large extent of those who belonged to the BAPS, supplemented by many overseas members. When in 1971 the Council received news of the falling attendances in some Sections, it reported that there was no cause for alarm here because attendance at meetings was in the region of 50% of the Section's membership; even so it was decided to encourage guests and maxillo-facial surgeons to join. Thus in 1980 the Society's Medical Services Secretary was pleased to report that the Section of Plastic Surgery was one of the few Sections that had improved its membership and maintained good attendances in recent years.[69]

The Presidency of Mr Roy Sanders (1989–90) reinvigorated activities after a period of temporary lethargy when meetings had been reduced to four a session. In contrast, nine were arranged for 1989–90 and the slightly austere atmosphere of the Section changed to one of teaching and encouragement. This more lively educational approach continued in 1990 with evening training meetings introduced on head and neck reconstruction, breast reconstruction, skin grafts and flaps, cosmetic surgery, facial trauma, burns and hand surgery. The 1990s brought stimulating and very open monthly meetings, as Mr Adam Searle remembered: 'these were always well attended and we used the tempter of short case presentations during the first hour of each meeting to build up an audience, and followed that with a debate or lecture on a topic of relevance to our specialty. A relaxed air of enjoyment pervaded the meetings and the Section was blessed with very good attendances from both junior and senior doctors'.[70]

The Section has attracted eminent guest speakers, notably Professor Paul Tessier of Paris, the world authority on craniofacial surgery (1994), and the highlight of the millennium year was an address from Professor Darina Krastinova-Lolov on 'Orbito-palpebral surgery', illustrated by cases. She pioneered a radical facelift procedure, which she tested on herself with conspicuous success, but she has made it her vocation to reconstruct the faces of deformed children and burns victims at the Hôpital Foch in Paris. Professor Krastinova-Lolov was awarded the Honorary Fellowship of the Society in the year 2000.

## Section of Oncology

The Institution for Investigating the Nature and Cure of Cancer was established in 1801, supported by Dr Matthew Baillie, Mr John Abernethy, Mr George Pearson and Mr Everard Home who all became founder-members of the Medical and Chirurgical Society when it was formed four years later. Over the ensuing century papers on cancer were published regularly in the Society's *Transactions* and from 1907 in the *Proceedings* of the RSM.

Cancer hospitals, societies, charities and voluntary organizations proliferated in the early 20th century, and the RSM appointed a Prevention of Cancer Committee with

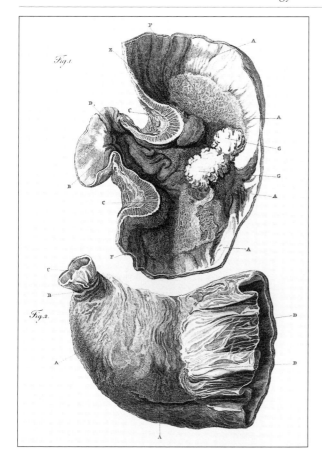

An engraving by W Clift in Matthew Baillie's *Morbid anatomy of some of the most important parts of the human body* (1812) showing some of the appearances of cancer of the stomach. Figure 1: a section of the stomach near the pylorus affected with cancer. Figure 2: a section inverted where in one part its coats had been affected by the action of the gastric juice. Dr Baillie's work on morbid anatomy was the first to present the pathological changes caused by diseases. He presented this volume of his work to the Library.

admirable but unfulfilled intentions in the 1920s (see page 200). Several Presidents of the RSM made significant contributions to cancer research and treatment: Sir Henry Morris and Sir William Selby Church were founders of the Imperial Cancer Research Fund in 1902, Sir John Bland-Sutton's *Cancer clinically considered* was published in 1909, Sir Gordon Gordon-Taylor (like Bland-Sutton) worked for the Middlesex Hospital's Cancer Charity, and Lord Webb-Johnson's Bradshaw lecture of 1940 was entitled 'Pride and prejudice in the treatment of cancer'.

After the Second World War advances were made in the knowledge of the nature, prevention, diagnosis and treatment of cancer. The growth of scientific knowledge and clinical practice accelerated and, as Sir Ronald Raven has pointed out, from its synthesis the multidisciplinary subject of oncology emerged. He defined this subject as being compounded of the arts and sciences and dealing with the aetiology, prevention, diagnosis and definitive treatment of the group of diseases known traditionally as cancer, and with the rehabilitation and continuing care of patients suffering from them.[71]

Raven, who devoted more than 50 years of his life to cancer, and Dr Manuel Lederman, an internationally renowned head and neck radiotherapist, were the chief sponsors of the Section of Oncology. They were supported by 30 Fellows of the Society who felt isolated because of the impossibility of keeping abreast with the increase in knowledge of cancer, its causes and the multiplicity of methods available for its treatment. 'They feel strongly', the Council reported, 'that all concerned with laboratory and clinical research or those responsible for investigating the treatment of human cancer should meet together regularly so that they may profit mutually from the total fund of knowledge in this field. The purpose of such a Section would be to facilitate progress in all aspects of oncology by regular meetings for discussion of medical, surgical, radiotherapeutic, pathological, chemotherapeutic research and other problems related to neoplasia in man'.[72]

Several Council members expressed doubts about the wisdom of founding the Section, because oncology was a subject dealt with in part by many existing Sections. Other Fellows were unfamiliar with the word oncology, which is derived from the Greek word meaning mass, tumour or swelling. There was also strong resistance to the creation of any new Section at a time when older ones were failing: it was felt that new Sections would detract from existing ones and lead to the further fragmentation of medicine. Thus proposals surfacing in the 1960s for sections of venereology, medical care, neurosurgery and nephrology were rejected.[73]

The number and standing of those promoting a Section of Oncology was impressive, however: the original 30 supportive Fellows had been joined by another 100, so while reluctant to concede, the Society's Council placed the matter in the hands of an advisory committee. On the strength of the committee's recommendations the Council agreed to the formation of the Section and a preliminary meeting was held in March 1970 with Sir Alexander Haddow in the chair.[74]

## Sir Alexander Haddow

The inaugural meeting of the Section on 7 October 1970 was attended by 137 of the 277 founder-members. There was now wide enthusiasm for the venture and the presidency of Sir Alexander Haddow acted as a magnet; he preferred to pay homage to the early efforts of Raven, Lederman and Sir Eric Riches in founding the Section. Haddow went on to entice members by outlining the programme for the forthcoming session: novel matter on the aetiology of cancer of the large bowel arising from the recent work of Burkitt and others, a critical survey of the prospects of immunotherapy, a clinical and pathological review of the lymphomas, a description by Professor Richard Doll of the prevalence of cancer in five continents and lastly an account of the highly intriguing discovery of the inappropriate production of hormones by functional tumours.

In defining the scope of oncology Haddow mentioned the earliest clinical contributions, from chimney-sweep's cancer described in 1775 to 'the most dramatic modern addition to cancer incidence – the social habit of cigarette smoking'. Chemotherapy, immunology, carcinogenesis, molecular repair and wound healing were other aspects requiring the attention of the Section at an exciting time. 'After 40 years I can truthfully say that cancer research is more expansive, exciting and vibrant than ever before. We are now in the presence of a ferment and welter of imaginative ideas... It is our prayer that this new Section of our Society will play its proper part in the encouragement of ideas and in the more than ever vital task of communication between the clinical and experimental worlds. Oncology finds itself at a climacteric or watershed and the new vista which I have attempted to describe must inspire us to the spirit of Cortez'.[75]

At the Chester Beatty Institute Sir Alexander Haddow was renowned for his capacity for sustained analytical thought, yet he was no 'ivory tower' worker. He was particularly concerned to apply new research knowledge to the problems of cancer treatment and patient care and he fostered the exchange of information and ideas. He suffered from diabetes and blindness, yet was not deterred from taking a leading role on numerous councils and foundations such as the International Union Against Cancer and the British Cancer Council.

Shortly after Haddow's death in 1976 the current President, Professor E Cotchin, paid him tribute and within a few months the Section's Council was planning a memorial to which all members were invited to subscribe £3. The amount raised by contributions and by the investment of a donation from the British Association for Cancer Research founded the Sir Alexander Haddow Memorial lecture, first given by Sir Peter Medawar in 1977 who told 'The story of tumour immunity'. The second Haddow lecture was attended by no more than a dozen – a sad indication that the Section was in the doldrums.

## A strong Council

With the assistance of the pugnacious Scot Professor Sir John Bruce, Regius Professor of Clinical Surgery at Edinburgh, a prestigious Section Council was recruited: Ronald Raven was the foremost cancer surgeon at the Royal Marsden Hospital, founder President of the British Association of Surgical Oncology and of the Association of Head and Neck Oncologists of Great Britain and the author of a comprehensive treatise on *Cancer* (1960). Dr Manuel Lederman was a past President of the Section of Radiology and soon to be President of the Association of Head and Neck Oncologists – in 1972 he endowed the Leah Lederman lecture and his name was given to Library carrels at the RSM. Dr DP Burkitt recognized a malignant tumour in the jaws of African children known as Burkitt's lymphoma. Professor Richard Doll was already a Fellow of the Royal Society and is perhaps best known for his work on the effects of smoking on health; he was to be awarded the RSM's Gold Medal in 1997. Dr RW Baldwin headed cancer research at the Nottingham laboratories. Dr Graham Bennette of the British Cancer Council was to be Medical Services Secretary of the RSM from 1977. Mr Ian Burn was surgeon to Charing Cross Hospital, a President of the Clinical Section (1974–75), member of the Surgical Section and Honorary Secretary to the RSM for nine years. Dr T Symington was co-author of *Scientific foundations of oncology* (1976). Other officers and Council members of the new Section were KD Bagshawe, Dr Nigel Compston, EH Cooper, RS Handley, Dr RJC Harris, IDA Johnston, Thomas Lodge, Sir Ronald Bodley Scott, Professor John Stallworthy, Sir Eric Riches and the veterinary surgeon Professor Cotchin.

## Meetings

As promised, cancer of the large bowel was soon on the agenda: at the December meeting Denis Burkitt ventured to suggest that there appeared to be a direct relationship between the prevalence of non-infective disease of the large bowel and the cellulose content of the

Sir Ronald Raven, President of the Section of
Oncology 1973–74; he was also President of the
Section of Proctology 1956–57.

diet. 'It may therefore be possible to reduce the incidence of these diseases by retaining the cellulose in carbohydrate foods' he surmised. Burkitt was to be the pioneer of the high-fibre diet for bowel cancer.[76]

The first Leah Lederman lecture was given in April 1973 by Sir Hedley Atkins, who was coming to the end of his term as President of the Society. He had started a breast clinic at Guy's Hospital in 1936 and his subject was 'The treatment of breast cancer'. By 1973 over 12,500 patients had passed through the clinic and Atkins gave his audience at the RSM the benefit of his 37 years' experience. The lecture was followed by a glimpse of future technology: 'it would seem that mammography is acceptable as a diagnostic screening procedure', commented the radiologist Professor Eric Samuel.[77]

Ronald Raven's presidential address of March 1974 looked at 'Future trends in oncological research and treatment': 'The birth of surgical oncology as a multidisciplinary subject was a historic landmark and awakened considerable interest and enthusiasm', he asserted, his own enthusiasm leading to the formation of the Association of Head and Neck Oncologists of Great Britain in 1968, this Section in 1970 and three years later the British Association of Surgical Oncology. The term 'oncology' was clearly gaining ground and Raven urged colleagues to discard the word 'cancer' with its depressing influence and adopt instead the general term 'oncological diseases'.[78]

## Clinical oncology course

Raven was untiring in his promotion of oncology yet, as Sir Richard Doll emphasized in a letter to the Section and the Royal Colleges, there was concern in several quarters 'at the delay in accepting oncology as a specified subject for specialist training'. Young people were not coming forward for training because there were no consultant appointments in the field and the appropriate posts could not be established in the absence of recognition for oncology by the Colleges.

While the Royal Colleges deliberated, the Section of Oncology took an initiative in establishing a postgraduate course in clinical oncology. This was organized by Mr Ian Burn and Dr Graham Bennette in September 1976 and aimed to give clinicians an overall view of recent advances in treatment and research in selected areas of the cancer field. Nearly 50 chairmen, speakers and lecturers contributed and some 130 delegates attended, almost half of them from overseas. Another similar course was planned for 1977 and the Section of General Practice took up the idea with equal success (see page 392).[79]

## Decline and revival

By March 1977 it was clear that many members of the Section rarely if ever came to meetings, and many distinguished oncologists did not participate in its activities at all. The Sections and the Society lacked vigour; this Section blamed the high subscription, poor facilities at 1 Wimpole Street and regretted that the luncheon arrangements at Chandos House had ceased (the Society's acquisition of Chandos House and the uses made of the building are described on pages 462–64). Efforts were made to recruit new members to the Section and joint meetings were arranged with the British Association for Cancer Research, the British Breast Group, the Association of Head and Neck Oncologists, the Blair-Bell Research Society and the Oncology Club, in addition to the combined meetings with other Sections that had always been a feature of the programme. By holding joint meetings with outside bodies the Section of Oncology gave the appearance of being adequately attended, but when meetings were not supported by outsiders, numbers were few. The President addressed an audience of just 12 in 1983, and the following year the President's meeting had to be cancelled because the level of registration was so low.[80] In these circumstances the future of the Section came under review and members were circulated: 66 replies to a questionnaire were received, and the overall response was negative.

The main problem was a surfeit of meetings of cancer associations and societies in London: the only note of optimism was struck by Professor K Hellman who was confident that the opening of the extended and refurbished building at 1 Wimpole Street would lift morale (as it did) and he persuaded the Council to defer the decision to close the Section.

In 1988 another questionnaire was posted to the 315 Section members, eliciting 179 responses and 66 resignations. Catapulted into action, the Section embarked upon an ambitious programme for 1988–89 with meetings on AIDS-related tumours, molecular biology, cancer genetics, animal tumours, cytology and screening, most of them held in conjunction with the Oncology Club or the BACR.

In 1997 a new prize was founded by Professor Kenneth Bagshawe, a founder-member of the Section and an Honorary Fellow of the Society, in memory of his wife, Professor Sylvia Lawler. This provides two awards centred on the annual Sylvia Lawler prize meeting, one is given for the best scientific paper and one for the best clinical paper.

As the Section approached its 30th anniversary in 2000 attendances at regular meetings rose to between 40 and 60, a notable exception being a joint meeting with the Section of Coloproctology on 'Colorectal cancer' in December 1999 which was attended by over 90. The anniversary meeting in October 2000 proved to be another successful meeting when an audience of over 100 heard talks by some of the Section's founder-members.

Many of the subjects of papers and discussions that come before the Section are familiar – thyroid cancer, Hodgkin's disease, colorectal cancer, cutaneous lymphoma and cancer immunotherapy. It is the new approaches, fresh ideas and concepts, news of recent research and technologies, the interchange of information and above all the promise of a genetic revolution that makes the meetings interesting.

## Open Section

This Section came into being as a direct result of the recommendations of the Working Party appointed under the chairmanship of Dr Gordon Wolstenholme 'to consider the Society's role and that of the Sections in the organization of medical meetings and as a forum for conducting medical education' (1973).

One of the main recommendations of the Working Party was that the Society should welcome and encourage exchanges of information and opinion between the medical profession and those in public life at all levels. It was suggested that Members of Parliament, trade unionists, teachers, judges, personalities in the media, economists, industrialists, academics and students should be given opportunities to take part in the activities of the RSM for mutual benefit. Wolstenholme personally fostered the concept of an open forum of professionals who could tackle difficult national issues in health, and it was envisaged that this might be accomplished by the RSM if the Library and Lay Section was reorganized and at the same time a new medico-lay forum was composed of an equal number of medical and lay members. Thus in October 1974 the Library and Lay Section was abolished and reverted to its former role as the the Library (Scientific Research) Section, and the Open Section was inaugurated to provide a channel of communication between the medical profession and those in other walks of life.

The core of the Open Section was formed by members and Fellows who had belonged to the Library and Lay Section and the inaugural meeting on 26 November 1974 was attended by a total of 84 Fellows, members and guests, with Professor AW Wilkinson in the chair. Professor WW Holland of St Thomas' introduced the subject of the first papers which centred on screening programmes. At this and subsequent meetings on 'Tobacco substitutes' and 'The induction question' several papers on the subject were presented by medical and lay speakers giving different perspectives. The first paper to reach the pages of the *Proceedings* in 1976 was from His Honour Mr Justice Sebag Shaw on 'Law and the expert witness'.[81]

## The Section falters

The resignation of a lay member from its Council brought into focus the concern felt by many members of the Section that they were marginalized by the Society. Lay members felt hard done by because they were not entitled to full Society privileges, albeit for a reduced subscription. More to the point, the meetings arranged for the Section had been few, dull and predictable and Dr GE Paget thought the Section was in danger of collapse. 'If the most interesting and exciting innovation in the Society in the last 20 years is not to founder – or even worse, perish from inanition – plainly action must be taken to correct this state of affairs'. Paget's paper of December 1975 commented forcefully on the unsatisfactory state of the Section, which had yet to define its role and establish its place in the RSM. A special meeting called in June 1976 was attended by Sir Gordon Wolstenholme as President of the Society and recommendations for changes were put forward. As a result lunch-time meetings were commenced at Chandos House offering a buffet; the first was held in February 1977 on 'Child health services' and was highly successful, with an attendance of 91.

The Section had turned the corner and was set on a fair course under the presidencies of Dame Anne Bryans (1980–82) and the journalist Katharine Whitehorn (1982–84), with Claire Rayner of *Woman's Own* as an energetic Honorary Secretary who organized a meeting on 'Sexual disorder – can the doctors cope?' in December 1980.

## The 1980s

Changes at the RSM in the 1980s favoured the Open Section. Meetings of a multidisciplinary nature were encouraged and the Open Section acted as a link in this development. The setting up of the Fora and the incorporation of a social aspect to meetings were welcomed by this Section and Ms Whitehorn was the first to suggest that perhaps wine and cheese might add to the conviviality of a meeting, leading to buffet suppers and even dinners.

The Open Section was exceptionally successful in securing publication of its proceedings in the *Journal*; the meeting on 'Alternatives to western medical care', for instance, was reported as a lively, quick-firing discussion that questioned the necessity of a medical qualification. It also provoked the comment that it was time for doctors to examine their consciences and decide whether they were primarily interested in their patients or in their own professional interests.[82]

The Section regularly addressed ethical and controversial questions such as 'Experiments on embryos' and 'Lessons from the Savage enquiry'. The latter concerned Mrs Wendy Savage who had been suspended from her post by Tower Hamlets District Health Authority for alleged professional incompetence. Mrs Savage and Mr Beaumont, the barrister who chaired the enquiry, both came to the Section meeting, which emphasized the need for an expert conciliation service in such cases.[83]

Community care, the question of how health services should be funded, AIDS, migraine and genetic engineering were some of the subjects debated by this Section. The meeting on AIDS in February 1987 was held at a time of public panic, and Sir Donald Acheson, Chief Medical Officer of the DHSS, Tony Whitehead of the Terrence Higgins Trust and Dr Roy Porter of the Wellcome Institute for the History of Medicine attempted to dispel some myths while not denying the serious clinical and ethical problems that the pandemic posed.

Some relief was allowed: in June 1991 members went to the Royal Academy at Burlington House, Piccadilly, for a joint meeting with Academicians and in July 1998 a joint meeting was arranged with other Sections on 'Music, the brain and the mind', concluding with a concert.

The Open Section offers programmes of a variety and topicality unique within the RSM, as Lady Jean Lovell-Davies pointed out in an address entitled, appropriately, 'Open Section – open minds'.

ROYAL ACADEMY OF ARTS.
PICCADILLY, LONDON, W1V 0DS

Telephone : 071-439 7438
Fax : 071-434 0837
Telex : 21812

ROYAL ACADEMY OF ARTS

AND

ROYAL SOCIETY OF MEDICINE

Symposium in honour of the late Dr. Arthur M. Sackler

Friday, 14th June, 1991

at

The Jill and Arthur M. Sackler Galleries, The Royal Academy of Arts

THE MIND'S EYE

9.00 am      **Arrival and Registration**

9.30      **Welcome**

     Roger de Grey, President, Royal Academy of Arts
     Dr Zarrina Kurtz, President, Open Section of the Royal
     Society of Medicine.

     **Introduction**

     Professor Richard Gregory, CBE, Emeritus Professor of
     Neuro Psychology at the University of Bristol

10.00      **Mental Images**

     Professor Colin Blakemore, PhD, ScD, DSc., Waynflete
     Professor of Physiology, University of Oxford and Fellow
     of Magdalen College, Oxford.

     Physical and Mental Images

     Professor Horace Barlow, MBBCh, MD, ScD, FRS, Fellow
     of Trinity College, University of Cambridge

     Innate Releasers and Eigen-Images

The meeting of the Open Section at the Royal Academy of Arts, Burlington House, Piccadilly, on 'The mind's eye', in June 1991.

In the year before the NHS Review was published the Section carried out its own review, featuring Mr Enoch Powell, a former Minister of Health, and Sir Raymond Hoffenburg, President of the Royal College of Physicians. The 1989–90 session considered issues then being examined by Parliament or the media, for example the Health Service and Community Care Bill, the supply of clean water and the Broadcasting Bill. When discussions coincide with a high level of public awareness they are guaranteed to be vigorous.[84]

## Linking clinical and lay concerns

The breadth of view of the Open Section is encapsulated in its title but this evaded many, so in 1998 the Section's purpose was clarified by the addition of the sub-title 'Linking Clinical and Lay Concerns'. The balance between medical and lay interests is maintained on the Section's Council, and Presidents usually alternate between clinical and lay members.

Ms Katharine Whitehorn, Dame Deirdre Hine, Lord Soulsby and Mrs Jean
Gaffin at the Open Section's 25th anniversary dinner,
November 1999.

The Section celebrated its 25th anniversary with a dinner in November 1999 attended
by over 80 members and guests and ten past Presidents, one of whom, Ms Katharine
Whitehorn, gave a sparkling account of the Section's history and prospects. This was soon
followed by a millennium meeting on the sober subject of 'Social exclusion: the role of
health and health services'. The Section also organized a lively debate for the Millennium
Members' Open Day on 'Modern medicine: dying or thriving?'.

## Section of Hypnosis and Psychosomatic Medicine
originally Medical and Dental Hypnosis

The history of hypnosis within the RSM begins in 1833, some 20 years after the death of
Franz Anton Mesmer. In this year Professor John Elliotson, physician and mesmerist, was
elected President of the Medical and Chirurgical Society of London, the parent of the
RSM. Elliotson was Professor of Medicine at University College at the time; he opened a
Mesmeric Infirmary and was a friend of the painter and illustrator George Cruikshank and
of the novelist William Thackerary, whose life he had saved. In gratitude Thackeray
immortalized Elliotson as Doctor Goodenough in his novels *Pendennis* and *The adventures of Philip*. Another friend was Thomas Wakley, the founder of the *Lancet* – Wakley
supported Elliotson's work with mesmerism to start with but later denounced him for
holding public demonstrations, thus obliging Elliotson to resign his professorship in 1838
(see pages 68, 82 and Plate 65).

In the 23 volumes of his journal the *Zoist*, Elliotson published many accounts of surgery
accomplished without pain under the influence of mesmerism. These reports faded into
obscurity with the advent of chemical anaesthesia and mesmerism slid into the backwaters
of medical practice, at the same time replacing 'ether frolics' and 'the laughing gas' as stage
and music-hall entertainment. Meanwhile, Elliotson and his successors realized that the
trance state that Anton Mesmer had supposed to be a response to magnetism was better
understood as a variant of sleep, hence the change of name from mesmerism to hypnotism
(*hypnos* meaning sleep in ancient Greek).[85]

## Into the mainstream

A century after the combination of Elliotson's disgrace and the impact of the arrival of chemical anaesthesia had displaced mesmerism, a series of events brought hypnosis into mainstream medical practice. The Second World War saw troops massed for retraining, and to maintain morale singers, comedians and stage hypnotists provided entertainment for the forces. Some army medical and dental officers witnessed stage hypnosis and used the opportunity to learn the technique of trance induction, discussing its potential application to medical and dental practice. When the war ended these army doctors and dentists returned to civilian practice with an interest in hypnosis.

The criticism and, at worst, persecution endured by those who had promoted hypnosis in the past persuaded the BMA to investigate the potential value and proper place of hypnotism in medicine, and in 1955 the subcommittee appointed by the Psychological Medicine Group of the BMA produced its report. It advised the avoidance of extravagant claims and sensationalism, suggested further scientific research and recommended the teaching of hypnosis at undergraduate and postgraduate level. A key sentence of the report reads: 'The subcommittee is satisfied after consideration of the available evidence that hypnotism is of value and may be the treatment of choice in some cases of so-called psychosomatic disorder and psychoneurosis. It may also be of value for revealing unrecognized motives and conflicts in such conditions'.

## Societies

In 1956, confident of BMA support, doctors joined with those dentists who in 1952 had formed the British Society of Dental Hypnosis in a new Medical Society for the Study of Hypnosis, merging in 1961 with another group to become the British Society of Medical and Dental Hypnosis. The last-named subsequently organized regular postgraduate hypnosis courses and started an accreditation scheme for the clinical practice of hypnosis in medicine and dentistry.

International contacts were established during the postwar years and in particular with the North American societies of medical and dental hypnosis. In 1978 clinical psychologists working alongside medical and dental colleagues founded the British Society of Experimental and Clinical Hypnosis.

## Section of Medical and Dental Hypnosis

When the proposal to form a Section of Medical and Dental Hypnosis came before the RSM Council in April 1977, there was some apprehension. The British Society of Medical and Dental Hypnosis supported the proposition but the Council of the RSM wanted to know how many members of that Society were laymen, doctors or dentists: it was feared that the formation of the Section might encourage an influx of non-medical members of the Society.[86] A committee appointed to investigate the problems reported positively, so the Council agreed in October 1977 to establish the Section. [87]

The Metropolitan Branch of the Society of Medical and Dental Hypnosis had been meeting at 1 Wimpole Street for many years. It was a vigorous branch of a national society with a distinguished membership of men and women qualified as doctors and dentists and many of them supported the new Section, which made a good start with 69 founder-members who were already Fellows of the RSM and 88 newly elected Fellows. Dr David Waxman of the Department of Psychological Medicine, Middlesex Hospital, was elected the first President and at the inaugural meeting of 22 June 1978 he declared that 'The formation of the Section of Medical and Dental Hypnosis within the established disciplines of the Royal Society of Medicine marks the beginning of a new era in the chequered history of a phenomenon as old as man himself. Beset with folklore, mystique and misunderstanding, hypnosis has emerged from beneath the lilac cloak of the 18th century into what is now recognized as a specific weapon in the psychotherapeutic armamentarium'. The Section aimed 'to extend the knowledge of the hypnotic state, to investigate further its neurophysiology and to promote interest in its clinical use'.[88]

For the first session of 1978–79 meetings were arranged on the training of psychotherapists, hypnosis and suggestibility, pain problems in dentistry, hypnosis and paranormal phenomena; a short-paper meeting and a dinner were also held. The Council was keen to 'spread the gospel of the use of hypnosis within other Sections', so members of the Sections of Orthopaedics, Odontology, Anaesthetics and Surgery were invited to appropriate meetings.[89]

The Section initiated a conference on 'Psychological influences and illness: hypnosis and medicine' in 1982, attended by speakers from the USA, Australia, Israel, Sweden and Britain. As this was an international event, Sir John Stallworthy, President of the RSM, took the chair.

### Section of Hypnosis and Psychosomatic Medicine

In 1987 the fourth European Congress of Hypnosis and Psychosomatic Medicine Conference was held at Oxford, sponsored by the RSM, and following this most successful meeting the Section President, Dr David Pederson, instigated the change of title to the Section of Hypnosis and Psychosomatic Medicine, this being more in keeping with the nature of its meetings. He explained that 'the original title had come from the British Society of Medical and Dental Hypnosis, some of whose members had grouped together to found the Section, making that name at the time a natural choice… We now feel similarity of names leads to some confusion, furthermore hypnosis is part and parcel of the psychosomatic field of medicine even when used within the framework of dentistry'. The Society concurred, approving the change of title in July 1988.

The renamed Section aimed to hold eight meetings each session, with guest speakers and an annual teaching symposium. This formula, combined with an increased interest in hypnosis and psychosomatic medicine, resulted in a rise in the membership figures to 430 for the session 2000–2001.

## Section of Accident and Emergency Medicine (Plate 66)

Accident and emergency medicine developed as a specialty in Britain between the 1960s and the 1980s from roots established in the 19th century. The first President of the Section, Dr Vera Dallos, traced the origins of the specialty to an article expressing concern about the country's casualty service in the *Lancet* of 1869;[90] others saw the first manifestation of accident and emergency medicine in the arrangements set up by the orthopaedic surgeon Robert Jones to deal with casualties among those building the Manchester Ship Canal in 1883.

The authorities were forced to organize emergency care for the wounded during two World Wars, and in 1941 the Birmingham Accident Hospital and the accident services of the Radcliffe Infirmary, Oxford, swung into operation. Train and bus disasters of the 1950s and a series of official reports from 1959 drew attention to serious inadequacies in the casualty service. Sir Henry Platt's Report of 1962 suggested that 'accident and emergency' should replace the word 'casualty', and this stirred debate. Perhaps the most constructive work was achieved after the foundation of the Casualty Surgeons' Association in 1967 under the leadership of Mr Maurice Ellis whose work at the General Infirmary, Leeds, set a shining example and whose *Casualty surgeon's handbook* laid the foundations of the literature of the specialty.

A working party chaired by Sir John Bruce reviewed accident and emergency services with the result that 32 experimental consultant posts were established in accident and emergency departments as a pilot scheme in 1971, and the first academic consultant appointment in accident and emergency medicine was established at Manchester eight years later. The 1980s saw the launch of the Emergency Medicine Research Society and two journals devoted to accident and emergency medicine.

At the RSM Sir John Stallworthy received a proposal for a Section of First Aid (or possibly Emergency Care) in 1980, which failed to enthuse him. The idea emanated from Mr Ronald G Macbeth, who had been involved with the St John Ambulance Service for many years. He acknowledged that a new section of the RSM 'does not spring in full beauty like Venus from the waves and maybe a symposium might be a way of introducing putative parents' for a first aid section. He pointed out that emergency medicine had expanded beyond the jurisdiction of orthopaedics: 'no longer are the Orthopods the chief priests of First Aid, the anaesthetists are in there and even the ENTs with their concern about the airways', and it was time to involve all doctors. Dr Bernard Lucas extended the idea from first aid to emergency care, but it was still several years before these proposals reached fruition as the Section of Accident and Emergency Medicine.[91]

## Mr Tabone-Vassallo founds the Section

In August 1984 Mr Mario Tabone-Vassallo, Senior Registrar of the Casualty Department of St Stephen's Hospital, London SW10, tested the ground about a Section of Accident and Emergency Medicine of the RSM. He must have received some encouragement, although it was nearly a year before a meeting was convened between himself and the President, Sir John Walton, Ian Burn and Robert Thomson. Tabone-Vassallo convinced the officers of the Society that 45 members of the Casualty Surgeons' Association would join the Section, that meetings of the Section would not clash with those of the Association and that accident and emergency medicine was an expanding specialty with an ever-increasing number of practitioners. Therefore in March 1986 the RSM Council agreed to establish the Section for a probationary five-year period. Tabone-Vassallo, Dr Vera Dallos, Dr John Thurston and Mr Richard Warren then met to draft the regulations and aims of the Section: 'to promote high standards of all aspects of accident and emergency practice'.[92]

At the inaugural meeting on 19 January 1987 Dr Dallos was in the chair and Tabone-Vassallo took the post often assigned to the originator of a Section – Honorary Secretary. Thirty-seven founder-members were elected and the President of the RSM, Sir Gordon Robson, described how the Section had come into being. In addition to Dr Dallos' presidential address on the development of accident and emergency medicine in this country, Mr William H Rutherford located the milestones in the specialty. He had spent 20 years working at a mission hospital in India before returning to the UK and embarking on a career in accident and emergency medicine, notably at the Royal Victoria Hospital, Belfast, at the height of the 'Troubles', and he edited the textbook on *Accident and emergency medicine* (1979, 1989).

The Section was highly organized from the beginning, its officers having arranged an all-day symposium on 'The medico-legal aspects of accident and emergency medicine' to cap the inaugural meeting. The President took care to publicize the Section in the *Archives of Emergency Medicine*, trumpeting the advance this represented. 'It is nearly 25 years since the Platt Report of 1962 stated that accident and emergency work is "unlikely to provide a satisfactory career for a consultant"…Those 25 years have seen the establishment, development and flowering of accident and emergency medicine led by a consultant body who can afford to smile at those "famous last words". There is no better occasion for joy and pride in our achievements than the recognition of our specialty by the Royal Society of Medicine'. Dr Dallos announced that the Section planned to hold three symposia a session on 'burning issues', also clinical meetings which would often be held jointly with related specialties. She hoped to recruit Fellows and Associate Fellows who would be involved with the running and development of the Section, and others were welcome to attend meetings and to bring their nursing and medical staff.[93]

## Symposia, newsletter and prize

The symposia proved successful, attracting sponsorship from the pharmaceutical industry, experts in different fields as speakers and an average attendance of over 100 senior accident and emergency personnel. Symposia on 'The trauma service: cause for concern?' and 'The elderly patient in the accident and emergency department' set a pattern of excellence and, as Tabone-Vassallo reported, they were intended to contain 'the required degree of controversy'. He claimed that some of the meetings had stimulated national debate on such matters as 'no fault' compensation and trauma centres. In respect of trauma centres a Working Party of the Royal College of Surgeons reported in 1988 and the DHSS agreed to support one trauma centre at Stoke. The debate continued at the Section in September 1989 when the Minister for Health, Mr David Mellor, opened the symposium on 'Trauma – the way ahead'.[94]

The Section's proceedings and symposia required more coverage than the RSM *Journal* could offer, so the Section launched its own *A & E Letter* in 1988, sponsored for the first two years by Eli Lilly and Co and edited by Gordon S Laing. Thus papers on 'ENT and ophthalmic emergencies', 'Accident and emergency nursing', 'Road safety and vehicle design', 'Aspects of violence' and 'Infectious enthusiasm' – to name but a few – reached the printed page.

Perhaps the most ambitious symposium organized by the Section was on 'Emergency medicine in a united Europe', attended by 96 delegates from the UK, France, Germany, Portugal, the Netherlands and Denmark. Their aim was to lay the foundations of a common accident and emergency policy throughout the European Community and it was hoped that the symposium would prompt the foundation of a European association for accident and emergency medicine.

Meanwhile other meetings dealt with rheumatology, psychiatry and the forensic and legal aspects of accident and emergency medicine, to which members of other Sections were invited. Dr Dallos was keen to arrange a combined meeting with the Emergency

The first issue of the *A & E Letter*, 1988. The photographs, top, are of Dr Vera Dallos, first President of the Section 1986–87, and Mr M Tabone-Vassallo, the Section's founder and its President 1990–91.

Medical Research Society in Manchester during her presidency but this had to be abandoned when the Section was cold-shouldered by the EMRS, which wished to maintain 'a crisp distinction' between it and the Section.[95]

After six years as the chief advocate of the Section, Tabone-Vassallo gave notice of his intention to make way for younger men in 1991. His gracious letter thanked all those who had supported 'my efforts in the establishment of the Section', which had been successful in itself and had provided a stimulus for the formation of other new and active Sections. This Section was financially sound, its newsletter found new sponsorship, there were plans to establish a prize for unpublished research (first awarded to Mr A Mark Dalton during the 1992–93 session), a presidential badge and chain had been purchased together with jewels for past Presidents.[96]

At the sixth AGM in July 1992 it was reported that the Council of the RSM had approved the Section's annual prize, that the number of fully paid-up Fellows of the Section continued to rise and this Section was one of the most popular and influential within the Society. Prosperity continued with symposia on 'Occupational health risks in accident and emergency medicine' opened by Dr Kenneth Calman, Chief Medical Officer of Health, on 'Accident and emergency medicine – training and being trained', with contributions from the President and the Dean of the recently founded Faculty of Accident and Emergency Medicine, and a symposium on 'Sports and soft tissue injuries' was opened by Sir Roger Bannister in 1996. The Section celebrated its tenth anniversary with a dinner, and the millennium papers looked at the challenges of the past and the opportunities of the future.

## Section of Clinical Forensic and Legal Medicine (Plate 67)
originally Clinical Forensic Medicine

In the preliminary negotiations surrounding the formation of the RSM (1905–07), the Medico-Legal Society was invited to join the amalgamation. That Society had been founded in 1901 to promote the study of legal medicine and at that time it was the only learned society in the country devoted to the subject. Although the Council of the Medico-Legal Society agreed in principle to an amalgamation, it did not participate in the final negotiations, choosing instead to pursue an independent course that it has followed to this day. Its membership is fairly evenly shared between the two senior professions of the law and medicine and it publishes its proceedings in a quarterly journal.

Other organizations emerged later: the British Academy of Forensic Sciences and the Forensic Science Society, both of which were concerned, *inter alia*, with the forensic aspects of medicine. In 1951 the Association of Police Surgeons was founded and this was specifically concerned with clinical forensic medicine. Both forensic pathology and forensic psychiatry are recognized by academia as specialties, but clinical forensic medicine has not received that accolade. There was no academic body that was devoted to clinical forensic medicine, and this was a cause of concern to those doctors who practised their skills in this discipline, gathering medical evidence in criminal cases and giving oral evidence in Magistrates' and Crown Courts.

### Founding the Section

Dr Neville Davis, the chief founder of this Section who has written this account, recalls that when on 2 July 1986 Her Majesty Queen Elizabeth II opened the refurbished premises of the RSM, the President Sir John Walton (later Lord Walton of Detchant) spoke in his address of the need to broaden the Society's activities. Dr Davis, who had held office in the Association of Police Surgeons, heard this address in the West Hall. He regarded it as an invitation and wrote at once to Sir John proposing the establishment of a Section of

Clinical Forensic Medicine. On 25 July 1986 he received a reply from the Society's Executive Director suggesting a meeting which might lead to the presentation of a report to the Honorary Officers. A Steering committee was appointed and a feasibility study showed that the proposed Section was viable and that its core was likely to be drawn from the membership of the Association of Police Surgeons. That Association nevertheless had its anxieties as to whether a Section of Clinical Forensic Medicine would usurp its own functions. In the end the argument that the multidisciplinary structure of the RSM was the right place for an academic body for clinical forensic medicine prevailed, and the Association supported the project.

On 23 April 1987 the Executive Director, Mr Robert Thomson, wrote to Davis, 'I am very pleased to tell you that at the meeting of Council held on Tuesday this week it was decided that Council would give notice of its intention to establish a Section of Clinical Forensic Medicine for five years in the first instance'.

The Section was officially established in October 1987 and held its inaugural meeting on 23 January 1988. Sir Gordon Robson, who had succeeded Sir John Walton as President of the RSM, was in the chair and he welcomed the new Section warmly. Among those present were Miss Margaret Pereira, representing the Home Office, and Mr Sydney Chapman MP (later Sir Sydney Chapman). Dr Neville Davis was elected President and the other medical members of the Steering committee were also elected to office.

The Section's first symposium on 'Forensic aspects of fitness' was held in conjunction with the Association of Police Surgeons. The list of attendees included Mr Peter Bottomley MP, the current Under-Secretary of State at the Department of Transport, Michael Bennett of the Police Federation, Mr D Mills, Legal Attaché with the US Embassy, Dr David Paul, President of the British Academy of Forensic Sciences and Sir John Wickerson, immediate past President of the Law Society.[97]

*Meetings and membership*

Meetings were held three times a year on Saturdays in January, June and October. They were preceded by informal dinners on the previous night, the first having been held prior to the inaugural meeting. It was hoped to hold one meeting a year in the provinces.

Not only was the multidisciplinary structure of the RSM exploited, but a new dimension – multiprofessional – was added. It soon became evident that the legal content of the meetings was attractive to lawyers, and so judges, barristers and solicitors applied to join the Section. This was a departure from normal practice, since the Society's charter specified that the professions eligible for election to the Fellowship were medicine, dentistry and veterinary surgery. The Membership committee and the Council of the RSM took the view that distinguished lawyers with an interest in the medico-legal interface would contribute greatly to the work of the Section and would thereby benefit the RSM. Accordingly they looked upon their election with favour. Similarly with forensic scientists: Dr Frances Lewington, not medically qualified, but an eminent forensic scientist who later received an OBE for her work in training doctors, was elected to the Fellowship and served on the first Council of the Section and subsequently as Honorary Secretary.

This liaison between medicine and the law was an invaluable symbiosis in the Section meetings. Richard Ferguson QC, prefacing his paper on 'The violent offender in court', referred to the suspicion, resentment and on occasion outright hostility that existed between the two professions, which, he said, the meetings of the Section served to eradicate.[98] Dr Davis, writing in *Clinical forensic medicine* (published in 1996 by the Association of Police Surgeons and edited by Dr David McLay, the first editorial representative on the Section Council), declared, 'There is little doubt that the Section has forged valuable links and has contributed greatly to mutual understanding between the two noble professions of medicine and the law'. He expressed the hope that such contacts would lead to the establishment of international links and would lead to productive co-operation in education and training in clinical forensic medicine. [99]

Bearing in mind that the original membership of the Section was concerned with the criminal area of the medico-legal interface, it is not surprising that this would be reflected in the subject matter of the Section's symposia. Titles such as 'Death, sudden and unexpected', 'Bang and crash' and 'Murder, rape and assault' aroused considerable interest. At a symposium on 'The forensic aspects of violence' in 1988 Dr RT Shepherd gave a graphic account of the Hungerford shootings in which the killer fired 119 shots, at his own mother among others. A Northern Ireland surgeon added to the horror with slides illustrating the dreadful injuries which were caused by terrorist activity. Sir Peter Imbert, then Commissioner of the Metropolitan Police, struck a sombre note at that symposium, expressing the hope that 'we strive together towards that common goal of ours of improving the quality of life in the face of the disturbing increase of violence in society'. [100]

Dr Robin Moffat, first Honorary Secretary of the Section, succeeded as President in 1989 and concluded his term in office with a valedictory address on 'Corporal punishment: the end of an era'. Dr Raine Roberts, who followed Moffat, was well known for her work in Manchester with victims of sexual assaults. She hosted a symposium in Manchester on 'Child abuse' which illustrated the multiprofessional, multidisciplinary nature of the Section, with papers from a paediatrician, a child psychiatrist and a lawyer. [101]

In September 1992 the Section successfully applied to the RSM Council for permanent establishment, having completed its five-year probation. Doctors Roberts and Moffat reported a membership of over 200 and an average attendance at meetings of 70. They wrote, 'We trust the Council of the RSM will look kindly upon our endeavours' and concluded, 'our aim is to cultivate high-quality medical testimony at the Courts, improve the quality of Clinical Forensic Practice and enhance undergraduate training in the legal aspects of medical practice. We have made a promising start!'. [102]

In 1995 the members of the Section were prominent in organizing a Society Conference on 'The medical aspects of terrorism'. This was a great success with international speakers of repute, including Sir John Dellow, a former Deputy Commissioner of the Metropolitan Police, who spoke about his experience at the siege of the Iranian Embassy; Professor John Gunn dealt with the role of the psychiatrist in the siege; Lord Harris, a former Minister in the Home Office, spoke of the political dimension of terrorism and Dr Yamashina talked about the 1995 attack on the Tokyo subway with sarin gas. Other speakers covered the Waco siege in Texas, the Piper Alpha and Lockerbie disasters, and all present were moved by a memorable address from Terry Anderson, who was for seven years a hostage in Lebanon.

### Clinical Forensic and Legal Medicine

By 1996 it was clear that there was a need to cover the civil area of medico-legal practice. Mr Adrian Marston, Honorary Dean, addressed the Section's Council and encouraged it to expand its horizons to include matters such as medical negligence, personal injury, medical ethics and family law. At the same time the RSM was negotiating with the embryonic Expert Witness Institute to become a founding sponsor. It was clear that if the Section was not prepared to accommodate the civil area, another section or forum would have to be formed. There was considerable resistance to the move, which was nevertheless supported by Dr Davis. Eventually agreement was reached; Davis had mooted a change of title to Section of Legal Medicine but old loyalties died hard and in the end the new title was settled as Section of Clinical Forensic and Legal Medicine. The change took place in 1997 during the presidency of Dr Paul Knapman, the Westminster Coroner. The October symposium in that year was devoted to 'The expertise of the expert medical witness', and it was well supported by doctors and lawyers alike. [103]

*The 10th anniversary*

In January 1998, with its membership standing at 335, the Section celebrated its 10th birthday. Dr Peter Dean, both a coroner and a forensic medical examiner, succeeded to the presidency and the Section went from strength to strength. As Dr Moffat wrote in *RSM News*, 'The Section is determined to enhance the quality and precision of expert medical testimony provided pre-trial and in the civil and criminal courts'.[104] During Dr Dean's presidency the Section was a leading resource for a Society conference on 'Medical aspects of death in custody'. High-profile speakers included Dr Stephen Karch, a world authority on cocaine addiction, and Mr Peter Moorhouse, Chairman of the Police Complaints Authority. If it were not for the regulations limiting the capacity of the Barnes Hall, some 300 delegates might have attended: there was not an empty seat in the auditorium.

*Current status*[105]

Dr Diana Wetherill, a police surgeon from West Yorkshire, was President for the millennium year. The millennium meeting in June 2000 was entitled 'Forensic medicine and the seven ages of man' and featured eminent speakers such as Professor Astrid Heger from the University of Southern California, the doyenne of child sexual abuse, and Mr Alan Levy QC, a member of the Section and a prominent lawyer in the field of legislation about children. At the suggestion of the President, the Council of the Section agreed that there should be a two-day symposium, jointly organized by the Section and the Association of Police Surgeons, in York in October 2000, as Dr Wetherill was keen that members from the north should be able to attend meetings more easily.

The membership has risen to 651 and many members are acknowledged experts in their field.

## Section of Geriatrics and Gerontology

Six new Sections were inaugurated in the early 1990s, bringing a considerable expansion of activity at the RSM which then housed a record number of 40 Sections. The first of the group to be established was the Section of Geriatrics and Gerontology in 1991.

The first English book on geriatrics was Sir John Floyer's *Medicina gerocomica*, written in 1724, which began by recommending that old men, 'when they leave off all Employments, they must take care of themselves, in Eating, Exercise, Frication, Bathing, Passions, Evacuations etc'. Nearly a century later (1817) Sir Anthony Carlisle's *Essays on old age* reiterated a common-sense approach in the 'judicious management of the disorders of senility'. The best-known name in 19th-century geriatrics was that of Professor JM Charcot, an Honorary Fellow of the RMCS who inaugurated a course in geriatrics at the Salpêtrière Hospital in 1866. Charcot's *Leçons cliniques sur les maladies des vieillards* is in the RSM Library, along with the works of Floyer and Carlisle.

Geriatrics emerged as a specialty in Britain during the 1950s after the government gave hospitals the responsibility for the care of the chronic sick. Since then the specialty has expanded to be the leading authority on the provision of acute, rehabilitative and long-term care of older people. During the 1950s the British Geriatrics Society was founded, Dr Alex Comfort's book *The biology of senescence* first appeared and the Ciba Foundation's symposia on ageing were held. By the 1990s the increasing number of ageing people in Britain was commanding medical and social recognition: longevity had become the norm and the problems associated with it came to notice as never before.

As Professor Millard stated in his letter of 1989 proposing the Section to the Council of the RSM, the time was right for the development of a Section of Geriatrics. There were several existing societies – the British Geriatrics Society with over 1,500 members, the British Society of Social Gerontology, the British Society for Research on Ageing and the British Association for Service to the Elderly in addition to a Teachers of Geriatrics Club in

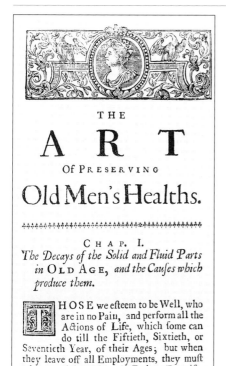

THE

# ART

Of Preserving

## Old Men's Healths.

✝✝✝✝✝✝✝✝✝✝✝✝✝✝✝✝✝✝✝✝✝✝✝✝✝✝✝✝✝✝✝✝✝✝✝✝✝✝✝

CHAP. I.
*The Decays of the Solid and Fluid Parts
in* OLD AGE, *and the Caufes which
produce them.*

THOSE we efteem to be Well, who
are in no Pain, and perform all the
Actions of Life, which fome can
do till the Fiftieth, Sixtieth, or
Seventieth Year, of their Ages; but when
they leave off all Employments, they muft
take care of themfelves, in Eating, Exercife,
A                     Frication,

Sir John Floyer's *Medicina gerocomica* was the first English book devoted to geriatrics (1724).

London, but none of them possessed the unique characteristics of a Section of the RSM. Millard reminded the Council that 15 years before Professor Grimley Evans had tried to establish a Section for Medical Gerontology, and indeed still favoured it, but this had failed to attract enough support.

The name of the proposed section was contentious: 'geriatrics' (preferred by Millard on the grounds that it would attract members from all disciplines),[106] 'medicine in the elderly' and 'medical gerontology' were considered before the title of Geriatrics and Gerontology was chosen and the object of the Section was defined as the study, promotion and advancement of the science of ageing and clinical care within the specialty.[107]

No less than 230 Fellows of the Society registered interest in the proposed section, so in 1990 the Society's Council gave its approval, announcing that the inaugural meeting of the Section of Geriatrics and Gerontology would be held in March 1991. At this meeting Dr Alex Comfort was elected President, although he was absent through illness. Professor Peter Millard, the Eleanor Peel Professor of Geriatrics at St George's Hospital Medical School, who had done so much to bring the Section into being, was chosen as Honorary Secretary and identified as President-elect.

The first subject to come before the Section was 'Driving in old age'. Many European countries tested cars but not drivers as they aged, and the high number of drivers over the age of 70 combined with the prevalence of dementia in the elderly gave cause for alarm. The wide interest and implications of the meeting led to it being reported in the Society's *Journal* under the heading of 'Dementia and driving'.[108]

Another early meeting on 'Drugs and the ageing population – current issues' was held jointly with the Forum on Clinical Pharmacology and Therapeutics and attracted an audience of about 100. The Section organized an annual regional meeting, a clinical meeting, combined meetings with other Sections and for the 1993–94 session a two-day European meeting on 'Cerebrovascular ageing' with the British Society for Research on Ageing.

## AC Comfort Memorial lecture

The first President of this Section, Dr Comfort, was one of the country's leading academic gerontologists and became widely known as the author of *The joy of sex*. He established a fund to commemorate his father, AC Comfort, in 1981 and a few years later he donated his collection of books on gerontology to the RSM Library. The fund was to provide an annual award either in the form of a prize for a paper on some aspect of clinical research in geriatric medicine, written by a practitioner of no more than five years' standing or by a student; alternatively it could pay for a lecture on geriatric medicine. The first AC Comfort lecture was given by Professor David Weatherall of the Institute of Molecular Medicine at the John Radcliffe Hospital, Oxford, who spoke about 'The biology of ageing' in 1995. Studies had already shown that the ageing process 'must be under some kind of genetic programming' and Sir David predicted that the biology of ageing was to be an extremely exciting field of research.[109] Two years later Professor Grimley Evans of Oxford University raised the issue of ageism in his lecture 'The menace of ageism: a call to arms' (1997).

## Fully established

The Section was on trial for the first five years of its life, which were completed in 1996, when Professor Millard applied for full recognition. He was delighted with the support his Section had received and with the ambience the RSM provided. 'We now have over 250 active members and a programme of three day and three evening meetings', he reported.[110]

Osteoarthritis, osteoporosis, Alzheimer's disease, stroke prevention and treatment, nutrition in old people and the management of depression are just some of the topics of recent meetings. The unique feature of the Section is that it brings together biological, medical and social aspects of ageing and meetings attract experts in many fields to the RSM. For example, a meeting in October 1996 on 'Madness in old age' was attended by an audience of 77 including psychiatrists, general practitioners, researchers, nurses, an ophthalmic surgeon and a dental officer in addition to geriatricians. The Section also examines current services and projects, as in 1996 when changes in the NHS prompted a debate about the development of the 'Hospital at home' concept, and in 1999 there was a debate about the recommendations of the Royal Commission on Long Term Care.

The burgeoning population of elderly people, both fit and ill, indicates that this Section will be fully occupied long into the future. The presidential address given by Professor Anthea Tinker (the first social scientist to be elected President) in March 2000 posed the interesting question of whether differences in old age would persist in the new millennium, and a conference later in the session examined 'Ethnicity, ageing and health'.

## Section of Respiratory Medicine

After a successful meeting of October 1990 held at the Royal College of Surgeons on 'Advances in the understanding and treatment of asthma', a questionnaire was sent to those who had been present to assess interest in the formation of a Section of the RSM to pursue the subject further. Of those who responded, 83 were in favour of a new Section, 57 promised they would join and only 18 were already Fellows of the RSM, so the Section promised to boost the Society's membership figures.[111]

A Steering committee was appointed in April 1991 and the Medical Services Secretary, Dr RD Mann, reported to the Executive Director, Mr Thomson, that 'the Respiratory people are very enthusiastic about the need to bring together the medicine, the surgery and the underlying science of their subject. They feel that the Society can play a unique role in the development of these subjects by overcoming the schism that presently tends to develop between the medical, surgical and scientific aspects. The Section is very keenly interested in the opportunities to link with American and European Groups and to hold

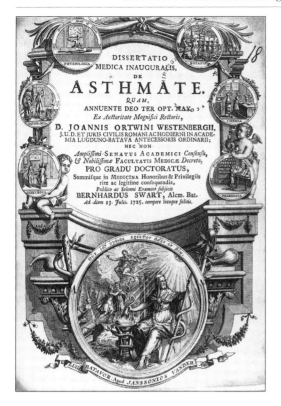

An early dissertation on asthma: *Dissertatio medica inauguralis de asthmate* by Joannis Westenbergii (1725), from a volume in the Library.

Anglo-American and Anglo-European meetings'. Initially it was planned to name the Section Respiratory Medicine and Surgery, although the Honorary Officers favoured the title of Respiratory Section. Its formation coincided with plans for a Cardiovascular Section – as the Medical Services Secretary pointed out, the Society had no Sections representing the heart and circulatory system, the lungs and the gut. 'These three huge branches of medicine have not been represented in our corporate life, although we have many Sections devoted to quite small specialties. I suggest that having a proper heart and circulation Section (the Cardiovascular Section) and a proper lung Section (the Respiratory Section) would fill two of these three great gaps'.[112]

The Council of the RSM approved the founding of the Section of Respiratory Medicine, announcing in the same breath that the Section of Geriatrics and Gerontology would be inaugurated in March 1991, the Cardiothoracic Section would begin work early in 1992, and that a Forum on Medical Audit and Accountabilty was being planned (this materialized under the title of Quality in Health Care).

The inaugural meeting of the Section of Respiratory Medicine with its first President, Dr John Costello in the chair, took place on 14 October 1991 when papers were presented on 'Opportunistic infections in the lung'. The Section next met for a symposium on 'Beta-agonists in the treatment of asthma: state of the art'. The capacity audience included several distinguished guests – Professor Sir James Black (Nobel Laureate), Professor W Asscher (Chairman of the Committee on Safety of Medicines) and Professor Peter Burney, a respiratory epidemiologist. The debate was not just about efficacy but also about safety and the papers resulted in an important publication (1992).[113]

For the 1993–94 session there were four meetings but by the following year several posts on the Council were vacant, including that of President. Even so, the Section gained recognition as a full Section in 1996 and revived under the presidency of Professor Clive Page with a meeting on 'Mechanical ventilation and intensive care' and a day-long meeting with the Section of Paediatrics on 'The wheeze in early life', with speakers from Australia and America. Two eponymous lectures have been founded, one honouring Dr Philip Ellman whose legacy of 1960 established a lecture on chest and rheumatic diseases, and another in memory of Professor Priscilla Piper who had been President for 1993–94.

The presidency of Dr Brian O'Connor began with the provocative question of how to stop people smoking; Dr O'Connor served for 1997–99 and also saw the Section into the 21st century with meetings on 'Allergic disease – an epidemic in the new millennium?', 'Imaging in respiratory disease', 'Current controversies in respiratory medicine' and of course 'Asthma'.

## Cardiothoracic Section
originally Cardiothoracic Surgery

'The formation of the Cardiothoracic Section was long overdue and it has got off to a good start', its first President, Sir Terence English, wrote to colleagues. The Section was instigated by Mr James Roxburgh and Mr Graham Venn, both of them cardiothoracic surgeons of St Thomas' Hospital and Fellows of the RSM.

Its inception was driven by two considerations. Primarily, there was no significant forum for topic-orientated teaching and debate within the specialty. Secondly, several cardiothoracic trainees had used the RSM Library during their research year and had been surprised to find that despite the prevalence of cardiovascular disease within the community there was no cardiac-orientated Section.[114]

Tudor Edwards, one of the founding members of the Society of Thoracic Surgeons of Great Britain and Ireland in 1933, had proposed in 1944 that physicians, radiologists, pathologists and anaesthetists interested in thoracic problems might be included in that Society. The idea was not accepted, nor was his suggestion that the RSM might form a section devoted to chest diseases, so Tudor Edwards founded the Thoracic Society in 1945,

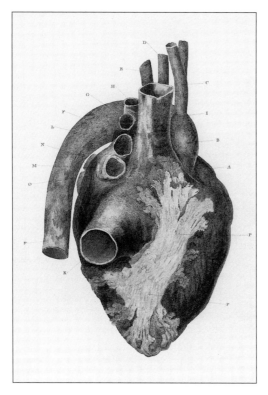

One of the exceptional plates by William Clift in Dr Matthew Baillie's *Morbid anatomy of some of the most important parts of the human body* illustrated a large ossification on the surface of the heart (1812).

which in 1984 amalgamated with the Society of Thoracic Surgeons to form the Society of Cardiothoracic Surgeons.

In 1990 James Roxburgh and Graham Venn mounted another campaign aimed at instituting a section of the RSM. Before approaching the Society's Council they posted a questionnaire to 144 consultants in their specialty to ask whether they would support the formation of a section of cardiothoracic surgery. Affirmative replies were received from 116 people of whom only 18 were Fellows, so an appreciable influx of new Fellows could be expected if the Section was launched. The Council of the RSM was quick to appreciate this and gave approval for the formation of the Section in 1991.

The most appropriate title for the section was more problematic. 'Cardiovascular and thoracic surgery', 'cardiac and vascular surgery', the 'cardiovascular section' or 'section of cardiothoracic surgery' were options, and the original title of Section of Cardiothoracic Surgery was soon altered to Cardiothoracic Section.[115] Its objects were to cultivate and promote cardiac, vascular and thoracic surgery and medicine and the sciences connected with them. It was hoped that cardiac and thoracic surgeons, respiratory physicians, anaesthetists and cardiologists would support the Section and they were encouraged to give case presentations.[116]

The inaugural meeting was held on 19 May 1992, at which time the President, Sir Terence English, who had performed Britain's first successful heart transplant in 1979, was President of the Royal College of Surgeons. The following October a particularly successful meeting was arranged on the topical subject of 'Video-assisted thoracic surgery'. The introduction of new technology allowing the surgeon to accomplish complicated procedures without opening either the thorax or abdomen introduced a new era of surgery and members were privileged to hear reports from three surgeons active in the field since its inception: Mr McAnena, Mr SW Fountain and Dr J Weerts from Belgium. Their presentations were followed by a brisk discussion and 'the prevailing mood seemed to be that these techniques had such a tidal wave of support that they were unstoppable'. The afternoon of the same day was devoted to papers on 'Intraoperative myocardial protection', opened by Professor David Hearse of St Thomas'.[117]

After the trial period the Section was confirmed as fully established in January 1997, since when meetings have been both technical ('Molecular biology in alliance with cardiothoracic surgery') and general ('Cardiothoracic surgery: future and past', in conjunction with the History of Medicine Section).

The aim has been to establish a meeting-place where subjects of topical interest are presented and discussed in a friendly environment at a level appropriate to trainees and established consultants alike. The meetings commence at mid-morning so as to allow those living out of London to attend, and they are divided into morning and afternoon sessions (one of which usually centres on thoracic matters and the other on cardiac topics), broken by a buffet lunch and concluded with a reception and dinner. The Section has received substantial, invaluable support from industry, without which it would not have been able to attract the high calibre of international speakers for meetings.

Cardiothoracic trauma, carotid disease, the changing professional and legal environments and cardiothoracic surgery at the extremity of age have been under discussion and in September 2000 the Section joined forces with the Department of Psychiatry and Behavioural Science of UCL and the Section of Anaesthesia in organizing the Fifth International Brain and Cardiac Surgery Conference at the RSM. This brought together in one conference lasting three days 119 anaesthetists, psychiatrists, neurologists, cardiologists, physicians and surgeons who were invited to present new research.

## Section of Transplantation (Plate 70)
originally Organ Transplantation

The brothers Cosmas and Damian, represented in the coat of arms of the RSM, were sanctified in recognition of their miraculous first transplant. Legend has it that at some time in the third century AD they amputated a man's gangrenous leg and grafted in its place the leg of a dead Moor.

In modern history, transplantation is associated with Alexis Carrel, who was awarded the Nobel Prize in 1912 for his work on the suturing and transplantation of organs. Carrel used his Nobel lecture to urge a more fundamental study of the biological relationships existing between living tissues so as 'to render possible the benefits to humanity which we hope to see accomplished in the future'.[118] Carrel had begun to transplant kidneys, hearts and the spleen, the main problem that he encountered being rejection of the new organs, and it was not until after his death that the work of Peter Medawar heralded the first successful kidney graft (between twins in 1954). This led to successful lung, liver, spleen and heart transplantations in the 1960s and more recently, pancreatic transplants.

The history of skin transplantation advanced with the achievements of Sir Harold Gillies in the First World War, recognized by an Honorary Fellowship of the RSM in 1959.

The name of Christiaan Barnard of Groote Schuur Hospital, Cape Town, must also be mentioned in association with heart and lung transplantation. He had performed the first human-to-human heart transplant in December 1967, and in 1981 he submitted a paper to the RSM (jointly with Cooper), recording 13 years' experience. He claimed that as a result of his leadership several hundred heart transplants had been performed throughout the world by 1981.[119]

At the Society's Council meeting of 20 April 1993 it was agreed to establish three new Sections: Nephrology, Sports Medicine and Organ Transplantation. The third of these had been proposed by Professor Richard Wood and Mr Maurice Slapak in 1992. Dr Niall Quinn then suggested the name be changed because the term 'organ transplantation' appeared to bar people involved in neuronal cell and bone marrow transplantation.

The Section was especially concerned to stimulate and encourage the younger generation, and at its meetings the presentation of clinical cases and research from the under-35 age group was given preference. It was also hoped that the Section would act as a facilitating organization for the establishment of multi-centre control trials and co-operation in multi-organ procurement.[120]

As President of the RSM, Sir George Pinker launched the Section on 9 March 1994, when Professor Wood was elected the first President and gave an address on 'Bowel transplantation'. Meetings were arranged on 'Xenotransplantation' and 'Organ donation' in 1995, but the Section was struggling: there was plainly a conflict of interests with the British Transplantation Society. Dr Richard Moore, elected President in 1998, tried to rejuvenate the Section and after a hiatus meetings recommenced with a joint event with the British Transplantation Society in Cardiff in March 2000, followed by a joint meeting with the Section of Nephrology.

The aim has been to develop a rapid response to topical issues in transplantation on a two- or three-yearly basis and to broaden the membership by attracting those representing solid organ transplantation and members of the scientific community.[121]

## Section of Nephrology (Plate 69)

Dr John Moorhead of the Department of Nephrology at the Royal Free Hospital, later Emeritus Professor, had urged the formation of a Section devoted to his specialty in 1969 on the grounds that the number of nephrologists was growing, particularly in association with dialysis and transplantation centres. Although nephrology and renal transplantation were still small specialties, it seemed to Dr Moorhead that this was the time to take the initiative in what was then a most exciting and rapidly growing field of medicine. It was, after all, the first time in history that an artificial organ had worked reliably in end-stage renal failure, and cadaver transplants were beginning to achieve some success. Moreover nephrology had recently been recognized as a specialty by the Department of Health. The Council of the RSM was besieged by demands for new sections in the 1960s, however, and nephrology was one of those rejected. In retrospect, the Society's decision to ignore the first 25 years of nephrology seems inexplicable, if not a catastrophe.[122]

The second attempt to found a Section of Nephrology originated with Dr Barry Hoffbrand, whose aim it was to bring together Fellows interested in all aspects of renal physiology, pathology, medicine and surgery and the treatment of renal disease. It was also expected that some non-clinical scientists involved in immunological aspects of renal disease and transplantation would wish to join the Section.[123]

The founding of the Section of Nephrology, as with the Sections of Respiratory Medicine, Geriatrics and Gerontology and the Cardiothoracic Section, reflected the decline in the scope of general medicine as a result of increasing specialization, a phenomenon that was plain to see in the Section of Medicine, Experimental Medicine and Therapeutics. Another consideration was, in the case of nephrology, the pre-existence of the Renal Association. When Dr Hoffbrand was assessing interest in founding the Section, senior nephrologists gave little support, possibly due to the feeling that the Section would weaken the Renal Association by dividing loyalties. Lack of interest was also attributed to poor perceptions of the RSM among those who knew little of it.

Hoffbrand and his supporters were nevertheless convinced that a Section would strengthen nephrology as a specialty and that it would be complementary to the Renal Association, whose programmes had become ever more research-based. This has proved to be the case and the success of the Section is that it fulfils the needs of practising nephrologists, established and in training, and those whose own specialty impacts on nephrology.[124]

Professor Andrew Rees, formerly of the Royal Postgraduate Medical School, Hammersmith Hospital, was invited to be founding President and Dr Hoffbrand was an Honorary Secretary. The inaugural meeting was held on 15 March 1994, within a fortnight of the death of Mr Robert Thomson, who had been the Society's Executive Director from 1982 to 1992 and who had encouraged the formation of this and other new Sections. The formal business of inauguration and the appointment of officers were followed by papers on 'The management of nephrotic syndrome' and a buffet supper.

Dr Hoffbrand's optimism about the Section has been justified by its increasing success under the presidencies of Dr Paul Sweny of the Royal Free Hospital and Professor Charles Pusey of Imperial College School of Medicine, Hammersmith Hospital. There have been positive attempts to involve Fellows from outside London and from the non-teaching hospitals. The format of most meetings has been a clinical symposium on a selected topic, with a distinguished and international faculty. The first regional meeting was held in Manchester in November 1999 and it is proposed to continue to hold three meetings a year, one of which will be outside London. There is a deliberate policy to choose topics that will be of multidisciplinary interest and also to hold joint meetings with other Sections. The success of this approach is reflected in consistently good attendances at meetings, by both consultants and trainees. Recent meetings have attracted over 50 participants and in some cases up to 150. Thus in the space of six years the Section was well established and clearly fulfilled a role distinct from that of the Renal Association.[125]

## Section of Sports Medicine (Plate 68)

Mr Basil Helal, consultant orthopaedic surgeon to the London Hospital, suggested a Section of Sports Medicine in 1982, but received a negative response from the Medical Services Secretary of the RSM, who pointed to the British Association of Sport and Medicine and suggested that perhaps a forum would be more appropriate.[126]

The power of exercise in the treatment of disease has long been recognized and was extolled by Francis Fuller in his *Medicina gymnastica*, which went into several editions in the early 18th century. The first English work to concentrate specifically on sports medicine was written by Dr Charles B Heald in 1931, *Injuries and sport. A general guide for the practitioner*, which gave advice on the diagnosis and treatment of sports injuries.

The discipline received recognition when the Society of Apothecaries introduced a Diploma in Sports Medicine in 1988, and in 1992 the second proposal for a Section of the RSM was received more sympathetically than the first. This time the initiative lay with the orthopaedic surgeon Mr Michael Laurence, who was requested to assess the numerical support to be expected and the type of programme he envisaged – some members of the Council still doubted that sports medicine justified its own Section. Laurence listed 17 different specialties he believed would have a particular interest in some aspect of sports medicine, which he was sure would soon be a major career throughout the world. It was already a clearly identifiable medical specialty with its own profile of clinical conditions, pathological mechanisms, methods of investigation and treatment. Its problems range from drugs to deliberate injury, as the recent winter Olympics had demonstrated. Its specialists, both clinical and non-clinical, are drawn from a variety of other specialties and health care professions.[127]

The Society's Council endorsed the recommendation of the Education committee and the Honorary Officers that a Section of Sports Medicine was justified in April 1993, with a view to an inaugural meeting during the 1993–94 session. The object of the Section was to bring together the various medical and scientific disciplines interested and involved in the subject of sports medicine and to improve the state of knowledge in this specialty by encouraging the exchange of ideas, and on this basis the new Section attracted 43 founder-members.[128]

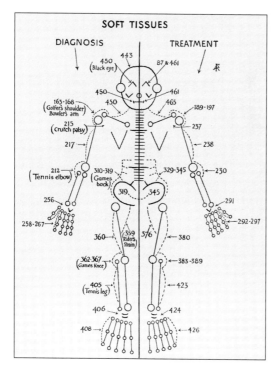

An illustration from Dr Charles B Heald's book *Injuries and sport. A general guide for the practitioner* (1931). This was the first book in English on the diagnosis and treatment of sports injuries (the numbers refer to the pages in the text).

Sir Roger Bannister, the London neurologist (and the first four-minute-miler), was persuaded by Mr Laurence and the cardiologist Dr Dan Tunstall-Pedoe to take the post as first President of the Section. Laurence and Dr Mark Harries were the first Honorary Secretaries and Laurence was to succeed as President for 1999–2000. At the inaugural meeting on 7 April 1994, opened by Sir George Pinker as the Society's President, Sir Roger spoke on 'The birth of the Section and the niche it would fill'. Mr David Cowan gave a paper on 'Drug use, abuse and enhancing agents', followed by Professor MA Ferguson-Smith on 'Gender verification', Professor Archie Young on 'Ageing and sport' and Mr GR McLatchie on 'Head injuries'.

Further meetings were held on 'The management of life-threatening conditions in sport', 'Sport and the law', 'Health benefits and dangers of exercise' and 'Sports and neurological disorders'. In October 1995 Dr Robert Jackson, one of the pioneers of sports medicine in America, spoke at a meeting on 'Structural failure and overuse injury' in the legs of athletes, while in 1996, as past President, Bannister chaired a joint meeting with the Section of Accident and Emergency Medicine on 'Sports and soft tissue injuries' when Dr D Tunstall-Pedoe gave a fascinating talk on 'Sixteen years of the London Marathon'. Other speakers highlighted the medical problems associated with the sports injuries presented at Accident and Emergency Departments and there were presentations on head, groin and shin injuries, drugs in sport, medico-legal aspects and strategies for the prevention of sports injuries.

In 1997 an educational/recreational day was given a place in the Section's calendar. This was the first joint clinical education and golf event held at Wentworth: lectures in the morning, golf in the afternoon and a dinner and prizes in the evening. Away meetings are a strong feature of the Section's activities and have been held, for instance, at Arsenal Football Club and the Guttman Sports Stadium, Stoke Mandeville (in conjunction with the British Wheelchair Sports Foundation); at Lords Cricket Ground members toured the injury treatment areas.

Another regular feature of the programme has been a meeting on current areas of research, presented by staff and students of university departments of sports medicine from the Royal London School of Medicine, the Queen's Medical Centre University Hospital, Nottingham, and Loughborough College.

## FORA

The creation of multidisciplinary Fora was a major development for the RSM and demonstrated the Society's willingness and ability to adapt to the demands of the late 20th century. The idea took shape in 1981 and over the next 20 years a total of 18 Fora were established. As topic-related, multidisciplinary study groups they have promoted open discussion at many levels on subjects ranging from computers in medicine to food and health.

The concept of the Fora originated in the recommendations of the Working Party chaired by Sir Gordon Wolstenholme in 1973. This brought the future role of the RSM under the microscope and recommended the need for a modern building, the continuing pursuit of an academic role and the development of a medico-lay forum as the way ahead. The medico-lay forum came into being as the Open Section in 1974, adding a new dimension to the Society by bringing people from many disciplines together to discuss questions of mutual concern, and after a faltering start this Section proved lively and successful. Efforts were also made at this time to encourage joint meetings of Sections on interdisciplinary themes, yet there were difficulties on obtaining full co-operation and when such meetings did take place there was no continuity of work once the meeting concluded.

With the signing of the agreement to redevelop the Post Office site adjacent to the Society's house in 1981, thoughts turned to the new building and the manifold opportunities it would offer. The future role of the Society came up for discussion once again and as part of this process the President, Sir John Stallworthy, invited Section Presidents to discuss current problems facing the Society and to suggest new approaches. These informal meetings gave an impetus to those looking for ways to increase the academic vitality of the RSM. A memorandum of March 1981 'To consider what new role the RSM can play and how might this be realized' proposed 'that the Society should establish a certain number of forums (working party/study groups) with a multidisciplinary structure'. The memorandum was the work of Dr Luke Zander, President of the Section of General Practice, in conjunction with the Medical Services Secretary, Dr Graham Bennette, and it had the backing of Dame Anne Bryans, Mr GVP Chamberlain, Mr JA Dormandy, Dr P Mellett, Dr NC Mond, Dr D Morris and Professor M Sandler. It was welcomed by Sir John Stallworthy, and given unanimous approval by the Society's Council in July 1981, and it formed the blue-print for the Fora.[129]

It was expected that the interdisciplinary Fora would seize upon subjects of wide interest and pursue them indefinitely. Their membership was to include people who would not usually participate in Section meetings such as nurses, psychologists, social workers, administrators and other non-medical professionals whose work was of key importance in many aspects of medical practice. It was understood that the activities of the Fora would vary from one to another: seminars, debates, workshops, study groups to comment on some official report affecting medical practice, teaching sessions and symposia were within their scope and there was no requirement for members to be Fellows of the Society, although it was hoped that many would take this step. Initially, members of a Forum were usually recruited by the Steering committee and the membership of each Forum was not expected to exceed 100; this was later extended and by 2000 some Fora boasted over 500 members.[130]

The setting up of a Forum depended on the enthusiasm of the founder(s), the appointment of an effective Steering committee and the approval of the Forum sub-committee. The enthusiasm of the founders was sometimes generated by an exceptionally successful conference or meeting on a subject that required further investigation. For example, the Forum on Pregnancy Care aimed to continue work begun at the conference on 'Pregnancy care for the 1980s', which had been held in the spring of 1981 by the Sections of General Practice and Obstetrics and Gynaecology. Similarly, the Forum on Clinical Haemorheology was prompted by the success of the second European Conference on Clinical Haemorheology organized by Mr John Dormandy, nominally initiated by the Section of Measurement in Medicine (of which he was President 1979–81) and the Section of Pathology, and held at Kensington Town Hall in 1981. A third Forum came into being as a result of meetings of the planning committee for the European Symposium on Scientific Studies in Mental Retardation. Those meetings, involving senior workers in genetics, neurosciences, psychology, psychiatry, biochemistry and educational and sociological research had the character of an interdisciplinary study group and it became obvious to the participants that mental retardation was ideally suited for study by a Forum. Thus three subjects for study by Fora were immediately apparent: pregnancy care, clinical haemorheology and mental retardation.

*The first Fora commence meetings*
Pregnancy care, the first subject suggested for study by a Forum, materialized as the **Forum on Maternity and the Newborn** in the 1983–84 session. Meanwhile the first Forum to be operational was the **Forum on Clinical Haemorheology,** which like the conference that preceded it, was master-minded by Mr JA Dormandy. The Forum's primary function was to undertake work that was not being done by any existing organization and to bring together those working in cardiology, neurology, diabetology, vascular surgery, haematology, ophthalmology and biophysics. It was expected that the Forum would continue

Forum on Clinical Haemorheology,
1982.

studies along the lines suggested by the recent European Conference and it was not beyond the realms of possibility that the Forum would develop into a national society. With Dormandy as Chairman, the Forum was inaugurated in May 1982 with a meeting on 'Red cell deformability', at which members presented brief accounts of their various projects and work in progress; the occasion was made all the more enjoyable by an excellent meal at Chandos House. Members were primarily concerned with the study of the factors inherent in blood that affect its ability to flow, and the papers and discussions of the first two meetings were judged to be very successful. By the end of the first session 75 people had joined the Forum and meetings had been held at the Royal Infirmary, Glasgow, and the Institute of Neurology, Queen Square. The Forum issued a news-sheet and the Steering committee (which included three members of the European Clinical Haemorheology Co-ordinating committee) organized joint meetings with La Société Française d'Hemorheologie Clinique. A conference at Leeds was held in 1993, a two-day Anglo-Scandinavian meeting in 1994 and a spring meeting at Birmingham in 1995, which was to be the last time the Forum met. By this time it was clear that the main fields of interest were being adequately represented by the Venous Forum (formed in 1983) and the Forum on Angiology (formed in 1987, see page 445). A merger with one or both of these Fora was a possibility suggested by the Society's Honorary Dean, and although no formal amalgamation took place, the Forum on Clinical Haemorheology ceased to hold independent meetings because its members found their interests well covered by others.[131]

The 1983–84 session saw the inauguration of the **Forum on Maternity and the Newborn** and the **Venous Forum.** The former held its inaugural meeting in September 1983, opened by its founder, Dr Luke Zander, who explained to an audience of about 100 what he saw to be the purpose of this Forum and how this was to be realized. The intention was to draw together people from a wide range of differing disciplines and perspectives to share ideas on issues of common interest and concern. To achieve this, the multidisciplinary nature of the Forum would be reflected in the composition of its Steering committee, which has always included individuals from general practice, midwifery, obstetrics, the behavioural sciences and representatives of the receivers of care, as well as frequently including disciplines such as neonatal paediatrics, physiotherapy, health visitors and community medicine. The meetings were to be unusual in that they were characterized by having contributions from the different disciplines and at least half the time was devoted to open discussion in order to maximize the opportunity for interdisciplinary exchange. Wherever possible meetings were followed by a buffet supper so that discussion could continue in a more informal setting. Dr Ian Chalmers reported in the RSM *Journal* that 'the quality and intensity of the discussion which took place at the first meeting of this Forum augurs well for its future'.[132]

Topics and speakers for the meetings are chosen by the Steering committee as a whole to ensure they are truly interdisciplinary. The proceedings, initially reported intermittently in the Society's *Journal* and for a while in the *Journal of Maternal and Child Health*, were, by 2000, appearing regularly in the *Midwives' Journal*.

The Forum has been keen to explore and challenge areas of controversy, particularly when this has related to differences in views held by the providers and receivers of care, and has endeavoured to do this in a spirit that does not antagonize any one professional group. One of the most memorable meetings, undertaken in March 1986 against the advice of the Society's Honorary Officers, was entitled 'The Savage suspension – its significance and implications'. This explored the implications of the suspension by the Tower Hamlets District Health Authority of Mrs Wendy Savage from her post as consultant obstetrician at the Royal London Hospital, and was held at a time when this was causing widespread debate. The following October the Open Section also addressed the question of what could be learned from the Savage case for the future handling of professional disputes (see page 420).[133] Mrs Savage (now Professor) was reinstated in her post and was chosen to succeed Zander as Chairman of the Forum.

To mark the new millennium the Forum held its third decadal two-day conference, 'Pregnancy care in 2000 – a model for leadership for health care in the twenty-first century' (a sequel to 'Pregnancy care in the 1980s' and 'Pregnancy care in the 1990s', the proceedings of which had been published in book form). The millennium meeting was highly unusual in that it was built round the contribution of someone quite outside medicine, Benjamin Zander, an orchestral conductor and teacher known internationally as a charismatic speaker on creativity, accomplishment and leadership. Baroness Julia Cumberlege wrote appreciatively, 'Thank you for a most remarkable two days. I learnt such a lot; leadership, music, humour, language and love of human kind. It was wonderfully uplifting at a time when maternity services are at a low'.[134]

Professor Dormandy (as he became), founder of the **Forum on Clinical Haemorheology**, also initiated the **Venous Forum,** the first phlebological group in this country. In almost every other European country there was a national society of phlebology and the Venous Forum intended to fill the gap in the United Kingdom. The Forum was promptly invited to represent Britain at the Union Internationale de Phlébologie, and its Steering committee jointly organized the first major international meeting on phlebology in September 1985; with 777 participants this was the biggest event ever held under the auspices of the RSM and was a resounding success, with a practical outcome in the publication of a new journal under the aegis of the Venous Forum. The week concluded with a banquet at Guildhall attended by Princess Alexandra.

From its inauguration in June 1983 the Forum incorporated into its programme Anglo-French meetings such as the gathering of physiologists, dermatologists, plastic surgeons, general surgeons and others interested in venous disorders that took place at Chichester in

Venous Forum, 1983.

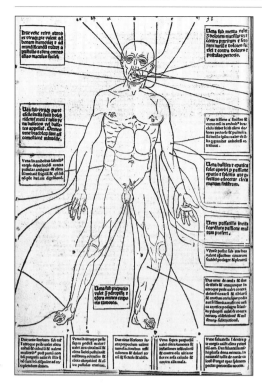

A table on 'Flebotomy' showing 'the vein man' from Johannes de Ketham's *Fasciculus medicinae* (1513). This book is a collection of short medical treatises illustrated with traditional woodcut diagrams.

April 1984. In spite of the temptation to wander around the town in the spring sunshine, the scientific sessions were well attended, and this was remembered as an exceptionally happy and successful event that further cemented links between French and British phlebologists.[135] Dr Georges Jantet, a future Chairman of the Forum, was given a vote of thanks for his rapid and clear translations from French; together with Dormandy, he was instrumental in forging Anglo-French connections that were so important to this Forum.

The Venous Forum held a Scottish meeting at the Royal College of Surgeons of Edinburgh in 1984, and has also arranged meetings with the Italian Group for Clinical and Experimental Phlebology and with the American Venous Forum.

Unfortunately the Forum ran into debt as the result of a conference held at the Barbican in 1995, raising the question of financial liability for such an event. Although this took three years to settle, the Forum survived into the first year of the new millennium with meetings organized in Chester and Gloucester as well as London.

In May 1984 the **Forum on Lipids in Clinical Medicine** was launched under the Chairmanship of Dr Norman Miller, with a membership of 125 from many disciplines. This Forum aimed to bring together physicians, biochemists, epidemiologists, nutritionists and others with an active interest in lipids who need to keep abreast of developments in other specialities. At the first meeting Dr Ingvar Hjermann of Oslo and Dr Robert Duffield (London) presented evidence from their own epidemiological studies for a beneficial effect of reduction of plasma lipid concentrations in hypercholesterolaemic men.

In 1986 BUPA sponsored a meeting on 'Lipids, alcohol and the liver', and other meetings focused on 'Coronary heart disease prevention' and 'The new genetics'. In 1996 the Forum with the Nutrition Society and the Biochemical Society Lipid Group hosted a two-day session when an international panel addressed the results of research showing connections between an impaired ability to clear fat from the bloodstream after a meal and susceptibility to coronary heart disease. More recently an international symposium was organized with the Association for the Study of Obesity, the Nutrition Society and the British Hyperlipidaemia Association on 'Reducing cardiovascular disease risks'.

With four Fora up and running and the possibility of others on medical communication, mental retardation and clinical cytology being investigated, the Society's Council reviewed the situation with some satisfaction. Attendance figures were pleasing and seemed to indicate the continuing commitment of members to go to meetings after the initial display of curiosity. Occasionally the numbers present, including guests, were greater than the registered number of members of the Forum and this was thought to be unique in the history of the Society's regular meetings.[136]

It had taken several drafts before the Constitution of the Fora was agreed in April 1983; finances, membership and administration needed to be carefully thought out and were subject to revision. Responsibility for approval, finance and academic activities was placed with the Forum sub-committee, which vets proposals for new Fora to ensure that the work projected is not being adequately pursued by other groups and that there is a definite need for the subject to be studied in an interdisciplinary way.

Two subjects that new Fora were encouraged to pursue were **Mental Retardation** and **Medical Communication**. The **Forum on Mental Retardation** came about as the result of the enthusiastic response to the first European Symposium on Scientific Studies in Mental Retardation held at Oxford in 1983. This had been organized by Dr David Morris, who was the chief instigator and first Chairman of the Forum; its inaugural meeting was held in February 1984 to discuss whether Down's syndrome was a progressive condition. The next year the Forum was included in a symposium with the British Institute of Mental Handicap at the Institute of Psychiatry, a three-day event that was over-subscribed and generated £1,000. The subject was 'Behavioural disorders and retardation', and Professor John Searle of the University of California gave the main lecture. The next meeting was held at the Institute of Neurology on the subject of 'Brain development, genetic control and brain plasticity'. It was an illuminating meeting because all the speakers addressed this highly specialized subject in a way that was fully understood by members from widely differing fields of work – a prime example of the function of a Forum.

Members of the Forum also took part in two major meetings in 1986 with the Commonwealth Association for Mental Handicap and Developmental Disabilities and with the Royal Society for Mentally Handicapped Children. After the death of its founder Dr Morris, the Forum held a meeting in his memory in September 1990 on 'Services for children with severe learning disability'. The following year Professor James Hogg suggested a change of name for the Forum. Its title had been chosen five years previously because of its link to an international classification that was no longer current in this country. The Forum assumed the new title of **Learning Disability** in 1993 and continues to discuss problems at many levels.

The **Forum on Medical Communication** was launched in November 1984, invitations having been sent to 280 people by Dr Robert Murray's Steering committee. Professor Richard Eiser of the Department of Psychology, Exeter University, was the prime mover behind the Forum, posing the question 'What is medical communication?' at the first meeting. He made it clear that the scope of the Forum would be broad and that it would examine why people sought information about health, illness and medical practice, from whom they sought it, what kind of information was given to them and how it was interpreted. The Forum was concerned to improve communication between doctors, their patients and the public generally.[137]

Since the Forum was formed the media have done much to facilitate communication between the medical profession, the public and patients who clamour for accurate, acceptable information. Communication skills are therefore more necessary than ever, in medical schools and beyond. The Forum changed its name to **Communication in Health Care** in 2000, and with 642 members for the session of 2000–2001 it set a record as the largest Forum.

The President of the Society from 1982 to 1984, Sir James Watt, pointed out that there was a strong case for a Forum on aspects of nutrition and medicine and his suggestions materialized as the **Forum on Food and Health** in December 1984. Its first Chairman was Sir Francis Avery Jones, a past President of the Section of Proctology, and its membership expanded faster than that of any other Forum, reaching 227 by the end of the 1984–85 session.

Public interest in food allergy and intolerance was and is intense and the Forum held an excellent symposium on 'Food intolerance' in June 1985, well attended by most disciplines but disappointing in respect of the few gastroenterologists present. The one-day meeting gave the message that the greatest need was for more thorough, systematic research. The British Nutrition Foundation, among others, had reservations about the activities of the Forum, in particular a meeting on 'Sugars' in 1986, so the meeting was extended to two days to ensure that all aspects of sugars in health and disease were presented in an unbiased manner.

The health aspects of unusual and exotic diets such as Asian, Eskimo and Masai have come under scrutiny by the Forum and in October 1995 a meeting on 'Food, people and health' attracted an international audience who heard the case for a return to the diet of our prehistoric ancestors. This Forum has obtained generous sponsorship, for instance from Rank Hovis MacDougall for a meeting on 'Bread and health', while the Brooke Bond Tea Company subsidized a symposium on flavonoids (surveys have showed that tea, onions and apples are important sources of flavonoids).

The finances of the Fora came under review in 1985, when a 60% increase in subscriptions for non-Fellow members was proposed. This caused an outcry: the Fora on Clinical Haemorheology and Lipids stated that they would recommend disbandment if such an increase was implemented. When it was pointed out that the number of Forum members stood at 1,100 of whom two-thirds were not Fellows, the Council was persuaded to raise their subscriptions by a more modest 20% (to £30 per annum). At the same time the finances of the Fora were placed of a firmer footing by the introduction of a registration fee for meetings, and all Fora were encouraged to seek sponsorship (the Society provides a launching fund for each new Forum after which it has to be self-financing).

With the Society settled in larger premises, two new Fora commenced work during the 1986–87 session. The **Forum for Sexual Medicine and Family Planning**, the eighth Forum, was inaugurated at a one-day meeting in November 1986. It had competed for its existence with a proposed forum on sexually transmitted diseases and the Forum sub-committee found it hard to decide which of the two proposals to sanction. The RSM was already providing a base for the Medical Society for the Study of Venereal Diseases and it was apparent that there were several means of pursuing the subject of sexually transmitted diseases – through the MSSVD, at Society conferences or symposia, not to mention an impending Anglo-American Conference – without the need for a Forum. It was therefore decided to encourage the alternative proposal for a Forum on Sexual Medicine and Family Planning.[138] This Forum flourished under the Chairmanship of Mr FA Patterson (who also chaired the Forum on Medical Communication) and in September 1987 it hosted the Helena Wright Memorial lecture given by Dame Josephine Barnes on 'Family planning then and now'. Another eminent speaker, Rabbi Julia Neuberger, addressed the Forum in 1990 speaking on 'Religious and cultural aspects of family planning' at a time when changes in the abortion law and the issue of embryo research were making news. The Forum altered its title to **Sexual Health and Reproductive Medicine** in 2000.

The **Forum on Angiology** originated in a suggestion from Dr John Tooke in 1986 that the Forum sub-committee might consider an affiliation with the recently formed British Angiology Group. The Steering committee of the latter, already convened and including Dr Tooke, Mr Dormandy and Dr Jill Belch, was unanimous in its desire to become the

Forum on Angiology, 1987.

Angiology Forum: 'the reputation of the RSM structure for cross-discipline fertilization making it our natural aspiration'. The aim was to bring together people from a range of medical, scientific and paramedical disciplines with the objective of furthering understanding of diseases of the peripheral circulation. The proposers promised the careful selection of subjects so as not to overlap with the Venous Forum or the Forum on Clinical Haemorheology, maintaining that the proposed Forum was as 'a necessary clinically orientated umbrella' as opposed to another splinter group. The Medical Services Secretary replied positively, explaining the procedure that required the proposer of a forum to present his ideas to the Forum sub-committee and that 'a troublesome feature of Forums is that their Chairmen must be Fellows of the RSM'. Once the formalities were complete the Forum on Angiology was approved, although progress was complicated by the Council's determination to raise the subscription for non-Fellow Forum members; hence the inaugural meeting did not take place until February 1987. Eligible members were canvassed by the Forum's energetic Secretary (who as Professor Belch was later its Chairman), with the result that the Forum started out with a membership of 96 and a two-day meeting on central topics. The Forum forged links with the Swedish Society of Medical Angiology and the Swedish Vascular Club, leading to a meeting in Stockholm in 1988. The success of this conference prompted further British-Swedish meetings in the 1990s; joint or tripartite meetings with international radiologists, vascular surgeons, and with other Sections and Fora have proved the most successful.[139]

The founder Chairman of the **Forum on Clinical Pharmacology and Therapeutics**, Professor Paul Turner of the Department of Clinical Pharmacology, St Bartholomew's Hospital Medical College, was to be the Society's first Academic Dean. His argument for establishing the Forum was that existing groups concerned with pharmacology were very specialized and parochial and did not provide the means for gathering the various specialist groups into one body. The Medical Services Secretary realized that there was a danger of duplication between the proposed Forum and the Library (Scientific Research) Section, which was increasingly concerned with pharmaceutical medicine and was considering a change of name to reflect this. Nevertheless, there was strong outside support for the proposed Forum, which aimed to further understanding in the role of drugs in the treatment of disease.

Professor Turner assembled the Steering committee and organized the first meeting on 'Towards safer drugs' in March 1988.[140] The Forum expected to incorporate members of the defunct Section of Medicine, Experimental Medicine and Therapeutics and did not

Forum on Clinical Pharmacology and Therapeutics, 1988.

expect to conflict with the interests of the Library (Scientific Research) Section. But when the latter developed into the Section of Pharmaceutical Medicine and Research in 1994, the objectives of the Section and the Forum were acknowledged to be broadly similar, so the Forum was absorbed by the Section in 1998. This was the first merger between a Forum and a Section.

A preliminary survey to assess interest in a **Forum on Computers in Medicine** drew favourable responses from 90 enthusiasts in 1989. Therefore the Forum was constituted in order to provide a means by which clinicians from different medical specialties could meet to discuss the problems and solutions in medical applications of computers. While there was a demand for such a Forum in 1990, the use of computers in medicine soon became commonplace and the need for a special Forum on the subject passed; having been inactive for several years, the Forum was therefore disbanded in 1996. It was always the policy that a Forum should disband when its work was complete, although this has rarely been the case.

Forum on Computers in Medicine, 1989.

Several proposals for new Fora surfaced in the 1990s: complementary medicine, ethics in health care, breast health, primary care and Caribbean medicine all came up for consideration by the Forum sub-committee. Five new Fora received prompt approval: **Quality in Health Care, Palliative Care, Catastrophes and Conflicts, Telemedicine** and **Sleep and its Disorders**. The titles alone denote some of the preoccupations of the late 20th century. Reviewing the position of the Fora over the decade 1981–91, the Society's Honorary Officers were pleased, reporting that the Fora were active, in credit and that many of them were successful in finding sponsorship. Their popularity posed the question of whether or not they might become Sections.[141]

Meanwhile, the formation of new Fora was encouraged: the **Forum on Quality in Health Care** began life as **Medical Audit and Accountability** under the Chairmanship of Dr Charles Shaw of the King's Fund. It arose out of the Society's Anglo-American Symposium on Medical Standards, Peer Review, Audit and Accountability held at the Royal College of Physicians in 1990 under the title of 'Quality in health care'. From 1992 onwards, the Forum broadened its scope; it was felt that it should cover issues beyond the measurement of medical structure, such as working with other clinical professions, quality management, the discussion of practical issues and organizational standards. Recent meetings have examined quality in maternity care, the quality of emergency services and the question of quality in the new millennium.

Forum on Quality in Health Care, 1992.

The **Palliative Care Forum** grew out of the hospice movement and the establishment of the specialty of palliative medicine in 1987. Debate over ethical dilemmas at the end of life and an increasing awareness of the need to develop a scientific approach to palliative care provision led to the formation of the Forum. Its founder, Baroness Ilora Finlay, explained to the Society's Council that the aim of the Forum would be to promote a scientific approach to and understanding of the palliative management of patients, their families and their carers. There was limited scientific evidence in the field due to the large number of disease groups and the short lifespan of the patients. The Forum would address this matter while ensuring that the large number of professionals involved in palliative care could meet together under the auspices of the RSM.[142]

Palliative care depends on good inter-professional working relationships, and recruitment from professions other than medicine has been actively encouraged. The Forum's meetings commenced in the 1996–97 session, many of them being held jointly with the Association for Palliative Medicine Science Committee or with Sections and other Fora of the RSM (the Forum has resisted being associated with euthanasia pressure groups). The content of meetings has focused on establishing a scientific evaluation of different concepts of palliative care; attendance at meetings has been good and evaluation enthusiastic.

Telemedicine, defined as the application of electronic communications technology to improving medical care, is becoming important in treatment, medical education, diagnosis and clinical management. It has the potential to revolutionize the practice of medicine throughout the world: telepathology, telepsychiatry and teleradiology could all replace out-patient referrals, and all aspects of telemedicine and telecare have a part to play in

The inaugural meeting of the Telemedicine Forum, June 1997.

industrialized and developing countries. Professor Richard Wootton, Director of the Institute of Telemedicine and Telecare at Queen's University, Belfast (the first such institute in the UK), was instrumental in forming the **Telemedicine Forum** in order to promote research into telemedicine, the dissemination of good practice and the establishment of standards, with the aim of providing a focal point for telemedicine in Britain. The Forum also serves as a link between countries and stimulates local applications between members.

The inaugural meeting in June 1997 was a high spot of that year at the RSM: Ms Tessa Jowell, Minister for Public Health, was there to experience a three-way link between London, the Hong Kong Telemedicine Association Conference and Beijing. This spectacular start was followed by information on current practices in telemedicine, covering the whole spectrum from remote physical monitoring of patients to the interpretation of X-rays, psychiatric and accident and emergency consultations. The second meeting was an international conference, Telemed 97, which attracted over 170 people from 22 countries; these numbers were exceeded at Telemed 98. The Forum makes extensive use of video-conferencing and the expertise that has been acquired to support this Forum can be used by other Fora and Sections. The RSM Press published the first volume of the *Journal of Telemedicine and Telecare* in 1995, also the *Introduction to Telemedicine* edited by Richard Wootton and and John Craig (1999). The Forum has established three awards for researchers or clinicians working in telemedicine and telecare, and on the Millennium Members' Day at the RSM the Forum laid on demonstrations with two overseas links.

A proposed forum on disaster medicine/medical catastrophes/medical care of catastrophes emerged as the **Forum on Catastrophes and Conflicts** in July 1999. Professor Jim Ryan and Professor John Lumley opened the campaign for a Forum on the medical care of victims of catastrophes in 1998, targeting doctors, engineers, linguists and people from many other disciplines. The Society of Apothecaries had recently established a Diploma in the Medical Care of Catastrophes and the United Nations launched the International Decade for Natural Disaster Reduction. These separate initiatives gave formal recognition

The inaugural meeting of the Forum on Catastrophes and Conflicts on 'Humanitarian aid in the hostile environment – a team approach', July 1999.

to disaster training and increased worldwide awareness of the need for disaster reduction and management. The RSM's *Handbook of the medical care of catastrophes* by Lumley, Ryan and Baxter (1996) provided the textbook, yet there was as yet no dedicated group for those working in the field. The Forum intended to fill the gap by providing a meeting-place for the discussion, debate and promulgation of ideas and activities in disaster medicine. 'The need for the activity is demonstrated by the 15 to 20 wars taking place worldwide at any one time, and the increasing number of natural disasters. Out of the 23 cities with greater than 10 million population by 2100, 17 will be sited in hazard-prone zones', Professor Lumley pointed out.[143]

The application bore 35 signatures,and the Forum's inaugural meeting on 16 July 1999 on 'Humanitarian aid in the hostile environment' was attended by approximately 100. The title of the Forum was soon altered to give prominence to the humanitarian element: **Catastrophes and Conflicts – Humanitarian Health Care.** The programme is designed to appeal to all aid workers, whether independent or in government departments or organizations, and all those interested in humanitarian aid activities.

The 'Sleep Forum' was long in gestation, from a proposal made by Professor Chris Idzikowski in 1997 to approval by the Academic Board in 1998, culminating in the Forum's first meeting in October 1999. The **Forum on Sleep and its Disorders** was set up to promote the understanding of sleep and its disorders. The objectives are to run symposia and produce publications, and it is intended that this Forum should be a place for discussing rather than dictating where things should be going. The membership includes anaesthetists, basic research scientists, clinical pharmacologists, ENT specialists, general practitioners, health care professionals, neurologists, nurses, occupational medicine physicians, oncologists, respiratory physicians, psychiatrists, psychologists and physiologists. The Forum's first Chairman was its founder, Professor Idzikowski, Director of the Sleep Assessment and Advisory Service.

The Sections of the RSM were and are established in response to the continuous evolution of medicine and medical technology; some Sections have ceased to be relevant so have died, while proposals for new ones surface regularly. The same principle applies to the Fora: from the small group that came into being in the early 1980s a total of 16 Fora have addressed a variety of subjects; 13 continue to meet regularly, two Fora were wound up, one merged with a Section and in 2000 the RSM Council announced plans for two new Fora – on **Black and Ethnic Minority Health** and on **Primary Health Care.** When the first Fora were established in the 1980s their meetings were not considered worthy of record in the Society's *Calendar*; by 2000 the membership of some Fora exceeded that of some Sections and Forum meetings were given emphasis equal to Section meetings in the RSM *Bulletin*. Such shifts and changes have always characterized medicine and in the kaleidoscopic 21st century it is a function of the Royal Society of Medicine to encourage the development of medicine and all its branches.

1 RSM, *Annual Report 1982–83*.
2 BMJ (i) 9 April 1955 pp. 865–70. Hoff, EC and PM, *The life and times of Richard Lower, physiologist and physician 1631–91* (1936).
3 CM 19 June 1928.
4 *Lancet* (i) 20 January 1923 pp. 130–32. BMJ, *The endocrines in theory and practice* (1937). Hall, Diana Long, 'The critic and the advocate: contrasting British views on the state of endocrinology in the early 1920s' in *Journal of the History of Biology* vol 9 (1976) pp. 269–85.
5 Correspondence and papers relating to the founding of the Section 1944–46 compiled by Dr Greene, MS/20/f1.
6 GM Section of Endocrinology 22 May 1946, MS/20/b1.
7 *Lancet* (ii) 12 October 1946 pp. 546–48.
8 PRSM vol 39 (1945–46); this edited account does not include the postscript which is to be found in Sir Geoffrey Keynes' obituary of

Langdon-Brown in the *Lancet* (ii) 12 October 1946 pp. 546–48.

9 *Lancet* (i) 1 June 1946 p. 828.

10 GM Section of Endocrinology 1946–50, MS/20/b1.

11 BMJ (i) 9 April 1955 pp 565–70.

12 *Ibid*.

13 CM Section of Endocrinology 1950–70, MS/20/a1.

14 *Lancet* (i) 7 January 1950 p. 27.

15 BMJ (i) 25 March 1950 p. 709.

16 *Lancet* (ii) 22 July 1950 p. 139.

17 CM 20 June 1950.

18 BMJ (ii) 21 October 1950 p. 935.

19 Obituary, *Journal of Royal College of General Practitioners* vol 28 (1978) pp. 765–66.

20 Gray, DJ Pereira (ed), *Forty years on. The story of the first fifty years of the Royal College of General Practitioners* (1992) p. 24. Horder, John (ed), *The writings of John Hunt* (1992) p. 20.

21 Hunt, Lord, 'The foundation of a College' in *Journal of the Royal College of General Practitioners* vol 23 (1973) pp. 5–20. Fry, John, Hunt, Lord and Pinsent, R (eds), *A history of the Royal College of General Practitioners. The first 25 years* (1983) pp. 1, 8, 12.

22 PRSM vol 44 (1951).

23 BMJ (ii) 29 December 1951 pp. 1575–81.

24 PRSM vol 58 (1965).

25 Loudon, Irvine, Horder, John and Webster, Charles (eds*)*, *General practice under the National Health Service 1948–1997* (1998).

26 GM Section of General Practice 1991, MS/24/B2.

27 RSM, *Annual Report of Council 1955–56*. Regulations, Library (Scientific Research) Section 1956, MS/34/a1, Box 62.

28 Report of Library representative, CM Library (Scientific Research) Section 1958, MS/34/a1, Box K62. PRSM vol 55 (1962), vol 69 (1976).

29 PRSM vol 53 (1960). RSM, *Annual Report of Council 1959–60*. In 1970 Frohlich was appointed a Director of the RSM Foundation, and from 1981 Frohlich visiting professorships were established.

30 CM Library (Scientific Research) Section 1970–72, MS/34/a1.

31 Education Committee Minutes 24 February 1994.

32 Schilling, RSF, 'Developments in occupational health over the last thirty years' in *Journal of the Royal Society of Arts* November 1963 pp. 933–84.

33 CM 19 November 1963.

34 Carter, Tim, 'Diseases of occupations: a short history of their recognition and preven-

tion' in *Hunter's diseases of occupation* (2000) pp. 917–25.

35 Formation of Section of Occupational Medicine 1964, K96, Box 47. RSM, *Annual Report of Council 1963–64*.

36 PRSM vol 58 (1965).

37 Schilling, RSF, *A challenging life. Sixty years in occupational medicine* (1998) pp. 129–43.

38 *Ibid* pp. 121, 129–43. PRSM vol 59 (1966).

39 PRSM vol 60 (1967).

40 CM Section of Occupational Medicine 1966, MS/50/a1.

41 PRSM vol 69 (1976).

42 CM Section of Occupational Medicine 1975–77, MS/50/a1. RSM, *Annual Report 1977–78*.

43 JRSM vol 78 (1985).

44 *Ibid* vol 79 (1986).

45 CM Section of Measurement in Medicine 14 February 1979, MS/36/a1.

46 *RSM News* Issue 9 (1996–97) p. 4.

47 Formation of the Section of Measurement in Medicine 1963–65, K63, Box 47.

48 Presidential address, PRSM vol 63 (1970).

49 PRSM vol 58 (1965). CM Section of Measurement in Medicine 1964–86, MS/36/a1.

50 CM Section of Measurement in Medicine 1965–66. PRSM vol 61 (1968).

51 I am grateful for comments from Mr Adrian Marston.

52 I am grateful to Dr Carice Ellison for her help with this Section.

53 Formation of Section of Clinical Immunology and Allergy 1965, K17. Box 46.

54 PRSM vol 61 (1968).

55 *Ibid* vol 59 (1966).

56 *Ibid* vol 61 (1968).

57 *Ibid* vol 65 (1972).

58 JRSM vol 77 (1984) pp. 971–77.

59 Section of Medical Education 1966–82, K64, Box 47.

60 *Ibid* 1965–83, MS/38/f2, Box 112. PRSM vol 60 (1967).

61 PRSM vol 60 (1967).

62 *Ibid* vol 61 (1968).

63 *Ibid* vol 70 (1977).

64 Anon, 'A retort', February 1981, MS/38/f1, Box 63.

65 CM 19 April 1983.

66 BMJ (ii) 10 September 1966 p. 641.

67 RSM, *Annual Report of Council 1966–67*. Formation of Section of Plastic Surgery 1966–68, K160, Box 48.

68 PRSM vol 71 (1978).

69 CM Section of Plastic Surgery 1970–80, MS/70/a1.

70 I am grateful for information from Mr Adam Searle.

71 Raven, Ronald W, *The theory and practice of oncology* (1990).
72 RSM, *Annual Report of Council 1968–69.*
73 Proposed Sections 1961–85, Box 81.
74 CM 15 July 1969.
75 PRSM vol 64 (1971).
76 *Ibid.*
77 *Ibid* vol 67 (1974).
78 *Ibid.*
79 CM Section of Oncology 1975–76, MS/54/a1. RSM, *Annual Report 1976–77.*
80 RSM, *Annual Report 1985–86.*
81 PRSM vol 69 (1976).
82 JRSM vol 74 June 1981. GM Open Section 1981, MS/56/b1.
83 GM Open Section 1986 MS/56/B1.
84 JRSM vol 83 August 1990.
85 Most of the history of this Section is written by Dr Anne Mathieson, to whom I am grateful.
86 CM 19 April 1977.
87 *Ibid* 18 October 1977.
88 Regulations June 1978, MS/30/f1, Box 112.
89 RSM, *Annual Report 1977–78.* PRSM vol 72 (1979). Dr Waxman is commemorated in an annual lecture. CM Section of Medical and Dental Hypnosis 1978–79, MS/30/a1.
90 Presidential address, JRSM vol 81 1988 pp. 130–31. PRSM vol 57 (1964).
91 Correspondence on proposed First Aid Section 1980, MS/02/f1.
92 CM Section of Accident and Emergency Medicine 1987, MS/02/a1, and GM 1987, MS/02/b1.
93 *Archives of Emergency Medicine* March 1987 vol 4 no 1 p. 63.
94 GM Section of Accident and Emergency Medicine 1988–89, MS/02/b1. Letter Tabone-Vassallo to Hewitt, CM 15 October 1991.
95 CM Section of Accident and Emergency Medicine 1988, MS/02/a1.
96 *Ibid* 1991.
97 CM Section of Clinical Forensic Medicine 1988, MS/10/91, Box 74. JRSM vol 81 1988 p. 555.
98 JRSM vol 82 1989 p. 310.
99 Davis, Neville, 'Contemporary clinical forensic medicine' in McLay, WDS (ed), *Clinical forensic medicine* (1996) pp. 5–6.
100 JRSM vol 82 1989 pp. 309–11.
101 *Ibid* vol 86 June 1993 pp. 363–67. Section programmes 1991–98, MS/10/e1.
102 Letter Roberts and Moffat to Thomson 1 September 1992, CM 20 October 1992.
103 Renaming of Section 1997, MS/10/f1.
104 *RSM News* Issue 12 (1997–98), p. 12.
105 I am grateful to Dr Diana Wetherill for information on the status of the Section in 2000.
106 CM 18 July 1989. I am grateful for Professor Millard's comments on this Section.
107 *Ibid* 17 October 1989.
108 JRSM vol 85 1992 pp. 199–202.
109 *Ibid* vol 88 1995 p. 698.
110 Letter Millard to Green 15 March 1996, CM 1996.
111 RSM, *Annual Report 1990–91.* CM 15 January 1991.
112 Memorandum Mann to Thomson July 1991, CM 16 July 1991.
113 Costello, J and Mann, RD (eds*), Beta agonists in the treatment of asthma* (1992).
114 This Section's history, written by a founder-member, Mr Bruce Keogh, is available on the Internet: ctsnet.org/doc/540; it provides much of the information for this Section. I am grateful to Mr Graham Venn for pointing this out.
115 *Ibid.* I am grateful for information from Mr James Roxburgh.
116 Cardiothoracic Section programmes 1991–98, MS/06/e1.
117 JRSM vol 86 1993 pp. 305–06.
118 *Nobel lectures in physiology or medicine 1901–1921* (1967) pp. 442–66.
119 *Ibid* vol 74 (1981) pp. 670–74.
120 RSM, *Annual Report 1993–94.*
121 I am grateful for information from Dr Richard Moore.
122 Proposed Sections 1961–85, Box 81. I am grateful for comments from Professor John Moorhead.
123 RSM, *Annual Report 1993–94.*
124 I am grateful for information on founding the Section from Dr Barry Hoffbrand.
125 Information kindly supplied by Professor Charles Pusey.
126 Proposed Sections 1961–85, Box 81.
127 Education Committee Minutes, 27 October 1992.
128 Section of Sports Medicine, planning 1993.
129 CM 21 July 1981.
130 Establishment of Fora 1982–83, MF/01, Boxes 1999/10, 1999/21.
131 Forum on Clinical Haemorheology, correspondence and meetings, 1982–83, MF/04/a1 and f1, Box 2000/8. I am grateful for information from Professor John Dormandy and Dr Gerald Nash.
132 JRSM vol 77 1984 pp. 340–42.
133 *Lancet* (i) 12 April 1986 pp. 837, 864–65, 3 May 1986 p.1036. Honorary Officers' Minutes (bound) 4 March 1986. JRSM vol 80 1987 pp. 588–89.
134 I am grateful to Dr Luke Zander for information.

135 JRSM vol 77 1984 pp. 968–70.

136 RSM, *Annual Report 1983–84.*

137 JRSM vol 78 1985 pp. 872–74.

138 Forum on Sexual Medicine and Family Planning, correspondence 1985–86, MF/22/f1, Box 1999/21.

139 Forum on Angiology, correspondence 1986–87, MF/02/f2, Box 2000/17.

140 Forum on Clinical Pharmacology and Therapeutics Steering committee minutes and correspondence 1985–87, MF/06/a1 and e2, Box 2000/9.

141 Honorary Officers' Minutes (bound) 3 December 1991.

142 CM 8 October 1998. I am grateful to Professor Finlay for information about this Forum.

143 Letter Lumley to Marston 25 June 1998, CM 21 July 1998.

# Chapter 10

## The Society in the 20th century

THE AMALGAMATION OF 15 medical societies within the Royal Society of Medicine under the charter of 1907 put the Society on a strong footing as it entered the 20th century. The acquisition of the site on the south-east corner of Wimpole Street was a bold and brilliant move and the opening of the Society's house there in 1912 received a good deal of publicity and applause. The century was to bring fluctuations in the effectiveness and popularity of the RSM, however.

*Overview*

As long as MacAlister held the reins as Secretary, expansion was the theme. With Sir William Osler's support he strove to draw all specialties into the Society and to create the best medical library in the world. The RSM continued to grow steadily despite the succession of disruptions resulting from the First World War, the death of MacAlister, the General Strike, the Depression and a Second World War. The Sections, for the most part self-sufficient and dominated by those working at the London voluntary hospitals and the medical schools, recorded the papers given at meetings in the *Proceedings*, which often extended to three substantial volumes annually. The publication was highly regarded by the medical profession, and the Society's reputation was such that the Ministry of Health and other government departments looked to its Sections and committees for guidance.

The Society emerged from the Second World War relatively unscathed: there was inevitably some disruption of meetings and the United Services Section was suspended altogether. On the other hand the Inter-Allied Conferences brought a refreshing diversity of doctors in the armed services to 1 Wimpole Street. In the immediate aftermath of the war, the most portentous event of the century for doctors was the passage of the National Health Act in 1946 and its implementation in 1948, surrounded by conflict, controversy and hard bargaining. The RSM, in accordance with its established policy of eschewing involvement in national politics, took no part in the negotiations. The President, Sir Maurice Cassidy, preferred to leave such matters to the BMA and the Royal Colleges and neither the Council of the RSM nor the *Annual Reports* of its Executive committee made any pronouncement on the issue.

The Society provided a welcome venue for discussions on the science of medicine and on the practical problems of medical care, and there were many doctors returning from active service who were anxious to pick up the threads of civilian practice and learn about the technical advances in their specialties. At that time few other organizations offered such opportunities, and the rapid specialization of medicine together with the upgrading of provincial and former local authority hospitals created a new demand. The wider professional participation in the work of the Society was reflected in the formation of the Section of General Practice in 1950.

By 1955 the RSM was composed of 26 Sections, most of them thriving, and an invaluable Library which had been extended to a second floor in 1953. Its maintenance, however, stretched the Society's finances to the limit. In 1955 the 150th anniversary of the founding of the Medical and Chirurgical Society was celebrated by a lavish dinner at the Dorchester

Hotel in the presence of HRH the Duke of Edinburgh, yet in the same year the Council recorded the difficulty of 'making ends meet'.[1] The primary difficulty was that the cost of the services provided at 1 Wimpole Street exceeded the income from Fellows' subscriptions, and this was to be a recurrent problem. Other sources of funding had to be found if subscriptions were to be kept at a level acceptable to a sufficient number of Fellows.

Mr Richard Hewitt had been appointed Secretary in 1952 and he held the post, under the new title of Executive Director, until 1982. He exercised a major influence on the development of the Society during those years, giving priority to securing its financial position and acquiring accommodation into which it could expand; with these objectives in mind it was perhaps understandable that he gave less attention to the academic development of the Society.

Firstly, Hewitt persuaded the pharmaceutical industry to finance the Library (Scientific Research) Section: companies were willing to pay large membership fees for the privilege of access to the Library for their scientific staff. Although this arrangement was not a major financial coup, over the years numerous contributions were forthcoming from the pharmaceutical industry in the form of capital grants and sponsorship, sometimes causing concern about covert promotion of their products. Whatever the reservations, the support of the pharmaceutical industry was indispensable to the growth of the Society.

Another of Hewitt's initiatives lay in the United States of America. After a series of visits he organized the Royal Society of Medicine Foundation as a channel for fund-raising, and in later membership drives he recruited a large number of American affiliate members. Ultimately, America did not prove to be the gold mine that Hewitt had hoped for; nevertheless his efforts promoted many lasting professional contacts across the Atlantic.

Hewitt also worked indefatigably towards the extension of 1 Wimpole Street into the adjacent Post Office site. This was always a long-term plan and it proved tantalizingly difficult to achieve. Meanwhile the Dering Yard property behind 20 Hanover Square accommodated some of the Society's activities but it was the acquisition in 1964 of the lease of Chandos House, close by in Queen Anne Street, that gave the Society much-needed additional accommodation. There the splendid reception rooms and the residential accommodation in the Domus Medica gave a tremendous boost to the Society although at some cost, specifically the financial burden and the administrative difficulties of operating on three sites.

Throughout the 1960s and 1970s the rapid expansion of specialist medicine and surgery in the NHS hospitals meant that there were exciting possibilities in the founding of new Sections, and the Section meetings and the services of the Library fulfilled the requirements of most Fellows admirably. Unfortunately attendance at some of the older Sections fell, often as a result of the increasing activities of local postgraduate centres or national specialist associations, and the Society, although able to offer superior club facilities, lacked academic cohesion. A Working Party under Sir Gordon Wolstenholme addressed the issue and as a result of its recommendations the Open Section was established in 1974, giving recognition to the fact that health care was not the exclusive preserve of the medical profession. Regrettably, other recommendations put forward by the Working Party (for instance, the formation of a Science Council) were defeated by inflation, mounting costs and inadequate accommodation.

Matters came to a head in April 1978 when Richard Hewitt announced to the Council that the RSM was at the crossroads: it could no longer survive in its present form by simply going on as before, beset as it was by serious financial and academic problems, not to mention the sudden resignation of the President (see page 468). In these circumstances the redevelopment of the Society's house and the reinvigoration of the academic life under steady leadership became imperative. Later that year it at last became possible to purchase the freehold of the Post Office and although this was just the start of long and difficult negotiations, when the building opened in 1986 it gave the Society new impetus. Hewitt, who had become a little dictatorial, retired in 1982 having seen the building project so close to his heart well on its way to completion. The commissioning process was left to his successor, Mr Robert Thomson, who had already served a long apprenticeship and who saw little need to change the administrative system.

The appointment of a Medical Services Secretary, Dr Graham Bennette, in 1978 was intended to stimulate academic development both within the Sections and by commercially sponsored conferences. The older Sections did not always take kindly to 'interference' but one initiative that was to prove a major success (due in part to Bennette's influence) was the establishment of the Fora. These were at first intended to be transient groups tackling specific issues of the day, in which there would be major participation by the paramedical professions. Most of the Fora proved to be popular and long-lasting, and they now constitute a significant element in the Society's programme.

The last decade of the 20th century was one of rapid change as the Society adapted to the cultural shift which had so altered the relationship between the medical profession, the politicians and the public. By the later 1980s the impetus given by the new building was flagging and the administration was again showing signs of strain. On the academic side the change from a salaried Medical Services Secretary to an Honorary Dean in charge of a Continuing Medical Education Department set in motion a spectacularly successful trend that included the establishment of an Academic Board. The death of Robert Thomson in 1993 and the appointment of Dr John Green as Executive Director transformed the Society's administration in three turbulent years. It was a necessary correction but a painful one and there was a warm welcome for the calmer but no less efficient regime of Dr Anne Grocock, who was appointed Executive Director in December 1996.[2]

## Early years at Wimpole Street

The occupation of 1 Wimpole Street in 1912 heralded a period of expansion, physically and academically, as the Society settled into its grand and spacious house and its Secretary gathered Sections and sub-Sections under its roof. Several thousands of medical men attended the 'at homes' held at 1 Wimpole Street in November 1912 when exhibitions and demonstrations showed the Society and its house to advantage. The phenomenal success of the RSM was clear to see: one correspondent to the *BMJ* wrote of its 'hydra-like advancement into fields of medical activity hitherto unprovided with the essential accessories of development', of the buoyancy and exuberant vitality the Society brought to the medical life of the metropolis and of its valuable educative influence.[3]

During the First World War the Emergency Surgical Aid Corps was based at 1 Wimpole Street (see pages 195–96) and when the Society's Council resumed normal business in June 1918 it reported that in spite of war conditions the activities of the RSM had been well maintained.[4]

During the interwar years the Society took a close interest in the plans of the Ministry of Health and elected representatives to committees on anaesthetics, cancer and radiology (see pages 197–200). The *Annual Reports* of the 1930s tell of steady development, 'another year of excellent progress' (1936–37) and consolidation. Finances were in a healthy state and shortly before the outbreak of the Second World War membership reached a record high of 5,000.

## The Second World War

A note of foreboding was sounded in June 1939: 'the selection of the essentials to restart the Society in the event of destruction is under consideration'.[5] On the declaration of war in September the house at 1 Wimpole Street was shut for a fortnight but thereafter it was business as usual as far as circumstances allowed. Among the precautions such as sandbags, fire-watchers and black-outs it was decided to move irreplaceable journals and books to the comparative safety of St Albans, Hertfordshire (see below).

During the war the Society organized joint discussions on topical subjects such as the treatment of burns, blast injuries and 'trench mouth'. The Section of Surgery was eager to improve the protection of men in the fighting forces by body armour, and the resulting recommendations were sent to the government. With the exception of the United Services Section, which lapsed because its members were otherwise engaged, Section meetings were sustained, although on a reduced scale, and they tended to focus on the medical, surgical and psychological problems of war. The publication of papers in the *Proceedings* was limited as a result of paper shortages, and the Society's property in Dering Yard was completely destroyed by enemy action, yet Sir Henry Tidy, President from 1942 to 1944, was optimistic. Casting his memory back, he described the 1920s as the seriously bleak years for the RSM, encumbered as it had been by a debt of over £50,000; Sir John MacAlister was a dying man and nearly all the Society's income was then swallowed up by the *Proceedings*. By contrast, in 1942 the life of the Society was flourishing and its debt was amortized. Tidy was bursting with ideas: he quickly saw that the RSM Library could be instrumental in replacing medical literature destroyed in the war, he presided over a series of Inter-Allied Conferences at the Society's house and he urged the completion of 1 Wimpole Street by a fourth floor.

The Inter-Allied Conferences on Military Medicine (or War Medicine) were for the benefit of medical officers of the British, Dominion and Allied forces and were on subjects of immediate practical importance. They were widely acknowledged to have been valuable in discussing the training and problems of medical officers in battle and they forged long-standing bonds between Allied medical officers. From 1942 until the last conference in July 1945 the facilities of 1 Wimpole Street were put at the disposal of the conferences. Each man attending made a contribution of two shillings and sixpence towards the cost of lunch and one shilling for tea, which was augmented by a subsidy from the Society.

Sir Gordon Gordon-Taylor remembered the Barnes Hall being 'thronged to capacity, preponderantly by medical officers of the Army of the USA in the European theatre of military operations. Apart from the exchange and interchange of information that was germane and valuable to the war effort, perhaps the forging and cementing of firm friend-ships between the surgeons of the Allies was the finest feature of the conferences'.[6] At the conclusion of the 24th and last conference it was calculated that over 6,500 officers had attended them.

There were lessons to be learnt from the war. In March 1946 the Society organized an exhibition showing the influence of war on medical science; members of Sections contributed and papers were presented and later published in the British Council's *Medical Bulletin*. Sir Henry Tidy, meanwhile, agreed to edit the proceedings of the Inter-Allied Conferences and these were published in 1947.

The Society's house emerged from the war with little damage; the guttering and exterior had been disfigured by shrapnel but compared with the Royal College of Physicians or the Royal College of Surgeons, the RSM was fortunate. When the first of these took a direct hit in October 1940 its Comita met instead at 1 Wimpole Street, and when a second bomb caused more serious damage the College's books and collection of engravings were rescued through the exertions of the RSM's Library staff 'just in time to save them from further damage by heavy rain'.[7] Likewise when the Royal College of Surgeons was bombed in 1941 the RSM offered hospitality and assistance. The prospect of rebuilding the Royal Colleges after the war raised the possibility of closer association between the Colleges and including the RSM; Lord Webb-Johnson, the Society's President from 1950 to 1952, wanted this to take the form of a gargantuan Academy of Medicine at Lincoln's Inn Fields.

## The introduction of the National Health Service

The RSM remained aloof from the difficult negotiations that led up to the inauguration of the NHS in 1948. Only once had the Society ventured into the debate, when 30 years previously it held three meetings on the 'Future of the medical profession under the proposed Ministry of Health'. A Ministry of Health committee was set to work and with the Royal Colleges the Society supported the Consultative Council which aimed to give specialized guidance on health policy. The influence of Lord Dawson of Penn (President of the Society 1928–30) was pervasive at this time, although his proposals for a comprehensive state medical service were shelved.

The President of the Society during the crucial years between the passing of the National Health Act and its inauguration (1946–48) was Sir Maurice Cassidy, a cardiologist who was not interested in medical politics, administration or committee work. He took no part in the debate surrounding the establishment of the NHS nor did he encourage the RSM to do so. The battle was essentially between the Rt Hon Aneurin Bevan, Minister of Health for the Labour government, and the BMA, with the Royal Colleges acting as peacemakers.

At a time when a large proportion of the profession was energized by the impending reorganization of the country's health service, the Society concentrated on domestic matters and enjoyed a period of expansion. Although many Fellows had died or could not be traced after the war, the Society's membership roll lengthened in the postwar years. During a period of scarcities, food rationing, a housing crisis and general hardship the Society grew and flourished. Men returning from the war needed the facilities the Society provided; the Library was expanding its services, the United Services Section resumed meetings, other Section meetings gained momentum lost during the war, and from 1948 the RSM Club enabled Fellows to entertain at the Society's house.

Although the Society kept its silence in the debate over the NHS, two Sections did express concern about its effects: the Section of Radiology held a discussion on the place of the radiologist under the proposed State health service in July 1946, and the Section of Psychiatry was anxious to ensure the development of psychiatry under the new system. Once the NHS was operational its impact on the RSM was evident in the creation of the Section of General Practice by those who were frustrated, overworked and unrepresented by a college. Over the next 50 years the Society approved the formation of 17 new Sections devoted to the specialties that had gained recognition as a result of the expansion of health services under the NHS.

## The Library

As Resident Librarian from 1887, and later as consultant Librarian and the Society's Secretary, MacAlister dominated the Library until his retirement in 1925. His successor as Librarian, Mr HE Powell, had been recruited in 1907 as an unpaid assistant and was 'a gentle and lovable colleague, cultivated in literature, and a man of upright character and goodwill', well liked by Fellows.[8] During Powell's 27 years with the RSM demands for references, abstracts and translations were an important part of Library services, as was the parcelling and posting of books to Fellows. The figures for the academic year 1929–30 record that 23,068 readers used the Library, 21,892 books were borrowed and 4,747 parcels were sent. Donations and gifts were received regularly: the valuable Chalmers Library in 1922, £500 given by Lord Illingworth which formed the nucleus of the Library Endowment Fund in 1930, and the donations of Miss Medwin and Mrs Law were other generous benefactions.

After Powell's death in 1934 Mr GF Home became Librarian. He was a scholar and 'something of a recluse'.[9] Nevertheless he was not averse to innovations such as microfilm copying and he introduced the first formal classification system. To the ever-growing collection of journals he added the most complete collection of French and German encyclopaedic works, while bibliographical and translating tasks continued to expand. Home collapsed with a coronary thrombosis in July 1940, returning to part-time work and determined to keep the Library open during the war.[10] In view of the fact that the nearby John Lewis building had been gutted by a fire bomb and the neighbourhood was regularly bombarded, in 1940 some 40,000 of the most valuable books and 18th- and 19th-century journals were sent for storage at 'Waterways', a house in St Albans. This effort was financed by regular grants from the Rockefeller Foundation, which had been alerted to the need to preserve the Society's collection by Professor F Golla, President of the Section of Psychiatry at the outbreak of war. At St Albans the collection was guarded by two resident members of the Library staff who were responsible for bringing items to London when required.

With the arrival of peace, Home and his sub-Librarian, WJ Bishop, made great efforts to fill gaps in the Library sets of important foreign works. Home soon found himself in the new post of Director of the Central Medical Library Bureau and Bishop departed to the Wellcome Historical Museum.

## Central Medical Library Bureau

One of the first resolutions of the Society's Council at the first peace-time meeting for several years was to implement a plan to rehabilitate medical libraries of Europe that had suffered losses owing to damage by the enemy. The scheme was handled by the Central Medical Library Bureau, which aimed to supply microfilm copies of journals to medical institutions whose collections had been depleted. A grant of £61,725 from the Rockefeller Foundation in 1946 enabled microfilm readers to be sent to the associated libraries and by the time the service was terminated in 1949, 10,357 complete volumes of out-of-print medical journals had been dispatched to 142 medical libraries in all parts of the world and 175 microfilm readers had been supplied.

The Central Medical Library Bureau was superseded by the RSM's Photographic and Film Unit, which from 1949 onwards was housed in Dering Yard, rebuilt after war damage.[11] The Unit provided medical institutions, universities and individuals with micro-film, photocopying and photography of patients and specimens. Work was undertaken for the Institute of Ophthalmology and for Charing Cross Hospital and the Unit was soon assisting the Admiralty, Colonial Office, UNESCO and WHO. Renamed the Audio-Visual Department, it moved from Dering Yard to 1 Wimpole Street after its redevelopment in the 1980s.

## Wellcome Research Library

Mr Home retired from the post of consultant Librarian in 1952, so it was the Librarian Mr Philip Wade who oversaw the opening of a major extension to the Library in 1953, generously funded by the Wellcome Trustees. As President of the Society, Sir Henry Tidy had recognized the need for an additional storey at 1 Wimpole Street, and in 1944 Council approved plans. A building fund was opened in the expectation of raising £50,000 but it was soon recognized that war-time stringencies and the national shortage of housing meant the deferral of plans at Wimpole Street until the 1950s. Sir Henry Tidy's ambitions were supported by Sir Henry Dale, President of the RSM 1948–50, who as Chairman of the Wellcome Trust was in a position to promote this cause.

A fourth floor to top 1 Wimpole Street had always been an option and when it was eventually decided upon the Society looked to the architect JJ Joass, who had been associated with the original building. Joass' plan placed the extension on the floor directly above the existing Library while the Council Room, the President's room, the Secretary's office, the kitchen and restaurant moved to a new fourth floor. The weight of the additional floor demanded the installation of two massive steel stanchions from the foundations to the top

1 Wimpole Street, showing the fourth floor added in 1953.

of the building. This solution, together with Joass' use of aluminium facing for the new floor, was regarded as masterly.[12]

Beginning with an initial grant of £80,000 in 1950 the Wellcome Trust gave a total of £125,000 to the building fund; Fellows contributed £8,500 and the deficit was borrowed. The second-floor Library opened in 1953, having been completed after Joass' death the previous year by his associate, Mr Lesslie K Watson. An account of the official opening of the Wellcome Research Library in December 1953 refers to Joass' 'natural and jealous pride in his own plans and ideas'– he was said to be likely to burst into flame under criticism. Far from criticizing, Sir Henry Dale praised the austere beauty of the new Library.[13]

The Wellcome Trustees were particularly concerned that the RSM Library should be open to younger medical graduates and those from overseas. Therefore the Trust donated an additional sum to sponsor 300 Wellcome Associates annually; a similar arrangement for 100 Associateships was sponsored by the Leverhulme Trust Fund and in 1964 the Ciba Foundation sponsored 20 postgraduate students' memberships of the RSM.

Within a few years of the opening of the Wellcome Research Library benefactions enabled the Library to recover from a position of overspending and lack of space to one of development. It received a grant of £24,000 from the Rockefeller Foundation, and further contributions from the Wellcome Trustees and from the Pfeiffer Research Foundation allowed the Library both to develop and to preserve its resources. Furthermore, in 1966 a generous £50,000 was received from the Reginald M Phillips Foundation to establish a library endowment fund for the purchase of books and journals in perpetuity. The formation of the Library (Scientific Research) Section in 1956 brought another source of income and a broadening of the function of the Library (see pages 394–95). But the need for additional accommodation for the Society as a whole was becoming more acute with each passing year.

While the opening of the Wellcome Research Library solved the immediate problem of book space and reading facilities, the President of the Society, Lord Webb-Johnson, was casting an eye over the Western District Post Office adjacent to 1 Wimpole Street as a potential site for expansion. Persistent negotiations with the Post Master General brought an assurance that the RSM would have the option of acquiring that site at some future date. This process was to take over 30 years and meanwhile additional accommodation had to be found in order to continue the Society's activities satisfactorily. The expansion of the Society since it had moved to Wimpole Street was a measure of its success. When the house was opened in 1912 it was used by some 3,000 Fellows, 15 Sections held 130 meetings a year and the Library housed 80,000 volumes. By 1963–64 the membership had reached 12,000, there were 27 Sections (and two more in the course of formation) with 430 meetings held in the building annually; by then the Library contained an estimated 400,000 volumes and required an extra 150 yards of shelving each year.[14]

Possible solutions to the lack of space ranged from building on an entirely new site in Regent's Park to a move to the west side of Portman Square or expanding into the Royal College of Nursing, all of which were rejected. The Society clung to the hope of acquiring the Post Office site and decided on a modest extension at the top of 1 Wimpole Street for the time being.

## Expansion

### Cockayne Suite

In 1957 the Society was named as a residuary legatee of the estate of Dr EA Cockayne, a Fellow from 1912 to 1956, President of the Section of Paediatrics 1938–39 and a member of three other Sections. When Cockayne's estate was wound up in 1962 the Society benefited to the extent of over £22,500, and this was immediately put to good use in building offices and a committee room above the fourth floor. Another legacy, from Dr Bolton Corney, was applied to the same end and the two bequests covered the entire extension, built by Kyle Stewart in 1963–64.[15]

### Chandos House

It became increasingly clear that the wait for the Post Office site was to be a long one, so when it came to notice that Chandos House in Queen Anne Street was to be auctioned on 5 December 1963, the Society's Council moved swiftly. On 23 November the Honorary Officers alerted the Council about the forthcoming auction and advised that an offer of £260,000 should be made forthwith. A contract was signed on 3 December and the sale was completed in January 1964, with the Society agreeing to pay £265,000 for a 99-year lease (later extended) with a small ground rent and an additional £7,200 due for fixtures and fittings. An appeal was launched to cover the cost of the purchase, conversion and furnishing and this was an astounding success, reaching £585,000 – more than its target.

Chandos House, Queen Anne Street, London W1, acquired by the RSM in 1964 and sold in 1986.

The generosity of individual benefactors was acknowledged by electing them to a Court of Benefactors, on to which professional advisers and others who materially assisted the Society were also elected.

The Council congratulated itself on the acquisition of Chandos House with its 'splendid ground and first floor rooms, many of them with fine hand-painted Adam ceilings, Adam fireplaces, polished floors and superb chandeliers'.[16] It was indeed a fine house, designed by Robert Adam in 1769–71 for the third Duke of Chandos. The unassuming stone front gave little indication of the superb decoration of the main rooms within. *The buildings of England* waxes lyrical over the exquisite doorcases, decorative ceilings, the marble fire-

The 18th-century ballroom in Chandos House.

place carved with a sacrificial scene, medallions painted by Angelica Kauffmann... all in all one of Robert Adam's best London town houses.[17]

In 1815 the house became the Austro-Hungarian Embassy and was the scene of extravagant entertainments hosted by Prince Esterhazy. In the early 20th century it was a residence of the aristocracy, housing the Countess of Strafford, the Earl of Shaftesbury and Viscount Kemsley in turn.

The building underwent conversion and restoration work to meet the Society's needs, and when this was complete in 1967 Chandos House became a favourite rendezvous for Fellows at lunchtime. Receptions and concerts were held there and the Domus Medica (guest bedrooms) established in the former mews at 10 Duchess Street took more than 300 reservations in the first six weeks of opening. Chandos House provided the RSM with book storage in the basement, magnificent rooms for meetings and receptions, offices, and rents – the College of Pathologists, the Nutrition Society, the Royal Medico-Psychological Association and the Excerpta Medica Foundation all took short leases.

The attractive facilities of Chandos House and the Domus Medica, together with the formation of three new Sections (Measurement in Medicine, Occupational Medicine and Clinical Immunology and Allergy) brought 600 elections to the Fellowship in the years 1964–65. The Society's Executive Director was seeking a foothold in North America and the mood was optimistic: the Council detected a developing corporate spirit and this was fostered by reinstating the Society's annual dinner.[18]

## Royal Society of Medicine Foundation

The RSM Foundation was the brainchild of Richard Hewitt as Executive Director. He took his cue from International Co-operation Year (1965) and the consequent formation of the Society's International Office, which aimed to promote relations between members

The original logo of the Royal Society of
Medicine Foundation *c*.1968.

of the medical profession in Britain and overseas. As a part of this drive to encourage international co-operation and in the hope of fund-raising, Hewitt undertook the first of several visits to America in 1957.

Hewitt returned to America in 1960, 1964 and 1965, putting his proposals for representation in America to the Society's Council in 1964. He pointed out that 1,000 of the Society's members lived in the USA and 300 in Canada. The Society already enjoyed reciprocal agreements with the New York Academy of Medicine, the Academy of Medicine of Toronto, the National Library of Medicine in Washington DC and it had benefited greatly from the generosity of the Rockefeller Foundation. What further benefits might accrue from closer links with North American colleagues, with the American pharmaceutical industry and medical publishing houses? American tax legislation had recently been tightened, however, and 'the only possibility of getting clearance for a project of fund-raising from US individuals and corporations would be the establishment of a US incorporated committee or charity for broad medical and scientific purposes'. This 'incorporated committee or charity' materialized in February 1967 as the Royal Society of Medicine Foundation.[19]

The Foundation was authorized 'to receive and maintain a fund or funds of real or personal property or both ... for the scientific purposes of the Royal Society of Medicine and other charitable, religious, scientific or literary or educational purposes'. Its professed purpose was 'to promote communication between members of the medical profession in the United States and Britain and to enable the academic, scientific and practical experience of the profession in both countries to be shared in a way that will create better doctors, better medicine and a better long-term relationship between all specialties in medicine'.[20]

The first President of the Foundation was Mr Francis Boyer, Director and former Chairman of SmithKline French Laboratories; Dr Howard Craig, Director Emeritus of the New York Academy of Medicine was Secretary, there were two Nobel prizewinners on the first Board (Dr AF Cournand and Dr F Peyton Rous) and Sir Arthur Porritt, currently President of the RSM, was another of the 12 original Directors. Once established, several eminent figures in American medicine and public life were recruited on to the Board of the Foundation including Dr Purnell W Choppin, Professor of Virology at Rockefeller University and later Director of the Howard Hughes Foundation, Dr Jeremiah Barondess (later President of the New York Academy of Medicine) and Professor Alexander Bearn,

President 1976–79 and Professor of Medicine at the Rockefeller Institute for Medical Research, later the Medical Director of Merck, Sharp and Dohme (USA).

In addition to providing an annual sum for the RSM and $100,000 for the redevelopment of 1 Wimpole Street, the RSM Foundation sponsored travelling Fellowships (1969–77), visiting professorships from 1977 and from 1980 reciprocal arrangements to sponsor British physicians visiting the USA. The Foundation contributed towards the Liver Unit of King's College Hospital (1970) and with the RSM organized Anglo-American Conferences, beginning in 1971 with one on 'Medical care'. The objective of these conferences was to discuss comparative issues such as health care services, medical education, scientific research and practice standards.

From 1978 conferences and symposia organized by the Foundation were published in the RSM's International Congress and Symposia Series, providing sponsors with a means of publishing proceedings of meetings held anywhere in the world. Another series of publications known as the Round Table Series commenced in 1985 following a panel discussion at the RSM on 'Safety aspects of non-steroidal anti-inflammatory drugs'; by 2000 over 70 titles had appeared in the series.

To begin with the Foundation was run on a part-time basis from Greenwich Village, but in 1985 an office was established with the Archbold Foundation at 7 East 60th Street, New York, in the splendid building of the Metropolitan Club. The same year saw the appointment of its first full-time Executive Director, Mr William O'Reilly, an emigré Australian. At this time the President of the RSM, Lord Walton, and its Executive Director, Robert Thomson, visited New York twice a year to attend Board meetings, staying at the University Club and making many contacts with US colleagues. Lord Walton presented the first Richard T Hewitt Award in 1984, sponsored by the SmithKline Beckman Corporation in recognition of Hewitt's outstanding contribution to the RSM and the Foundation. The award, consisting of a cheque for $10,000 and a commemorative silver-gilt column, is given every two years for distinguished achievement in the improvement of human health. On the first occasion, at the Helmsley Palace Hotel, New York, the award went jointly to Group Captain Leonard Cheshire (later Lord Cheshire), founder of the Cheshire Homes in the UK, and to Dr Howard Rusk, an outstanding figure in America in the development of rehabilitation services for the disabled and founder-Chairman of the World Rehabilitation Fund.[21]

By the early 1990s the RSM Foundation possessed about 3,000 members in the USA and a Board of 30 Directors. Its 25th anniversary was celebrated by a week-long series of events organized under the presidencies of Sir George Pinker at the RSM and Mr Arthur J Mahon of the Foundation. Initially the Foundation had been generously sponsored – among the major donors were SmithKline, Burroughs Wellcome, and Merck and Company – but by 1992 the balance sheet showed a shortfall, with disbursements exceeding revenue by $16,316.

In 1993 the newly appointed Chief Executive of the RSM, Dr John Green, found that the Foundation lacked financial records and he ordered a restructuring and a cut in running costs. Accordingly, the New York office moved to smaller premises and staff costs were reduced. Even so, the finances of the Foundation were insecure and it was predicted in 1996 that without a fresh source of income it could face bankruptcy. The office moved once again, from 150 East 58th Street to the top floor of the English Speaking Union building at 16 East 69th Street, and financial constraints forced the Foundation to operate on a reduced basis throughout 1997. A strategy review later that year urged a re-evaluation of the 'mission' and activities of the Foundation. In 1998 a new President, Dr Richard Wilbur, took office, and in the following year he came to 1 Wimpole Street to present the Richard Hewitt Award to Sir Richard Doll (Plate 71); the Board of Directors of the Foundation met the next day with several new members, a new Secretary and a new

Treasurer. These changes, and the removal of its base from New York to Lake Forest, Illinois, put the Foundation on a more viable footing.

## Medico-Pharmaceutical Forum

Another purpose of Hewitt's visits to America was 'to study the close relationship between the pharmaceutical industry and the medical profession in the United States, which has been of such advantage to both, and to consider to what extent that relationship can properly be fostered in this country by this Society'.[22]

Hewitt reached the conclusion that the RSM should cultivate a close ethical relationship between the medical profession and the pharmaceutical industry, from which both parties might stand to gain. The excellent relationship between the physician and the pharmaceutical industry in America had been the subject of an address given to the Library (Scientific Research) Section in 1960 by Mr LW Frohlich of New York, and the Medico-Pharmaceutical Forum was founded with the intention of promoting a similar arrangement in this country.

When it was established in 1968 the Forum aimed to consider matters of joint interest to the medical profession and the pharmaceutical industry, and to undertake, sponsor and promote studies of mutual concern. The foundation meeting took place in May 1968, supported by the Association of British Pharmaceutical Industry and attended by representatives from nine medical organizations including the Royal Colleges, the BMA and the Society of Apothecaries. Lord Cohen represented the RSM and the Society provided secretarial assistance and accommodation.[23]

Within the space of a year the Forum had convened two working parties, one on 'Academic–industrial relations' and another on 'Clinical pharmacology'. Its first report was on 'Facilities for the early clinical studies of new medicine'; it was published in 1969 and was widely distributed. By all accounts the Forum gained in strength for its first few years; by 1973, however, it was being criticized by several medical bodies on the grounds that its output was insubstantial and its impact negligible. It received scant publicity, had little influence and failed to come to grips with really controversial issues. The BMA and the Royal College of Pathologists resigned from membership and the future of the Forum lay in the balance.[24] A revival in the late 1970s resulted in two further reports and the meetings continued until in 1990 it had to be admitted that the Forum no longer had a significant role.

When the Medico-Pharmaceutical Forum disbanded in 1990 it did so in the belief that its original objectives of establishing liaison between the medical profession and the pharmaceutical industry had been fulfilled. The British Association of Pharmaceutical Physicians, the RSM's Forum on Clinical Pharmacology and Therapeutics and especially the Faculty of Pharmaceutical Medicine rendered the Medico-Pharmaceutical Forum redundant.

## The RSM at the crossroads

Despite the initiatives described above, some of the older Sections of the Society languished and many meetings were poorly attended. Specialization under the NHS had encouraged the proliferation of postgraduate institutions, colleges and associations throughout the country whose activities tended to detract from the meetings of the older, less specialized Sections of the RSM.

The Society was also in difficulty; it lacked cohesion and members complained about the lack of communication between the Council and the Sections. The Wolstenholme Working Party Report of 1973 emphasized the desirability of rehousing the Society in one modern building (among several other recommendations for the reinvigoration of the Society and its Sections) but this was delayed. Meanwhile, acute problems due to shortage of space and staff in the Library, the resignation of the President in January 1978 and adverse publicity marked a low point in the Society's history.

Sir John Dacie had succeeded Sir Gordon Wolstenholme as President of the Society in the summer of 1977. Dacie was well known for his work on *The haemolytic anaemias*; he was a past President of two Sections and had been President of the Royal College of Pathologists 1973–75. Within a few months of presiding at the RSM, however, criticism of his style of leadership was being voiced. When Dacie heard that the Honorary Officers were discussing with a past President, behind his back, problems that they attributed to his indecisiveness, his resentment was such that he felt his resignation was the appropriate action.[25]

Other factors were also involved in the President's resignation, such as differing views on the function of the Society's Council *vis-à-vis* the Executive (it was perceived by some that the Council was no more than a rubber stamp); there was a conflict of personalities on the Council (15 members were on the point of resigning); the method of choosing the President was regarded as unsatisfactory and there was discontent with the low profile of the Society and its ailing Sections.

In the history of the Society since 1805 no other President had departed in such haste. Andrew W Barclay had resigned after one year in office (1881–82), J Warrington Haward likewise served just a year (1906–07) and Lord Porritt departed after a first year to take up the Governor Generalship of New Zealand in 1967, but there had been nothing like the departure of Sir John Dacie after just a few months. The hiatus was filled by Sir Gordon Wolstenholme (the immediate past President) until Lord Smith of Marlow, a recent President of the Royal College of Surgeons, took office for 1978–80. The 'unhappy and unprecedented events' of the first half of 1978 were followed by inaccurate press comments based upon speculation, and an ascending spiral of rumour threatened to erode confidence in the Society at a time when the united support of the whole membership was particularly important.

It was in these precarious circumstances that the Executive Director reported to the Council in April that the Society was at the crossroads. It had been caught up for six years in the maelstrom of inflation and was beset by financial problems – the estimated deficit for 1977–78 was £108,000. The reason for this state of affairs was the rising cost of the traditional academic services provided by the Society – the Library, the *Journal* and the *Calendar*, administration and meetings. The Society was also threatened by the alternative range of academic activities offered locally at a time when the travel expenses of a single visit to Wimpole Street by a provincial Fellow could exceed his annual subscription. Hewitt painted a gloomy picture, alleviated only by his proposed remedies: the redevelopment of the Society's house, a wholehearted recruitment drive, interdisciplinary meetings and trading activities.[26]

Not surprisingly, the Annual General Meeting in July was 'singularly ill-humoured'. Doubtless the great majority of those who voiced their discontent at this meeting were genuinely bewildered by conflicting rumours, by adverse comment in *World Medicine* and lampoons in *Private Eye* – the front cover of *World Medicine* for 14 June drew attention to an article by a Fellow under the heading 'Odd smell at the RSM?'.[27]

The meeting of July 1978 was uncomfortable but it did produce proposals for improved communications within the Society and by the end of the year reforms were in hand. A Medical Services Secretary, Dr Graham Bennette, was appointed to revive the academic life of the Sections, which were encouraged to hold fewer, more substantial meetings of multidisciplinary interest; a Working Party was examining the structure and function of the Society and RSM Services was formed to promote commercially sponsored activities in conference management, publications and audio-visual productions. Most promising of all was the purchase in August of the freehold of the Western District Post Office next door. Prosperity was still several years away but 1978 can be seen as a watershed.

Meanwhile the Council continued to receive complaints that the Fellowship felt aggrieved over the lack of the information about the Society's affairs, and changes to the established method of nomination to Council were called for. A steady hand was required and Sir John Stallworthy, who had been President for 1973–75, agreed to serve a second term, the only time in the history of the Society that this has occurred. He faced a formidable task. Inflation rose from 11% to 22% in 1979 compelling the modification of plans for 1 Wimpole Street, notably the omission of a lecture theatre to seat 350, and negotiations with a pension fund to develop the site fell through. The Sections were also suffering: the Medical Services Secretary reported in 1979 that six Sections sustained vigorous and successful meetings, the other 28 had disappointing attendances and some showed a constantly poor and declining performance.[28]

Stallworthy began by holding luncheons and suppers aimed at improving channels of communication between Section Presidents and the officers of the Society. Changes in the Society's by-laws were made to allow representation on Council to Sections if their President was absent, and to increase the number of Fellows on the Scientific and Executive committee. Section regulations were to be revised and each was encouraged to appoint a Treasurer and to organize large-scale meetings that could command a registration fee and sponsorship. After years of dissatisfaction with the *Journal*, a decision was taken that it should reflect the meetings of the Society and its Sections more closely and that it should be published by the RSM alone.

Possibly the most constructive element to emerge from these events was the memorandum on what new role the RSM could play and how this might be realized, prepared by Dr Luke Zander in consultation with the Medical Services Secretary in 1981 (see page 440). This stressed the continuing importance of the RSM as a unifying force in an age of increasing specialization and presented the idea of study groups/ working parties, which as Fora were to grow into a new and useful limb of the Society.

The tide was beginning to turn, and in September 1981 an agreement was signed between the RSM and the Heron Property Corporation for the development of the former Post Office site. This heralded the regeneration of the Society and was the occasion for rejoicing. The up-beat announcement of the news in the Society's *Annual Report* predicted that every facet of the Society, Section and Forum activity would be enhanced by the redevelopment; discontent within the membership would be healed and staff morale would soar. The RSM was on course to become the foremost postgraduate centre in the country with the most efficient medical library to be found. It was hoped that 'the Open Section can in truth become a wide forum for all the professions, a complete conference service for the Society and others can be offered, with assembly areas, publishing and audio-visual facilities, catering and overnight accommodation, homeless societies can be gathered under the Society's wing and administered, an Academy of Medicine, if others will unite in forging it, can be housed and serviced here'. With these optimistic words an appeal for £3.5 million was opened.[29]

Sir John Stallworthy bowed out in 1982, as did Richard Hewitt, whose business acumen, foresight, graciousness and quiet efficiency were acknowledged in glowing terms. Unfortunately his successor, Robert Thomson, fell ill almost immediately, whereupon Hewitt agreed to fill the gap until Thomson's return. Hewitt was made an Honorary Fellow of the Society in 1985 and his name lingers in the Richard T Hewitt Award and in the Hewitt room where his portrait hangs.

## Redevelopment of the Society's house 1981–86

The agreement of 18 September 1981 with the Heron Property Corporation to redevelop the Western District Post Office (Kingsley House) was described at the time as 'one of the most important events in the Society's entire history'.[30]

The Western District Post Office, built 1908–09 and shown here *c.*1915. The sign at the door indicates the counter service of the Post Office; the large archways gave access to the sorting office, which was served by an underground railway. The nearest arch is now the main entrance of 1 Wimpole Street.

The property became available in the autumn of 1977, whereupon negotiations commenced between the Post Office, the planning authorities and potential partners in the development. Almost a year later, in August 1978, the freehold was purchased by the RSM for £750,000 'in what must have been the bargain of the century'.[31] The Post Office leased back part of the building for three years so as to retain a counter service while the Society, the Department of the Environment, Westminster City Council and the principal architect, Mr Alan Roberts of Elsom, Pack and Roberts, discussed plans and planning permission.

The 'historic' agreement of 1981 yielded the freehold of the site to the Heron Corporation in exchange for a lease expiring in 2912 to the RSM for a peppercorn rent of £400 per annum payable to Howard de Walden Estates Ltd on condition that Heron constructed the new building, half of which was to be occupied by the RSM and half by offices paying rent to Heron.

Purchase and demolition cost the Society £1,500,000, the costs of the modernization of the old building amounted to £3,304,000 and the total financial responsibility falling on the Society stood at £6 million. Sir John Stallworthy headed an energetic Appeal committee, confident that the Society had secured a good deal and that the sale of Chandos House might yield nearly £2,000,000 towards the cost of redeveloping 1 Wimpole Street (it eventually sold for £1,864,200 in August 1986).

The contractors for the redevelopment, Sir Robert McAlpine and Sons, were delayed by a year, so it was not until May 1985 that the new building was complete and the modernization of 1 Wimpole Street began. One year later the Society occupied an extended and refurbished house, opened by HM Queen Elizabeth II and HRH the Duke of Edinburgh on

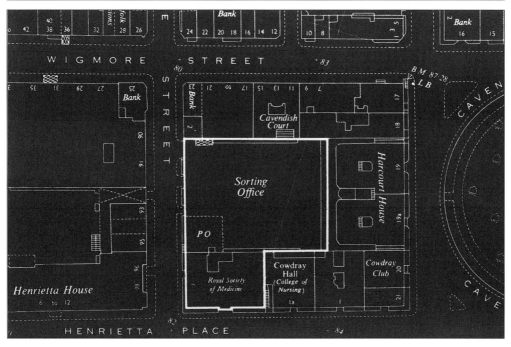

The site of the Western District Post Office was acquired by the Society in 1981.

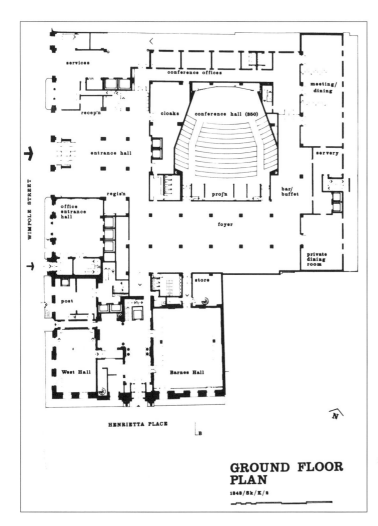

**GROUND FLOOR
PLAN**

1843/Sk/K/2

Plans of 1979 by the architects Elsom, Pack and Roberts included an auditorium to seat 350, which was not executed.

2 July 1986 (Plate 72). It was a memorable occasion, not least for the warmth of the day (the Library windows failed to open) and a sticky fountain pen that meant that the Queen signed her name with a ball-point.

Number 1 Wimpole Street had been transformed from a club-like house with out-dated furnishings and equipment into a modern headquarters where all the interests of the Society converged. The main entrance was through the southernmost arch of the former sorting office, leading to what had been the hall of the Post Office, now paved with Brazilian granite and Sicilian marble. The flamboyant Edwardian façade of Portland stone, designed by Sir Henry Tanner in 1908–09, had been cleaned and the building that lay behind it had been set on a reinforced concrete raft to cover the tunnels of the Post Office's underground railway network. Tanner was architect to the Office of Works with a wealth of experience in Post Office building, besides hotels (the Strand Palace and the Regent Palace) and much of Regent Street.

As soon as 1 Wimpole Street was ready for reoccupation the RSM *Journal* alerted Fellows to the new club area centred on the conservatory, the quiet room with its green baize walls and a common room with sycamore panelling. The Barnes and West Halls and the Marcus Beck Room had been modernized, new offices built on the third and fourth floors and the Domus Medica offered 20 single and 10 double rooms. The Library benefited from the generosity of the Wolfson Foundation and a gift of £100,000 from Mrs Vera Lederman in memory of her husband provided reading carrels; rolling stacks for basement storage and a mezzanine floor were also installed (Plates 73, 74 and 75).[32]

The refurbishment had meant the removal of some 2,500 boxes of pre-1900 printed books from the Library's basement for storage at the Wellcome Institute, Euston Road. At 1 Wimpole Street Library services were maintained in difficult conditions: the main service counter and work room operated in the basement, with current books housed in the wine store, current journals on the mezzanine floor and during the disruption reading desks were provided in the Domus Medica.

It took some while for the Society to face up to the additional costs of running the larger building – the revelation that this was likely to amount to some £400,000 for 1985–86 caused alarm. Additional staff were needed, day-to-day running expenses were higher than before, catering and the *Journal* made losses and there had been a fall in membership numbers during the disruptive building work. Fortunately a recruitment drive attracted large numbers of affiliate members, and climbing profits from the Publications Department allayed concerns about a financial deficit.

## Conventional medicine and complementary therapies

In a series of Colloquia held between April 1984 and January 1987 the Society made a brave attempt to dispel suspicion about complementary medicine and to encourage collaboration between conventional practitioners of medicine and qualified practitioners of complementary therapies. The debate had been stimulated by a speech made by the Prince of Wales to the BMA in its 150th year, in which he appealed to doctors to treat the whole individual, if necessary by the use of complementary methods. There was widespread disillusionment with 'high-tech' medicine at this time, encouraging a surge of interest in alternative methods, although on the whole the medical profession remained wary.

In response to the Prince's speech, the BMA set up a working party to consider possible methods of assessing the value of alternative therapies. At the RSM there were already moves afoot to bring together *bona fide* practitioners of complementary medicine and medically qualified people, and the President, Sir James Watt, discussed with Lord Kindersley the possibility of a forum on the subject of therapies. Watt, encouraged by the Prince of Wales, then took the initiative by organizing a series of Colloquia between medical practitioners and complementary practitioners. Several Sections were represented, along with speakers from six complementary therapies – osteopathy, chiropractic, acupuncture, naturopathy, medical herbalism and homeopathy. The first meeting, held at Chandos House, was opened by Sir James Watt and Lord Kindersley but as confrontation between different groups was anticipated, the Prince of Wales was advised not to attend (in the event confrontation was avoided although the exchanges were certainly frank and the issues controversial). The Prince did attend three subsequent Colloquia, and he wrote the Foreword to the resulting publication *Talking health. Conventional and complementary approaches* (1988), which was edited by Sir James Watt and Dr Clive Wood.[33]

The Colloquia established a dialogue between different methods of healing and they acted as a catalyst in the establishment of the Centre for Complementary Health Studies at Exeter University and in the foundation of the Council for Complementary and Alternative Medicine. At the RSM a new section of homeopathic medicine was proposed in 1989 but rejected by the Council. Two years later a meeting of the Section of General Practice considered whether alternative medicine should be taken seriously: the main stumbling-block was identified as non-medically qualified practitioners who brought alternative methods into disrepute.

## Save-a-Life campaign

In 1984 the Society embarked upon another new venture: to educate the public in emergency resuscitation. Following a joint meeting with St John Ambulance on 'Mass education in emergency aid: a valid concept?' organized by Dr Andrew Raffle early in 1984, a co-ordinating committee of representatives from the Society, the Department of Health, the Health Education Council and voluntary associations set in motion the biggest national campaign of its kind ever mounted in this country to train the public in elementary cardiopulmonary resuscitation.

The campaign was supported by BBC Television, which produced seven 10-minute programmes (repeated) designed to arouse public interest and to draw attention to leaflets and training courses. The campaign was organized by Mrs Penny Webb with a small team at 1 Wimpole Street, and it depended entirely on donated funds. Training sessions in resuscitation at centres throughout Britain were organized and by February 1988 some 135,000 people had attended the classes. It was estimated that dozens of lives had been saved by trainees of the scheme and as the campaign drew to a close in September 1987, Prince Michael of Kent presented awards at a ceremony at the Society's house.

## BMTV

A third venture of the 1980s proved less successful. This was launched in association with British Medical Television as an exciting and rewarding initiative in postgraduate education aimed principally at provincial members of the Society. The Executive Director believed it to be a great opportunity for the Society that could be achieved at no cost; there appeared to be no disadvantages and the Honorary Officers were enthusiastic.

Through an agreement between the RSM and BMTV members were promised daily news programmes, weekly clinical programmes and monthly programmes covering Society and Section meetings. The initial response was encouraging: 4,500 requests were received from Fellows for the direct television receivers and the Society's symposium on 'No-fault compensation' was chosen as a test-run in 1989. Nine films were made before BMTV went into receivership in February 1990, whereupon the project was taken over by Community Services Broadcasting and further programmes were produced, on 'Malaria in Britain', 'BSE' and 'The use and abuse of drugs in epilepsy', for example. These were broadcast on BBC2 at 2am on the last Thursday of each month and Fellows were reminded to set their video recorders accordingly.

CSB met with no more success than BMTV, although by the time the project died in

1990 a total of 21 programmes had been made. Dr Ronald Mann (shortly to resign as Medical Services Secretary) continued to believe in the viability of a RSMTV Distance Learning project and two programmes (on 'Prescribing in the 1990s' and 'Hormone replacement therapy') were approved for Postgraduate Education Allowance (PGEA).

## Publications

In 1978 RSM Services was established with responsibility for publishing the commercially sponsored International Congress and Symposium Series and the Round Table Series. Under the chairmanship of Dr Raffle RSM Services expanded its list of publications and produced welcome profits. The Society's *Journal* and *Tropical Doctor*, on the other hand, experienced difficulties – *Tropical Doctor* had a small circulation and relied on grants, while dislike of the *Journal* had been voiced ever since it replaced the *Proceedings* in 1978. The Honorary Officers dealt with a succession of verbal and written complaints from Sections about the editorship of Dr Victor Bloom, and there was continuous debate as to whether the Society should publish a journal of scientific excellence or a record of the proceedings of the Society and its Sections. It was decided in 1981 that the *Journal* should reflect the activities of the Society and Sections more closely, and that it should be published by the Society alone.

This was not the end of the story: the *Journal* continued to be a loss-making operation and differences between Bloom and the Society's officers widened. Bloom was requested to resign his position but refused, and appealed to an industrial tribunal (the matter was settled out of court in 1986). Bloom's successor, Professor AJ Harding Rains, was previously editor of the *Annals of the Royal College of Surgeons of England* and he brought a new look to the Society's *Journal*. From January 1986 the format changed from quarto to A4, the design improved and priority was given to reports and articles emanating from meetings. Professor John Swales took over as Editor in 1995, and Dr Robin Fox in 1996.

The future of *Tropical Doctor*, which the Society had published for the benefit of doctors in developing countries since 1971, looked less rosy. The grants that supported it came to an end in 1986 and the far-flung, thinly distributed circulation of the publication made it an unlikely commercial success. Nevertheless, circulation figures increased to 1,695 in 1990, special issues were published and as *Tropical Doctor* approaches its 30th anniversary it remains greatly valued by those who need it. Another cause for concern, though a short-lived one, voiced in the Council room at 1 Wimpole Street in 1986 was the publication of *Growing up*, a booklet on sex education published by the RSM in association with Modus Books. The explicit text and illustrations offended some Council members, and one past President complained that it was 'highly explicit and amoral'.[34]

The editorial and publications departments merged in 1985 under the directorship of Mr Howard Croft, and developed into the RSM Press in 1994. The list of journals under its imprint expanded steadily and among the most recent titles are the *Journal of Medical Biography*, the *British Medical Bulletin*, the *Journal of Telemedicine and Telecare* and the *Journal of Laryngology and Otology*. Monographs on eponymists in medicine and on medical history began to be published from the 1980s, followed by the mighty tome on the Society's Presidents by Dr JH Moll (1996) and *Clinical governance: making it happen* (1999) by Dr Myriam Lugon and Dr Jonathan Secker-Walker, which topped the *BMJ* best-selling list for several months. Mr Peter Richardson took over the directorship in 1997.

## Change and reform in the 1990s

During the last turbulent decade of the 20th century the pace of change quickened as the Society took steps to strengthen its academic reputation and to adapt to the challenging circumstances in which doctors found themselves. From the appointment of an Academic Administrator in 1991 to the recommendations of the Strategic Academic Review Group in 1999 the goal has been to reinforce the RSM as an academic institution dedicated to medical professional development.

The Medical Services Secretary, Dr Mann, resigned in 1991 believing that he was not given the scope to carry through his policies, and the choice of his successor, designated the Academic Administrator, proved unfortunate. Dr Robyn Young's appointment was not confirmed at the end of her probationary period and this caused disquiet. A combination of circumstances gave rise to suspicions that 'All's not well at the Royal Society of Medicine', this being the title of an article in the *BMJ*; this was soon followed by a letter from Dr Bloom, formerly editor of the RSM *Journal*, criticizing the publication policy and the Society's alleged 'don't rock the boat' mentality.[35] As a consequence of these ructions, the President, Sir David Innes Williams, strongly recommended that the post of Academic Administrator (as a salaried position subordinate to the Executive Director) should be replaced by the appointment of a Dean as one of the Honorary Officers (with an allowance for expenses) and that a senior doctor with experience of administration and postgraduate education should be recruited for the post.

The Honorary Officers' 'Think Tank' accordingly set to work to consider this proposal in the context of the national role of the Society and its relationship with the medical profession and the lay public. The resulting report of 1992 affirmed that the academic strength of the Society lay with the Sections and Fora, that the Library was its most prized possession and that the Society's conferences made a contribution to public debate on a wide variety of subjects. It was also agreed that the academic content of the conferences and meetings would be fortified by the appointment of a Dean and happily Professor Paul Turner, who had been forced through ill health to retire from full-time work as Professor of Clinical Pharmacology at St Bartholomew's Hospital, accepted the post in 1993. In the two years before his sudden death he established a new regime in the Continuing Medical Education Department upon which his successors were able to build. An international conference on that subject was held at 1 Wimpole Street and the Society was pleased to announce that its meetings would have CME accreditation, beginning with the 1994–95 session. This was good news for Fellows, who could now fulfil the CME requirements at no cost other than their membership subscriptions.

While the 'Think Tank' was deliberating, so was the Policy and Procedures Review committee. Their report of 1993 recommended the abolition of ambiguous by-laws, the reform of procedures and increased representation for Fora on the Society's Council. Reform was in the air when the Executive Director, Robert Thomson, resigned due to ill health in January 1993. His successor, Dr John Green, a mathematician from Queen's College, Cambridge, took the post of Chief Executive and brought an aggressive management style to the RSM. The purse strings were tightened and financial accountability, maximum efficiency, reorganization and redundancies were the orders of the day. During Green's whirlwind directorship a new corporate identity was stamped on the Society, reflected in the *Annual Report*, the *Journal* and the *RSM News*. After some problems an integrated computer system was introduced and Genesis went live early in 1995. For the first time the Library was able to offer a computerized catalogue to readers (previously the card catalogue had been produced using a monstrous tape typewriter and then a primitive word processor). As computerization took hold in the 1990s the Library progressed to the Unicorn system in 1997, and the online catalogue followed the next year. As Librarian between 1977 and 1995 Mr DWC Stewart nursed the Library through a difficult transition period, ensuring that it embraced the emerging electronic world without losing touch with its curatorial heritage or neglecting its historical collection. His successor and namesake, Mr David Stewart, took the new title of Director of Information Services, and he was succeeded in the post by Mr Ian Snowley in 1999.

As the Publications Department developed into the RSM Press, the CME Department was also transformed into the Academic Department under Mr Adrian Marston as Honorary Dean. The Society took over the administration of the Medical Society for the Study of Venereal Diseases and provided accommodation for the Academy of Royal Medical Colleges. The RSM Foundation was subject to reforms and the revision of by-laws advanced: thus Green's presence was felt at every level of the Society, from the Academic Department to the kitchens.

Dr Green left the RSM abruptly in July 1996, whereupon the Society found stability and confidence under the presidency of Sir Christopher Paine and with the appointment of Dr Anne Grocock as Executive Director. The Academic Board came into being and agreement on new by-laws was reached; attendances at Section and Forum meetings rose, the number of Society conferences increased to 30 for the 1996–97 session, a new post of Honorary Sub-Dean was created and fresh appointments in the RSM Press and Library and Information Services heralded vigorous developments in these departments.

The Academic Board chaired by Dr Richard Lansdown immediately began to explore new initiatives, improvements in the organization of meetings and the co-ordination of programmes. The revision of the by-laws provided the Society with a more effective Council and a more efficient committee structure, and led to a petition for a new Supplemental Charter (Plate 76). This was granted on 21 October 1998 and formally signed in Letters Patent of 10 February 1999, 165 years after King William IV had granted the original charter to the Royal Medical and Chirurgical Society and nearly 200 years since the foundation of the Medical and Chirurgical Society in 1805. During that span of time the Society has remained loyal to the first, unanimous resolution of its founder-members that a society 'comprehending the several Branches of the medical profession be established in London for the purpose of conversation on professional subjects, for the reception of communications and for the formation of a library'.

The Library, one of the largest postgraduate biomedical libraries in Europe, now boasts a collection of some 10,000 periodical titles and in the region of 500,000 volumes. Through its Library, its members, meetings and publications the Society has both influenced and reflected the achievements of medicine and surgery over two centuries – advances such as the first transfusion of blood in humans, the use of anaesthetics in major surgery, the development of antiseptic surgery, the application of radiology to medicine, the discovery of penicillin and the unravelling of the human genome. As horizons expanded, so did the Society – by the creation of 40 Sections devoted to the specialties,

The commemorative bronze medal designed by Dr John Moll is awarded from time to time to distinguished people on occasions such as the millennium. It was first presented to the Princess Royal when she received the Honorary Fellowship and gave a lecture 'A little knowledge is a dangerous thing' in 1998.

through the work of the multidisciplinary Fora and by organizing conferences to address issues of public interest. Thus the Royal Society of Medicine has cultivated and developed the academic principles on which the Medical and Chirurgical Society was founded in 1805.

1 RSM, *Annual Report of Council 1954–55.*

2 I am most grateful to Sir David Innes Williams for his major contribution to this chapter.

3 BMJ (ii) 21 December 1912 pp. 1725, 1732.

4 CM 18 June 1918.

5 RSM, *Annual Report of Council 1938–39.*

6 Supplement to PRSM vol 52 (1959).

7 Clark, Sir George and Cooke, AM, *A history of the Royal College of Physicians of London* vol iii (1972) p. 1074.

8 Davidson, Maurice, *The Royal Society of Medicine. The realization of an ideal 1805–1955* (1955) p. 122.

9 *Ibid* p. 123.

10 BMJ (ii) 5 December 1953 pp. 1264–66.

11 CM 1945–49.

12 New building 1950–51, H7.

13 PRSM vol 47 (1954).

14 RSM, *Annual Report of Council 1963–64.*

15 *Ibid 1962–63.*

16 CM 27 November 1963.

17 Cherry, Bridget, and Pevsner, Nikolaus, *The buildings of England. London 3: North West* (1991) p. 653. The name of Robert Adam's brother James appears in the rate book of 1771, also on a survey of 1797–99. Some designs for the interior decoration of Chandos House survive at the Sir John Soane Museum.

18 RSM, *Annual Report of Council 1964–65.*

19 Letter Wells to Boyer 18 March 1964. The Royal Society of Medicine Foundation Inc, 'A twenty year retrospective', typescript 1987. RSM Foundation, ' A celebration of 25 years of service', typescript 1992. I am grateful to Claire Jackson for her resumé of the RSM Foundation.

20 O'Reilly, William G, 'Report on RSM Foundation' (1996).

21 Walton, John, *The spice of life* (1993) pp. 474–75.

22 I am grateful to Claire Jackson for a copy of her memorandum of the Medico-Pharmaceutical Forum, June 1999.

23 CM 23 April 1968.

24 RSM, *Annual Report of Council 1970–71, 1973–74, 1974–75.*

25 Dacie's letter of resignation 9 January 1978, CM 17 January 1978.

26 CM 18 April 1978.

27 The article was written by Dr Barbara Evans, *World Medicine* 14 June 1978 pp. 21–23. Subsequent correspondence (12 July 1978 p. 17) claimed that the RSM had lost its way. *Private Eye* libelled three Fellows, CM 22 August 1978.

28 RSM, *Annual Report 1979–80.*

29 *Ibid 1981–82.*

30 *Ibid.*

31 *Ibid.*

32 JRSM vol 78 July 1985 pp. 599–602.

33 Complementary Medicine Colloquia 1982–86, MC/01, Box 112.

34 CM 15 July 1986.

35 BMJ vol 304 9 May, 20 June 1992 pp. 1201, 1636.

# General Bibliography

Particular references are given in the Notes to each Chapter.

Acierno, Louis J, *The history of cardiology* (1994).

Atkinson, Richard S and Boulton, Thomas B (eds), *The history of anaesthesia* (1989).

Austoker, Joan and Bryder, Linda (eds), *The Medical Research Council* (1989).

Berrios, E Germann and Porter, Roy, *The history of clinical psychiatry* (1995).

Blair, JSG, *In arduis fidelis: centenary history of the Royal Army Medical Corps 1898–1998* (1998).

Blandy, John and Williams, JP, *The history of the British Association of Urological Surgeons 1945–1995* (1995).

Bynum, WF, Lock, Stephen and Porter, Roy (eds), *Medical journals and medical knowledge* (1993).

Bynum WF and Porter, Roy, *Companion encyclopedia of the history of medicine* 2 vols (1993).

Clark, Sir George and Cooke, AM, *A history of the Royal College of Physicians of London* 3 vols (1964–72).

Copeman, WSC, *A short history of the gout and the rheumatic diseases* (1964).

Cartwright, FF, *The development of modern surgery* (1967).

Collins, ET, *Moorfields Eye Hospital* (1929).

Cooter, Roger, *In the name of the child: health and welfare* (1992) and *Surgery and society in peace and war: orthopaedics and the organization of modern medicine 1880–1948* (1993).

Davidson, Maurice, *The Royal Society of Medicine. The realization of an ideal 1805–1955* (1955).

Dixon, Allan St J, *Rheumatology in the United Kingdom: 50 years of progress in treatment and education* (2000).

Duncum, Barbara D, *The development of inhalation anaesthesia* (1994).

Dunnill, Michael, *The Plato of Praed Street: the life and times of Almroth Wright* (2000).

Ellis, Harold, *Surgical case histories of the past* (1994).

Fairbank, HAT, Bristow, W and Platt, H (eds), *The Robert Jones birthday volume* (1928).

Holmes, Sir Gordon, *The National Hospital, Queen Square* (1954).

Lawrence, Christopher, *No laughing matter, historical aspects of anaesthesia* (1987).

Le Vay, AD, *The history of orthopaedics* (1990).

Loudon, Irvine, *The tragedy of childbed fever* (2000).

Major, RH, *Classic descriptions of disease* (1945).

Medvei, VC, *The history of clinical endocrinology* (1993).

Moll, JMH, *Presidents of the Royal Society of Medicine. Illustrated profiles 1805–1996* (1996).

Moore, Norman and Paget, Stephen, *The Royal Medical and Chirurgical Society of London. Centenary 1805–1905* (1905).

Munk, William *et al*, *The roll of the Royal College of Physicians of London* 9 vols (1878–1994).

Osler, Sir William, *The evolution of modern medicine* (1921).

Partington, JR, *A history of chemistry* vol 3 (1963).

Pelling, Margaret, *Cholera, fever and English medicine 1825–65* (1978).

Peterson, MJ, *The medical profession in mid-Victorian London* (1978).

Pettigrew, TJ, *Medical portrait gallery. Biographical memoirs of the most celebrated physicians, surgeons etc* 3 vols (1838–40).

Porter, Roy, *The greatest benefit to mankind* (1997).

Power, Sir D'Arcy *et al*, *Plarr's lives of the Fellows of the Royal College of Surgeons of England* 2 vols *et seq* (1930–70).

Power, Sir D'Arcy, *Masters of medicine* (1936) and *British medical societies* (1939).

Poynter, FNL, *Evolution of medical practice in Britain* (1961).

Raven, Sir Ronald, *The theory and practice of oncology* (1990).

Rosen, George, *The specialization of medicine* (1944).

Shorter, Edward, *A history of psychiatry: from the era of the asylum to the age of Prozac* (1997).

Shryock, Richard H, *The development of modern medicine* (1948).

Singer, Charles and Underwood EA, *A short history of medicine* (1928).

Starr, Douglas, *Blood: an epic story of medicine and commerce* (1998).

Wallace, Anthony F, *The progress of plastic surgery. An introductory history* (1982).

Walton, John, Barondess, Jeremiah and Lock, Stephen (eds), *The Oxford medical companion* (1994).

Waugh, William, *A history of the British Orthopaedic Association* (1993).

Webster, Charles, *The health services since the war* 2 vols (1988,1996).

Weir, Neil, *Otolaryngology: an illustrated history* (1996).

White, Sir William Hale, *Great doctors of the nineteenth century* (1935).

# Appendix

## The Presidents of the Society 1805–2000

William Saunders 1805–08
Matthew Baillie 1808–10
Sir Henry Halford 1810–13
Sir Gilbert Blane 1813–15
Henry Cline 1815–17
William Babington 1817–19
Sir Astley Cooper 1819–21
John Cooke 1821–23
John Abernethy 1823–25
George Birkbeck 1825–27
Benjamin Travers 1827–29
Peter Roget 1829–31
Sir William Lawrence 1831–33
John Elliotson 1833–35
Henry Earle 1835–37
Richard Bright 1837–39
Sir Benjamin Brodie 1839–41
Robert Williams 1841–43
Edward Stanley 1843–45
William Chambers 1845–47
James Arnott 1847–49
Thomas Addison 1849–51
Joseph Hodgson 1851–53
James Copland 1853–55
Caesar Hawkins 1855–57
Sir Charles Locock 1857–59
Frederic Skey 1859–61
Benjamin Babington 1861–63
Richard Partridge 1863–65
Sir James Alderson 1865–67
Samuel Solly 1867–69
Sir George Burrows 1869–71
Thomas Curling 1871–73
Charles Williams 1873–75
Sir James Paget 1875–77
Charles West 1877–79
Sir John Erichsen 1879–81
Andrew Barclay 1881–82
John Marshall 1882–84
Sir George Johnson 1884–86

George Pollock 1886–88
Sir Edward Sieveking 1888–90
Timothy Holmes 1890–92
Sir Andrew Clark 1892–93
Sir Jonathan Hutchinson 1894–96
William Dickinson 1896–98
Thomas Bryant 1898–1900
Frederick Pavy 1900–02
Alfred Willett 1902–04
Sir Richard Douglas Powell 1904–06
John Warrington Haward 1906–07
Sir William Selby Church 1907–10
Sir Henry Morris 1910–12
Sir Francis Champneys 1912–14
Sir Frederick Taylor 1914–16
Sir Rickman Godlee 1916–18
Sir Humphry Rolleston 1918–20
Sir John Bland-Sutton 1920–22
Sir William Hale-White 1922–24
Sir St Clair Thomson 1924–26
Sir James Berry 1926–28
Viscount Dawson of Penn 1928–30
Thomas Watts Eden 1930–32
Vincent Low 1932–34
Sir Robert Hutchison 1934–36
Sir John Parsons 1936–38
Sir Girling Ball 1938–40
Sir Archibald Gray 1940–42
Sir Henry Tidy 1942–44
Sir Gordon Gordon-Taylor 1944–46
Sir Maurice Cassidy 1946–48
Sir Henry Dale 1948–50
Lord Webb-Johnson of Stoke-on-Trent
    1950–52
Sir Francis Walshe 1952–54
Sir William Gilliatt 1954–56
Sir Clement Price Thomas 1956–58
Sir Geoffrey Marshall 1958–60
Lord Adrian of Cambridge 1960–62
Sir Terence Cawthorne 1962–64

Lord Cohen of Birkenhead 1964–66
Lord Porritt of Wanganui, NZ, and
    Hampstead 1966–67
Sir Hector MacLennan 1967–69
Lord Richardson of Lee 1969–71
Sir Hedley Atkins 1971–73
Sir John Stallworthy 1973–75
Sir Gordon Wolstenholme 1975–77
Sir John Dacie 1977–78
Lord Smith of Harlow 1978–80
Sir John Stallworthy 1980–82

Sir James Watt 1982–84
Lord Walton of Detchant 1984–86
Sir Gordon Robson 1986–88
Sir Christopher Booth 1988–1990
Sir David Innes Williams 1990–92
Sir George Pinker 1992–94
Sir Donald Harrison 1994–96
Sir Christopher Paine 1996–98
Lord Soulsby of Swaffham Prior
    1998–2000
Dame Deirdre Hine 2000–02

# Index

Information on *italicized* pages is to be found in an illustration or caption.

*A & E Letter* 426
Abel, Lawrence 373, 374
Abercrombie, Lord 158, 160
Abercrombie, George F 389, 390, 391
Abercrombie, George F, jr 356
Abercrombie, J 28
Abernethian Society 2
Abernethy, John 2, 10, 11, *41*, 48, 50, 414
Academy of Royal Medical Colleges 476
accident and emergency medicine *see under* Royal
      Society of Medicine: Sections
Acheson, Sir Donald 420
Acton, William 78–9, 153
Adam (lawyer) 53
Adam, Robert 463–4
Adams, Aileen 308
Adams, Joseph E 200
Adamson, Messrs (builders) 117
Addison, Christopher (Viscount Addison) 197
Addison, OL 356
Addison, Thomas 29, 30, 43, 84, 91, 97, 230, 382
Addison's disease 43–4, *Pl*.10, *Pl*.11
Adrian, Lord 265
AIDS 409, 420
Aikin, Arthur 26, 28, 59
Aikin, CR 5, 6, 10, 11, 26, 41, 58
Aikin, John 9, *Pl*.1
Aitken, D McCrae 358
Albee, Frederick 221, 359
Albers, JA 18, 56
Alderson, James 144
Alexandra, HRH Princess 442
alkaptonuria 28, 29, 153
All Russian Association of Neurologists 268
Allbutt, Thomas Clifford 80–81, 85, 149, 157, 290,
      291, 330, 365, 366, 367, *Pl*.21
Allchin, Sir William 182, *Pl*.21
Allen, JS 93
Allen, William 18, 19, 26
allergy *see under* Royal Society of Medicine:
      Sections, Clinical Immunology and Allergy
Althaus, Julius 264
American Neurological Association 268
American Proctologic Society 374
American Rhinology Society 275
Amies, Hardy 391
amnesic syndromes 327, 328
anaesthesia 112–13, 127–31, 199, 331
      *see also under* Royal Society of Medicine: Sections
Anaesthesia History Association 308

Anatomical Society of Great Britain 121, 172
Anatomy Act (1832) 96
Ancell, Henry 101
Anderson, Mr 371
Anderson, Louisa Garrett 246
Anderson, Terry 429
Andrewes, Christopher 234
Andrewes, FW 227
Andrews, Henry Russell 249, 251
angiology 441, 445–6
Anne, HRH, Princess Royal 316, *476*
Antibody Club 407
antisepsis 119, 134–7
aphasia 266
Apley, A Graham 364–5
Apothecaries Act (1815) 96
appendectomy 138–9
Arnott, James M 58, 78, 86
Arnott, Melville 399
Arnott, Neil 74, 96, 103
Arthritis and Rheumatism Council 318
artificial joints 363–4
Ashdown, Edwin 163
Ashley, Lord *see* Shaftesbury, Earl of
Ashton, Norman 341
Ashwell, Dr 104
Asscher, W 433
Association of Anaesthetists of Great Britain and
      Ireland 216, 306–7
Association of British Neurologists 267, 268
Association of British Pharmaceutical Industry 394
Association of Clinical Pathologists 229
Association of Coloproctology 374
Association of Coloproctology of Great Britain and
      Ireland 375–6
Association of Head and Neck Oncologists of Great
      Britain 418
Association of Industrial Medical Officers 398, 400
Association of Medical Advisors to the
      Pharmaceutical Industry 406
Association for Palliative Medicine 448
Association of Physicians of Great Britain and
      Ireland 214
Association of Police Surgeons 427, 428, 430
Association of Registered Medical Women 301
Association for the Study of Medical Education 410
Association for the Study of Obesity 443
asthma 408, 433
Astronomical Society 61
Athletae 3

Atkins, Sir Hedley 418
'aurorascope' 272
Aveling, JH 244

Babantini, Signor 30
Babington, Benjamin Guy 74, 75, 77, 79, 103, 104,
    108, 147, 230, 269, Pl.1
Babington, William 2, 11, 12, 18, 26, 29, 36, 44, 58,
    59, 74
Bacon, John 73
    medallion 73, 163, 180, Pl.16
Badcock, Mr 240–41
Bagshawe, KD 417, 419
Bailey, JB 157, 165
Baillie, Matthew 10, 11, 19, 20–21, 24, 34, 42, 50,
    51–3, 54, 414
    gifts to Library 19, 54
    Morbid anatomy 2, 10, 45, 54, 415
Bain, Dr 111–12
Baker, AWW 241
Baker Brown, Isaac 132, 244–5
Baldwin, Aslett 371
Baldwin, Sir Henry 241, 242
Baldwin, RW 417
Baldwin, Stanley 251
Ball, JB 270
Ball, William Girling 227, 352
Ballance, Charles 219, 255, 275, 276
balneology see under Royal Society of Medicine:
    Sections, Rheumatology and Rehabilitation
Baly, William 76, 85
Banister, Richard 87
Bankart, AS Blundell 357, 358, 359, 361
Banks, Sir Joseph 9, 10, 36, 58
Banks, William Mitchell 138, 144
Bannister, Sir Roger 427, 439
Banting, FG 293
Bantock, George 135
Barber, Geoffrey 388, 389, 390, 391
barbiturates 292–3
Barclay, AE 282, 287
Barclay, Andrew Whyte 119, 468
Barcroft, Sir Joseph 312
barium meals 282
Barker, Arthur 138
Barlow, Thomas 68, 120, 163, 182, 254, 255, 309
Barnard, Christiaan 436
Barnes, Henry, lectures 397
Barnes, Josephine 253, 445
Barnes, Robert 105, 167, 182, 244, 245
Barnes, Stanley 266
Barondess, Jeremiah 465
Barr, Dr 275
Barrett, Lady 249
Bashford, HH 235
Bass, Rolf 397
Bastian, H Charlton 141, 227, 263
Bateman, Thomas 16, 34, 54, 56, 57, 91, 92, 259
Bateman's disease see molluscum contagiosum
Bateson, William 190
Batten, FE 265, 334
Batten, George 282, 285
Battle, Richard 223, 413, 414
Bauwens, Philippe 320, 321
Baxter, P 450
Bayer Diagnostic 349

Bayley, Dr 330
Bayliss, RI 385, 387
Bayon, Dr 190
Beach, Sir Hugh 348
Bearn, Alexander 465–6
Beaumont, Mr 420
Beaumont, William 78
Beck, Marcus 182, 192
Beck, Roger 182, 192
Becquerel, Henri 280
Bedson, SF 229
Beevor, Charles 265
Belch, Jill 445, 446
Belcher, John 163, 172, 175, 180–81, 183, 185, 239
Belcher and Pite (architects) 163
Bell, Charles 34–5
Bell, Commander Digby 198
Bell, Thomas 74, 91
Bence-Jones, Henry 77, 93, 94–5, 309
Bennett, EA 327
Bennett, FJ 240
Bennett, John Hughes 140, 263
Bennett, Michael 428
Bennette, Graham 329, 417, 418, 440, 457, 468
Bensley, Sir William 72
Bentley, Edward 103
Berger, JF 17, 59
Berkeley, Comyns 245, 246, 251
Bernard, Claude 118, 119, 382
Bernaux, Thiébaut de 56
53 Berners Street 58, 62, 69, 71–6, 104, 108,
    116–17, 157, 163
Berry, EU 166
Berry, James 219, 222, 371
Berry, RJ 289
Berzelius, Jacob 16, 18, 26–7, 46, 59
Berzelius Symposium 237
Best, Mr Justice 60
Bevan, Aneurin 459
Bevan, Sylvanus 59
Beveridge Report 381
Bierer, Joshua 328
Billings, JS 177
Binnie, George 287
Biochemical Society Lipid Group 443
Biraud, Yves 236
Bird, Cuthbert Golding 87, 113
Birkbeck, George 1, 2, 6–7, 12, 19, 20, 26, 34, 42
Birt, JS 30
Bishop, PMF 382, 384, 386–7
Bishop, WJ 460
bismuth meals 282
Black, Sir James 203, 433
black and ethnic minority health 450
Blacker, George F 249, 251
Blair-Bell, William 245, 246, 251, 252
Blair-Bell Medal 250, 252, 253
Blair-Bell Research Society 418
Bland-Sutton, Sir John 135, 141, 219, 221–2, 246,
    252, 345, 415
Blandy, John 356
Blane, Gilbert 10, 24, 25, 46
blast injuries 223
blindness, definition 336
Blizard, William 3, 5, 10, 11, 16, 18
Blomfield, GW 288

Blomfield, Joseph 302, 305
blood transfusions 31–4
Bloom, Victor 474, 475
Blumenbach, JF 18
Blundell, James 29, 31–4, 43, 46
BMTV 473–4
Bodmer, Sir Walter 405
body armour 222–3
Boeck, Professor 153
Boer War 154
Boghurst, William 230
Bohr, Christian 167
3 Bolt Court, Fleet Street 5, 20
Bolton, Roger 397
Bombelli, Renato 364
Bonney, Victor 245, 246–7, 250, 351
Bostock, John 2, 9, 18, 25, 26, 29, 31, 37, 38, 39, 51,
    59, 69–70, 114
    interest in chemistry 27–8
    papers 19, 46, 84
    on *Transactions* 41, 42, 44
Bottomley, Peter 428
Bourne, Aleck 249
Bourne, Wesley 205, 306
Bowdler-Henry, C 243
Bowlby, Sir Anthony 198, 221, 255
Bowlby, John 313
Bowles, RL 112, 149
Bowman, William 76, 89, 137, 141, 333, *Pl.*21
Boyd, Mrs Stanley 182
Boyer, Francis 465
Boyle, HE 303–4, 305
Boyle, Helen 326
Boyton, James 171, 172, 180
Bradley, WH 236
Bradshaw lecture 415
*Brain* 264
Brain, Russell 265, 266, 268
brain surgery 140–41
Braine, F Woodhouse 301–2
brainwave studies 327
Brande, Everard 8, 15
Brande, WT 97
Brazier (patient) 32
breast cancer 137–8, 223–4, 411, 418
breastfeeding 312
Breathing Club 406
Brewster, Sir David 70
Bridport, Viscount 158, 160
Bright, Richard 26, 28, 29–30, 43, *83*, 103, 230
Bright, Timothy *323*
Bright's disease 30, 114, 148, *Pl.*9, *Pl.*69
Bristow, W Rowley 359, 361
Bristowe, JS 263
British Academy of Forensic Sciences 427
British Allergy Society 407
British Angiology Group 445
British Association for the Advancement of Science 70
British Association for Cancer Research 416, 418,
    419
British Association of Dermatology 261
British Association of Otolaryngologists 278
British Association for Physical Medicine 320, 322
British Association of Plastic Surgeons 411–12, 414
British Association for Psychopharmacology 329
British Association of Radiographers 287

British Association of Radiologists 285
British Association of Radiology and Physiotherapy
    200, 285
British Association of Rheumatology and
    Rehabilitation 322
British Association for Service to the Elderly 430
British Association of Sport and Medicine 438
British Association of Surgical Oncology 418
British Association of Urological Surgeons 354, 355,
    356
British Balneological and Climatological Society
    116, 172, 175, 301, 316–17
British Breast Group 418
British Council of Physical Education 198
British Dental Association 195, 238, 242
British Diabetic Association 386
British Electro-Therapeutic Society 173, 200, 213,
    280–81
British Geriatrics Society 430
British Gynaecological Society 121, 163, 173, 213,
    214, 244, 245
British Hyperlipidaemia Association 443
British Institute of Mental Handicap 444
British Institute of Radiology 200, 285, 289
British Laryngological, Rhinological and Otological
    Association 173, 213, 269–70
British League Against Rheumatism 321
British Medical Association 97, 99, 110, 281,
    324
    Psychological Medicine Group 423
*British Medical Journal* 101
British Nurses Association 163
British Nutrition Foundation 445
British Orthopaedic Association 358
British Orthopaedic Society 356, 357
British Paediatric Association 312
British Pathologists' Association 229
British Pharmacopoeia 203, 294
British Postgraduate Hospital and Medical School
    197
British Proctological Society 369, 370
British Rheumatism Association 321
British Small Animals Veterinary Association 368
British Social Hygiene Council 353
British Society of Audiology 279
British Society of Dental Hypnosis 423
British Society of Experimental and Clinical
    Hypnosis 423
British Society for Immunology 407
British Society of Medical and Dental Hypnosis 423
British Society of Radiotherapists 285
British Society for Research on Ageing 430, 431
British Society for Rheumatology 322
British Society of Social Gerontology 430
British Society for the Study of Orthodontics 241
British Transplantation Society 436
British X-ray and Radium Protection Committee
    284
Broadbent, Sir William 170, 263
Brocq, Louis 260
Brodie, Benjamin 15, 30–31, 36, 48–9, 68–9, 70, 71,
    85–6, 101, 111, 198, *350*
    papers 30–31, 46, 80, 86, 322
    on *Transactions* 49
Brook, Arthur L 364
Broster, LH 384, 386

Brown, Louise 253
Brown, Maud Forrester 359
Brown, TE Burton 289
Brown-Séquard, CE 110
Browne, Denis 313, 361
Browne, Sir George Buckston 192
Bruce, David 344
Bruce, Sir John 417, 424
Bruce, W Ironside 281, 283, 284
Brunel, Isambard Kingdom 30, 48–9
Brunton, Sir Thomas Lauder 206, 217, 220, 290
Bryans, Dame Anne 420, 440
Bryant, Thomas 133, 143–4
Buchanan, Colin 396
Buchanan, George S 230, 233
Buckley-Sharp, MD 411
Budd, George 83
Budd, William 83, 84
Bunnel, Sterling 361
Burd, HE 87
Burden Neurological Institute 267
Burdett-Coutts, Baroness 119
Burgess, Milner 310
Burghard, Colonel 195
Burkitt, Denis P 416–17
Burlington House, Piccadilly 107
    joint meeting with Royal Academy 420, *421*
Burn, Ian 417, 418, 425
Burn, John 76
Burnet, FM (Sir Macfarlane Burnet) 234, 408
Burney, Fanny 138
Burney, Peter 433
Burns, Kenneth 367
Burrows, Sir George 108, 109–10, 118, 139, 144,
    *Pl*.21
Burrows, H Jackson 362–3
Burt, WJ 179
Busk, George 83
Butcher, W Deane 281, 285
Butler, T Harrison 338
Butlin, HT 144
Buxton, Dudley W 128, 130, 131
Buxton, St JD 360
Buzzard, Sir Edward Farquhar 218, 265, 266, 267,
    326
Buzzard, Thomas 264
Byrne, Oscar 74

Cade, Sir Stanford 223
Cairns, Hugh 222, 266–7, 277
    memorial lecture 267
Callender, GW 139–40
Calman, Kenneth 427
Calnan, Charles 263, 408
Cameron, Sir Roy 229
Cameron, Thomas WM 367–8
Campbell, Janet 249
Campbell, Meredith 356
cancer 200, 223–4, 229, 247, 287, 288, 372, 414–19
Cannizzaro, Duchess of 158
Cantlie, James 290, 342
Capener, Norman 360, 362
Capon, NB 312
cardiothoracic medicine *see under* Royal Society of
    Medicine: Sections
Carew, FAE 368

Carleton, Alice 261
Carling, E Rock 222, 227, 354, 357, 370
Carlisle, Sir Anthony 430
Carne, Stuart 391
Carnegie, Andrew 177
Carpenter, George 310
Carpue, JC 413
Carrel, Alexis 436
Cartwright, Samuel 91, 106, 238, *Pl*.42
Carver, Field Marshal Lord 348
Carwardine, H 99
Case, Robert 401
Cassidy, Sir Maurice 455, 459
Casualty Surgeons' Association 424
cataract 341, *Pl*.19
Caton, Richard 331
Cattell, Richard 372
15 Cavendish Square 72, 142, 186–8, 245
Cawadias, AP 332
Cawthorne, Terence 278, 332, 395, 399
Celsus, *De medicina* 188, 206, *Pl*.36
Central Council of Recreative Physical Training 198
Centre for Complementary Health Studies (Exeter
    University) 473
Chadwick, Edwin 77, 97
    memorial prize and medal 348–9
Chain, Sir Ernst 227
Chalmers, AJ 206
Chalmers, Ian 441
Chamberlain, GVP 440
Chamberlain, Neville 198
Chamberlen, Peter, obstetrical instruments 99, *100*,
    330
Chambers, Dr 149
Chambers, William 71–2, 73
    chimneypiece 73, 163, 180, *Pl*.17
Champneys, Francis 165, 188, 207, 216, 245, 252,
    301, 330, 350
Chandos House 269, 418, 420, 456, 462–3, 470
11 Chandos Street 172, 259
Chaplin, Arnold 332
Chapman, Sydney 428
Charcot, Jean-Martin 118, 148, 430
Charles, HRH, Prince of Wales 346, 472, 473
Charlesworth, Mrs 397
Charnley, John 363–4
Cheatle, Arthur 275, 276
Chemical Club 16, 39
Cheselden, William 349, *350*
Cheshire, Leonard (Lord Cheshire) 466
Cheyne, William Watson 120, 135, 150, 153–4, 199
Childe, Charles 200, 247
Chippingdale, Dr 318
chloroform anaesthesia 112–13, 129, 130–31, 137,
    302–3
cholera 83–4, 104, 120
Choppin, Purnell W 465
Christian, James S 110, 111
Church, Sir William Selby *170*, 186, 190, 207, 214,
    331, 342, 415
    and birth of RSM 170, 173, 177, 213
    and Wimpole Street building 180, 185
Churchill (bookseller) 76
Churchill, Rt Hon Winston 204
Ciba Foundation, sponsored students 461
Clark, Sir Andrew 151, 158, 219

Clarke, Archibald 165
Clarke, Ernest 334, 338
Clarke, Jackson 357
Clarke, JFL 12, 19, 48, 94, 101
Clarke, John 92, 309
Clarkson, Patrick 411, 413
Clayton, Cuthbert 166
Clayton, Janet 191
Clegg, Hugh 343
Clendinning, John 74, 88
Cliffe, Percy 403–5, 406
Clift, William 45, *46*, 70, *415*
climatology and balneology 115–16
    see also under Royal Society of Medicine: Sections,
        Rheumatology and Rehabilitation
Cline, Henry 10, 12, 19, 24, 28, 29, 32, 36, 50
Clinical Endocrinology Trust 387
clinical medicine see under Royal Society of
    Medicine: Sections
Clinical Society of London 102, 103, 106, 109, 161,
    163, 172, 213, 254, 279–80
clitoridectomy 245
Clover, JT 113, 127, 128, 130
Clowes, William 186
Clutterbuck, Henry 6–7, 12, 39
Cobham, Viscount 158
Cock, Edward 89–90, 128
Cock, FW 330
Cockayne, EA 462
Coga, Arthur 31–2
Cohen, Lord 322, 332, 387, 405, 406, 407–8, 410,
    467
Cohen, B 243
Cohen Report 390
Cole, RH 324
Coleman, WS 264
College of Dentists of England 238
College of Obstetricians and Gynaecologists 245
Collette, Charles 186
Collier, James 266
Collier, Josephine 278
Collins, E Treacher 334, 338, 339
Collins, Thomas 71, 73
Collinson, Nelson 220
colocystoplasty 356
coloproctology see under Royal Society of Medicine:
    Sections
colour blindness 340
Colyer, JF (Sir Frank Colyer) 239, 240, 241, 242
Colyer Prize 205
Comandon, Jean 190–91
Comfort, AC, lecture 432
Comfort, Alex 430, 431, 432
Commonwealth Association for Mental Handicap
    and Developmental Disabilities 444
communication in health care 411, 444
community medicine 236–7
    see also under Royal Society of Medicine: Sections,
        Epidemiology and Public Health
Community Services Broadcasting 473–4
comparative medicine see under Royal Society of
    Medicine: Sections
complementary therapies 472–3
Compston, Nigel 417
computers in medicine 406, 447
Conan Doyle, Arthur 169

Conjoint Examining Board 121
contact lenses 340
Cooke, John 16, 39, 54
Coolidge, William 282
Cooper, Astley 2, 10, 11, 17, 29, 30, 34, 35, 37–8, 39,
    49, 50, 58, 60, 68–9, 70, 74, 85, 87, 109–10, *Pl.8*
    arterial surgery 18, 23, *41*, 46
    ear surgery 89
    on mastectomy 137–8
    and Moorfields Hospital 89
    report of lecture 48
    spina bifida surgery 27
Cooper, Bransby 87
Cooper, EH 417
Cooper, Samuel 57–8, 87
Coote, Holmes 128, 129
Cope, Sir Zachary 332, 351
Copeman, Sydney Monckton 200, 235
Copeman, William SC 318, 321, 322, 332–3
Copland, James 61, 74, 101, 147
Corbett, RS 373
corneal transplantation 339
Corner, Beryl 313
Corney, Bolton 462
Corvisart, Jean 17, 18
Cosmas, Saint 436, *Pl.70*
Costello, John 433
cot death 315
Cotchin, E 416, 417
Coulson, William 349
Council of British Ophthalmologists 338
Council Club 191–2
Council for Complementary and Alternative
    Medicine 473
Cournand, AF 465
Courtland (clerk) 40
Cowan, David 439
Craig, Howard 465
Craig, John 449
Craig, Sir Maurice 292–3, 324
Crawfurd, Raymond 330
creosote 68
cretinism 148, 382, *383*
Crichton, George 289
Crichton-Brown, James 263, 264, 275
Crimean War 99
Critchett, Sir George Anderson 334, 337, 338
Critchley, Macdonald 266, 268, 338, 347
Crocker, H Radcliffe 258
Croft, Howard 474
Croft, John 120, 154
Croft, Richard 8
Crombie, Donald 391
Crosby, Sir Thomas Boor 181–2
Crosse, John G 37
croup 115
Crown and Anchor 15, *Pl.2*
Cumberbatch, Alphonso 275, 285
Cumberlege, Baroness Julia 442
Cumming, William 89
Cumston, Charles 204–5
    lectures 205
curare 307
Curie, Pierre and Marie 199, 200, 280
Curling, Thomas B 109, 113, 114, 130, 148, 382, *383*
Curran, Desmond 292, 327, 329

Curry, James 2, 16, 23, 29, 34, 59, 88
Cushing, Harvey 267
Cushny, AR 290, 291
Cuthbert (subtenant) 61
Cuvier, Georges 18
cyclothymia 326
cystic fibrosis 316
Czermak, Johann 79, *80*, 269

Dacie, Sir John 229, 269, 408, 468
Dalby, Sir William 275
    memorial prize 205
Dale, Sir Henry 205, 291, 294, 305, 328, 386, 397, 460, 461
Daley, William Allen 218, 235
Dalling, Sir Thomas 367
Dallos, Josef 340
Dallos, Vera 424, 425, 426
Dalrymple, John 89, 94–5
Dalrymple-Champneys, Weldon 233, 235–6
Dalton, A Mark 427
Dama, Charles 264
Damian, Saint 436, *Pl*.70
Dandy, Walter 266
D'Arcy, ED 354
Darier, Ferdinand-Jean 261
Darwin, Charles 95, 115, 118–19, 145
    home and Museum 368
Darwin, Leonard 188
David, TJ 316
Davidson, Sir James MacKenzie 282, 284, 288
Davis, Dr 46
Davis, John A 315
Davis, Neville 427–9
Davy, Humphry 9, 16, 19, 26, 27, 29, 36, 58
Davy, John 81, 93
Dawkins, Massey 308
Dawson, Sir Bertrand (Viscount Dawson of Penn) 194, 197, 198, 203–4, 284, 381, 459
Dawson Report 197, 381
de Morgan, Campbell 101
de Santi, PRW 147
de Valois, Dame Ninette 391
de Watteville, A 263, 264
Dean, HR 228
Dean, Peter 430
Debarry, Richard 60, 61
Dellow, Sir John 429
dental caries 240
Dental Federation of Japan 242
Dentists Act 238, 242
Dering Yard 456, 458, 460
Dermatological Society of Great Britain and Ireland 92, 173, 213, 214, 258
Dermatological Society of London 92, 121, 172, 213, 214, 258
dermatology 91–2
    *see also under* Royal Society of Medicine: Sections
Deville, Pierre 261
Dick, W 154
Dick-Read, Grantly 252
Dickinson (shorthand writer) 271
Dickinson, WH 114, 115, 154
Dickson, Air Vice Marshal 279
digitalis 290, *Pl*.47
Dill, JF Gordon 198

Dimsdale, Mr 5
diphtheria 82, 115, 234, 235
Dixon, James 76, 77
Dixon, WE 291, 292
    memorial lecture 205, 291, 293, 294, 397
Dobell, Horace 109
Dodd, Harold 370, 373–4
'Dogger Bank itch' 400
Dogs' Protection Bill 199
Dohi 261
Doll, Sir Richard 232, 237–8, 284, 400, 406, 416, 417, 418, 466, *Pl*.71
Domus Medica 456, 464, 472
Donald, Archibald 248
Donald, KW 397
Doniach, Deborah 408
Dore, SE 258, 261
Dormandy, JA 406, 440, 441, 442, 443, 445
Doucet, Dr 42
Doveton, Major-General 179
Dowdeswell 120
Dowling, GB 262
Dowling Oration 262
Druitt, R 129
Dubois, Nicholas 158
Duckworth, Sir Dyce 240
Dudgeon, Professor 343
Dudley, Sir Sheldon 347, 349
Duffield, Robert 443
Duffin, EW 98
Duke-Elder, Phyllis 339
Duke-Elder, Sir Stewart 334, 339
Dukes, E Cuthbert 352–3, 373
Duncan, HM 128–9
Duncan, J Matthews 135
Dundas, David 8, 24, 30
Dundas-Grant, Sir James 202, 272, 275, 276, 277
Dunlop, Sir Derrick 203
Dunn, John 50
Dunn, Naughton 359
Dunn, TL 329
Durham, AE 79
Durning-Lawrence, Sir Edwin 182
Dwyer, FC 364
Dyke, SC 227

Earle, Henry 39, 50, 71
East, Norwood 327
Eccles, A Symons 120–21
eclampsia 249
Eden, T Watts 207, 246, 249, 251, 252, 286, 319
Edinburgh Club 16
Edinburgh, HRH Prince Philip, Duke of 456, 470, *Pl*.72
Edis, RW 117
Edridge-Green, FW 340
Edward, Prince of Wales (*later* Edward VIII) 198
Edward VII, King 131, 139, 167, 215
Edwards, Alan 257
Edwards, Frederick Swinford 369, 370
Edwards, Geoffrey 201, 208
Edwards, George 307, 384
Edwards, Robert G 252–3
Edwards, Tudor 222, 434
Ehrlich, Paul 153
Eiseman, Ben 348

Eiser, Richard 444
electro-convulsive therapy 328
electrotherapy 113–14
    see also Royal Society of Medicine: Sections,
        Radiology
Elgood, FM 158, 179, 180–81
Elizabeth II, Queen 427, 470, 472, Pl.72
Elliot, Lt Colonel 336
Elliotson, John 30, 68, 69, 70, Pl.65
    and mesmerism 82, 101, 422
Ellis, JS 364
Ellis, Maurice 424
Ellison, Carice 404
Ellison–Cliffe lectures 404–5
Ellman, Philip, lecture 434
Elmslie, RC 221, 357, 358, 359, 362
Elsom, Pack and Roberts (architects) 470, 471
Emergency Medicine Research Society 425, 426–7
Emergency Surgical Aid Corps 195–6, 457
Emery, John L 315
Empire Rheumatism Council 318, 321
Endocrine Society 252
endocrinology 290
    see also under Royal Society of Medicine: Sections
engineering in medicine 406
English, Sir Terence 434, 435
epidemics 82–5
Epidemiological Society of London 75, 97, 99, 102,
    104, 108, 172, 202, 213, 230, 231
epidemiology see under Royal Society of Medicine:
    Sections
Erichsen, John 77, 78, 110, 119, 128, 133, 144, Pl.21
erysipelas 29–30
ethanesal 305
ether anaesthesia 112, 113, 127–30, 303
Eugenics Education Society 188, 189
European Conference on Clinical Haemorheology
    440
European Symposium on Scientific Studies in
    Mental Retardation 440, 444
Eustachi, Bartolomeo 89, 90
Evans, DE Laming 357, 358, 359, 362
Evans, Grimley 431, 432
Everidge, John 354
Excerpta Medica Foundation 464
experimental medicine see under Royal Society of
    Medicine: Sections
Expert Witness Institute 429
eye banks 339
Eyre, JW 240
Eysenck, Hans 327

Facial Pain Symposium 244
facial palsy 279
Faculty of Child Psychiatry 316
Faculty of Occupational Medicine 402, 403
Faculty of Ophthalmologists 338
Fagge, C Hilton 148, 345, 382, 383
Fairbairn, John S 249, 251, 252
Fairbank, Sir Thomas 312, 357, 359–60, 361
Fairley, G Hamilton 407, 408
Falkland Islands campaign symposium 348
Family Doctor Charter (1966) 392
Faraday, Michael 12, 70, 97, 99, 107
Farquhar, Sir Walter 10, 19, 24, 50
Farre, Arthur 16, 77

Fayrer, Sir Joseph 153
Featherstone, HW 306
Federation of Medical and Allied Societies 198
Fenwick, Edwin Hurry 349–50, 356
Fenwick, Samuel 85, 149
Ferguson, John 397
Ferguson, Richard 428
Ferguson, Robert 59
Ferguson-Smith, MA 439
Fergusson, JD 355–6
Fergusson, William 25, 78, 85, 87, 129
Ferrier, David 117, 140, 141, 207, 263
fevers 82
Findlay, L 311
Finlay, Ilora 448
Finzi, Isobel 288
Finzi, Neville 255, 286, 287, 288, 325
Finzi, Winifred 288
Finzi lecture 288, 289
Fish, E Wilfred 242–3
Fitton, Dr 45
FitzWilliams, Duncan 223–4
Fixsen, JA 365
Fleming, Alexander 194, 218, 227–8, 255, 290, 293,
    334, 340, 367
Fleming, GWT 328
Fletcher, Charles M 395, 399
Fletcher, Ernest, memorial lecture 321
Flockhart, William 160–61
Florence, Henry L 182
Florey, Sir Howard 227, 228, 293
Floyer, Sir John, Medicina gerocomica 430, 431
Foerster, Professor 221
food and health 445
Fordyce, Dr 2
forensic medicine see under Royal Society of
    Medicine: Sections, Clinical Forensic and Legal
    Medicine
Forensic Science Society 427
Formby, Myles L 405
Forrest, Sir Patrick 224
Forshall, Isabella 313
Forsyth, Harry 240
Foster, WD 227
Foster Kennedy, Robert 265
Fothergill, John 2, 82, 115
Fothergill, William 248
Fountain, SW 435
Fowler, Christopher 356
Fowler, James Kingston 216
Fox, Robert Fortescue 316, 317–18, 321
Fox, Robin 474
Fox, T Colcott 206, 258, 259, 260
Foxen, EH Miles 278
Fracastoro, Girolamo 152
Franck, James 20, 59
Frangenheim, Hans 252
Frank, Howard 180
Frank, J 16
Fraser, Russell 387
Frederick, Crown Prince of Prussia 147
Freemasons' Tavern
    anniversary dinners 61
    meetings at 7–8, 12, 16–17, 54, 104
Freind, John 330
Freud, Anna 315, 325, 328

Freud, Sigmund 325
Freudenberg, RK 328
Freudenthal, Walter 261, 262
Freyer, Sir Peter 351
Frohlich, LW 395, 467
Fry, John 392, 393, 398, 411
Fuller, Francis 438
Furnivall, Percy 370

Gabell, Douglas 242
Gabriel, WB 372, 373, 374
Gaffin, Jean *422*
Gairdner, William 76
Galbraith, Walter 352
gall stones 138
Gamble, Norman 205
  prize 205, 277
Gant, FJ 154, 166
Garcia, Manuel 79, 269
Gardner-Hill, H 384
Garner, Alec 341
Garrod, Sir Alfred 30, 153
Garrod, Sir Archibald E 29, 115, 153, 154, 170, 254, 332, 334
Garthshore, Maxwell 11
Gary, Dr Albert 279
Gascoyen, George 114, 153
Gask, George 222, 303
Gaskell, Walter H 117, 131, 167
Gauvain, Sir Henry 284–5, 361
Gauvain, Suzette 401–2
Gay, John 100–1
Gee, Samuel 217
Gemmell, Sir Arthur 252
general practice *see under* Royal Society of Medicine: Sections
Geological Society 58–9, 70
George IV, King 37
George V, King 186, 203, 319
George, Phyllis 224
geriatrics and gerontology *see under* Royal Society of Medicine: Sections
German Dermatological Society 260
Gibb, GD 79
Gibbs, James 178–9
Gibbs, Sir Vicary 51
Gibson, William, memorial prize 205
Gilford, Hastings 142
Gill, Richard 302
Gilliatt, Sir William 252
Gillies, Sir Harold 223, 224, 256, 293, 411, *412*, 413, 436
Gilpin, Dr 25
Gilson, JC 401
Girdlestone, GR 360
Gissane, William 364
glass eyes 337
glaucoma 137
Glaxo Prize 224
Glenny, AT 232
'glottiscope' 79, 269
Goadby, Kenneth 240
Godber, Sir George 405, 406
Goddall, EW 233
Godfrey, Martin 393–4
Godlee, Rickman J 103, 134, 138, 142, 154, 165,

195, 207, 219, 301, 344
  brain surgery 140, 263
G Godson and Sons (builders) 180
Goldmann, E 216, 219
Golla, FL 265, 266, 292, 326, 328, 460
Gooch, Dr 94
Good, John Mason 20
Goodall, Dr 235
Goodhart, Sir James 138, 190
Goodsall, DH 370
Goodwin, Sir John 344, 345
Gordon, JA 58
Gordon, WA 318
Gordon-Taylor, Sir Gordon 223–4, 346, 373, 415, 458
Gordon-Watson, Sir Charles 371, 372, 373
Gosse, Edmund 205
Gould, Sir Alfred Pearce 182, 201
Goulden, Charles 340
Gowers, William 117, 138, 141, 190, 264, 265
Graefe, Albrecht von 137
Granville, Lord 107
Granville, AB 60, 104
Gray, Archibald 260
Gray, Cecil 307
Gray's medical walking stick 96
Great Exhibition (1851) 96
Great Ormond Street Hospital 93, 309
Green, John 457, 466, 475, 476
Green, Stanley 281
Greene, Raymond 382, 384, 385
Greenhow, Edward Headlam 106, 254
Greenough, GB 58, 59
Greenwood, Arthur 204
Greenwood, Major 233
Gregory, George 84
Greig, William 406
Gretton, JH 158
Griffiths, Eldon 396
Grimble, AS 398
Grimsdale, Harold 336
Grocock, Anne 457, 476
group therapy 328
Groves, EW Hey 220–21, 362
*Growing up* 474
Guillemeau, Jacques 87, *88*
Gull, William 84, 114, 146, 148, 382–3
Gulliver, George 81
Gullstrand, Professor 338
Gunn, A Rugg 340
Gunn, JA 292
Gunn, JC 429
Guthrie, Douglas 332
Guttman, Ludwig 268, 328
Guy's Hospital, Physical Society 2, 11, 24, 36
Gynaecological Visiting Society 245, 251
gynaecology *see under* Royal Society of Medicine: Sections, Obstetrics and Gynaecology

Haber, Henry 261
Haddow, Alexander 218, 416
  memorial lectures 416–17
Hadfield, Charles 305
Hadfield, Geoffrey 229
haemorheology 406, 440–41, 445
Haighton, John 2, 8, 9, 29, 31, *Pl.*1

Haldane, Lord 323
Hale-White, Sir William 190, 255, 366, 371
Halford, Sir Henry 34, 50, 51–3, 54, 69, 74
Hall, Edward 78
Hall, Marshall 40, 46, 58, 80, 93–4, 110–11, 182
    memorial prize 82, 117–18, 182, 265
Hall, Simson 276
Hall-Edwards, JF 280, 283
Halliburton, Dr 148
Hallpike, CS 266, 267, 277
Halsted, William 138
Halton, John 307
Hamer, William 230, 233
Hamerton, Lt Colonel Albert 344
Hamilton, James 18
Hamilton, Max 405
Hamilton-Russell, Mrs 292
Hammond, TE 354
Hancock, Dr 6
Handfield-Jones, D 110
Handley, RS 417
Handley, Sampson 221, 370, 371
Hanley, Howard G 355, 356
20 Hanover Square 72, 121, 150–51, 158–63, 172,
    214, 239, 245, Pl.27
    leased from RSM 180
    master key 154, Pl.23
    possible rebuilding 175
Hare, Dr 108
Harley, George 113
Harley, John 110, 118, 137
Harman, N Bishop 265, 311, 334, 335, 336
Harris, E Vincent 180
Harris, Lord 429
Harris, RJC 417
Harris, Wilfrid 265
Harrison, Benjamin 44
Hart, Bernard 218, 324, 326
Harvey, William
    book on circulation 187, 188
    memorial 118
Hastings, Sir Charles 110
Hastings, Somerville 277
Hatchett, Charles 9, 19
Haward, J Warrington 129, 173, 214, 219, 468
Hawkins, Caesar 99, 103, 113
Hawley, Lt Colonel Alan 348
Hawthorne, CO 198
hay-fever 28
Hayes, W 229
Haywood, Brigadier 257
Head, Henry 117, 167, 264, 265–6
Heald, Charles B 438
Heald, Professor RJ 371, 376
Hearse, David 435
heart surgery 139–40
Heaviside, John 11
Heberden, William 9
Heberden Society 322
Hedley, WS 280
Hedley-Whyte, Dr 372
Heger, Astrid 430
Helal, Basil 438
Hellman, K 419
Helmholtz, Hermann von 118
Hench, Philip 294

Henderson, Sir Donald 232
Hendry, William 356
Hennen, John 78
2–5 Henrietta Street 72, 178–80
    see also 1 Wimpole Street
Henry, Alexander 101
Hepburn, Doreen 397
Hepworth, Barbara 362
Heron Property Corporation 469, 470
Herschel, John 61, 97, 107
Hertz, Dr 282
Hewer, C Langton 305, 307
Hewitt, Charles 165, 194, 207
Hewitt, Frederic W 128, 130–31, 302
Hewitt, Graily 109
Hewitt, Prescott 119
Hewitt, Richard 456–7, 464–5, 468, 469
    award 466, Pl.71
Hewlett, Professor 227
Hickman, Henry Hill 110, 204, 306
    commemorative medal 205, 306
Hicks, Sir William Joynson 198
Higgins, Peter 391
Hill, Lord 395
Hill, Sir Austin Bradford 236, 399, 400
Hill, Denis 327, 329
Hill, Sir Robert 344, 345
Hilton, John 42–3, 87, 129
Himmelweit, Hilde 315
Hine, Dame Deirdre frontispiece, 422
Hinton, James 90, 277, 278
hip
    congenital dislocation 313, 360, 361
    replacement 362
Hippocratic oath 54
History of Anaesthesia Society 308, 309
history of medicine see under Royal Society of
    Medicine: Sections
Hjermann, Ingvar 443
Hobday, Frederick 218, 227, 270, 365–6, 367
Hobhouse, Neill 326
Hocken, Edward O 89
Hodgkin, Thomas 15, 29, 30, 42–3, 44, 79, 81, 167
Hodgson, Joseph 98
Hoffbrand, Barry 437
Hoffenburg, Sir Raymond 421
Hogg, James 444
3 Holborn Row 36, 55, 56, 57, 58–60
Holborow, EJ 407, 408
Holborrow, Christopher 413
Holland, Eardley 252
Holland, Sir Henry 59, 102, 115
Holland, WH 237
Holland, WW 419
Holmes, Gordon 265, 266, 334, 336–7, 396
Holmes, Timothy 47, 114, 121, 130, 150, 151, 157,
    161
Home, Everard 8, 20, 414
Home, GF 459–60
Hooke, Robert 81
Hooker, Sir William 70, 107
Hope-Simpson, RE 392
Hopkins, Frederick Gowland 203, 290, 332
Horder, JP 391
Horder, Sir Thomas (Lord Horder) 223, 318, 320,
    351, 352

Horne, F Jobson 272
Horner, Francis 59
Horner, Leonard 60
Horrobin, David 397
Horsley, Sir Victor 120, 138, 148, 219, 263, 264, 265, 275
  on anaesthesia 131
  on Pathological Society 225
  spinal surgery 141
Houghton, WH 292–3
Hovell, JH 243
Hovell, Thomas Mark 271
Howard, Benjamin 112
Howard, Edward 9
Howard de Walden and Seaford, Lord 182, 207
Howells, John G 329
Howitt, Frank D 319–20, 322
Howship, John 45, 81
Hughes, Cecil 306
Hughes, Edward 58
Hughlings Jackson, John 68, 101, 117, 141, 142, Pl.21
  Gold Medal and lecture 205, 264, 266, 267
Hulke, HW 137, 165
humanitarian health care 349, 447, 449–50
Hume, Sir Abraham 59
Humphrey, John 409
Hunt, John 389, 390–91
Hunt, RH 347
Hunter, Charles 114
Hunter, Donald 399
Hunter, John 2–3, 11, 30, 54, 55, 91
Hunter, William 2, 11, 133
Hunterian Society 3, 39
Hurst, Arthur 372
Hutchinson, John 79, 96
Hutchinson, Sir Jonathan 43, 68, 89, 92, 120, 133, 141, 163, 186, 263, Pl.21
  studies of syphilis 114, 142, 149, 153
Hutchison, Alexander, memorials 237–8
Hutchison, Robert 290, 311
Huxley, Thomas Henry 119
Hyde, Samuel 316, 317
  memorial lecture 205, 319, 321
hypnosis see under Royal Society of Medicine: Sections
hypodermic medication 114
Hyslop, TB 326

Idzikowski, Chris 450
Illingworth, Lord 207, 459
Imbert, Sir Peter 429
immunology see under Royal Society of Medicine: Sections, Clinical Immunology and Allergy
in vitro fertilization 253
incontinence 352
Index Medicus 165–6
India Office, drugs enquiry 216, 293
industrial medicine 235–6
infectious diseases 233
infertility 356
influenza 232, 234
Ingram, H Vernon 342
Inman, Dr 366
Institute of Laryngology and Otology 278
Institution of Electrical Engineers 288

Institution for Investigating the Nature and Cure of Cancer 414
Inter-Allied Conferences on Military (War) Medicine 196, 217, 345, 374, 455, 458
Inter-Allied Fellowship of Medicine 196–7
International Brain and Cardiac Surgery Conference (2000) 435
International Congress of Otology and Laryngology 276
International Congress of Physical Medicine 320, 321
International Congress of Radiology (1925) 284
International Congress of Rheumatology 321
International Decade for Natural Disaster Reduction 449
International Endocrine Congress (1964) 387
International Health Bureau (proposed) 189
International Health Conference (1919) 235
International Medical Congress (1881) 68, 119, Pl.21
International Medical Congress (1913) 357, 370
International Neurological Congress 328
International Society of Endocrinology 387
International Symposia on the History of Anaesthesia 308
intra-ocular lenses 341
iritis 334
Isherwood, I 289

Jackson, Sir Barry 373
Jackson, Robert 439
Jameson, Dr 154
Jameson, Sir Wilson 389, 390
Jamison, Kay 329
Jantet, Georges 443
Japp, Sir Willliam 251
Jastrow, Morris 331
Jebens, Erna 359
Jefferson, Geoffrey 222, 266
Jeffreys, Julius 88
Jeffries, B Joy 130
Jenner, Edward 12, 41, 42, 45, 408, Pl.1, Pl.6
  commemorative medal 202, 230, 231–2, 235
  and smallpox vaccination 24, 84, Pl.64
Jenner, William 84, 93, 115, 135, 230, Pl.21
Jessop, WHH 206
Joass, JJ 163, 180, 181, 183, 185, 460–61
Joffe, Michael 237
John of Arderne 369
  medal 375
Johnson, George 29, 30, 79, 83, 114, 128, 154
Johnson, James 43, 47
Johnston, IDA 417
Johnstone, George 158
Jolly, Hugh 315
Joly, Swift 352–3
Jones, A Rocyn 359, 360
Jones, Ernest 325, 327
Jones, Francis Avery 372, 374, 445
Jones, JR 59
Jones, Lewis 280, 281
Jones, Rt Rev Noel 348
Jones, Robert 220, 221, 310–12, 319, 357–8, 362, 424
  memorial lecture 360
Jones, T Wharton 81

Joseph, Sir Keith 315
*Journal of the Royal Society of Medicine* 224, 256–7, 268, 316, 469, 474
Jowell, Tessa 449
Joy, AB 118
Joynes, Henry 60
Juler, Ernest 338
Jung, Carl Gustav 325
Jurasz, Antoni 353

Kalinowski, Lothar 328
Karch, Stephen 430
Kay, AB 409
Keighley, M 375
Keith, Sir Arthur 371
Kekwick, A 394
Kennedy, Ludovic 348
Kent, Duke of 25
Kent, Prince Michael of 473
Keogh, Sir Alfred 195
keratoderma blennorrhagica 259, *260*
Kerr, GM 388, 389
Kerr, JM Munro *250*, 252
Kersley, George 322
Ketham, Johannes de, *Fasciculus medicinae 220, 410, 443*
Kettel, Karsten 278
Kettle, EH 227
Key, Charles Aston 23
Keynes, Geoffrey 213, 223, 268
Kidd, Frank 351, 352
Kiernander, Basil 394, 395
Kilner, Pomfret *412*
Kindersley, Lord 472, 473
Kindler, Theresa 261
Kipling, Rudyard 204
Kirkes, WS 110, 139
Klebanoff, Seymour 409
Knapman, Paul 429
Knill, Sir John 181
Koch, Robert 68, 83, 85, 119, 120, 135, 149–50
Kovaks lecture 321
Krastinova-Lolov, Darina 414
Krivsky, Professor 249
Kyle Stewart (builders) 462

Laing, Gordon S 426
Laird, James 58
Lambert, F Barrie 358
Lambrinudi, Constantine 361
*Lancet, The* 48, 76, 99–100
Lane, James 153, 154
Lane, William Arbuthnot 190, 207, 208, 220
Lang, Basil 335
Lang, William 334
Lang lecture 335
Lang Medal 334–5
Langdon-Brown, Walter 194, 332, 334, 351, 352, 382, 383, 384, 385–6
Langdon-Down, R 326
Langstaff, George 45
Langton, John 170
Lansdown, Richard 476
laparoscopy 252–3
Larrey, Baron 25, 138
Laryngological Society of London 148, 163, 172, 173, 213, 269

Laryngological Summer Congress (1919) 271–2
laryngology *see under* Royal Society of Medicine: Sections
laryngoscope 79, *80*, 147
laser ophthalmoscope 342
Latham, Arthur 171, 172, 173, 180, 185, 189, 201
Laurence, Michael 438, 439
Law (clerk) 35–6
Law, Ellen 207, 459
Lawler, Sylvia, memorial prize 419
Lawrence, TE 267
Lawrence, William 29, 34, 40, 56, 60, 82, 89, 99, 133
Lawrie, Surgeon Lt Colonel 130
learning disability 444
Lederman, Leah, lecture 417, 418
Lederman, Manuel 415, 417
Lederman, Vera 472
Ledingham, JCG 227
Lee, Henry 77, 152
Lee, Robert 46, 78, 93, 98–9, 108, 112, 133, 330
Legge, Dr 399
Lehner, T 243
Leiper, RT 368
Leishman, Sir William 343, 344
Leslie, Robert Murray 202
Lett, Hugh 310, 354
Lettsom, John 2, 3, 5, 6–7, 10, 21, *Pl.1*
Lever, Dr 104
Leverhulme Trust Fund, sponsored Associateships 461
Levi, David 312
Levick, G Murray 191
Levy, Alan 430
Levy, Alfred Goodman 302
Lewin, Lord 348
Lewington, Frances 428
Lewis, Aubrey 326, 328
Lewis, Harry 316
Ley, Gordon 249
Library Association 166
Liebig, Justus von 17, 97, 332
Life Assurance Medical Officers Association 172
life, origin of 227
30 Lincoln's Inn Fields 35, 39, 60
57 Lincoln's Inn Fields 60–61, 62, *Pl.13*
Lind, James 399
Lindsay, Lilian 205, 243
lipids in clinical medicine 443, 445
Lister, Joseph (Baron Lister) 15, 81, 119, 128, 135, 146, 163, 167, *Pl.21*
  and antisepsis 134–7
  biography 207
  and mastectomy 138
  operation on Queen Victoria 135
Lister, Joseph Jackson 81
Lister, WT 336–7, 338, 340
Liston, Robert 30, 79, 85, 86–7, 103, 112, 127, 128–9
Little, E Graham 258, 259
Little, E Muirhead 356, 357, 358
Livingstone, Wing Commander 340
Llewellen, Craig 348
Lloyd, Dame Hilda 252
Lloyd-Davies, Oswald 37
Lloyd-Roberts, George 364
Lloyd-Williams, Katherine 308

lobectomy 307
Lockhart-Mummery, Hugh E 371, 374, 375
Lockhart-Mummery, JP 369, 370, 371, 372, 373,
    398
Locock, Sir Charles 244
Lodge, Thomas 417
London County Council Act (1920) 284
London Medical Gazette 48
London Thyroid Club 386
Long, John St John 61
Louis, Pierre 17, 85, 97
Love, Kerr 277
Lovell-Davis, Lady Jean 420
Low, GC 234, 343
Lower, Richard 31, 382
Lowsley, O 353
Lucan, 3rd Earl of 158
Lucas, Bernard 425
Lucas, Clement 120, 310
Lugon, Myriam 474
Lumley, John 449, 450
lunatic asylums 85
Lyceum Medicum Londinense 3, 36
lymphadenoma 44
Lyster, Cecil 280, 283

MacAlister, Donald 208
MacAlister, JYW 116, 135, 154, 166, 167, 330, 342,
    343
    appointments
        Resident Librarian 121, 144, 157, 163–5
        Secretary and consulting Librarian 165–6, 167
    and Emergency Surgical Aid Corps 195–6
    financial mismanagement 201–2
    and 20 Hanover Square
        lease 180
        purchase 157–8, 161, 163
        residence 164, 166
    health problems 166, 207
    and Index Medicus 165–6
    knighthood 196, 207
    portrait 208, Pl.24
    and postgraduate medical education 196–7, 198
    retirement and death 207–8
    and RMCS centenary 167
    and RSM Council Club 191
    and RSM formation 151, 169–70, 171, 173–5,
        213–14, 301, 345
    and RSM Proceedings, editor 201
    and RSM Sections
        Experimental Medicine and Therapeutics 290
        Odontological 239, 240
        Ophthalmological 334
        Proctology 370, 371
        Tropical Medicine and Parasitology 342–3
    and 1 Wimpole Street 180, 181, 182, 183, 185–6,
        193
MacAlister, Lady, portrait 208
McAlpine, Douglas 266
McAlpine, Sir Robert, and Sons (building
    contractors) 470
McAnena, Mr 435
McArthur, Colonel NP 349
Macbeth, Ronald G 425
McBride, Peter 275–6
McCann, Dr 249

MacCarthy, Dermod 314
McCarthy, J 136
MacCormac, H 262
MacCormac, Henry 149
MacCormac, Sir William 119, 154, Pl.21
McCrea, Moreland 195, 196
McDonagh, JER 259, 260
MacDonald, Ramsay 204
MacDonald, SG 351
McDougall, William 325
Macewen, William 140–41, 275, 279, 357
McFadyean, Sir John 366
McGregor, JS 328
Macgregor, Patrick 92
McGrigor, DB 287
MacGrigor, Sir James 39, 70
McIlroy, Louise (Dame Louise) 247, 252
McIndoe, Sir Archibald 223, 347, 361, 412, 413
McIntosh, J 228–9
Macintosh, Robert 308
MacIntyre, William 94, 95
Mackay, George 333
Mackay, Helen 312–13
McKee, GK 363–4
McKenzie, Dan 274, 279
Mackenzie, Hector 217
MacKenzie, James 290
Mackenzie, Morell 79, 146–7, 269, 271, 273
    portrait 272
MacKenzie, W 129
McLatchie, GR 439
McLay, David 428
Maclean, Sir Ewen 249, 251
MacLennan, Sir Hector 252
McLintock, JS 402
Macloghlin, Eliza 206
McNalty, Sir Arthur 235, 332
Macnaughton-Jones, H 245, 246, 247
McNeil, Charles 316
macular coloboma 338
McVail, John 233
McWhirter, R 223
Magendie, François 97
Magill, Ivan 305, 306, 307
Mahon, Arthur J 466
Makins, Sir George 221, 255
malaria 151–2
Manfredi, Hieronymus Pl.12
manic-depressive psychosis 326
Mann, Ida 338–9, 340, Pl.55
Mann, Ronald D 331, 432–3, 474, 475
Manson, Patrick 151–2, 227, 233, 342, 343
Manson-Bahr, P 343
Mapother, Edward 265, 266, 325, 326, 328
Marcet, Alexander 5, 6, 7, 10, 11, 16, 17–18, 20, 34,
    45, 50, 51, 54, 58–9, Pl.5
    anxiety concerning MCS 35, 39
    enquiry on fevers 82
    Foreign Secretary of MCS 10, 30
    gifts to Library 56
    interest in chemistry 10, 26–9, 46, 153
    service at military hospital 25
    and smallpox vaccination 24
Marcet, Jane 17, 24
Marcet, William 85, 149, 163
Marcus Beck Laboratory 182, 192–3

Marcus Beck Library 193, 472
Margaret, HRH Princess 189
Marie Louise, HRH Princess 271
Marsh, Howard 138, 150
Marshall, Dr (Queen's physician) 135
Marshall, Sir Geoffrey 218, *303*, 304
Marshall, John 113, 119, 121, 138, 144, *Pl*.21
Marston, Adrian 397, 429, 476
Marston, Archibald 307
Marston, JA 152
Martin, CJ 233
Martineau, Philip M 28
Mary, Queen 186
Mason, R Michael 322
massage 120–21
mastectomy 137–8, 144, *145*, 223–4
maternal mortality/morbidity 247, 250–51, 252
maternity and the newborn 440, 441–2
Mathys, Robert 364
Maudsley, Henry 323
Maudsley Hospital 326–7, 329
Mayer, E 271, 292
Mayer-Gross, W 326, 327, 328
Mayou, MS 337–8, 339
measurement in medicine *see under* Royal Society of
    Medicine: Sections
Medawar, Sir Peter 234, 408, 416–17, 436
Medical Act (1858) 97, 99
Medical Act (1886) 121
Medical and Chirurgical Club 16
Medical and Chirurgical Society Club 16–17, 191
Medical and Chirurgical Society of London 2, 3,
    5–21, 23–62
   150th anniversary of founding 455–6
   Library 5, 16, 18, *19*, 39, 54–8
   Obligation Book 12, *13*
   royal charter 50–54, 62, 68–70, *Pl*.15
   seal 53, *69*
   *see also* Royal Medical and Chirurgical Society
medical communication 411, 444
Medical Disability Society 322
medical education 2, 409–11, 475
   community medicine 236
   comparative medicine 368
   general practice 392
   history of medicine 333
   laryngology and otology 272, 274, 278
   obstetrics and gynaecology 249, 251
   orthopaedics 361
   postgraduate 196–7, 198
   proctology 371
   psychology 326
   *see also* BMTV *and under* Royal Society of
     Medicine: Sections
medical electricity 113–14
Medical Insurance Agency Prize 224
Medical Officers of Health 233
Medical Parliamentary Committee 197–8
*Medical and Physical Journal* 47
Medical Research Club 225
Medical Research Committee 199
Medical Research Council 199
   Radiology committee 200
Medical Society of Edinburgh 1
Medical Society of London 3, 5–7, 12, 20–21, 36,
   39, 40, 135, 238, 310

Founders' Picture 36, *Pl*.1
   mergd with RMCS 170–72
   merged with Westminster Medical Society 97
Medical Society for the Study of Hypnosis 423
Medical Society for the Study of Venereal Diseases
   445, 476
*Medical Times and Gazette* 101
Medico-Botanical Society 188
*Medico-Chirurgical Review* 47
*Medico-Chirurgical Transactions* 40–47, 78, 97, 101,
   102, 151, 173
Medico-Legal Society 327, 427
Medico-Psychological Association 109, 172, 324
Medwin, Gladys M 207, 459
Mellanby, Edward 311, 367
Mellanby, May (Lady Mellanby) 242
Mellett, P 440
Mellor, David 426
Melville, Stanley 283
Mendelian inheritance 233
Ménière's disease 277
mental retardation *see* learning disability
Mental Treatment Act (1930) 326
Merrick, Joseph (the 'Elephant Man') 103
Merriman, S 82
Meryon, Edward 99, 101, 107, 113–14
mesmerism 82, 422
Metcalfe, Percy 264
Meyer, Alfred 326, 327, 328
Meyer, Hans Wilhelm 138
Microscopical Society 81
microscopy 81
Middlesex Hospital Medical Society 2
Middleton, EM 345
Midwives Act (1902) 244
Miles, WE 370, 371
Millard, Peter 430–31, 432
Miller, H Crichton 326
Miller, James 82
Miller, Norman 443
Milligan, ETC 373, 374
Milligan, Sir William 272, 273, 275, 276
Millin, Terence 352, 354
Mills, D 428
Milman, Sir Francis 9, 51
Milton-Thompson, Sir Godfrey 347
Ministry of Health 196, 197, 198, 200
Minnitt, RJ 304
Misiewicz, JJ 347
Moffat, Robin 429, 430
Moir, Chassar 252
Moll, JH 205, 474
Mollison, William 277
molluscum contagiosum 91, 259, *Pl*.20
Moncrieff, Alan 312
Mond, NC 440
Moniz, Egaz 266
Montrose, 1st Duke of 158
Moon, RO 332
Moore, Charles H 81, 137–8
Moore, James Irwin 271–2
Moore, Norman 165, 167, 186, 331
Moore, Richard 436
Moore, SG 249
Moore, Thomas 352, 356
Moorfields Eye Hospital 88–9, 333

Moorhead, JF 398, 436–7
Moorhouse, Peter 430
Morison, JM Woodburn 285, 286
Morley, George 347
Mornington, Countess of 179
Morris, Professor 400
Morris, David 440, 444
Morris, Henry 144, *145*, 170, 185, 188, 191, 206,
    260, 323, 331, 349, 415
Morris, Malcolm 258, 259
Morson, A Clifford 353, 354
Morson, Basil 371
Morton, Reginald 280, 281, 282
Morton, WT 128, 129, 131, 331
Mott, Frederick 227, 292, 311, 323, 324, 326
Mott, Valentine 42
Mouillot, FA de T 318
Mowlem, Rainsford *412*
Moynihan, Sir Berkeley (Lord Moynihan) 80,
    219–20, 371
Muir, Sir Edward 373, 394
Müller, Johannes 17, 97
Mummery, John Howard 238, 239, 240
Mummery, Norman Howard 235, 301
Mummery, Stanley 240
Munk, William 99
Munro, Air Commodore D 345
Murchison, Charles 84
Murley, Reginald 223, 224
Murphy, Sir Shirley 233, 235
Murray, GR 290, 383, 385
Murray, Robert 444
Murray, Thomas 16
mustard gas 340, *Pl.55*
myasthenia gravis 268
Myers, Hart 11, *Pl.1*
Myers, Lt Col 171
myope classes 335
myxoedema 148, 382, 383

Nabarro, D 311
Nachbar, John 201
Napoleonic wars 25, 87
Nasmyth, Alexander 91
National Association of General Practitioners 97
National Fund for the Acquisition of Radium 203
National Health Act (1946) 381, 455
National Health Insurance Act (1911) 196, 247–8,
    381
National Health Service, introduction 381, 459
National Institute for the Deaf 277
National Veterinary Medical Association 199, 365
Nattrass, F 268
Negus, VE 278
Neligan, GE 354
Nelson 120
Neonatal Society 316
nephrectomy 138
nephrology *see under* Royal Society of Medicine:
    Sections
Nettleship, Edward 333, 334
Neurological Society of the United Kingdom
    (*previously* Neurological Society of London)
    141, 173, 205, 213, 263–4
neurosciences *see* Royal Society of Medicine:
    Sections, Clinical Neurosciences

New Health Society 190
Newhouse, Molly 400, 401
Newman, Sir George 200, 249, 251, 305, 318
Newsholme, Arthur 230, 232–3
Newson-Smith, Lord and Mundy (accountants) 201
Newton, DRL 322
Nicholls, Thomas 20
Nichols Prize 205
Nicolaier, Arthur 133
Nightingale, Messrs (builders) 161
Nightingale, Florence 88, 95
Nisbet, Williaam 29
Nissen, Karl 364
Nitch, Cyril 351, 352, 354
nitrous oxide anaesthesia 130, *131*, 303, 304
Niven, James 233, 234
Noguchi, Hideyo 190, 191
noise deafness 279
Norbury, Lionel 372, 374
Norman, Leslie 401
Norman, Sir William 344
Normanby, Viscount 68, 69
Northcroft, George 241
Nosworthy, MD 305
Nourse, Chichele 270
nuclear medicine 406
Nutrition Society 443, 464

Oates, Geoffrey D 376
obstetric pain relief 304
Obstetrical Society of London 97, 99, 102, 104–6,
    108, 109, 163, 171, 172, 173, 213, 214, 215,
    244–5
obstetrics *see under* Royal Society of Medicine:
    Sections
occupational medicine *see under* Royal Society of
    Medicine: Sections
Odier, Professor 18
O'Donovan, WS 261
Odontological Society of Great Britain 106, 171,
    172, 173, 213, 215, 238
    centenary 243
    Odontological Museum 239, 242
Odontological Society of London 91, 97, 99, 102,
    106, 238
odontology 91
    *see also under* Royal Society of Medicine: Sections
O'Dowd, Michael 254
O'Dwyer, JJ 399
oestrogens 287
Ogilvie, Sir Heneage 374
Oliver 385
O'Malley, JF 277
oncology *see* cancer *and under* Royal Society of
    Medicine: Sections
Oncology Club 418, 419
Openshaw, TH 356–7, 358, 362
Ophthalmological Society of the United Kingdom
    89, 121, 172, 206, 333, 338
ophthalmology 87–9, 141–2
opium 88
Optical Society 163
Ord, William 115, 148, 149, 382, *383*
O'Reilly, William 466
organ transplantation *see under* Royal Society of
    Medicine: Sections

Organe, Geoffrey 307, 308, 394, 396
Ormerod, FC 277, 278
Orr, David 324
orthopaedic surgery 220–21
   *see also under* Royal Society of Medicine: Sections
Orton, G Harrison 281, 284
Osler, William 119, *Pl.*21, *Pl.*53
   and Dogs' Protection Bill 199
   donation to building fund 182
   and postgraduate medical education 196–7
   and RSM formation 169, 173–4, 177, 213–14,
      342, 371
   and RSM Library 187–8
   and RSM Sections 301
      Clinical 255
      Epidemiology 235
      Experimental Medicine and Therapeutics 290
      History of Medicine 131, 330–31
      Medicine 217
      Pathology 227
   tuberculosis resolution 189
   wartime meetings 194
Osmond-Clarke, H 362
Otological Society of the United Kingdom 172,
   173, 213, 275
otology 89–90
   *see also under* Royal Society of Medicine: Sections
otosclerosis 276–7
Otty, JH 274
ovariotomy 87, 98–9, 132–4
Owen, Isambard 161
Owen, Richard 43, 76, 97

Pacini, Professor 112
paediatrics 92–3
   *see also under* Royal Society of Medicine: Sections
Page, C Max 357
Page, Clive 433
Page, Max 223
Paget, GE 396, 420
Paget, James 43, 48, 68, 76, 81, 83, 109, 110, 119,
   144–6, *Pl.*21
Paget, Rosalind 249
Paget, Stephen 167, 226
Paget's disease 144–5, *146*
Paine, Sir Christopher 476
palliative care 44, 448
Palmer, Edward 128
Palmer, Raoul 252
Pampiglione, G 367
'panhysterectomy' 247
Paramore, RH 247
parasitology *see under* Royal Society of Medicine:
   Sections
Parker, Rushton 221
Parkinson, James 8, 30, 59, 82
   bicentenary 268
Parkinson, John 30
Parry, CB Wynn 321
Parry, T Vincent 332
Parry, Thomas 73
Parsons, Herbert 266
Parsons, HJ (Sir John) 334, 338, 339
Parsons, Sir Leonard 312
Pasteur, Louis 118, 119, 408
Pasteur, William 197, 255, 345

Paterson, Donald 312
Paterson, J Ralston 288
Paterson, RS 287
Paterson, WB 240
Pathological Society of Great Britain and Ireland
   229
Pathological Society of London 74–5, 97, 102–3,
   107, 108, 109, 132, 161, 163, 172, 213, 225–6,
   365
   centenary 228–9
pathology 78
   *see also under* Royal Society of Medicine: Sections
Patient's Charter 393
Paton, Leslie 264, 334, 336, 338
Paton, Noel 311
Paton, William 308
Patterson, FA 445
Patterson, Norman 277
Paul, David 428
Pavloff, IP 167
Pavy, Frederick 153
Payne, J Lewin 240, 242
Payne, Joseph Frank 230, 330
Pearson, George 5, 414
Pearson, John 19, 20
Pearson, Karl 190
Pearson, RS Brice 408
Peel, Sir John 252
Pegler, L Hemington 270
Pellizzari 261
Pendlebury, Herbert 180
penicillin 227, 228, 293
Pennant, Richard 158
Pepys, Sir Lucas 9, 25
Pereira, Jonathan 77
Pereira, Margaret 428
peripheral nerve repair 61
Perkins, George 361
Petracek, Emile 261
Petrus de Montagnana *410*
Pettigrew, TJ 59, 94
Pfeiffer Research Foundation 462
Phaer, Thomas 309
pharmaceutical industry 467
pharmaceutical medicine *see under* Royal Society of
   Medicine: Sections
pharmacology 397, 431, 446–7
Philipp, Elliott E 254
Phillips, Benjamin 75, 87, 98
phlebology 441, 442–3
physical education 198
physical medicine 319, 320–21
   *see also under* Royal Society of Medicine: Sections
Physiological Society 106, 172
physiotherapy 285, 318
Pickles, William 389, 391
Pickworth, FH 292
Pictet, Marc-Auguste 16
Pincher, Chapman 395
Pinching, Anthony 409
Pinckard, Dr 6
Pinker, Sir George 252, 436, 439, 466
Pinsent, Robin 391
Piper, Priscilla, memorial lecture 434
Pirie, George A 282, 283
Pirquet, Clemens von 408

Pitcairn, David 10, 12, 19
plastic surgery 223, 347
 *see also under* Royal Society of Medicine: Sections
Platt, Sir Harry 359, 360, 361
Platt, Hugh 367
Platt Report 424, 425
Plumer, Sir Thomas 51
pneumoconiosis 402
Pogose, NG 305
poliomyelitis 234
Pollack, Margaret 392
Pollock, George 129
Pond, Desmond 329
population statistics 234
Porritt, Sir Arthur (Lord Porritt) 465, 468
Portal, Anthony 18
Porter, Roy 329, 420
Post, Felix 329
Postgraduate Medical Association 197
Pott, Percival 399
Potter, JP 86
Poulett, Earl of 158
poverty related to disease 232, 234
Pow-wow Club 3, 11, 17
Powell, Enoch 391, 421
Powell, HE 207, 459
Powell, Richard Douglas 149, 150, 207, 217, 281,
 330
 and formation of RSM 151, 167, 169–70, 171,
 213
 and RSM centenary 80, 168–9
Power, D'Arcy 190, 330, 331, 365, 367
Power, Sir William Henry 231
Pownall, George 75
Prados y Such, Miguel 326
premature babies 312, 341
preventive medicine 236
 *see also under* Royal Society of Medicine: Sections,
 Epidemiology and Public Health
primary health care 450
Prince, John 178
Pringle, JJ 260
prisoners, health of 85
Pritchard, Dr 275
*Proceedings* of the RMCS 101–2, 151
*Proceedings* of the RSM 173, 201, 208, 215, 216, 229,
 256, 262, 271, 281
Prochaska, George 94
proctology *see* Royal Society of Medicine: Sections,
 Coloproctology
Prophet, AS 243
prostatectomy 351–2
Prout, William 28–9, 46, 57, *350*
*Provincial Medical Gazette* 48, 101
Provincial Medical and Surgical Association 97
 *see also* British Medical Association
psychiatry *see under* Royal Society of Medicine:
 Sections
psychopharmacology 329
psychosomatic medicine *see* Royal Society of
 Medicine: Sections, Hypnosis and
 Psychosomatic Medicine
public health 199, 237
 *see also* Royal Society of Medicine: Sections,
 Epidemiology and Public Health
puerperal fever 249, 251

Pullinger, BD 340
Pulvertaft, RJV 229
Punnett, RC 233
Pusey, Charles 437
Pye-Smith, PH 153, 169, 226
pyorrhoea 240, 241, 334
Pyrah, LN 356

Quain, Richard 95–6, 103, 109, *Pl.21*
quality in health care 433, 447
Quarrier, Daniel 25
Quekett, John 78–9, 81
Quinn, Niall 436

Radcliffe, Charles 113
radiation injuries 283–4
Radiological Institute 200
radiology 199–200
 *see also under* Royal Society of Medicine: Sections
radium treatment 372
Raffle, Andrew 473
Rains, AJ Harding 474
Ramazzini, Bernardino 399
Ramón y Cajal, Santiago 167
Ramsay, Sir William 167
Rankin, Edward 73
Ransom, A 99
Rantzen, Esther 348
Raven (clerk) 36, 58
Raven, Ronald 374, 415, 417, 418
Rayner, Claire 420
Reading, Philip 278
Reece, RJ 234
Rees, Andrew 437
Rees, JR 328
Rees-Mogg, William 315
Reeves, Brian 365
reflex functions 93–4
Reginald M Phillips Foundation 462
rehabilitation 321
 *see also under* Royal Society of Medicine: Sections,
 Rheumatology and Rehabilitation
Reid, Mr 252
Reid, Archibald 282, 284, 285
Reilly, Mr 374
Renal Association 437
respiratory medicine *see under* Royal Society of
 Medicine: Sections
resuscitation techniques 110–12, 153, 305–6, 383,
 473
Reynolds, Russell J 286
rheumatology *see under* Royal Society of Medicine:
 Sections
rhinology 275
 *see also under* Royal Society of Medicine: Sections,
 Laryngology and Rhinology
Ricardo, David 59
Rich, Colonel Norman 348
Richardson, Sir John 410
Richardson, Peter 474
Riches, EW 218, 354, 356, 416, 417
rickets 255, 311
Ridge (inventor of invalid carriage) 78
Ridley, Frederick 340
Ridley, Sir Harold 341
Rigby, Edward 106

Rob, CG 394
Roberts, Alan 470
Roberts, David Lloyd 205
Roberts, Hubert 195
Roberts, Raine 429
Robertson, James 313
Robinson, James 127
Robson, AW Mayo 137, 138, 154
Robson, Sir Gordon 425, 428
Rockefeller Foundation 460, 462
Rodger, T Ritchie 279
Rogers, A Talbot 391
Rogers, Sir Leonard 343
Rogers, T Arnold 91, 106, 238
Roget, Peter 2, 12, 16, 29, 30, 34, 38–40, 55, 59, 61
  at Royal Society 40, 94
  attempt to purchase new premises 60
  editor of *Transactions* 45
  and Library catalogue 56
Roitt, Ivan 408–9
Rokitansky, Carl 97
Rolleston, Sir Humphry Davy 3, *199*, 207, 288
  and Radiology committee 200
  and RSM Council Club 191
  and RSM History of Medicine Section 331–2
  and RSM Radiology Section 284
  and RSM Section of Medicine 217
  and RSM Section of Paediatrics 311
  and RSM Section of Proctology 371, 372
  and RSM War Section 344
  work in endocrinology 383, 385
Rolleston, John Davy 254, 311, 332
Romilly, Sir Samuel 51, 53
Röntgen Centenary Congress (1995) 289
Röntgen Society 200, 254, 280, 283, 285, 288
Rook, AJ 262
Rose, F Clifford 269
Ross, Ronald 152, 182, 193, 331, 342
Rosse, T 46
Rösslin, Eucharius, midwives' textbook *246*
Roth, Martin 329
Roth, Paul B 357
Rous, F Peyton 465
Routh, Amand 188, 227, 246, 247–8, 311
Rowbotham, Stanley 305
Rowley, William 61
Rows, Richard G 324
Roxburgh, James 434, 435
Royal Astronomical Society 74
Royal College of Anaesthetists 307
Royal College of General Practitioners 389, 390–91, 410
Royal College of Obstetricians and Gynaecologists 251–2
Royal College of Ophthalmologists 333
Royal College of Paediatrics and Child Health 316
Royal College of Pathologists 229, 464
Royal College of Physicians 1, 7, 20–21, 61
  bomb damage 458
  committee on rheumatic disease 318
  Faculty of Community Medicine 236
  and MCS incorporation 50–53, 69
  reforming movement 68, 96
Royal College of Psychiatrists 324, 329
Royal College of Radiologists 287, 288–9
Royal College of Surgeons 1, 58, 85, 96, 375

bomb damage 354, 458
Faculty of Anaesthetics 216, 307
pathological collection 221–2
Working Party on trauma services 426
Royal College of Veterinary Surgeons 75
Royal Commission on Medical Education 410, 411
Royal Humane Society 110, 111, 112
Royal Jennerian Society 11
Royal Medical and Chirurgical Society 67–121, 213, 310
  amalgamation proposals 108–9, 151, 161, 167, 169–73, 213, 239, 269–70, 275, 289, 317, 333–4, 427
  centenary 149, *166*, 167–9, *Pl.28*
  House Dinner 154, *Pl.25*, *Pl.26*
  Library 76–7, 154, 163–6
    catalogues 76, 77, 166, *Pl.18*
  Obligation Book 70
  scientific committees 110–16
    chloroform 112–13
    climates and baths 115–16
    diphtheria and croup 114–15
    hypodermic medication 114
    medical electricity 113–14
    suspended animation 110–12
    vaccino-syphilis 114
  in World War I 193–4
Royal Medical Society of Edinburgh 1–2
Royal Medico-Psychological Association 328, 329, 464
Royal National Life Boat Institution 110, 111
Royal Society 1, 40, 94, 107
Royal Society of Health 368
Royal Society of Medicine 169–75, 177–208, 213–14
  Academic Board 457, 476
  Associate members 202
  coat of arms 203, 273, *Pl.33*, *Pl.34*
  Continuing Medical Education Department (*later* Academic Department) 475–6
  financial difficulties 201–2, 472
  Gold Medal 202, 265, 367
  jubilee dinner 243
  Library 175, 177, 182, 187–8, 206–7, 455, 459–62, 472, 475, 476
    Central Medical Library Bureau 460
    Chalmers Library 206, 459
    rare book collection 193
    wartime storage at St Albans 460
    Wellcome Research Library 460–62
  Photographic and Film Unit 460
  presidential badge and chain 203, 273, *Pl.22*, *Pl.32*
  presidential gown 203, *Pl.35*
  publications 466, 474
    see also *Journal of the Royal Society of Medicine*; *Proceedings* of the RSM; *Transactions* of the RSM; *Tropical Doctor*
  special discussions 189–90
  Supplemental Charters 476, *Pl.29*, *Pl.76*
  Trust Fund 203
  women members and Fellows 171, 175, 182, 243
Royal Society of Medicine: Fora 392–3, 439–50, 457
  Angiology 441, 445–6
  Black and Ethnic Minority Health 450

Royal Society of Medicine: Fora – *continued*
  Catastrophes and Conflicts – Humanitarian
    Health Care 349, 447, 449–50
  Clinical Haemorheology 406, 440–41, 445
  Clinical Pharmacology and Therapeutics 397,
    431, 446–7
  Communication in Health Care (*previously*
    Medical Communication) 411, 444
  Computers in Medicine 447
  Food and Health 445
  Learning Disability (*previously* Mental
    Retardation) 444
  Lipids in Clinical Medicine 443, 445
  Maternity and the Newborn 440, 441–2
  Medico-Pharmaceutical 467
  Palliative Care 447, 448
  Primary Health Care 450
  Quality in Health Care (*previously* Medical Audit
    and Accountability) 433, 447
  Sexual Health and Reproductive Medicine
    (*previously* Sexual Medicine and Family
    Planning) 445
  Sleep and its Disorders 447, 450
  Telemedicine 447, 448–9
  Venous Forum 441, 442–3
Royal Society of Medicine: Sections 172, 213–17,
  301, 381–2, 456, 459, 467, 469
  Accident and Emergency Medicine 424–7, 439,
    *Pl*.66
  Anaesthesia (*previously* Anaesthetics) 199, 216,
    223, 301–9, 424, 435, *Pl*.48
  Cardiothoracic 433, 434–5
  Clinical 254–7, 384
  Clinical Forensic and Legal Medicine (*previously*
    Clinical Forensic Medicine) 427–30, *Pl*.67
  Clinical Immunology and Allergy 407–9, 464
  Clinical Neurosciences (*previously* Neurology)
    263–9, 334, 340, *Pl*.40
  Coloproctology (*previously* Proctology) 301,
    369–76, 419
  Comparative Medicine 301, 365–9, *Pl*.59
  Dermatology 256, 258–63
  Electro-therapeutics *see under* Radiology
  Endocrinology 252, 381, 382–8
  Epidemiology and Public Health (*previously*
    Epidemiology; Epidemiology and State
    Medicine; Epidemiology and Preventive
    Medicine; Epidemiology and Community
    Medicine) 194, 215, 230–38, 248, 249, 382
  Experimental Medicine and Therapeutics
    (*previously* Therapeutics and Pharmacology)
    216, 217, 219, 228, 289–94, 352, 383, 384,
    408
  General Practice 216, 381, 388–94, 400, 418, 459
  Geriatrics and Gerontology 430–32, 433
  History of Medicine 216, 301, 323, 330–33, 435,
    *Pl*.52
  Hypnosis and Psychosomatic Medicine (*previously*
    Medical and Dental Hypnosis) 422
  Laryngology and Rhinology (*previously*
    Laryngology) 269–75, 278, 279, *Pl*.44
  Measurement in Medicine 403–7, 464
  Medical Education 409–11
  Medicine, Experimental Medicine and
    Therapeutics (*previously* Medicine) 217–19,
    294, 371, 381, 437

Nephrology 436–7
Obstetrics and Gynaecology 205, 215, 235,
  244–54, *Pl*.41
Occupational Medicine 398–403, 464
Odontology 195, 202, 215, 238–44, 424, *Pl*.39
Oncology 408, 414–19
Open 382, 419–22, 439, 442, 456, 469
Ophthalmology 195, 301, 333–42, *Pl*.54
Orthopaedics 301, 356–65, 424, *Pl*.58
Otology 205, 216, 222, 269, 270, 272, 274–9,
  *Pl*.46
Paediatrics and Child Health (*previously* Study of
  Disease in Children) 215, 256, 261, 309–16,
  434, *Pl*.49
Pathology 225–30, 352, 384, 406, *Pl*.38
Pharmaceutical Medicine and Research [*previously*
  Library (Scientific Research) *and* Library and
  Lay] 382, 394–7, 419, 447, 456
Physical Medicine 285–6, 319–20, *Pl*.50
Plastic Surgery 365, 411–14
Psychiatry 292, 323–9, 347, 459, *Pl*.51
Radiology (*previously* Electro-therapeutics) 200,
  216, 279–89, 319, 459, *Pl*.45
Respiratory Medicine 432–4
Rheumatology and Rehabilitation (*previously*
  Balneology and Climatology, *and* Physical
  Medicine) 195, 215, 285–6, 316–22
Sports Medicine 438–9, *Pl*.68
Surgery 219–25, 372–3, 411, 424, *Pl*.37
Transplantation (*previously* Organ Transplantation)
  436, *Pl*.70
Tropical Medicine (*previously* Tropical Diseases)
  and Parasitology 188, 261, 301, 342–3
United Services (*previously* War Section) 301,
  344–9, *Pl*.56
Urology 301, 349–56, *Pl*.57
War 196
Royal Society of Medicine Club 192, 459
Royal Society of Medicine Foundation 402, 456,
  464–7
Royal Society of Medicine Press 474
Royal Society of Medicine Services 468, 474
Royal Society for Mentally Handicapped Children
  444
Royal Society of Tropical Medicine 343
Royal Statistical Society 248, 406
Rumball, Sir Aubrey 405
Rush, Benjamin 18
Rushton, Martin A 241
Rusk, Howard 466
Rutherford, Sir Ernest 282
Rutherford, William H 425
Ryan, Jim 449, 450
Rycroft, BW 339
Ryder, Richard 50
Rymer, Samuel Lee 238

Sabatier, Professor 18
Sabouraud, R 259, 261
St Bartholomew's Hospital Medical Society 2
St Peter's, Vere Street 178
Salk, Jonas 234
Salmon lecture 375
Salter, H Hyde 110
salvarsan 188, 259, 291, 334
Samuel, Eric 418

Sanders, Roy 414
Sanderson, John Burdon 106, 110, 111, 135, 226, 254
Sandler, M 440
Sansom, AE 130
Sargant, William 327, 328, 329
Sargent, Percy 266
Saunders, Dame Cicely 274
Saunders, Edwin 91, 238
Saunders, John Cunningham 88
Saunders, Peter 254
Saunders, William 2, 6, 7, 10, 18–19, 24, 26, 34, 50, 51–4, *Pl.*1, *Pl.*3
    gifts to Library 54
Savage, George 263, 265, 324
Savage, Wendy 420, 442
Savage, WG 227
Save-a-Life campaign 473
Savill, Agnes 261
Savory, WS 110, 111, 114, 119, 135
Scarborough, Earl of 158
Scarff, RW 262
scarlatina 82
Scarpa, Antonio 18
Schäfer, EA *see* Sharpey-Schäfer, Sir Edward
Scharf, George 45–6, 47
Scharlieb, Mary 182, 248, 301
Scheer, Barry 244
Schelling, Carl 242
Schilling, RSF 399, 400, 401
Schofield, John 275
Schofield, Philip 375–6
Schonbein, Professor 99
Schuster, Norah 333
scoliosis 358
Scott (landlord) 62
Scott, EP 391
Scott, RH 399
Scott, Richard 391
Scott, Sir Ronald Bodley 408, 417
Scott, Sydney 277
Scott and Parsons, Messrs 73
Seale, Francis 178
Searle, Adam 414
Secker-Walker, Jonathan 474
Seddon, Professor 361
Semon, Felix 146–8, 163, 165, 206, 227, 255, 263, 264, 269, 270–71
Semon lecture 270–71, 272
Semon Medallion 270
Sequeira, JH 259, *260,* 261
sexual health/medicine 445
Shaftesbury, Earl of 92, 104
Shapiro, Dr 329
Sharpey, William 76, 84, 110
Sharpey-Schäfer, Sir Edward 112, 264, 383, 385
Shattock, SG 226
Shaw, Dr 20
Shaw, Alexander 91
Shaw, Mr Justice Sebag 419
Shaw, William Fletcher 245, 251, 252
Sheldon, Dr 2
shellshock 324–5
Shepherd, RT 429
Shepley, WH 328
Sheppard, CE 131

Sherman, William O'Neill 221
Sherrington, Charles 117, 265
    memorial lecture 265
Shield, Marmaduke 131
Shields, John 194
Shipway, Francis *303,* 304
Shore, Dr 131
Sibson, Francis 112–13, 128, 129
Sicard, JA 266
Sieveking, Edward 118, 154, 161, 163, 316
Silk, John F 131, 301, 302
Silvester, Henry, resuscitation method 110, 111, 112
Simmons, Dr 2
Simon, John 84, 104, 119, 230
Simpson, JD 389
Simpson, JY 87
Simpson, RR 279
Simpson, SL 384
Simpson, WJR 343
Sims, James 5, 6–7, 12, *Pl.*1
Sims, John 58, 78
Singer, Lady 207
Singer, Charles 331, 332
Skey, FC 6, 46, 76, 108
Sklarz, Ernst 354
Skottowe, Ian 329
Slapak, Maurice 436
Slater, Eliot 327, 328, 329
sleep and sleep disorders 447, 450
slit lamp *337,* 338
Sloan, Samuel 281
Sloane, Sir Hans 1
Smallpiece, Victoria 313
smallpox 84, *Pl.*64
Smith, Dr 114
Smith, Lord 468
Smith, J Morrison 407, 408
Smith, James Edward 9
Smith, PG 284
Smith, Priestley 336
Smith, Protheroe 78
Smith, R Percy 324
Smith, Thomas 138, 170
Smith-Peterson, MN 359
Smyly, Sir William 245
Snow, John 78, 83, 101, 104, 120, 127, 129, 230
Snowley, Ian 475
Soane, Sir John 58, 60
social medicine 236
Société de Neurologie de Paris 268
Société Française de Pédiatrie 315
Société Française d'Hemorheologie Clinique 441
Society of Anaesthetists 131, 163, 172, 175, 301–2
Society of Apothecaries 1
    Diploma in Medical Care of Catastrophes 449
    Diploma in Sports Medicine 438
    Faculty of the History of Medicine and
        Pharmacology 216
Society of British Neurological Surgeons 267, 268
Society of Cardiothoracic Surgeons 435
Society for Endocrinology 386, 387
Society of Endocrinology of the USA 387
Society for the Improvement of Animal Chemistry 27–8
Society for the Improvement of Medical and
    Chirurgical Knowledge 3, 11, 36

Society of Medical Officers of Health 163, 233
Society of Occupational Medicine 400, 403
Society of Radiographers 285
Society for the Relief of Widows and Orphans of
 Medical Men 74
Society for the Study of Disease in Children 172,
 175, 301, 310
 centenary 316
Society for the Study of Fertility 386
Society for the Study of Infertility 252
Society of Thoracic Surgeons 435
Society of Tropical Medicine and Hygiene 152, 188,
 342–3
Solly, Ernest 317
Solly, Samuel 94–5, 108–9, 144
Somerset House 73, 74
Sommering, Samuel T von 17–18
Sorsby, Arnold 340
Soulsby, Lord 301, 367, *422, Pl.*71
Sourdille, Maurice 276–7
South, John Flint 78
specialization 218
 hospitals 88, 89, 91, 92, 93, 96, 101, 146
 medical societies 102–6, 121, 151
Speke, William 158, 160
Spencer 221
Spencer, Herbert 245, 246, 249, 251, 332
Spencer, Walter 351
Spilsbury (Library catalogue compiler) 76
Spilsbury, Sir Bernard 227
spina bifida 27
sports medicine *see under* Royal Society of Medicine:
 Sections
Spriggs, EI 310
Spurzheim, JC 18
Squire, P 129
Squire, W 129
Stafford, RA 89
Stallworthy, Sir John 252, 253, 417, 425, 440, 469,
 470
Stanger, Christopher 19
Stanley, Sir Arthur 200
Stanley, Edward 58, 82
Stapleton, Thomas 316
Starling, EH 290, 385
statistics 405
Stawell, Lord 158
Stengel, Erwin 327, 328, 329
Stephens, James 72
Stephenson, Sydney 310
Steptoe, Patrick C 252–3
Stevens, A Edwin 395
Stevens, Edward 72
Stevens, Philip 72
Stevens, TG 251
Stevens lectures for the laity 395–6
Stewart, DWC 475
Stewart, David 475
Stewart, J 45
Stiles, HJ 310
Still, George Frederic 306, 312
stillbirths 235, 248
Stones, HH 242
Stonier, Peter 397
Storm van Leeuwen, W 305
Strange, FG St Clair 364

Stratford House 177
Strauss, Dr 328
Street, Alfred 318
Sturridge, Ernest 240, 241
sulphuric ether 131
Sunderland, Septimus 316
Surgeons' Company 1
suspended animation 110–12
Sutton, Henry 114, 148
Swales, John 474
Swan, RH Jocelyn 351, 352
Swedish Society of Medical Angiology 446
Swedish Vascular Club 446
Sweny, Paul 437
Sydenham Society 74
Syme, James 137
Symington, T 417
Symonds, Charters 255, 265, 270, 371
syphilis 114, 142, 152–3, 188, 248, 259, 260, 279,
 311

Tabone-Vassallo, Mario 425, 426, 427
Tagliacozzi, Gaspare *412*
Tait, Robert Lawson 119, 135–6, 138, 163
Tanner, Dr 149
Tanner, Sir Henry 472
Tanner, Norman, award 224, *225*
Tatham, John 230
Taverner, Deryck 278–9
Taylor, Margaret 266
Taylor, PJ 401
Teachers of Geriatrics Club 430
telemedicine 447, 448–9
Tennant, Smithson 9, 59
terrorism 429
Tessier, Paul 414
tetanus 133
Thackeray, William 422
Thackrah, CT 399
Thatcher, Margaret 315
Therapeutical Society 109, 172, 173, 213, 289
therapeutics *see under* Royal Society of Medicine:
 Sections, Experimental Medicine and
 Therapeutics
thermometer (clinical) 80
Thin, George 120
Thiselton-Dyer, Sir William 289, 290
Thomas, Clement Price 394
Thomas, EW Prosser 262
Thomas, JW Tudor 338, 339
Thomas splint 357–8
Thomason, Theodore 233
Thompson, AR 351
Thompson, E Symes 115
Thompson, Henry 68, 143, 349, 374
Thompson, RHS 405
Thompson, Silvanus 254, 279–80
Thompson, Theophilus 101
Thomson, A Todd 30
Thomson, David 193
Thomson, FG 319
Thomson, John G 193
Thomson, Robert 425, 428, 437, 457, 466, 469, 475
Thomson, Sir St Clair 196, 203, 207, 272, 273–4,
 277, 332, *Pl.*43
Thomson-Walker, JW 351, 352

Thoracic Society 434–5
Thornton, J Knowsley 135, 136, 138, 154
Thurnham, J 90
Thurston, John 425
Tidy, Sir Henry 201, 218, 345, 346, 458, 460
Tierny 70
Tilley, Herbert 271
Tinker, Anthea 432
Tizard, JPM 314–15, 341
Todd, Lord 411
Tomes, C 240
Tomes, John 96, 106, 238
Tonsils and Adenoids Report 273
Tooke, John 445
toxoplasmosis 338
Toynbee, Joseph 29, 30, 79, 90, *91*, 182, 276
*Transactions* of the RMCS *see Medico-Chirurgical Transactions*
transplantation surgery *see under* Royal Society of Medicine: Sections
trauma centres 426
Travers, Benjamin 16, 19, 29, 37, 46, 89, *Pl.19*
trawler fishermen 400
trephining 140
Trethowan 359, 362
Treves, Frederick 103, 136, 138–9, 154, 170
Trevor-Roper, Patrick 339, 341
*Trichina spiralis* 43, 81
*Tropical Doctor* 343, 474
tropical medicine 151–2, 188
    *see also under* Royal Society of Medicine: Sections
Trotter, Maxwell 183
Trotter, Wilfred 266
Trueta, Joseph 361
Trunkey, Donald 348
Tubby, Alfred H 206, 310, 356–7, 362
tuberculin 150, 153–4
tuberculosis 84–5, 149–50, 189, 235, 311
    in cattle 199
    of ear 277
    of larynx 273
    light treatment 284–5
tubocurarine 307
Tucker, JH 104
Tunstall-Pedoe, Dan 439
Turner, A Logan 272
Turner, G Grey 222, 372, 373
Turner, JG 240–41, 334
Turner, Paul 446, 475
Turner, Philip 351
Turner, William *116*
Twain, Mark 166
Tweedie, Dr 104
Tweedie, AR 277
Tweedy, E Hastings 247
Tyler-Smith, W 108, 133, 244
typhoid 84
typhus 84
Tyrell, Frederick 43, 89

ulcerative colitis 371, 372, 374
Underwood, EA 332
Union Internationale de Phlébologie 442
United Services Medical Society 344, 345
urinary calculi 28, 37, 143
urology 142–3

*see also under* Royal Society of Medicine: Sections
Uvarov, Dame Olga 367

vaccination 24, 84, 114, 235, *Pl.7*
vaccine therapy 190, 226
Vaughan, EJ 158
venereal diseases 188–9, 248, 353
    *see also* syphilis
venesection 153
Venn, AJ 193
Venn, Graham 434, 435
ventriculography 266
vertigo 278
2 Verulam Buildings *14*, 15, 58
Victoria, Queen 15, 70, 112, 129, 135
Vieusseux, Gaspard 18, 24
Villemin, Jean-Antoine 85
Vincent, Clovis 268
Vincent, T Swale 383
vinyl chloride 401–2
Virchow, Rudolf 119
'vitamines' 311

Wade, AB 242
Wade, Sir Henry 353
Wade, Philip 395, 460
Waggett, EB 271
Wainwright, Denys 364
Wakeley, Surgeon Rear Admiral Cecil 293, 340
Wakley, Thomas 40, 48, 94, 101, 422
Walcheren fever 25
Wales, Prince of (in 1905) 168
Walker, Dr 6
Walker, Flight Lt 340
Walker, HM 394
Wall, Martin 42
Wallace, Sir Cuthbert 351
Wallace, HJ 261, 262
Wallace, J Sim 240
Wallace Memorial committee 206
Wallis, CE 243
Wallis, RC Mackenzie 305
Wallis Memorial lecture 205, 243
Walshe, Francis 268, 394
Walter, W Grey 328
Walter Bird & Co 186
Walton, Sir John (Lord Walton) 425, 427, 466, *Pl.72*
Wander, Albert 392
    lecture 392, 393
Want, John 47
war
    injuries 241–2, 284, 293, 318, 336–7, 340–41, 345, 359, 361, 373
    neuroses 324–5, 327, 328, 347
    *see also* Royal Society of Medicine: Sections, United Services
Warburton committee 40, 50, 69, 70
Ward, Nathaniel 103
Ward, R Fowler 354
Ward, R Ogier 353, 354
Wardrop, James 46, 89
Ware, James 89, *Pl.1*
Warren, Richard 425
Warren, Thomas 108
Warren, Wilfred 327, 329
water-cures 115–16

Waters, ATH 111
Watson, Sir Charles Gordon 198
Watson, Donald 279
Watson, Lesslie K 461
Watson, Sir Thomas 106
Watson, TJ 279
Watson-Jones, Sir Reginald 363
Watt, Sir James 346, 347, 445, 472, 473
Waxman, David 423
Weatherall, Sir David 203, 432
Weatherall, Miles 294
Webb, Curtis 246
Webb, Penny 473
Webb Miles, Messrs (subtenants) 163
Webb-Johnson, Alfred 351, 354, 390, 415, 458, 462
Weber, Frederick Parkes 227, 255, 256, 262, 265,
    309, 312, 332
Weber, Hermann 149
Webster, John 85
Weerts, J 435
Wegg, William 77
Weinberg, Dr 194
Weiss, John 79
Wellcome Trust 333, 394, 460, 461, 462
    sponsored Associates 461
Wells, Charles 307
Wells, Thomas Spencer 49, 87, 99, 119, 130, 132–4,
    135, 136, 138, Pl.21
West, Charles 77, 92–3, 115, 167, 245, 309
West, James 140
Westenbergii, Joannis 433
Western District Post Office see under 1 Wimpole
    Street
Westminster Medical Society 36, 61, 97
Wetherill, Diana 430
Wheatley, Benjamin 76, 77–8, 121
Wheelhouse, CG 157
Whetnall, Edith 408
Whewell, William 107
Whimster, I 262
White, RG 407, 408
Whitehead, Dr 5
Whitehead, Tony 420
Whitehorn, Katharine 420, 422
Whitfield, Arthur 258
Whiting, MH 340
Whitman, Royal 361
Whittingham, HE 345, 349
Wickerson, John 428
Wickham, Louis 259
Wigg, Joseph 15
Wigg and Pownall (architects) 75
Wightman lecture 310
Wilbur, Richard 466, Pl.71
Wilde, Sir William 90
Wiles, Philip 362
Wilkinson, AW 419
Wilkinson, Darrell 263
Wilks, Samuel 30, 43, 44, 82, 84, 90, 103, 114, 149,
    167, 168, 263, Pl.21
Willan, Robert 54, 55, 91, 92, 399
Willcox, Sir William 241, 292–3
William IV, King 15, 70, Pl.14
Williams, C Theodore 116, 149, 182
Williams, Charles J B 77, 78, 103, 106, 110, 128,
    149, 225

Williams, Chisholm 280
Williams, Sir David Innes 203, 356, 475
Williams, H Lloyd 241
Williams, Leonard 318
Williams, MHC, memorial lecture 401
Williams, Robert 17, 84–5
Williams, Shirley 315
Williams, Thomas 40, 58, 76, 77
Williamson, Dr 249
Williamson, Mildred 168, 183, 196
Williamson-Noble 340
Willis, Thomas 263, 382
Wilson, Erasmus (Sir William) 91–2
Wilson, JA 68, 87
Wilson, James 19, 34
Wilson, SA Kinnier 266
1 Wimpole Street 73, 118, 181–6, 203, 244, 256,
    288, 419, 457, 458, 469
    Cockayne Suite 462
    construction of fourth floor 460–61
    development of adjoining site (Western District Post
        Office) 439, 456, 462, 468, 469–72, Pl.72–5
    naming of rooms 182
    opening 186, Pl.30, Pl.31
Windeyer, Sir Brian 410, 411
Winnicott, DW 314, 315
Winsbury-White, Horace P 354
    lectures 354, 355–6
Winter, Chester 355
Withering, William 290, 331, Pl.47
Witts, Leslie 267
Wolff, Eugene 341
Wolfson Foundation 472
Wollaston, WH 9, 18, 24, 26, 28, 59
Wolstenholme, Gordon 387, 395, 419, 420, 468
Wolstenholme Working Party Report 236, 396, 419,
    439, 456, 467
Wood, Alexander 114
Wood, Clive 473
Wood, Constance 288
Wood, John 135, Pl.21
Wood, Richard 436
Woodall, John 391
Woodhead, Sir Bernard Sims 365
Woodruff, Sir Michael 396
Woods, Samuel 59
Woods, Stanton 319, 320, 321
Woolf, Virginia 265, 324
Wootton, Richard 449
World Health Organization 236
World War I 193–5, 324, 345
    paper shortages 216
    Section meetings 215, 221, 235, 241–2, 260, 284,
        311, 318, 324, 336–7, 358–9
    treatment of war disabilities 318, 359
    X-ray tube shortage 282
    see also Emergency Surgical Aid Corps
World War II 243, 274, 320, 327, 360–61, 423,
    457–8
    blast injuries 223
    body armour 222–3, 458
    reconstructive surgery 223, 256, 413
    Section meetings 235–6, 256, 261, 287, 321, 327,
        328, 354, 361, 373
    see also Inter-Allied Conferences on Military
        (War) Medicine

Wren, Christopher *263*
Wright, Almroth 190, 194, 195, 203, 226–7
Wright, Helena, memorial lecture 445
Wright, JAS 243
Wunderlich, Carl 80
Wyatt, Samuel 160
Wylie, WD 308
Wyllie, Dr 313
Wynne, James 149
Wyon, Thomas 53

X-rays 254, 279, 280, 281–3
  cinematography 286

Yamashina, A 429
Yelloly, John 2, 5, 6, 7, 8, 10, 15–17, 20, 26, 30, 34,
    35, 39, 58–9, 71, *Pl*.4
  enquiry on fevers 82
  leaves London 36–7
  and MCS incorporation 50, 51, 53, 54, 68, 69–70
  MCS Library 16, 57

catalogue 55, 56, 76
  gift 54
  MCS publications 40–41
  papers 19
Yelloly, Sarah 11, 37
Yeoman (clerk) 35, 59
Young, Archie 439
Young, George W 16, *46*, 59
Young, Helen 292
Young, Sir Robert Arthur 218
Young, Robyn 475
Young, TM 308
Yule, George Udny 233

Zaimis, Eleanor 308
Zander, Luke 392–3, 440, 441, 469
Zieler, Professor 260
Ziff, Morris 321
*Zoist* 422
Zoological Society 74
Zuckerman, Solly 223, 353, 384

# William the Fou[rth]

of the United Kingdom of Great Britain and Ireland King Defender of the Faith **To all to whom** these Pr[esents]
...ston Cooper Baronet and John Yelloly Doctor of Physic have by their petition humbly rep[resented]
Physicians and Surgeons of eminence in London for the cultivation and promotion of Physic and Surgery and
the said Society has expended considerable sums of money in the purchase and collection of a large and valuabl[e]
...the said Petitioners have humbly besought us that we should give to them and to the other persons who
...ncorporation for imparting greater stability and effect to the designs of the said Society **Now know y[e]**
...motion willed granted and ordained And **DO** by these presents for us our heirs and successors will grant a[nd]
...as are now Members of the said Society or who shall at any time hereafter become Members thereof and o[ne]
Corporate by the name of *The Royal Medical and Chirurgical Society of* L[ondon]
...shall have perpetual succession and a Common Seal with full power to alter vary break and renew the same a[t]
...every Court of us our heirs and successors and be for ever able and capable in the law to purchase receive ho[ld]
...notwithstanding the Statutes of Mortmain to take purchase hold and enjoy to them and their successors an[y]
...thousand pounds computing the same respectively at the said rent which might have been had or gotte[n]
...sell alien charge or otherwise dispose of any real or personal property so to be by them acquired as afore[said]
...subjects being persons able and capable in the law or any other body politic and Corporate in our sai[d]
...Government of the said Society and for the better management of the concerns thereof there shall be from the[nce]
...manner hereinafter mentioned shall form the Council **And We do** hereby appoint the said John Y[elloly]
...the Council to continue in Office till the first day of March next **And We further Direct** that a[t]
...fields who shall be authorised by method of Ballot to elect eighteen fit and proper persons as officers and o[f]
...the Council shall be composed And that such additional persons shall likewise continue in Office till the[ir]
...pleasure is that the Fellows of the said Society shall and may on the first day of March One thousand
...same as conveniently may be assemble together at the then last or other usual place of Meeting of th[e]
...and other members of the Council as may with the President form the number of twenty one of whom w[ith]
...or other member of the Council within the space of three months next after such death resignation or rem[oval]
...member of the Council And Our further will and pleasure is that no Fellow who has filled the Office o[f]
...termination of his office and that not more than two thirds of the Fellows who have formed the Counci[l]
...declare that the Fellows of the said Society or any ten or more of them shall and may have power fro[m]
...place as shall have in that behalf been appointed by and with the consent of not less than four fifths of the Fell[ows]
...that fit and that the Council hereby directed to be appointed and the Council of the said Society for the time be[ing]
...and may have power according to the best of their judgment and discretion to make and establish such bye law[s]
...of its officers and also the times place and manner of electing and removing the Fellows of the said Socie[ty]
...and also for filling up from time to time any vacancies which may happen by death resignation removal or
...Society and for regulating and ascertaining the qualifications of persons to become Fellows of the said Society re[lating]
...wise towards carrying on the purposes of the said Society and also the number qualifications and privileges of such
...vary alter or revoke and make such new and other Bye Laws as they shall think most useful and expedi[ent]
...hereafter to be made or alteration or repeal of any Bye Law which shall hereafter have been established b[y]
...Bye Laws or such alteration or repeal of any Bye Laws shall after such notice to the Fellows as from time
...Society ten at least of the Fellows of the said Society being present and provided that no such Bye Law or
...Ballot that not less than two thirds of the Fellows present at such meeting shall have voted for the same And
...President or such other officer or officers as may by the Bye Laws hereafter to be made be designated for th[e]
...case the Council shall not agree to such new Bye Laws or alteration or repeal of any existing Bye Laws
...consideration of the Society at large and determined on by them in the same way as has been directed wit[h]
...these Our Letters to be made Patent **Witness** Ourself at Our Palace at Westminster this T[w]enti[e]th...